California Contractors License Law & Reference Book

2025 Edition

With Rules and Regulations

Contractors State License Board
STATE OF CALIFORNIA
Gavin Christopher Newsom, *Governor*

ISBN: 979-8-3417-0175-5

© 2025 California Contractors State License Board

© 2025 Matthew Bender & Company, Inc., a member of the LexisNexis Group.

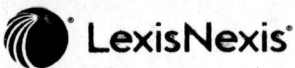

Matthew Bender & Company, Inc.
Editorial Offices
9443 Springboro Pike
Miamisburg, OH 45342
800-833-9844
www.lexisnexis.com

(Pub. 29700)

CONTRACTORS STATE LICENSE BOARD
OFFICERS & MEMBERS

Michael Mark, *Chair,*
Public Member - Labor Organization

Miguel Galarza, *Vice Chair,*
"B" Contractor Member

Alan Guy, *Secretary,*
"B" Contractor Member

Joël Barton, *Public Member*

Rodney M. Cobos, *Public Member*

Amanda Gallo, *Public Member*

Jacob Lopez, *Public Member*

Diana Love, *Public Member - Senior Citizen Organization*

Henry Nutt III, *"C" Specialty Contractor Member*

Steven Panelli, *Public Member - Building Official*

James Ruane, *"C" Specialty Contractor Member*

Thomas J. Ruiz, *Public Member*

Mary Teichert, *"A" General Engineering Contractor*

David R. Fogt, *Registrar of Contractors*

TABLE OF CONTENTS

Section I. The California Contractor License

Section II. Home Improvement

Section III. Business Management

Section IV. Construction Standards and Safety Regulations

Section V. The Department of Consumer Affairs

Page

Section VI. The Contractors State License Board; License Law, Rules and Regulations, and Related Laws

Introduction

The Contractors State License Board is introducing the 2025 law and reference book that includes only the essential information for consumers, contractors, and other stakeholders. Sections of law from state codes that are not from the Business and Professions Code that were included in editions before 2024 were removed because the laws are all available at www.leginfo.legislature.ca.gov. To provide your feedback on the 2025 edition of the California Contractors License Law & Reference Book please email cslbinfo@cslb.ca.gov.

SUMMARY OF RECENT CHANGES TO CONSTRUCTION OR CONTRACTORS' LAW

Effective January 1, 2025

Unless indicated otherwise

AB 2622 (Carrillo)

Amends Sections 7027.2 and 7048 of the Business and Professions Code, relating to CSLB.

This bill removes the existing license exemption for construction work where the price for labor, material, and all other items totals less than $500. Instead, this bill establishes a license exemption for construction work where the price for labor, material, and all other items totals less than $1,000, provided the construction work does not require a building permit or involve hiring any employees.

(Chapter 240, Statutes of 2024)

SB 1455 (Ashby)

Adds Sections 7000.5, 7011, 7025, 7040, 7059, 7065, 7068.1, 7071.9, 7076, 7076.2, and 7137 of, amends and repeals Section 7125 of, and adds Sections 7025.1 and 7125.7 to, the Business and Professions Code, relating to CSLB.

This bill extends CSLB's sunset provisions from January 1, 2025, to January 1, 2029, and makes other changes to the Contractors License Law including: (1) authorizing the licensure of federally recognized tribes and tribal businesses; (2) requires licensees who are subject to a workmanship complaint that results in a letter of admonishment or a citation to pay between $100 and $1,000 to reimburse CSLB's industry expert costs to investigate the complaint; (3) provides that license applicants pay examination fees directly to the examination vendor directly instead of CSLB; (4) clarifies that an awarding authority in a public works contract must select contractors in accordance with the licensing classification descriptions in the Contractors State License Law when determining the license class necessary to bid and perform a project; (5) delays the workers' compensation (WC) insurance requirement that all active licensees have WC from 2026 to 2028; (6) requires the board to consider a process for verifying (by audit or submission of proof or other means) how an applicant or licensee may obtain an exemption from WC from CSLB, by January 1, 2027; and, (7) removes the requirement that an applicant for licensure include a duty statement of their role and responsibilities planned for the license they are intending to qualify.

(Chapter 485, Statutes of 2024)

SECTIONS AFFECTED BY 2024 LEGISLATION

CSLB HISTORY & BACKGROUND

The Contractors State License Board (CSLB) was established in 1929 as the Contractors License Bureau under the Department of Professional and Vocational Standards. Today, CSLB is part of the Department of Consumer Affairs.

A 15-member board appoints CSLB's executive officer, or registrar of contractors, and directs administrative policy for the board's operations. CSLB's board includes nine public members (eight non-contractors and one local building official), five contractors, and one labor representative. The governor makes 11 appointments and four are made by the Legislature. The board holds regularly scheduled public meetings at various locations in the state. These meetings provide the public with an opportunity for input on agenda items and other issues.

CSLB licenses and regulates contractors in 45 license classifications that constitute the construction industry. Currently, there are around 285,000 contractor licenses in the state. The registrar oversees approximately 400 employees who work at the headquarters office in Sacramento and field offices throughout the state.

Headquarters staff receive and process applications for new contractor licenses, additional classifications, changes of license records, and license renewals. Staff also review and maintain records of disciplinary actions initiated by the field offices, provide verified certificates of licensure used in court or other legal actions, and provide other support services.

Headquarters directs the activities of field offices and initiates all disciplinary actions resulting from investigations. Field office staff investigate consumer complaints against contractors. The Statewide Investigative Fraud Team (SWIFT) addresses unlicensed activity.

CSLB's website, www.cslb.ca.gov or www.CheckTheLicenseFirst.com, provides the ability to look up a contractor by license number, name, or business name, and obtain the licensee's contact information, license status, CSLB legal actions (if any), classifications held, business type, and bond and workers' compensation insurance information. Home Improvement Salesperson registrations also are listed on the website's license look-up page.

Identical information is available through CSLB's automated public information line, (800) 321-CSLB (2752), which operates 24 hours per day. Also available is recorded information on licensing and examination procedures, complaint procedures and how to obtain information on a complaint that has been referred for legal action, the location and hours of CSLB offices, and current topics, such as recently passed laws or regulations. Callers also can order forms, applications, and other publications.

The "Find My Licensed Contractor" feature on CSLB's website allows users to search for licensed contractors in a specific classification by geographic area based on zip code or city. The randomly displayed results link to the license record and can be downloaded as either a PDF or a Word file.

CSLB aims to protect those whose homes and property are directly affected by disasters, such as wildfires, floods, mudflows, earthquakes, and pipeline explosions. CSLB offers materials at Local Assistance and Disaster Recovery Centers as well as monitors a Disaster Hotline, (800) 962-1125, to aid those in need.

CSLB offers a variety of publications and guides to help consumers make informed choices when contracting for home repairs and improvements. Speakers can be provided for groups interested in learning more about CSLB. Check the website for details or write to CSLB Public Affairs, P.O. Box 26000, Sacramento, CA 95826.

CSLB MISSION

The Contractors State License Board protects consumers by regulating the construction industry through policies that promote the health, safety, and general welfare of the public in matters relating to construction, including home improvement.

The Contractors State License Board accomplishes this by:

- Ensuring that construction, including home improvement, is performed in a safe, competent, and professional manner;

- Licensing contractors and enforcing licensing laws;

- Requiring licensure for any person practicing or offering to practice construction contracting;

- Enforcing the laws, regulations, and standards governing construction contracting in a fair and uniform manner;

- Providing resolution to disputes that arise from construction activities; and

- Educating consumers so they can make informed choices.

CONTRACTORS STATE LICENSE BOARD OFFICES

Headquarters
9821 Business Park Drive
Sacramento, CA 95827
(800) 321-CSLB (2752)

Mailing Address
P.O. Box 26000,
Sacramento, CA 95826

Website
www.cslb.ca.gov
www.CheckTheLicenseFirst.com

Northern Region

9821 Business Park Drive
Sacramento, CA 95827
Legal Action Disclosure (916) 255-4041
Case Management (916) 255-4027
SWIFT (Unlicensed Activity)
(916) 255-2924

Bakersfield Branch Office*
5800 District Blvd., Suite 300
Bakersfield, CA 93313
(800) 321-CSLB (2752)

Fresno Investigative Center
1277 East Alluvial Ave., Suite 106
Fresno, CA 93720
(559) 490-0580

Sacramento Investigative Center
P.O. Box 269115
Sacramento, CA 95826-9115
(800) 321-CSLB (2752)

Sacramento Intake & Mediation Center
P.O. Box 269116
Sacramento, CA 95826-9116
(916) 843-6515
Fax (916) 255-4449

San Francisco Investigative Center
301 Junipero Serra Blvd, Suite 206
San Francisco, CA 94127
(415) 469-6204

Southern Region

12501 East Imperial Hwy, Suite 600
Norwalk, CA 90650
Legal Action Disclosure (562) 345-7656
Case Management (562) 345-7656
SWIFT (Unlicensed Activity)
(562) 345-7600

Norwalk Intake & Mediation Center
12501 East Imperial Hwy, Suite 620
Norwalk, CA 90650
(562) 345-7530
Fax (562) 466-6064

Norwalk Investigative Center
12501 East Imperial Hwy, Suite 630
Norwalk, CA 90650
(562) 345-7610

Orange County Investigative Center
12501 East Imperial Hwy, Suite 640
Norwalk, CA 90650
(562) 345-7551

San Bernardino Investigative Center
1845 Business Center Drive, Suite 206
San Bernardino, CA 92408-3467
(909) 890-2205

San Diego Investigative Center
9246 Lightwave Ave., Suite 130
San Diego, CA 92123
(858) 300-5890

Santa Rosa Branch Office *
50 D Street, Room 400
Santa Rosa, CA 95404
(800) 321-CSLB (2752)

Valencia Investigative Center
25360 Magic Mountain Parkway, Suite 200
Santa Clarita, CA 91355
(661) 219-0066

West Covina Investigative Center
100 N. Barranca St., Suite 300
West Covina, CA 91791
(626) 332-1317

_____
* Limited office hours

Section I.

The California Contractor License

Chapter 1.

Enforcement Procedures: Complaints and Citations

Complaints against contractors may be filed with CSLB by homeowners, other contractors, subcontractors, material suppliers, or employees. Any entity may also file complaints.

Common complaints made against contractors involve poor workmanship; abandonment of a project; failure to pay subcontractors, suppliers, or employees; building code violations; lack of reasonable diligence in executing a construction project; use of false, misleading, or deceptive advertising; asking for excessive down payments or not including payment schedules in home improvement contracts; failure to obtain workers' compensation insurance; and violations of the law governing home improvement contracts.

COMPLAINTS AGAINST LICENSED CONTRACTORS

When a complaint is made against a licensed contractor, CSLB reviews it to determine if it falls within CSLB's jurisdiction. CSLB sends a confirmation to the person who filed the complaint and sends a notice to the licensed contractor to determine if the complaint can be resolved without further board involvement.

If the complaint has not been resolved after the contractor has been notified, a CSLB representative may contact the complainant and respondent (the licensee) to request additional information and, if necessary, documentation. If appropriate, CSLB will attempt mediation. If mediation is unsuccessful, CSLB may recommend settlement through its arbitration program, recommend that the complainant contact the surety company that issued the contractor's bond, file a claim in small claims court, or file a civil suit in superior court.

If CSLB finds that it's warranted, it may investigate to determine if there are violations of contractor state license law. An investigation may involve interviewing the complainant, the contractor, and any other parties who can furnish relevant information.

What happens if a violation is established?

If a violation is established but it is an isolated or minor one, CSLB may send the licensee an advisory notice. The advisory notice informs the licensee that CSLB is aware of the violation and that a future occurrence of the same violation may result in more stringent board actions.

For some violations, CSLB may issue a letter of admonishment. This may require the licensee to submit a corrective action plan showing compliance with the law and is publicly disclosable on the license record for one or two years.

If a more serious violation is established, the registrar of contractors may issue a citation, which can include an order to correct a project, make restitution to an injured party, and pay a civil penalty of up to $8,000 for most violations, and up to $30,000 for serious violations. *(See B&P §7099.2(b) regarding $30,000 citations for violations of B&P §§ 7110, 7114, 7118, and 7125.4.)*

If the licensee complies with the citation orders, CSLB takes no further action. If the licensee contests all or any part of the citation, an informal citation conference may be held to resolve the citation. If the matter is not settled, a hearing can be set before an administrative law judge of the State of California. At the hearing, the licensee can argue against the citation orders. If the licensee prevails at this hearing, CSLB takes no further action. If, however, the licensee does not prevail and does not comply with a final citation order, the license may be suspended and then revoked.

For flagrant violations of law, the registrar will take administrative action by filing an accusation with the state attorney general stating the board's intent to suspend or revoke the license. The licensee may be provided the opportunity to resolve the matter at an informal settlement conference. If the matter is not settled, the licensee is given an opportunity to defend themselves at a hearing before an administrative law judge.

The following procedures may be used to decide a case:

- The licensee may choose to have a hearing before an administrative law judge. The recommendation of this judge is used by the registrar in determining the appropriate action to take.

- The licensee and the registrar may negotiate a settlement of the case. This settlement is known as a "stipulation."

- If the licensee fails to respond to the accusation, the case will be considered in default. The registrar will decide on the appropriate action to take against the licensee.

The decision of the registrar may include various remedies:

- **Revocation of the License**

  The licensee's right to contract is taken away. The license shall not be reinstated or reissued for one to five years from the effective date of the decision.

  None of the official personnel listed in CSLB records for a revoked license and who have been found to have known about, or participated in, the acts or omissions constituting grounds for the revocation may apply for a license until the penalty period is over. The licensee also must show that they have complied with all provisions of the decision and settled any loss caused by the act or omission that resulted in the revocation of the license and must file a disciplinary bond in the amount set by the registrar. *(See B&P § 7071.8)*

- **Suspension of the License**

  The licensee is not entitled to operate during the period of suspension. A disciplinary bond must be filed before the license is reinstated or reissued.

- **Stay of Suspension or Revocation (Probation)**

  The licensee must abide by certain terms and conditions to keep the suspension or revocation from going into effect. They also must file a disciplinary bond to remain in business during this period. Suspension or revocation of the license will result if any of the terms of the agreement are violated.

- **Recovery of Investigation and Enforcement Costs**

  The licensee, to maintain good and clear standing or as a condition for renewal and reinstatement of their license, must pay the costs as ordered or as stipulated.

- **Dismissal with No Penalties**

  Matters that have been dismissed are not disclosed to the public.

- **Injunction against Unlawful Activity**

  Upon establishing that a blatant violation of the law has occurred, CSLB may go to court to request an injunction to immediately stop the unlawful activity.

- **Criminal Charges**

  If a blatant violation of the law has occurred, CSLB may refer the complaint to the local office of the district attorney for a possible criminal filing.

Complaint Disclosure

Once CSLB has determined that a probable violation of law has occurred, which, if proven, would present a risk of harm to the public—and for which suspension or revocation of the contractor's license would be appropriate—the date, nature, and status of the complaint will be disclosed to the public. A disclaimer stating that the complaint is, at this time, only an allegation will accompany this disclosure.

Citations will be disclosed to the public from date of issuance and for five years from the date of compliance.

Accusations that result in suspension or stayed revocation of the contractor license shall be disclosed from the date the accusation is filed and for seven years after the accusation has been settled, including the terms and conditions of probation. All revocations that are not stayed shall be disclosed indefinitely from the effective date of the revocation.

ADDRESSING COMPLAINTS AGAINST UNLICENSED CONTRACTORS

In California, it is a misdemeanor to engage in the business or act in the capacity of a contractor without a contractor license unless the contractor meets the criteria for exemption specified in Business and Professions Code sections 7040 through 7054.5.

When a complaint is filed against an unlicensed contractor, CSLB will verify that the accused individual or firm contracted without a license and will, with sufficient evidence, determine the amount of financial injury involved.

How does CSLB process complaints against unlicensed contractors?

When the board receives a complaint against an unlicensed contractor, it may issue an administrative citation or file a criminal action with the local district attorney's office. In some cases, it may initiate injunction proceedings against the non-licensee through the Office of the Attorney General or the district attorney.

- **Citation**

  The registrar may issue a citation to an unlicensed contractor when there is probable cause to believe that the person is acting in the capacity of a contractor or engaging in the business of contracting without a license in good standing (current and not under suspension) with CSLB. The citation includes an **order of abatement** to cease and desist and a **civil penalty** of up to $15,000. Unless the board receives a written appeal within 15 working days after the citation is served, the citation becomes a final order of the registrar. The civil penalty is paid to CSLB.

  If the citation is appealed, an informal settlement conference may be held to resolve the citation. If the matter is not settled, an administrative law judge will hear the appeal. The administrative law judge submits a decision to uphold, modify, or dismiss the citation. The decision is sent to the registrar for adoption.

  If the cited unlicensed contractor continues to contract without a license, the registrar may refer the case to the local district attorney for criminal action.

- **Criminal Action**

  CSLB may refer investigations to the local prosecutor to file criminal charges. If criminal charges are filed, the unlicensed contractor appears in local court, which renders a final decision on the case. The court may order a fine, probation, restitution, a jail sentence, or all of these.

- **Injunction**

  The registrar may apply for an injunction with the superior court of either the county in which an alleged practice or transaction took place, or the county in which the unlicensed person maintains a business or residence. An injunction restrains an unlicensed person from acting in the capacity or engaging in the business of contracting without a license in good standing with CSLB.

How does CSLB process complaints against unregistered salespersons?

The same citation process used for complaints against unlicensed contractors is used for complaints against unregistered home improvement salespersons. Disciplinary action also can be taken against the licensed contractor who employs the unregistered salesperson.

Statewide Investigative Fraud Team

In addition to the complaint process, CSLB established the Statewide Investigative Fraud Team (SWIFT), an arm of the Enforcement Division that focuses on the underground economy and unlicensed contractors who prosper at the expense of consumers and legitimate businesses. SWIFT has the authority to visit any jobsite without cause or complaint, ask contractors to produce proof of licensure in good standing, and cite those who are not properly licensed. *(See B&P Code §7011.4 and §7099.)*

SECTION II.
HOME IMPROVEMENT

Chapter 2.

Home Improvement

Home improvement is the repairing, remodeling, altering, converting, or modernizing of, or adding to, residential property and includes, but is not limited to, the construction, erection, replacement, or improvement of driveways, swimming pools (including spas and hot tubs), terraces, patios, awnings, storm windows, solar energy systems, landscaping, fences, porches, garages, fallout shelters, basements, and other improvements of the structures or land adjacent to a dwelling. Home improvement is also the installation of home improvement goods or the furnishing of home improvement services.

HOME IMPROVEMENT CONTRACTOR

A home improvement contractor, including a swimming pool contractor, is a contractor licensed by the Contractors State License Board (CSLB) who is engaged in the business of home improvement either full-time or part-time.

HOME IMPROVEMENT CONTRACTS AND SERVICE AND REPAIR CONTRACTS

The home improvement business in California constitutes a large portion of the state's construction industry. Problems can occur because of a misunderstanding of basic requirements and the agreement between the owner and contractor. Special legal requirements were enacted specifically for home improvement contracts to eliminate as many of these problems as possible. See B&P Code sections 7150 - 7159.9 (specific requirements are listed in Sections 7159 and 7159.5).

In 2004, through SB 30, and in 2005, through AB 316, the Legislature made significant additions to the information contractors must provide to the buyer of home improvements. The idea behind the legislation is to use the contract itself to inform homeowners of the

7

most important contract requirements to help them better understand the process. The availability of this consumer protection information is intended to reduce the number of disputes between contractors and homeowners and, therefore, the number of complaints that homeowners make to CSLB.

The following rules are required for improvement contracts: any changes made to contracts must be in writing, be legible, be easy to understand, and inform a consumer of their right to cancel or rescind the contract; and a home improvement contract must contain various information, notices, and disclosures for the protection of the consumer.

In addition, a **"service and repair contract"** must be used by licensed contractors for jobs of $750 or less, provided that the contract meets all four of the new requirements. There are various disclosure requirements applicable to the service and repair contract. In addition, a service and repair contract that does not meet specified requirements is subject to the requirements applicable to a home improvement contract regardless of the aggregate contract price. Any violation of the provisions of law applicable to home improvement and service and repair contracts subject the contractor to discipline.

The legislature occasionally revisits the home improvement contract and service and repair contract requirements to address consumer protection concerns.

AB 2471, effective January 1, 2021, extends the right to cancel home improvement contracts, service and repair contracts, Property Assessed Clean Energy (PACE) assessment contracts, and seminar sales contracts from three business days to five business days for those 65 years and older.

SB 1189, effective January 1, 2021, includes in the definition of home improvement the reconstruction, restoration, or rebuilding of residential property damaged or destroyed by a disaster for which a state of emergency has been declared by either the governor or the president.

SB 757, effective January 1, 2022, clarifies that a contract for a residential solar energy system is considered home improvement when installed on a residential building or property, for the purposes of the home improvement contract requirements. It also requires a home improvement salesperson to identify to the owner or tenant to whom a sale is being made the business name and license number of the contractor they are representing, and makes it a misdemeanor for a home improvement salesperson to assist, recommend, select, or otherwise guide an owner or tenant in the selection of a contractor for services unless CSLB receives notification of the salesperson's employment by the home improvement contractor. More information about home improvement salespersons is below.

In drawing up contracts, contractors should pay strict attention to the requirements for print typeface and point size of the notices and disclosures. For example, unless a larger print typeface is specified, text in any printed form shall be in at least 10-point type and the headings shall be in at least 10-point boldface type.

For more detailed information on home improvement contract requirements, visit www.cslb.ca.gov (search: home improvement contract). Contractors are encouraged to carefully review the free guide, "Contracting for Success," located on the CSLB website at https://www.cslb.ca.gov/Resources/GuidesAndPublications/Co ntractingForSuccess.pdf.

HOME WARRANTIES

Home warranties generally are not transferrable, except as provided for home roof warranties.

For home roof warranties, the California Civil Code provides:

> For any contract subject to this chapter that is entered into on or after January 1, 1994, the warranty obligations shall inure to the benefit of, and shall be directly enforceable by, all subsequent purchasers and transferees of the residential structure, without limitation, unless the contract contains a clear and conspicuous provision limiting transferability of the warranty (*Civil Code §1797.92*).

HOME IMPROVEMENT SALESPERSON REGISTRATION

Anyone who solicits, sells, negotiates, or executes home improvement contracts for a licensed contractor outside of the contractor's normal place of business, regardless of the dollar amount of these contracts, must be registered with CSLB as a Home Improvement Salesperson (HIS).

The law allows home improvement salespersons to file a single registration with CSLB, while still permitting them to represent multiple employers.

Licensees are required to notify CSLB in writing prior to employing an already registered HIS and to notify CSLB in writing when

Section II

employment of a registered HIS ends. These notification forms are available on CSLB's website: www.cslb.ca.gov (search: HIS forms).

Who is exempt from the HIS registration requirement?

Salespersons who only sell goods or negotiate contracts at a fixed business establishment where the goods or services are exhibited or offered for sale are not considered home improvement salespersons.

The official personnel listed in CSLB's records for the contractor license also are exempt from registration requirements. This includes individual contractors, qualifiers, partners, officers of the corporation, and responsible managing officers, members, managers, or employees of an LLC.

Other exemptions from the registration requirements include people who contact prospective buyers for the exclusive purpose of scheduling appointments for a registered home improvement salesperson, and *bona fide* service or repair people who are employed by a licensed contractor and whose repair or service calls are limited to the service or repair initially requested by the buyer.

What are the qualifications for a home improvement salesperson?

A home improvement salesperson must be at least 18 years old. There are no educational, residency, or experience requirements. However, a home improvement salesperson must submit their fingerprints to CSLB as part of the application process.

How do I apply for registration?

Complete an online easy-fill "Application for Registration as a Home Improvement Salesperson" by visiting www.cslb.ca.gov or obtain a copy of the application by downloading it from www.cslb.ca.gov or by calling (800) 321-CSLB (2752).

Then:

- Follow all instructions on the application.

- Submit the required nonrefundable, nontransferable application fee of $200 and your application to the CSLB headquarters office.

May I begin working as an HIS as soon as I have submitted my registration application and fee to CSLB?

No. CSLB must review your application and issue a registration number before you may legally work as a home improvement salesperson.

How long will it take to become registered?

CSLB's processing times vary depending on its workload, staff vacancies, etc. CSLB's website includes a processing time chart that lists the date of documents currently being processed, including HIS applications and renewals. The chart is updated weekly and helps keep applicants informed of current processing times. Visit www.cslb.ca.gov (search: processing times).

When does my HIS registration expire?

The HIS registration expires two years from the last day of the month in which it was issued. CSLB will mail a renewal application to your address of record several weeks before your registration expires. Upon verification of the renewal, a new registration certificate will be mailed showing the new expiration date.

What if my address has changed since my registration was issued or last renewed?

If your address has changed since your registration was issued or last renewed, it is your responsibility to notify CSLB in writing within 90 days of the change.

If you have not received an advance notification of renewal, notify CSLB. This should be done no later than three weeks before your registration expires.

What happens if a licensed contractor employs an unregistered salesperson?

According to B&P Code section 7154, a contractor who employs an unregistered person to negotiate home improvement contracts is subject to disciplinary action by the registrar. Furthermore, B&P Code section 7153 states that it is a misdemeanor for a person to act as a home improvement salesperson without being registered. In addition to possible criminal action, the same section provides that an administrative citation may be issued to any unregistered person who engages in the HIS occupation.

For additional information, refer to B&P Code sections 7150 through 7170 in Chapter 8 of this book.

HOME IMPROVEMENT CONTRACT REQUIREMENTS

B&P Code section 7159

This section provides basic information about some required elements in a home improvement contract but is not complete. For the full text of the home improvement contract requirements please visit

https://leginfo.legislature.ca.gov/faces/codes_displayText.xhtml?divisi
on=3.&chapter=9.&lawCode=BPC&article=10 or see Chapter 8 of this
book.

For free guides about home improvement contracts, consumers are
encouraged to review CSLB's "Terms of Agreement" at
https://www.cslb.ca.gov/resources/GuidesAndPublications/HomeImpr
ovementContractsConsumerGuide.pdf and contractors are
encouraged to review CSLB's "Contracting for Success" at
https://www.cslb.ca.gov/Resources/GuidesAndPublications/Contractin
gForSuccess.pdf.

Basic Requirements

- The contract and any changes to the contract must be in
  writing and signed by all parties. The writing must be legible
  and printed forms must be readable.

- Before any work is started, the contractor must give the buyer
  a copy of the contract signed and dated by both the contractor
  and the buyer.

- Unless a larger typeface is specified in the law referenced
  above, text in any printed form shall be in at least 10-point
  typeface and the headings shall be in at least 10-point
  boldface type.

- Except for a down payment, a contractor cannot demand or
  accept payment for work or materials until the work is
  completed or the materials are delivered. The down payment
  may not exceed $1,000 or 10 percent of the contract price,
  whichever is less.

- If the contract includes a salesperson's commission in the
  contract price, the payment to the salesperson shall be made
  on a pro rata basis in proportion to the schedule of payments
  made to the contractor.

- The contract must contain the name and registration number
  of the salesperson.

- The name, business address, and license number of the
  contractor must be included.

Contract must include full descriptions and information about the following:

- Description of work

- Description of materials and equipment

- The contract price

- Payment schedule
- Start and completion of work (dates and descriptions)
- Permits and tests
- Permissible delays
- Extra work
- Required release of mechanics' liens statements
- Owner's applicable right to cancellation

Please review the links above or Chapter 8 of this book for the complete requirements.

Required Notices and Disclosure Statements

Home improvement and swimming pool contracts in California are required to have the full text of several notices and disclosures. Some must be in the main body of the contract; others may be attached separately. The full text of the required notices and disclosure statements are not included here. Please review the link above or Chapter 8 of this book for the complete requirements.

- Extra Work and Change Orders
- Commercial General Liability Insurance
- Workers' Compensation Insurance
- Performance of Extra or Change-Order Work Notice
- Mechanics Lien Warning
- Contractors Board Information
- Applicable Right to Cancel and Notice of Cancellation Instructions

Common Problems with Home Improvement Contracts

- Missing notices and/or disclosures
- Excessive down payment requested or received
- Equipment to be used or installed is not detailed, and materials to be used not described specifically
- Job start and completion information not clearly stated and described including dates
- Bid or price not carefully or completely established
- Change orders not included

- License number and home improvement salesperson registration numbers missing
- Failure to identify required building permits or indicate who is paying for them
- No payment schedule

JOINT CONTROL AGREEMENTS

California Business & Professions Code provides for the optional use of a joint control agreement approved by the registrar of contractors "covering full performance and payment."

CSLB does not license joint control companies, nor does CSLB have legal jurisdiction over joint control company activities, nor does it maintain lists of approved joint control companies nor monitor their activities.

Contractors who furnish a joint control as part of the terms of a home improvement contract should be aware that the law prohibits them from having any financial or other interest in the joint control company. It is the contractor's responsibility to determine whether to use a joint control agreement, and responsibility for incorporating a joint control addendum into any agreement rests solely with the joint control company.

Contractors considering the use of a joint control agreement should first contact an attorney.

SECTION III.

BUSINESS MANAGEMENT

Chapter 3.

Managing a Business

This chapter will show how good management and accounting techniques can be applied to the construction industry. The numbers used in the examples were chosen to illustrate the average successful small contracting business.

THE CONTRACTOR MANAGER

Statistics show that a significant percentage of bankruptcies and business closures result from poor management. The specific reasons include an inability to plan, manage, and control business affairs; insufficient on-the-job supervisory experience or the inability to manage employees; and lack of knowledge about business practices.

The main duties of the contractor, who is also a manager, are to plan and direct the major activities of the business; coordinate employee work and materials; and train, direct, and advise employees in supervisory and non-supervisory positions.

PRINCIPLES OF MANAGEMENT

The most difficult part of changing roles from employee to manager may be in developing a clear understanding of what is important for successful management. Management theory has been divided into two different areas: functional and behavioral.

The Functional Areas of Management Include:

- **Planning**

   Good planning is one of the most important, but most neglected, management duties. Large amounts of information from within the business must be put together with information from outside the business to schedule business activities. Planning is essential to make sure that resources, money, people, and equipment are available to the business in the right amounts and at the right time.

15

- **Decision-Making/Delegation**

  Employees should be trained and encouraged to assume
  responsibility for routine decision-making. The manager's
  responsibility is to make sure that these decisions fit together
  with the plans for the project and the business.

- **Standardization**

  For the greatest efficiency, it is important to standardize
  methods for routine, ongoing operations. After you determine
  the best method, it should be adopted as the pattern for similar
  operations in the future. Standardization also makes it easier
  for decisions to be made at lower levels.

- **Controls**

  Controls are established to inform the manager when the
  actual business outcome is different from what was expected.
  Controls should be designed to warn the manager before the
  differences become too great. The manager can both check on
  the progress of the business and evaluate overall performance
  by comparing results with plans. Effective controls must be
  established and rigidly enforced. The manager can then adapt
  to change rather than resist it.

ESTABLISHING YOUR BUSINESS

Forms of Business

The legal form of the business will determine the available sources of
financing, the extent of personal liability, the extent of control, and
the tax liabilities. The legal form may change as the business grows
and should be reviewed as financing requirements change.

- **Sole Ownership**

  Sole ownership (often called personal ownership or sole
  proprietorship) is the simplest form of business organization
  and relies primarily on the financial resources available to an
  individual. The owner has sole responsibility and complete
  control. They must obtain all the financing and are personally
  liable for any claims against the business.

  For tax purposes, business income is reported as personal
  income.

- **General Partnership**

  General partnerships use the financial and personal resources
  of two or more individuals who share in the ownership and
  operation of the business. A general partnership requires

registration of the name of the business. Consult a lawyer to formalize the rights and responsibilities of the partners regarding management and profit-sharing.

Under most circumstances, a partnership agreement terminates with the death or withdrawal of a partner or the addition of a new partner. Some partnership agreements avoid termination by entering into a prior written agreement allowing the partnership to continue. However, when a contractor's license is issued to a general partnership and a general partner leaves for any reason or the partnership wants to add another general partner, the license is canceled.

The partnership is not an entity separate from the partners. Each partner may be personally liable to the extent of their personal assets and may be legally responsible for the negligent acts of the other partner(s). For tax purposes, an individual's share of the partnership income is taxed as personal income.

- **Limited Partnership**

  The limited partnership allows investors to join in a partnership without taking full responsibility for the business. The limited partner risks only their original investment. In this case, there must be at least one general partner who runs the business and who remains fully responsible for the liabilities of the business.

- **Corporation**

  A corporation is a separate legal entity created by the government. It can make contracts, be held legally liable, and is taxed. The corporation may raise capital by selling stock to private investors or to the public. Stockholders are usually not liable for claims against the corporation beyond their original investment. Creditors may claim only the corporate assets, although corporate officers may be personally liable.

  You can begin the process of incorporations by filing articles of incorporation with the Secretary of State. The corporation has no fixed life. The death of a stockholder or sale of one's personal investment will not disrupt the business.

- **"S" Chapter Corporation**

  "S" corporations must meet certain restrictions and can report the business income as individual income. This benefit is designed to remove tax considerations from the decision regarding the form of business organization for the small business. The business can operate in corporate form to reduce the owner's liability but is taxed like a partnership. Since the corporation is not taxed separately, only an information return similar to the partnership tax return needs to be filed.

- **Limited Liability Company**

  A California limited liability company (LLC) generally offers liability protection similar to that of a corporation but is taxed differently. Domestic LLCs may be managed by one or more managers or one or more members. In addition to filing the applicable documents with the Secretary of State, an operating agreement among the members as to the affairs of the LLC and the conduct of its business is required. The LLC does not file the operating agreement with the Secretary of State but maintains it at the office where the LLC's records are kept.

  To form an LLC in California, Articles of Organization (Form LLC-1) must be filed with the California Secretary of State's office.

Taxes and Permits

The owner(s) of the business is required to pay taxes and fees at the federal, state, and local levels. If the business is a sole ownership or partnership, estimated federal and state income taxes must be prepaid or paid quarterly.

A federal Employer Identification Number (EIN) must be requested from the Internal Revenue Service, and the federal income and Social Security taxes withheld from employee wages must be paid quarterly, monthly, or semimonthly, as required.

The contractor must register with the Employment Development Department, obtain a state EIN, and pay state payroll and unemployment insurance taxes for employees who earn over $100 in a calendar quarter.

California requires a Seller's Permit for businesses that sell tangible personal property. The State Board of Equalization can require a deposit of the estimated sales tax for the first six months. The contractor must collect the required sales tax from the customer unless the tax on materials was already paid at the time of purchase.

Before starting a job, determine if city or county permits are required. In addition, the contractor must be familiar with zoning laws and building codes.

Bonds

A requirement for bonding is generally mandatory for large jobs financed by institutional lenders, such as savings and loans, insurance companies, or commercial banks. In addition, many owners and lenders, as well as other contractors, impose bonding requirements. Bonds can be obtained from bonding companies for a percentage of the contract price, usually in the one to two percent range. This requirement is a cost of doing business that should be recognized when the bid is submitted. Bonds may be classified as follows:

- **Performance bonds** guarantee the project's completion according to the building plans and specifications. If the job is abandoned or the work is unacceptable, the bonding company has the option to hire another contractor to complete the work or settle for damages.

- **Payment bonds** assure the property owner that no liens for labor and materials will be filed against the property.

- **Contract bonds** guarantee both job completion and payment of all labor and materials.

In general, unless the bonding company has taken responsibility for completing the project, the bonding company will not have to pay more than the face amount of the bond.

The new contractor should be aware that bonding requirements may exclude the new business from bidding on desired jobs. Bonding companies will not take risks without verifying the technical and resource capabilities of the bonded contractor.

Contractor License Bonds

Contractor license bonds are different from performance, payment, and contract bonds. Each licensed contractor is required to carry a contractor bond. Unlike payment, performance, and contract bonds, which are usually written to cover specific projects, a contractor license bond is written to cover any project the contractor agrees to perform. The contractor license bond amount is $25,000. The bond for qualifying individuals is $25,000.

Limited Liability Company Surety Bond

A $100,000 surety bond (in addition to the $25,000 contractor bond) is required for the issuance, reissuance, reinstatement, reactivation, and renewal of an LLC license for the benefit of any employee or worker damaged by the LLC's failure to pay wages, interest on wages, or fringe benefits, as well as other contributions. (*See B&P Code §7071.6.5.*)

Commercial General Liability Insurance

Commercial general liability (CGL) insurance can shift the risk of liability for accidents and mistakes from the contractor to the insurance company. As the International Risk Management Institute explains in its *Guide to Construction Insurance*, commercial general liability insurance protects "the insured contractor from liability to members of the public (other than employees) for bodily injury, property damage, or personal injury caused by virtually any activity."

The insurance company:

- Provides a claim-handling process.

- Defends the contractor against insurance claims.

- Pays claims for covered damages.

- Pays for immediately necessary medical treatment, even when the contractor is not ultimately found liable.

Contractors State License Law does not require contractors to carry CGL insurance unless their business entity is a limited liability company (see below). Even though it is not universally required by licensing law, commercial property owners routinely require the contractors they hire to carry CGL insurance.

On the other hand, when a homeowner hires a contractor to perform home improvement work, they rarely require the contractor to carry CGL insurance. Most homeowners assume that a contractor would not work on the house without being insured. To alert homeowners to the value of CGL insurance, the California Code of Regulations (CCR) section 872(a), requires home improvement contractors to:

- Disclose in writing if they do or do not carry commercial general liability insurance.

- If they do carry CGL insurance, provide the homeowner with the name and telephone number of the insurance company, in writing, so the homeowner can verify coverage.

$1 Million Liability Insurance Minimum

Liability insurance with the aggregate limit of $1 million for licensees with five or fewer persons listed as members of the personnel of record is required for a limited liability company; plus, an additional $100,000 in insurance is required for each additional member of the personnel of record, not to exceed $5 million total. (*See B&P Code §7071.19*).

Workers' Compensation Insurance

California workers' compensation law establishes a no-fault insurance plan purchased by the employer-contractor and administered by the state to:

- Limit the employer-contractor's liability and possibly avoid costly lawsuits.

- Guarantee that an injured worker receives prompt and complete medical treatment and specific benefits for job-related injury or illness. Under some circumstances, an employer-contractor can be sued for damages.

   For example, the harmed parties may sue if an employee is injured when the employer is illegally uninsured, or if the employer conceals the existence of an employee's injury and its connection with employment. Check with the Department of Industrial Relations, www.dir.ca.gov, for more information.

Employer Liability

For a work-incurred injury or illness, an employer-contractor is required to provide weekly benefit payments (indemnity) and necessary medical and hospital treatment. This liability of the employer extends to employed relatives on the same basis as any other employee.

If the employer has one or more employees, even part-time, they are required to insure for workers' compensation claims. An "owner-operator" or "independent contractor" should pay particular attention to Labor Code §2750.5.

Workers' Compensation Insurance Coverage

The employer-contractor may provide insurance protection in one of three ways:

- A standard approved policy of workers' compensation insurance available through any licensed carrier; or

- Securing a permit from the Director of the state Department of Industrial Relations to become a self-insurer *(Labor Code §3700)*; or

- Participating in a collectively bargained alternative dispute resolution program recognized by the Division of Workers' Compensation *(Labor Code §3201.5)*.

In general, if a contractor carries workers' compensation insurance, the workers' compensation insurance company assumes the obligation of the contractor under the workers' compensation laws. Some exceptions include penalties based on:

- The contractor's serious and willful misconduct *(Labor Code §4553)*.

- Injury to an illegally employed person under 16 years of age *(Labor Code §4557)*.

- Instances where the employer discriminates against an employee because an industrial injury claim was filed *(Labor Code §132a)*.

Submission of Workers' Compensation Certificate or Certificate of Exemption to CSLB

B&P Code section 7125 provides that an applicant or licensee always have on file a current and valid Certificate of Workers' Compensation Insurance or Certification of Self-Insurance in the licensee's business name. The insurer can submit this information to CSLB electronically using the online submission system on CSLB's website: www.cslb.ca.gov.

Important note about workers' compensation exemption certificates. If you don't have employees, you must file an exemption from the workers' compensation requirement unless you hold one of these classifications which requires you to carry workers' compensation insurance: C-8 Concrete; C-20 Warm-Air Heating, Ventilating and Air-Conditioning; C-22 Asbestos Abatement; C-39 Roofing; C-61/D-49 Tree Service. Starting January 2026, all licensed contractor classifications must have a Certificate of Workers' Compensation Insurance on file with CSLB.

The contractor can submit an exemption to CSLB electronically using the online submission system on CSLB's website: www.cslb.ca.gov.

Reporting Occupational Injury or Illness

- An employer-contractor MUST file a complete report of every employee occupational injury or occupational illness that results in lost time beyond the date of injury or illness, or which requires medical treatment beyond first aid, with the Department of Industrial Relations through its Division of Labor Statistics and Research or, if an insured employer, with the insurer *(Labor Code §6409.1)*.

  The report filed shall be the original of the form required by the Division of Labor Statistics and Research. A report shall be filed concerning each injury and illness that has, or is alleged to have, arisen out of and in the course of employment, within five days after the employer obtains knowledge of the injury or illness. Each report of occupational injury or occupational illness must indicate the Social Security number of the injured employee (*Labor Code §6409.1*).

The insured employer must file with their insurer a complete report of every injury or illness to each employee. If a report is not filed with the insurance carrier, the Workers' Compensation Appeals Board may issue an order directing the insured employer to report the injury or illness within five days. Failure of the employer to comply with this order may be punished as contempt (*Labor Code §3760*).

- In every case involving a serious injury or illness, or death, in addition to the report described above, the employer must report immediately by telephone or email to the Division of Occupational Safety and Health (*Labor Code §6409.1*).

Employee Notification and Posting Requirements

Every employer-contractor subject to the provisions of the workers' compensation laws MUST:

- Give every new employee, either at the time of hiring or by the end of their first pay period, written notice of the employee's right to receive workers' compensation benefits should they be injured on the job while working for the employer. The content of the notice must be approved by the Administrative Director of the Division of Workers' Compensation and must contain the information listed in Section 9880 of CCR Title 8. *The notice shall be available in both English and Spanish when there are Spanish-speaking employees (Labor Code §3551).*

- Post conspicuously, in a location frequented by employees, a Notice to Employees poster. *The Notice to Employees must be posted in English and Spanish where there are Spanish-speaking employees.* The Notice to Employees poster must contain the information listed in Section 9881 of CCR Title 8 or the employer may post the Administrative Director's approved Notice to Employees poster provided in Section 9881.1 of CCR Title 8. Failure to keep such a notice conspicuously posted is punishable as a misdemeanor (*Labor Code §3550*).

- Post information regarding protections and obligations of employees under occupational safety and health laws, and related citations (*Labor Code §6408*).

- Give any employee who is a victim of workplace crime written notification that the employee is eligible for workers' compensation *(Labor Code §3553)*.

- The contractor or their insurance company should notify an employee, in case of an injury, of a physician who will provide professional care.

Benefits to Which Workers May Be Entitled

- **Medical Treatment**

  Employers are required to authorize medical treatment consistent with the American College of Occupational and Environmental Medicine's (ACOEM) Occupational Medicine Practice Guidelines or the treatment utilization schedule adopted by the Administrative Director to cure or relieve the injured worker from the effects of their injury. Within one working day of receiving the employee's claim form, the employer must authorize treatment for the alleged industrial injury and must continue to provide the treatment until the date that liability for the claim is either accepted or rejected by the employer. Until the date the claim is accepted or rejected, liability for medical treatment is limited to $10,000 *(Labor Code §§4600, 4604.5, 4610, 5307.27, and 5402)*.

- **Supplemental Job Displacement Benefit**

  The worker may be entitled to a supplemental job displacement benefit if they cannot return to work for the employer within 60 days following the end of the temporary disability period. The amount of the benefit is based on the employee's permanent disability level and must be used for retraining, skill enhancement, or job placement assistance *(Labor Code §4658.5)*.

- **Temporary Disability**

  The worker is also entitled to temporary disability payments while recovering from the injury. These weekly payments begin after the third day of disability and are based upon two-thirds of the weekly earnings, *up to a legal maximum*. The compensation insurance company should be able to provide information on current rates. Where temporary disability extends beyond 14 days or requires overnight hospitalization, the three-day waiting period is eliminated *(Labor Code §§4453, 4650, 4652, and 4653)*.

- **Permanent Disability**

  If a permanent disability arises out of an industrial injury, the worker is entitled to compensation based on the rated degree of disability. Benefits are based on the earning of the disabled worker, and the range of benefit amounts is set by state law *(Labor Code §4453)*.

- **Death Benefits**

  If the injury causes death, a benefit is payable to those dependent on the deceased for support at the time of injury. In addition, burial expenses are allowed up to a prescribed amount *(Labor Code §§4701 and 4702)*.

- **Compensation for Serious and Willful Employer Misconduct**

  The amount of compensation otherwise recoverable can be increased one-half, together with costs and expenses not to exceed $250, where the employee is injured by reason of the serious or willful misconduct of the employer or their managing representative, partner, executive, managing officer, or general superintendent. The insurance company is not liable for the increase and is not permitted to cover it under the insurance policy *(Labor Code §§4550 and 4553; Insurance Code §11661)*.

Penalties for Noncompliance

- Failure to secure payment of compensation as required by law is a misdemeanor *(Labor Code §3700.5)*.

- A contractor's license may be suspended or revoked by the registrar of contractors if the contractor fails to secure the payment of compensation *(Business and Professions Code §7110)*.

- The Department of Industrial Relations' Division of Labor Standards Enforcement also may take action against a contractor who has failed to secure the payment of compensation. This may include:

  o Issuing a "Stop Order," prohibiting the use of employee labor until insurance is provided *(Labor Code §3710.1)*.

  o Obtaining a restraining order in superior court against the contractor *(Labor Code §3712)*.

  o Issuing a penalty assessment order

(Penalties for an uninsured contractor may be either the greater of twice the amount the contractor would have paid in premiums during the period they were uninsured, or $1,000 per employee employed during that same period. If the contractor's uninsured status is discovered following the filing of a claim for compensation, the penalty shall be either $2,000 for each employee employed on the date of injury in non-compensable cases, or $10,000 for each employee in compensable cases (*Labor Code §3722*).)

o   Recording a lien against the real property and personal property of the contractor as a security interest *(Labor Code §3727)*.

- If a contractor willfully fails to provide compensation insurance for an employee and an injury occurs, the contractor must pay the disability compensation plus a penalty of 10 percent and attorney fees. They must also supply all necessary medical treatment. In addition, they are liable for damages in a civil action, with a legal presumption that the injury was caused by the employer's negligence. Contributory negligence of the employee is no defense *(Labor Code §§3706, 3708, 4554, and 4555)*.

- Every employer, and every employee having direction, management control, or custody of employment of any other employee, who willfully violates any occupational safety or health standard that causes the death of any employee or the prolonged impairment of the body of any employee shall, upon conviction, be punished by a fine and or imprisonment *(Labor Code §6425)*.

Additional Information

- Department of Industrial Relations
  Division of Workers' Compensation
  1515 Clay Street, 6th Floor
  Oakland, California 94612
  (510) 622-2866

- Visit the Division's website: www.dir.ca.gov/dwc.

- Call (800) 736-7401 for recorded messages.

FINANCIAL RESPONSIBILITY AND CONTROL

Records

State and federal agencies frequently specify that certain records must be maintained and made available for government audits and to substantiate tax reporting. For a description of the records specifically required under Contractors State License Law, see Business and Professions Code section 7111.

Accurate accounting records must be kept to provide the basis to construct financial statements. The information summarized in these statements highlights the total operational costs, individual job costs, and other costs that affect your ability to make a profit. Accurate records also provide information on cash receipts and a basis for control of disbursements. The contractor can, by reviewing these records, determine the cash flow requirements of other jobs that they have completed to help estimate the costs of future jobs.

Understand the Fundamental Terms of Accounting

- **Cash Basis of Accounting**

   Under the cash basis of accounting, revenue is recognized when cash is received, and expenses are deductible in the year paid (unless they should be taken in a different period to clearly reflect income).

   A cash basis of accounting may be appropriate where no prepaid expenses (e.g., insurance, rent), depreciable assets, or inventories exist, and where revenue is received during the accounting period.

   Information regarding cash flow, as provided by the cash basis of accounting method, can be valuable in judging the ability of the business to pay its debts, to finance replacement of productive assets, and to expand the scope of business operations. However, a strict cash method neither records receivables nor payables since these items have not been received or disbursed. This failure to match income and expenses for a given accounting period restricts the information available to the manager using a cash basis of accounting.

   Additionally, where depreciation and inventories are utilized, the accrual method is necessary to accurately reflect expenses and income. For federal income tax purposes, the accrual method is required when inventories are utilized.

The net increase or decrease in cash during a given period is not very useful in evaluating a company's operating performance because, although progress payments come in during a job, final profit cannot be determined until after the job is completed. For these reasons, the cash basis of accounting is not recommended for contractors.

- **Accrual Basis of Accounting**

The accrual basis of accounting recognizes revenues when earned and expenses when incurred, regardless of when payment is received or made. Thus, this method allows the matching of revenues and associated expenses for individual periods of time.

In a contracting business that has qualifying long-term projects, the accrual basis of accounting is often further modified using two methods: 1) the **percentage of completion**; and 2) the **completed contract**.

1) The percentage of completion method will report profits and losses regularly based on work accomplished on each job. For example, if the work performed each year is estimated to represent 50 percent of total performance under contract, then 50 percent of the total estimated revenue and profit is considered earned.

2) The completed contract method allows for the gross income and related costs for each contract to be reported in the year in which such a contract is completed.

- **Financial Statements**

The balance sheet and income statement summarize the firm's internal data. These statements, in turn, provide the information for ratio analysis that highlights the strengths and exposes the weaknesses of the company.

- **Balance Sheet**

The balance sheet is a statement of financial condition of an individual business at a certain point in time. The balance sheet is often referred to as a "snapshot." The accountant will usually provide two balance sheets, one for the current year just ending and another for the prior year. An example of a balance sheet for a corporation is shown on the next page. This balance sheet lets the reader compare where the company stood at the end of each of the past two years.

The balance sheet is a statement of the company's resources, financial obligations, and ownership investment. The balance sheet is divided into two sides: on the left are the assets; on the right are the company's liabilities and stockholders' equity (the owners' investment). Both sides are always equal or in balance. The company's assets include its cash, physical goods, and its financial claims on others. Liabilities represent the claims others have on the company. The stockholder's equity section includes the original investment of the owners. Since this example is a corporation, the equity section includes undistributed profits earned by the corporation to date (additional investment of earnings held by the corporation).

The following section briefly describes some of the important features of a balance sheet:

Typical Construction Company, Inc.
Balance Sheet
December 31, 2024

Assets	Current Year	Prior Year	Liabilities and Stockholders' Equity	Current Year	Prior Year
Current Assets			**Liabilities**		
Cash	$10,000	$15,000	Current Liabilities		
Retention	$40,000	$35,000	Accounts payable	$80,000	$60,000
Accounts Receivable	$70,000	$50,000	Notes payable	$25,000	$30,000
Total current assets	**$120,000**	**$100,000**	Accrued expenses payable	$20,000	$20,000
			Accrued payroll	$20,000	$18,000
Inventories			Misc taxes payable	$5,000	$10,000
Construction in progress	$200,000	$160,000	Federal income taxes payable	$30,000	$12,000
Less: partial billings or contracts	-$120,000	-$100,000	**Total, current liabilities**	**$180,000**	**$150,000**
Costs or contracts in excess of billings	**$80,000**	**$60,000**	Long-term liabilities		
Raw Materials	$30,000	$30,000	Bank loan, truck and equipment; 14% due	$100,000	$90,000
Total Inventories	**$110,000**	**$90,000**	**Total, Liabilities**	**$280,000**	**$240,000**
Prepaid Expenses (permits and licenses, etc.)	$20,000	$25,000			
Total, Current Assets	**$250,000**	**$215,000**	**Stockholders' Equity**		
			Common stock, $5 par value, authorized, issued and outstanding 10,000 shares	$50,000	$50,000
Property, plant and equipment					
Leasehold improvements	$4,000	$4,000	Retained earnings	$70,000	$60,000
Office furniture and fixtures	$2,000	$2,000			
Small tools	$10,000	$10,000	**Total, Stockholders' Equity**	**$120,000**	**$110,000**
Construction equipment	$154,000	$130,000	**Total, Liabilities and Stockholders' Equity**	**$400,000**	**$350,000**
Less: accumulated depreciation	-$20,000	-$15,000			
Net property, plant and equipment	**$150,000**	**$131,000**			
Other Assets		$4,000			
Total Assets	**$400,000**	**$350,000**			

ASSETS (left columns)

Assets are categorized as either current or fixed and are listed in order of declining liquidity. (Liquidity refers to the speed with which an item can be converted into cash or, put another way, the ability of the organization to pay its current debt.) Current assets are the first items listed on the left side of the balance sheet. These are the assets that are either cash or capable of being converted into cash in the normal course of business, generally within one year from the date of the balance sheet. In addition to cash (money on hand and deposits in the bank), the other items that will be turned into cash include retentions, accounts receivable, inventories, and prepaid expenses. After current assets, the balance sheet lists fixed assets.

All of these are briefly described below:

- **Cash**: Immediately available or liquid funds.

- **Retention**: A specified amount, usually 10 percent, withheld from progress payments to the contractor pending satisfactory completion and final acceptance of the project. This amount you have already earned even though you have not yet been paid.

- **Accounts Receivable**: The amounts due from customers (other than retentions) in payment for construction projects.

- **Inventory**: Includes all materials, labor, and direct and indirect overhead on jobs currently in progress. (For an example of direct and indirect costs, refer to the Internal Revenue Code Sections 263A [capitalization and inclusion in inventory costs of certain expenses] and 451 [general rule for taxable year of inclusion].)

- **Prepaid Expenses**: Goods or services the company buys and pays for before use. Examples are insurance premiums and office supplies.

- **Property, Plant, and Equipment**: Sometimes called fixed assets or plant and equipment, this group of assets includes physical resources a contractor owns or acquires for use in operations and has no intention to resell. Regardless of their current market value, fixed assets are valued at their original cost less accumulated depreciation. Sometimes property, plant, and equipment may be leased rather than owned. The value of the leased property is often included with the fixed assets and the lease payments are included with the liabilities.

- **Other Assets**: Resources not included under current assets, or under "Property, Plant, and Equipment" are placed here. Examples include scrap materials or equipment held for resale and long-term receivables.

LIABILITIES (right columns)

Liabilities, like assets, are broken down into two major categories: current liabilities and long-term liabilities. Liabilities represent obligations to pay money, pay other assets or render future services to others. The relationship of current and fixed assets and current and long-term liabilities will become apparent when you learn how to analyze the information presented in the financial statements.

Current Liabilities: This item includes debts of the company that become due within one year of the balance sheet date. Current assets are the source from which these payments are usually made. Management must be aware of this relationship and maintain sufficient current assets or control the amount of current liabilities to avoid becoming delinquent in its bills. In our example, Typical Construction Company, Inc. has $180,000 of current liabilities composed of the following items:

- **Accounts Payable**: Money owed to suppliers and subcontractors.

- **Notes Payable**: Balance of the principal owed on a written promissory note.

- **Accrued Expenses Payable**: Money owed for interest, services, insurance premiums, and other fees that are not included under accounts payable. Thus, expenses that have been incurred but are not due for payment on the date of the balance sheet are grouped under accrued expenses payable.

- **Accrued Payroll**: Salaries and wages that the contractor currently owes to employees.

- **Miscellaneous Taxes Payable**: Amounts estimated by the accountant to have been incurred during the accounting period and are owed to local and state governmental agencies.

- **Federal Income Taxes Payable**: Amount of liability for taxes owed to the federal government.

  NOTE: Different organizational forms will have different tax obligations.

LONG-TERM LIABILITIES

Long-term liabilities are notes or mortgages due one year beyond the balance sheet date. In our sample balance sheet, Typical Construction Company, Inc. owed $100,000 on a bank loan due more than a year in the future. This loan was secured by using certain equipment as collateral.

Stockholders' Equity (right column): The stockholders' equity section of the balance sheet, also called net worth or equity, represents the claim of the owners on the assets of the business. Different organizational forms use different names for this section of the balance sheet, but basically this is the original investment of the owners. Our example is a corporation, and the stockholders' equity section has two accounts.

Capital Stock: The total amount invested in the business by the contractor in exchange for shares of common stock at par value. Par value is arbitrarily established and need not be the same as the current market price of that share of stock.

Retained Earnings: Total corporation earnings from its beginning, minus the total dividends declared (distributions to owners) since the corporation was founded. This account represents additional investment by the owners who were willing to forego a larger distribution of the company's earnings.

INCOME STATEMENT

The income statement summarizes the operations of the company over a period of time. For the Typical Construction Company, Inc. (see next page) the period of time is one year. The balance sheets presented for Typical were year-end balance sheets with the income statement summarizing the operations during the intervening time period. Income statements are often prepared to cover shorter operational periods (e.g., quarter or month).

Basically, the income statement shows business revenue, expenses, and the resulting profit or loss for a given accounting period. Since the revenues are matched against the related costs and expenses, the difference between the two is how much the corporation makes or loses. This profit or loss is often called the "bottom line" because it is an important indicator of performance, and it is also the last line of the income statement.

Note, however, that this is only one performance indicator that financial statements report. The relationships of the various expense categories to total revenue presented in this statement must be understood if the company is to be effectively managed.

The components of this income statement are illustrated as follows:

Typical Construction Company, Inc.
Income Statement
for the year ending December 31, 2024

	Current Year	Prior Year
Sales of Residences	$1,250,000	$1,000,000
Cost of Operations		
Cost of Sales	1,030,000	850,000
General and administrative expenses	91,000	75,000
Operating expenses	23,900	22,000
Total operating expenses	1,145,000	947,000
Income Before Provision for Federal Income Tax	105,000	53,000
Provision for Federal Income Tax	30,000	12,000
Net Profit for year	$75,000	$41,000

Income: The revenue amount reflects all the billings made to customers for completed projects, as well as work in progress. This is an example of the accrual basis previously discussed. In our example for Typical Construction Company, Inc., the sales of residences for the current year were $1,250,000, which represents amounts billed for completed projects and work in progress.

Cost of Operations: Cost of operations in the contracting business is comprised of all costs and expenses associated with running the business, with the exception that federal income taxes are shown on another line. By totaling all the costs of operations and subtracting these from the revenue, the operating profit of the company can be found. In our example, Typical Construction Company, Inc., the total cost of operations for the current year is $1,145,000, which, when subtracted from the net sales, leaves an operating profit of $105,000. This represents the amount of profit earned by the contractor without taking into consideration federal income taxes.

Within the Cost of Operations section of the Income Statement are several important amounts:

Direct Labor: The actual cost for labor payroll for all jobs worked on during the period covered by the income statement. The amount of direct labor and the percentage of direct labor to the total cost of any project should be closely monitored by management. Direct labor expense is an important variable in determining the ultimate profit of the company. The labor percentage is also a direct measurement of the efficiency of the workers and the performance of supervision.

Direct Labor Burden: This includes all payroll taxes, insurance, and employee benefits associated with the labor payroll. If the workers belong to a union, the direct labor burden will include union benefit assessments and, in some cases, association fees.

Materials Used: This includes the cost of all materials used on the job and is usually the largest single expense item on the income statement. Since materials comprise such a large part of the total cost of contracting, this account should be carefully controlled and every effort made to ensure that purchasing is done efficiently.

Other Direct Costs: These costs include all items, other than those listed above, that are directly chargeable to individual jobs. For example, permits, bonds, insurance, and equipment rentals would be included here.

General and Administrative Expenses: This figure on the income statement is comprised of all items of expense of a general nature that cannot be specifically attributed to individual construction projects.

Whether individual expenses will be listed separately or combined with others will vary among accountants and contractors.

Pretax Income: To get this figure, the total operating expenses were subtracted from the sales of residences. This figure is called Income Before Provision for Federal Income Tax for those corporations that are subject to federal taxation. Certain corporations, as well as sole ownerships and partnerships, do not pay taxes on income; the income is reported on the owner's personal tax returns. This is another example of how the organizational form the contractor initially chooses will influence the content of the financial statements.

Net Profit for Year: This figure is often called net income and represents the sum of all revenues minus all expenses including

taxes, if applicable. Net profit or income is commonly referred to as
the "bottom line."

Statement of Changes in Financial Position

The Statement of Changes in Financial Position, also called the
Statement of Sources and Applications of Funds, is a third major
financial statement. It shows how funds were obtained and where
funds were used. We do not show an example of this statement
because in many small operations it is not used. However, if a
contracting company is going to be audited by certified public
accountants for the purpose of presenting financial statements to
creditors or others, a Statement of Changes in Financial Position may
be necessary.

Financial Analysis and Ratios

While the figures listed in the financial statements are meaningful
and important taken alone, they become even more valuable when
compared with other information. For example, comparing any
balance sheet item for the current year with the prior year
immediately provides added information. Did the figure increase?
Decrease? If so, by how much in absolute dollars? How much in
percentage terms?

The comparison of financial relationships is often done in three ways.

1. The first method is the comparison of current financial data
    with prior years. Very often, businesses will compare three to
    five years of key items, such as revenue and net income. This
    type of comparison gives the reader an idea as to the trends
    over time.

2. The second method is to compare the current financial data
    with that of other businesses within the same industry.
    Sources for industry data are provided by organizations, such
    as, Dun and Bradstreet, Inc., and Standard and Poor's, and
    are available on many websites that offer financial
    information. This information also can be found at large local
    libraries and at local college libraries.

3. The third method used in interpreting financial statements is
    ratio analysis. The relationship between any two figures
    within the current financial data is called a ratio. For
    example, if current assets are $100,000 and current liabilities
    are $50,000, the relationship of current assets to current
    liabilities ($100,000/$50,000) may be shown as 2 to 1, or 2:1
    (ratio). The bank loan officer who is to recommend the
    establishment of a line of credit (short-term loan) would be
    interested in the current ratio and quick ratio, as the bank

would expect the contractor to repay the loan in the near term.

Current Ratio

One very important kind of information that can be readily determined from the balance sheet is the ability of the company to pay debts when due (sometimes referred to as liquidity). The difference between the total current assets and the total current liabilities is called **working capital**.

One way of looking at working capital is that it represents the amount that is free and clear if all current debts are paid off. A comfortable amount of working capital gives a company the ability to meet its obligations and take advantage of opportunities.

Section III

What is a comfortable amount of working capital? To help answer this question, the current ratio provides additional helpful information. To calculate the current ratio, divide total current assets by total current liabilities. In the example of Typical Construction Company, Inc., the figures are:

$$\frac{\text{Current Assets } \$250,000}{\text{Current Liabilities } \$180,000} = 1.39$$

Therefore, for each $1 of current liabilities there is $1.39 in current assets to back it up.

Quick Ratio

The quick ratio is another, more conservative way of testing the adequacy of the current liquidity of the company. Instead of using current assets, quick assets are substituted because these are quickly converted into cash. One simple method of determining the quick assets is total current assets minus inventories. In our example:

Current Assets	$250,000
−Inventories	−$110,000
Quick Assets	$140,000

Quick Ratio:

$$\frac{\text{Quick Assets}}{\text{Current Liabilities}} \quad \frac{\$140,000}{\$180,000} = .78$$

For the above analysis, we can see that we have $.78 of assets that may readily be converted into cash for each $1 of current liabilities that will require cash payments shortly.

The long-term creditors (banks or insurance companies) would be interested in the ratio of total liabilities to net worth. This measure indicates the relative proportions of the contractor's assets supplied by creditors and owners. If the company defaulted on its debts, this ratio indicates the degree of safety for the creditors.

Net sales to net working capital, net sales to total assets, and net income to net worth are all measures of the efficiency of the company's use of its resources. These measures are important indicators to management. Net sales to net working capital (low ratio) might be attributed either to an excess of working capital or to inadequate sales. Management should examine each ratio, keeping in mind that if the ratios reflect a weakness, the manager then must analyze the problem area and develop possible solutions, e.g., more vigorous collection effort to reduce the size of receivables.

Keep in mind that the ratios also are interdependent. When the receivables are reduced, the cash generated by the collection effort may be used to reduce long-term liabilities and improve the debt ratio. Management must not focus its attention narrowly. The broad perspective created by knowledge of business principles is essential for success.

FINANCIAL MANAGEMENT

The financial management section focuses first on the need for financial resources; second, on the sources; and finally, on how to best determine if those financial resources are being fully utilized.

Capitalization

Capitalization refers to the total of financial resources made available to the owner. These financial resources are used to acquire the physical assets necessary to conduct the business. As you assess your financial requirements, the more obvious needs to finance the tools, vehicles, and other equipment (physical resources) used daily in the business are recognized first. The need for additional financing of office expenses, licenses, payroll expenses, bonding, rentals, etc. is critical for the business because of the differences between when you must pay and when you get paid.

The amount of working capital required depends on the type of contracting business. The progress payments required under contracts for custom building and remodeling may be used to meet payroll expenses and material costs. The typical contract provides for three or more payments, 90 percent during the construction phase and the final 10 percent upon completion and expiration of the lien period. This final 10 percent is the "retention." The contractor cannot collect more than the percentage already completed. The contractor must be aware that differences in the timing of expenditures and receipts may limit their capacity to finance the business, particularly if the company commits itself to new jobs before final payments on completed jobs have been received.

The significance of "retention" must not be underestimated. Retention usually exceeds profits and therefore represents a claim on working capital. Retention payments to the individual contractor may be held up through no fault of the contractor. The total project must be accepted before retentions are released. The problem is even greater for the subcontractor who completes their phase early in the project and must contend with a long waiting period. Since these funds are not available for use elsewhere in the business, the contractor must often finance the costs through borrowing.

Speculative builders require larger amounts of capital than custom builders. Consequently, speculative builders often must provide substantial financial resources to qualify for loan commitments.

Sources of Financing

The new business owner typically lacks the needed financial resources. Two types of external financing are available — **equity funds** and **debt**. Equity funds are supplied by investors who acquire some control of the business and a share of future profits. These funds remain in the business. Debt represents borrowed dollars that require both the repayment of the original amount and periodic interest payments. The owner does not normally give up control of the business.

EQUITY FUNDS

The typical sources of these funds are acquaintances of the new owner-contractor. Equity funds are sometimes available from private venture capital companies, small business investment corporations that are funded by the federal Small Business Administration, and minority enterprise small business investment companies. These sources are usually restricted to businesses with a proven track record in a growing industry.

DEBT

Long-Term

Banks may offer long-term financing to contractors with good credit ratings, technical knowledge, and capacity for repayment as evidenced by financial planning in the form of projected balance sheets, income statements, and cash budgets.

Section III

The Small Business Administration (SBA) does not make direct loans, but it does guarantee repayment of a loan. For more information, visit www.sba.gov.

Short-Term

The operating business may want to establish a line of credit with a bank to meet some of its short-term needs for working capital. Through the line of credit, commercial banks can provide the working capital necessary to complete the awarded contract, with the loan requiring repayment when the contractor is paid.

The bank loan officer will normally require balance sheets and income statements on the business for the current period, as well as over several prior years. The contractor is advised to have these reports prepared by a certified public accountant so that they meet professional accounting standards. The lender will expect to be provided with information on the contract up for bid, as well as all uncompleted contracts. The loan officer will evaluate:

> **Character**: Includes experience with similar jobs and locations; business reputation with lenders, suppliers, and subcontractors; and reasonableness of bid.

> **Capacity**: Requires an evaluation of current workload, availability of equipment, and financial resources available to withstand any reasonable loss. The financial strengths of the awarding agency, and subcontractors and suppliers also are important considerations.

> **Certainty**: What are the chances that repayment will be affected by unexpected losses on existing business? Are completion dates realistic? Is there a chance that penalties will be assessed for delays?

Bank loans to speculative builders may include funds necessary to provide off-site improvements, as well as the construction of buildings. Funding also may be arranged to acquire land for future development.

OPERATIONS MANAGEMENT

Job Selection

The planning involved in job selection requires knowledge of the general level of business activity in the local area, the need for new construction, costs of materials and labor, the contractor's current financial resources, the contractor's technical expertise, and any new architectural or structural advances.

Bidding and Estimation (Planning)

Accurate bidding requires that the contractor map out the entire construction process. The time spent on this detailed work ensures the accuracy of cost estimates necessary for the contractor to make a profit. Careful review of the job requires on-site inspection (walk the job), review of plans and specifications, identification of equipment required and the financing method (purchase, lease, rental), and the need for subcontractors.

Materials required are determined from takeoffs (quantity and measurements taken from plans) that are converted to costs on the estimation form. Prices should be obtained from published price lists and quotes from suppliers and subcontractors. It is important to include sales tax and freight costs. Cash discounts should not be included unless the contractor is certain that sufficient financial resources will be available so that accounts payable may be repaid during the discount period.

Labor costs are calculated according to work classification. These costs include not only the hourly wage rate, but also payroll taxes, health and welfare benefits, vacation pay, and required insurance.

Other direct costs that must be examined include permits and other fees; interest, loan commitment fees, points, and other charges on borrowed funds; equipment owned or rented; and any additional insurance that may be required.

Fuel and lubricant expenses, general maintenance, and small tools represent indirect costs that may be charged to the project and should not be overlooked.

The contractor also must identify the overhead expenses. Overhead normally includes such expenses as office rental, supplies and wages, advertising, bad debts, storage charges, and any other general administrative costs.

When all the costs have been totaled, the contractor must add profit. The contractor will seriously jeopardize the business by omitting the allowance for profit, especially if the bid has a low margin and there is any chance of underestimation. Insufficient profits threaten both capitalization (losses reduce retained earnings) and cash flow (payments to vendors may exceed receipts) to the extent that bankruptcy and/or dissolution may be the result.

Common pitfalls that can be avoided include the following: Bidding on projects for which the plans and specifications are not completely understood, insufficient planning so that hurried analysis becomes necessary, overextension of the managerial and/or financial resources of the company, and bidding against the competition and not on the job itself. It is easier to avoid financial difficulty by not bidding on a job for which you lack the capability than to try to salvage the job after a poor bid has been accepted.

The Construction Process (Coordination and Control)

The estimate that is the basis for the bid becomes a budget for the project. Without extensive planning and scheduling, lack of coordination can result in added costs that quickly reduce the profits.

If the estimation has been done properly, the job was broken down into a job schedule to arrive at the number of labor hours required. Actual construction, however, requires that materials and labor be brought together at the proper time. Two methods of production scheduling may be used to accomplish this coordination.

The **bar chart** (Figure 6.A) is a fundamental scheduling technique that shows graphically the starting and finishing times for the individual tasks that make up the job. This scheduling approach is simple but overlooks some interrelated tasks.

The **critical path** method (Figure 6.B) is a more complex tool that better interrelates the tasks. This technique derives its name from the key path through the network that considers all the tasks to be completed.

Any delay in one of these tasks will result in an overall delay of the project. This procedure, therefore, identifies the tasks on which the manager must focus attention to ensure completion of the project on time.

FIGURE 6.A
Building a New Home: Construction Schedule

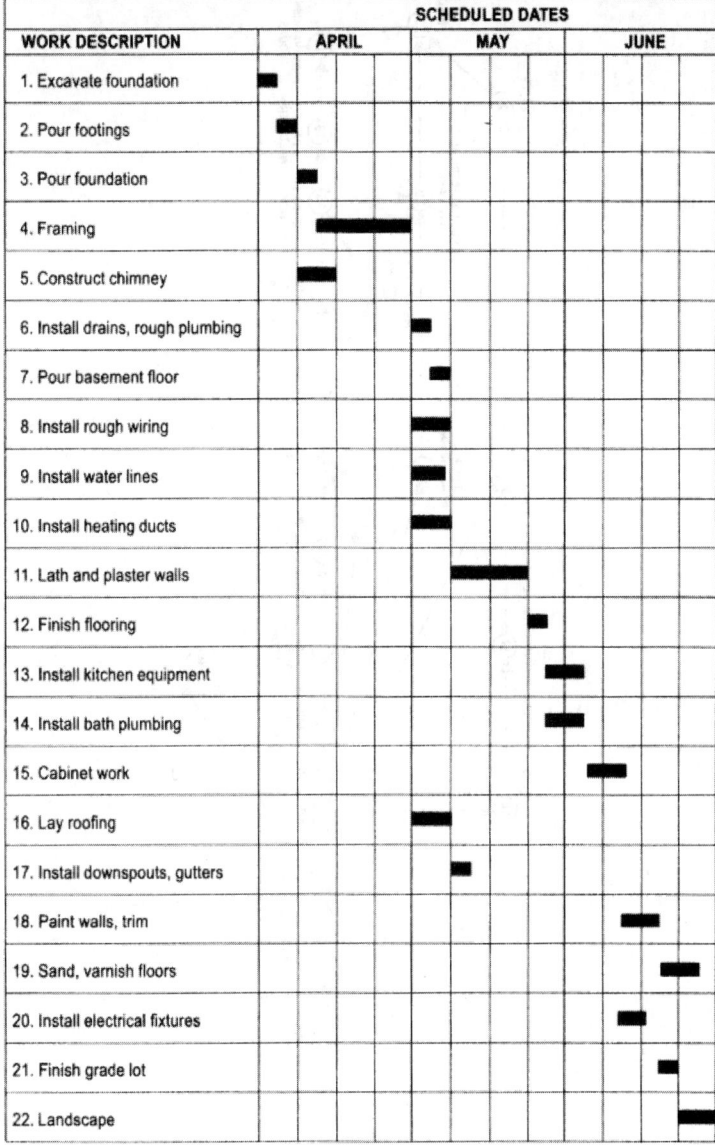

WORK DESCRIPTION	SCHEDULED DATES		
	APRIL	MAY	JUNE
1. Excavate foundation	▪		
2. Pour footings	▪		
3. Pour foundation	▪		
4. Framing	▬▬		
5. Construct chimney	▪		
6. Install drains, rough plumbing		▪	
7. Pour basement floor		▪	
8. Install rough wiring		▬	
9. Install water lines		▬	
10. Install heating ducts		▬	
11. Lath and plaster walls		▬▬	
12. Finish flooring		▪	
13. Install kitchen equipment		▪	
14. Install bath plumbing		▪	
15. Cabinet work			▪
16. Lay roofing		▬	
17. Install downspouts, gutters		▪	
18. Paint walls, trim			▬
19. Sand, varnish floors			▬
20. Install electrical fixtures			▪
21. Finish grade lot			▪
22. Landscape			▬

Section III

FIGURE 6.B
Building a New Home: Critical Path Analysis

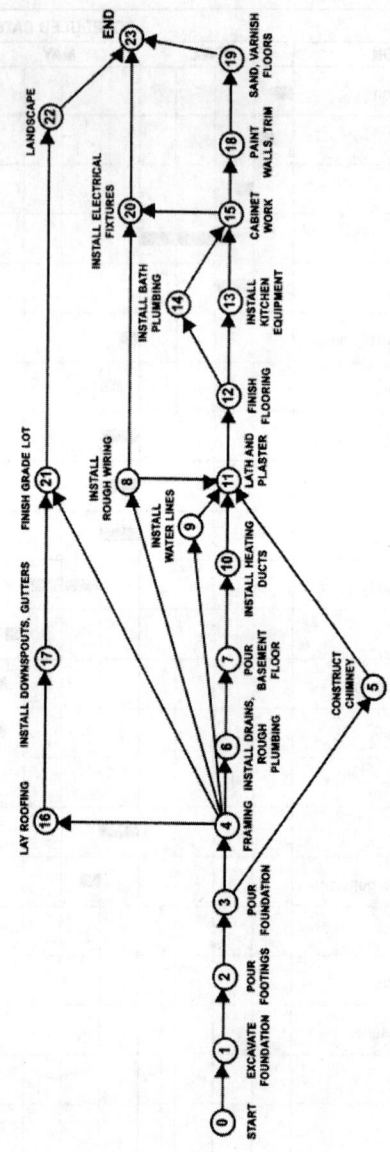

Controlling Costs

Contractors typically have a small permanent payroll that consists of a foreperson and skilled journeypersons. This force can be expanded by union hiring halls, which means that the contractor must be knowledgeable about the union's master labor contract. The work of the various subcontractors must be scheduled and coordinated with the overall job. The small contractor must expect to spend most of the day at the site, coordinating these activities and resolving conflicts. Subcontractors should be chosen based on their ability to perform, as well as cost, since untimely delays quickly eliminate the potential savings of the lowest bid.

Purchasing is an essential part of the job because of the high cost of carrying an inventory of materials. As with subcontractors, reliability is equally important as price. The contractor will typically develop trade relations with a limited number of suppliers. Costs are best controlled by checking with other suppliers if prices increase significantly, by verifying order quantities, by taking cash discounts when offered, and by not overstocking.

Risk Management

Businesses operate under conditions of uncertainty. Unexpected property and casualty losses can severely damage the business's prospects. Insurance is a means of reducing the company's exposure to risk. The contractor should consult an insurance agent or broker to design a comprehensive insurance package to meet the company's specific needs. This package could include:

- Workers' compensation insurance
- Fire insurance
- Liability insurance
- Automobile insurance
- Fidelity bonds
- Business interruption insurance
- Employee health and life insurance
- "Key person" insurance

If the contractor lacks sufficient funds for total coverage, a planned approach to risk management becomes necessary. Principles that should be followed include:

Section III

- Covering the largest loss exposure first; property and liability insurance should be reviewed yearly to reflect changes in valuation and take current court judgments into account.

- Using deductibles to significantly reduce costs.

- Reviewing coverage yearly to reflect changes in the business.

- Taking time to understand the implications of any changes in the insurer's contracts.

Marketing Management

Personal contacts represent the major source of business for the new contractor. Small and medium-sized contracting businesses rely on referrals. The extent of the marketing effort is limited by the sources available to the contractor.

LEGAL CONSIDERATIONS AND REMEDIES

A continuing relationship with an attorney familiar with the construction business can be helpful. Printed standard forms of agreements used in the industry are available from the contractor's particular trade association, the American Institute of Architects, or the Associated General Contractors of America. It is a good idea to have an attorney double-check the contract for compliance with all regulatory agency requirements.

In addition to helping with the interpretation of contracts, the attorney can help in choosing the form of business organization; making sure all necessary documents are filed with city, county, and state governments; and helping resolve any differences that might occur between the contractor and other business parties.

There are typically four types of contractual agreements between the builder and owner with which the contractor should be familiar. These are the lump-sum, the cost-plus, the unit-price, and the guaranteed-maximum cost contract. Each of these contract types specifies different terms and obligations with which the contractor must be familiar.

In addition, the contractor must be aware of the proper filing methods, the number of days for filing, and other documents, such as lien release notices, lien claims, and notices of completion. It is essential for the contractor to be familiar with the California mechanics lien law.

Disputes

At the outset, you should be aware that there is no good lawsuit. You will never be fully compensated for your out-of-pocket expenses, much less for the physical, emotional, and business disruption that a lawsuit can create. Therefore, you should do everything within reason to settle your differences. This can be done in several ways:

Get It in Writing

Besides the statutory requirement that certain contracts be in writing, it is extremely important that a contract of any significance at all be in writing. First, a written document will not be forgotten like a verbal agreement and is more likely to keep the parties aware of their rights and responsibilities.

Second, if there is a dispute and an arbitrator or judge is asked to interpret the agreement, they are more likely to find in accordance with your true intent if that intent is in writing.

Extras

"Changes" or "extras" added to a contract tend to contribute to disputes. To determine if something is in addition to or outside the scope of the original agreement, you must be able to accurately determine what the original agreement states. If the original agreement is well defined and in writing, it will be much easier to determine if something is added or changed.

Once you determine that a request is different than what was agreed to (whether more or less), document that fact in writing. You should also immediately negotiate the effect of the change, such as cost and time. Tell your customer what is going on and allow the customer to determine if the change is worth it. If you and your customer agree to the change, make sure both parties sign the written change order.

Communication

Whenever possible you should communicate with your customer and encourage your customer to communicate with you. Frequent "punch lists" are a good idea. A walk-through near the end of the job to determine the items that are left to be completed is recommended. Correct any deficiencies quickly.

It is a good idea to document the progress of the project and keep your customer up to date.

Section III

Closely allied with the communication of progress is frequent billing. By invoicing regularly, you will minimize your business's cash demands while keeping your customer informed. Let your customer know what is going on; and, if there is a problem, face it head-on before it becomes insurmountable.

Even if you have done everything you could, you may still find yourself involved in a dispute. You have various options:

Settlement

Lawsuits are costly, time-consuming, and disruptive. If possible, you should attempt to settle your differences.

Small Claims

If you are owed money and cannot settle your dispute, you might consider filing suit in small claims court rather than courts of greater jurisdiction. Although you cannot foreclose on a mechanics lien in small claims court, you may get a monetary judgment of up to $10,000 (see CCP §116.221). Aside from the fact that if a defendant loses, they have an automatic right of appeal, small claims judgments are as valid and binding as courts of greater jurisdiction.

Small claims courts are fast and economical. Your claim can usually be heard within one to two months and the entire cost should be minimal. You and your customer must represent yourselves. Neither you nor your customer may be represented by an attorney. For information about small claims court topics, such as filing a complaint and collecting a judgment, see the California Courts website: https://selfhelp.courts.ca.gov/small-claims-california. If the defendant loses in small claims court, there is an automatic right of appeal within 30 days of the ruling.

Arbitration

Another option for settling disputes is arbitration. CSLB has its own arbitration program, but many contractors choose to bring their disputes to private arbitrators.

Arbitration is different from court proceedings in several ways. Usually, both parties must agree to arbitration and can often have a say in choosing the arbitrator.

Either side may present its own case or use an attorney.

Because of its more informal nature, some of the protections afforded in court, such as the rules of evidence, are not always followed. Arbitrators tend to allow much more evidence than would be allowed in court. Most arbitration decisions are binding (the arbitrator's decision is final). Finally, there are very few grounds for appeal of an arbitration decision.

If you want potential disputes to be solved via *private* arbitration you must use the arbitration notice in Business and Professions Code section 7191. If the parties to the contract agree to such a notice, they will not be allowed access to CSLB's arbitration program (unless both parties later sign a waiver of the contractual arbitration clause).

CSLB Arbitration Program

To help resolve complaints filed with the board, CSLB offers two free arbitration programs: a mandatory program for disputes involving alleged damages of less than $25,000, and a voluntary program for disputes involving alleged damages of between $25,000 and $50,000. When the alleged damages are less than $25,000, CSLB can order the contractor into a mandatory CSLB arbitration.

To qualify for CSLB arbitration, disputes must comply with certain criteria:

- The contractor's license must be in good standing (current and not under suspension) at the time of the alleged violation.

- The contractor cannot have a record of prior violations.

- The parties cannot have previously agreed to private arbitration in the contract or elsewhere.

Mechanics Liens

Mechanics liens and "stop notices" are briefly touched on in this portion of the book; these two avenues are discussed in greater detail in the next portion. However, you should note that, as a contractor (one who enhances the value of property), you are entitled to a lien on the property and may be entitled to a lien on any construction funds. The way these liens are perfected is very technical and the time limits are short. You should be thoroughly familiar with the manner and means of perfecting your lien rights, such as giving the preliminary notice, recording the mechanics lien, filing a stop notice, and filing suit to foreclose. These remedies can be utilized by anyone who improves the property.

Section III

Filing Suit

Regardless of your mechanics lien rights, as with any other businessperson, you can file suit for breach of the construction contract if someone does not fulfill their obligation. Certainly, if the customer does not pay you money when it is due, you can sue them. If you have been unsuccessful in resolving the dispute and have not availed yourself of the mechanics lien rights due to the strict statutory requirements, you can still file suit. The seller of any product or service is entitled to compensation. You, as a contractor, also are entitled to your money.

If you are a corporation or limited liability company, you cannot represent yourself in court other than small claims court and must obtain the services of an attorney. If you are a partner or a sole proprietor, you can represent yourself in court and are not required to have an attorney represent you.

CALIFORNIA MECHANICS LIENS AND STOP NOTICES

Mechanics Liens

In California, mechanics liens are provided for in Article 14, Section 3 of the California Constitution:

> Mechanics, persons furnishing materials, artisans, and laborers of every class, shall have a lien upon the property upon which they have bestowed labor or furnished material for the value of such labor done and material furnished; and the Legislature shall provide, by law, for the speedy and efficient enforcement of such liens.

The manner in which mechanics lien rights are perfected is based on statutes. The California Supreme Court has held that mechanics lien rights are constitutional.

In order to file on mechanics liens, this does not mean that they must have a contract directly with the owner. However, they must have a contract with the agent of the owner and every contractor, subcontractor, architect, builder, or other person having charge of a work of improvement and held to be an agent of the owner.

A material supplier is not the agent of the owner and, therefore, a material supplier's supplier is not entitled to a statutory lien. Further, to perfect your lien, the work and/or materials, etc. must be incorporated into the structure. That is to say, it has to be installed.

Stop Notices

A mechanics lien is a lien on property. A stop notice is a lien on funds. You may use one or the other, or both. However, it should be noted that in public works, you cannot file a mechanics lien; therefore, your only remedy may be a stop notice. Since the stop notice is a lien on funds, it may be preferable to a mechanics lien in some instances.

Other Remedies

Even though you may be one of the people protected by the mechanics lien laws in California, you are not precluded from other remedies. You can still sue on a contract theory or on any other legal theory available. So, even if you have not availed yourself of the mechanics lien rights, you still have alternative legal remedies.

Procedure

The mechanics lien laws and stop notice requirements are relatively complicated and must be adhered to very strictly. Listed below is a procedural checklist to help you complete each step necessary in a timely manner.

Mechanics Lien and Stop Notice Checklist

I. Prior to Serving the Notices

Before serving the notices, it is important to do the following:

- ☐ Obtain the legal description of the property.

- ☐ Determine the name of the owner and the extent of the owner's interest in the property.

- ☐ Determine if the owner is the one requesting the improvement. (If not, what is the interest of the person requesting it and are there any others who claim an interest in the property, such as lenders, etc.).

- ☐ Determine if you are a prime contractor, subcontractor, laborer, or material supplier.

- ☐ Determine the name of the construction lender (if any).

- ☐ Consider the effect of a bond or joint control.

II. Subcontractors and Material Suppliers

A. Within 20 days from first furnishing labor or materials, serve a "Preliminary 20-day Notice" on the owner, the original contractor, and construction lender. No matter how many deliveries you make, or the time span over which you furnish labor or materials, only one Preliminary Notice is required.

The notice must include specific wording to inform a property owner of a new responsibility to notify anyone else who served a Preliminary Notice.

NOTE: You may also file the Preliminary 20-day Notice with the county recorder in the county in which the property is located. The county recorder will then notify you when a Notice of Completion or Notice of Cessation is recorded on the property.

The most common method for serving a notice is to use first class certified or registered mail, return receipt requested, postage prepaid, addressed to the residence or place of business of the person being served, or at the address shown by the building permit, or at an address contained on a recorded mortgage or trust deed. Be sure to keep post office receipts for later use if you need to file a claim and prove it in court. A Preliminary Notice also may be served by personal delivery or by leaving it with a "person in charge" at the residence or place of business of the person you wish to serve (must be an adult).

B. After the work is completed or ceases, the following apply:

1. If the owner records a Notice of Completion after completion of work of improvement (this requires signature of owner or owner's agent), you should not do additional work under the contract. (While this notice provision is designed to primarily protect the owner, it might serve to increase the funds accessible to satisfy your claim and indicate that you have performed your contractual obligations.)

2. Labor must have ceased for at least 30 days before the owner is entitled to record a Notice of Cessation. If the owner files a Notice of Cessation of labor or a Notice of Completion, then:

    (a) Within 30 days of the owner recording either a Notice of Cessation or Completion, the subcontractor must record a Claim of Lien with the county recorder. Also at this time, serve stop notices (see below).

NOTE: An owner who files a Notice of Cessation or a Notice of Completion must notify any potential lien claimants within 10 days of recording the notices. This notification is designed to let you, the potential lien claimant, know that the time for filing a Claim of Lien has been reduced. This provision does not apply to a residential property of four or fewer units.

  (b) File Lien Foreclosure Action within 90 days of recording a Claim of Lien and record a *lis pendens* at the same time. You must also file an action on the stop notice at this time, if applicable.

3. If no Notice of Completion or Notice of Cessation is recorded and either:

  (a) Labor ceases and the owner or agent uses work of improvement, or

  (b) The owner or agent accepts improvement, then:

    (1) Within 90 days of any of the above acts, record a Claim of Lien. Also, at this time, serve stop notices (see below).

    (2) Within 90 days of recording the lien, file a Lien Foreclosure Action and record a *lis pendens* at the same time.

4. Stop Notices:

  (a) Serve stop notices on the owner, bonded stop notices on the construction lender, or anyone holding funds.

  (b) If no mechanics lien has been recorded, and a surety payment bond has been recorded, then the notice must be served on the surety.

  (c) File suit on the notice at the same time that you file a Lien Foreclosure Action.

III. Prime Contractors

  A. Within 15 days after completion, you may record a Notice of Completion. (While this notice provision is designed to primarily protect the owner, it might serve to increase the funds accessible to satisfy your claim and indicate that you have performed your contractual obligations.) Do not do

Section III

additional work under the contract. This notice requires the signature of the owner or the owner's agent.

B. Within 60 days of recording the above, record the Claim of Lien.

C. Within 90 days of recording the lien, file a Lien Foreclosure Action and record a *lis pendens* at the same time.

D. If the owner records a Notice of Cessation of Labor or a Notice of Completion, do the following:

NOTE: Labor must have ceased for at least 30 days before the owner is entitled to record the Notice of Cessation.

1. Within 60 days of recording a Notice of Cessation or a Notice of Completion, the contractor must record a Claim of Lien.

2. Within 90 days of recording the Claim of Lien, file a Lien Foreclosure Action, and record a *lis pendens*.

E. If no Notice of Completion or Cessation is recorded, and either:

1. Labor ceases and owner or agent uses the work of improvement; or

2. Owner or agent accepts improvement, then:

(a) Within 90 days of any of the above acts, record a Claim of Lien.

(b) File a Lien Foreclosure Action within 90 days of recording Claim of Lien and record a *lis pendens* at the same time.

NOTE: Per AB 457, which took effect in 2011, the definitions of "claim of lien" and "mechanics lien" are the same. This law also requires that a Notice of Mechanics Lien be served on the owner or person believed to be the owner of the property or on the construction lender or original contractor, <u>and</u> that a "proof of service affidavit" to the above-mentioned party or parties be completed and signed by the person serving the Notice of Mechanics Lien. Failure to serve the mechanics lien and confirm a proof of service affidavit will cause the mechanics lien to be unenforceable.

GLOSSARY OF TERMS
ASSOCIATED WITH MECHANICS LIENS

Bonded Stop Notice is a bond that accompanies a stop notice to a construction lender and must be in a sum equal to 1 ¼ times the amount of the claim. The bond, along with the stop notice, must be delivered by certified or registered mail or in person, to the persons responsible for administering or holding construction funds. Should the claimant lose their action (lawsuit on the bond), then the claimant must pay all costs that may be awarded to the owner or contractor or construction lenders. This is the reason for the bond on the stop notice.

Claimant is the person claiming or asserting the right or demand (the person claiming mechanics lien or stop notice rights).

Claim of Lien (mechanics lien) is a written statement signed and verified by the claimant or by the claimant's agent that must state the following:

1. The amount of claimant's demand (after deducting credits and offsets).

2. The name of the owner or reputed owner, if known.

3. The kind of labor, services, equipment, or materials furnished by the claimant.

4. The name of the person who employed the claimant or to whom the claimant furnished the labor, services, equipment, or materials (the contractor who hired you if you are a subcontractor or the owner who hired you if you are the prime contractor).

5. A description of the site sufficient for identification.

Defendant is the person who defends themselves or who denies a claim. A defendant is the person against whom relief or recovery is sought in an action or suit.

Lien Foreclosure Action is a lawsuit to foreclose the mechanics lien.

Lis Pendens is a notice that a lawsuit is pending, and that the lawsuit affects real property. It warns everyone who might acquire the property that they may be bound by an adverse judgment.

Notice of Cessation is a written notice, signed and verified by the owner or their agent, stating:

1. Approximate date when labor on the job stopped.
2. Confirmation that no further labor has been performed since the recording of the notice.
3. Name and address of the owner.
4. Nature of the interest or estate of the owner.
5. Street address of the site, if any, or a description of the site sufficient for identification.
6. Name of the original contractor, if any, for the work of improvement.

Notice of Completion is a written notice, signed and verified by the owner or their agent, stating:

1. Date that the job was finished.
2. Name and address of the owner.
3. Nature of the interest or estate of the owner.
4. Street address of the site, if any, or a description of the site sufficient for identification.
5. Name of the original contractor, if any, for the contract covering the portion of the work of improvement completed.

The Notice of Completion must be recorded in the Office of the County Recorder of the county in which the site is located within 10 days after completion of the project. If the Notice of Completion is recorded, then the time within which you must record your mechanics lien is 60 days if you are a prime contractor and 30 days if you are a subcontractor. If this notice is not filed in a timely manner, you have a 90-day period within which to record the claim.

Notice of Non-Responsibility is a written notice, as described below, which is signed and verified by a person or that person's agent who owns or claims to have an interest in the property being improved and who has not caused the work of improvement. For example, the owner completes this notice when their tenant is requiring the work of improvement without the owner's direction. This notice must contain:

1. Description of the site sufficient for identification.

2. Name and nature of the title or interest of the person giving the notice.

3. Name of the purchaser or person holding the lease (lessee), if known.

4. Statement by the person giving the notice that they will NOT be responsible for any claims arising from the work of improvement.

Within 10 days of discovering the work of improvement, the person asserting non-responsibility must post this notice in a conspicuous place on the site and must record the notice in the Office of the County Recorder of the county in which the site is located.

Original Contractor, also known as prime contractor, is usually a general contractor.

Owner includes any person(s) having some title or interest in a parcel of real property.

Payment Bond is a bond usually procured by the owner or contractor in an amount sufficient to pay all claims of claimants. The bond gives the claimant the right to recover in any suit brought on the bond. Usually, the bond is used to protect against mechanics liens and substitutes the bond as security instead of the real property.

Prime Contractor, see "Original Contractor" above.

Stop Notice is a written notice, signed and verified by the claimant or the claimant's agent, that puts a lender or anyone else holding construction funds on notice that there is money due and owed to the claimant. It must state the following:

1. Type of labor, services, equipment, or materials furnished or agreed to be furnished by the claimant.

2. Name of the person to or for whom the labor, services, etc. were furnished.

3. Amount, based on value as near as possible, of the work or equipment already completed or furnished and the amount of the whole work agreed to be done or furnished.

If involving a private work of improvement, the notice must be delivered to the owner personally or left at their residence or place of business with a person in charge or delivered to their architect, if any; and, if the notice is served upon a construction lender holding construction funds and maintaining branch offices, it must be delivered to the manager or other responsible person at the office or branch administering or holding the construction funds.

If involving any public work for the state, the notice must be filed with the director of the department that initiated the contract.

If involving any other public work, the notice must be filed in the office of the controller, auditor, or other public disbursing officer whose duty it is to make payments under the provisions of the contract or with the commissioners, managers, trustees, officers, board of supervisors, board of trustees, common council, or other body by whom the contract was awarded.

Any stop notice may be served by registered or certified mail with the same effect as personal service.

The stop notice obligates the person holding construction funds to withhold sufficient funds to satisfy the amount in the stop notice. If the person holding the funds does not withhold sufficient funds to satisfy the stop notice, then the lender or whoever else is holding the funds may be responsible to the claimant directly.

To bind a construction lender, the stop notice must be bonded. The bond that accompanies a stop notice to any construction lender must be in the sum equal to 1 ¼ times the amount of the claim. The bond must be delivered along with the stop notice in person or by certified or registered mail to the persons responsible for administering or holding the construction funds.

Should the claimant lose in their action (lawsuit on the bond), then the claimant must pay all costs that may be awarded to the owner or contractor or construction lender. That is the reason for the bond on the stop notice.

Subcontractor is any person who does not have a contract directly with an owner. The subcontractor has a contract with and from the prime contractor or another subcontractor. A subcontractor is usually a specialty contractor but can also be a general contractor.

EXPERT ADVISORS

The new contractor must be prepared to seek out and utilize the expertise of specialists in business affairs, just as the contractor has come to rely upon skilled specialists in the building trades. If the business is to be organized as a partnership or corporation, an attorney, preferably one who specializes in drawing up partnership agreements or incorporation papers, should be consulted. The local bar association may be a good source for recommendations.

The accounting records should be prepared by a certified public accountant (CPA) whose practice specializes in building trade industry clients. The CPA or tax lawyer should be consulted for specialized tax problems.

The U.S. Small Business Administration (SBA) along with its resource partners, Service Corps of Retired Executives (SCORE) and Small Business Development Centers (SBDC), offer a wide variety of services to individuals wanting to start or expand their business. Contact them at:

> U.S. Small Business Administration
> (800) 827-5722
> www.sba.gov
> Email: answerdesk@sba.gov

BIDDING ON GOVERNMENT CONTRACTS

Contractors bidding in California should know that there are a variety of federal, state, and local governmental agencies, as well as public utilities and private corporations, which may require a bidder to take specific steps to achieve established minority, women, and disabled veteran business enterprise (DVBE) goals. For information on fulfilling these goals on bids for certain government contracts, check with the following agencies:

> California Department of General Services,
> Procurement Division
> Office of Small Business and DVBE Services (OSDS)
> 707 Third Street
> West Sacramento, CA 95605

> Phone: (916) 376-5000 or (916) 375-4940
> Email: OSDSHelp@dgs.ca.gov
> Website: http://www.dgs.ca.gov/pd/

Section III

The U.S. Department of Commerce Minority Business Development
Agency (MBDA) provides direct business development services to
minority businesses through a network of MBDA Business Centers
located in most major cities throughout the country. Services may
include identification of contracting opportunities, preparation of bid
proposals, identification of lending sources, preparation of loan
applications, etc.

For more information, visit http://www.mbda.gov.

SECTION IV.

CONSTRUCTION STANDARDS AND SAFETY REGULATIONS

Chapter 4.

Regional Notification Centers: Underground Service Alert

What is a Regional Notification Center?

A regional notification center is an association of owners and operators of subsurface installations (water, gas, electric, telephone, sewer, oil lines, etc.). Damage to these underground structures may result in the disruption of essential public services and pose a threat to workers, the public, and the environment. The purpose of the center is to provide a single telephone number that excavators can use to give the center's members advance notification of their intent to excavate. The operators of the underground installations are then responsible for providing information about the locations of the facility, marking or staking the approximate location of their facility, or advising the excavator of clearance. Operators are only responsible for facilities they own; operators are not responsible for facilities they do not own.

Contacting a Regional Notification Center is a Requirement—Not an Option.

California Government Code Sections 4216-4216.9 require anyone planning to excavate to contact the appropriate regional notification center at least two working days (but not more than 14 calendar days) before beginning excavation. The center will issue an inquiry identification number to the excavator as confirmation of the call.

NOTE: An excavation permit is not valid without this identification number.

Section IV

Who Must Comply:

- Any person or entity who plans to disturb the surface of the ground by digging, drilling, boring, etc.

Exempt Persons:

- An owner of private property who contracts with a California state-licensed contractor or subcontractor for an excavation project that does not require an excavation permit.

- An owner of private property (who is not a licensed contractor or subcontractor) who, as a part of improving their principal residence, does work that does not require an excavation permit.

- Any person or private entity that leases or rents power-operated or power-driven excavating or boring equipment to a contractor or subcontractor licensed pursuant to contractors' state license law, regardless of whether an equipment operator is provided for that piece of equipment, if the signed rental agreement contains the following provision:

  > "It is the sole responsibility of the lessee or renter to follow the requirements of the regional notification center law pursuant to Article 2 (commencing with Section 4216) of Chapter 3.1 of Division 5 of Title 1 of the Government Code. By signing this contract, the lessee or renter accepts all liabilities and responsibilities contained in the regional notification center law."

Steps Required for Compliance:

- Every contractor or subcontractor excavating at a jobsite must have their own Underground Service Alert (USA) identification (ticket) number for the excavation work they are performing.

- Excluding emergency situations, parties planning excavation activities must contact the appropriate regional notification center not less than two working days, nor more than 14 calendar days, prior to the start of work.

THE REGIONAL NOTIFICATION CENTER CALL IS FREE: 811/(800) 640-5137.

- Upon notification, the center will issue an identification (ticket) number. The ticket number will be valid for 28 calendar days. If work is to continue past 28 calendar days, the ticket number must be revalidated again by notifying the center before the ticket number expires.

- At the site, excavators must clearly mark the boundaries of the work area, usually with white paint.

- Within these boundary markings, operators of underground installations must then provide information about their facilities, mark or stake the location of their lines clearly using the appropriate color to show what type of installation is present or advise of clearance.

- During the course of the job, if the operator's markings become no longer visible, the excavator must contact the regional center and request that the operator re-mark the lines within two working days.

- Using the operator's markings, an excavator must determine the exact location of underground facilities with hand tools or a vacuum device before any power equipment may be used.

- After January 1, 2023, all new subsurface installations must be mapped using a geographic information system and maintained as permanent records of the operator.

- An excavator must notify the regional notification center within 48 hours of discovering or causing damage.

Section IV

Helpful Hints

- Provide the beginning date and time of your excavation.

- Give your name, company's name, company's mailing address, email address, telephone number where you can be contacted, nature of work (grading, drilling, etc.), whom the work is being done for, name of the foreman, permit name and number, if excavation has been outlined in white paint, and a description of the excavation site.

- When describing your excavation site, give the address or description where you will be digging (including side of street, the intersection corner, footage, and total distances or other tie-in measurements), and nearest intersecting street, city, and county.

Penalties

- Any operator or excavator who negligently violates any portion of Government Code sections 4216–4216.9 is subject to a fine not to exceed $10,000.

- Any operator or excavator who knowingly and willfully violates any portion of Government Code sections 4216–4216.9 is subject to a fine not to exceed $50,000.

- Any operator or excavator who knowingly and willfully violates any of the provisions of this article in a way that results in damage to a gas or hazardous liquid pipeline subsurface installation and that results in the escape of any flammable, toxic, or corrosive gas or liquid is subject to a civil penalty in an amount not to exceed one hundred thousand dollars ($100,000).

- An excavator also may be subject to third party claims for damages arising from the excavation work.

- Violation of Government Code sections 4216–4216.9 could result in disciplinary action and possible revocation of your contractor license by CSLB.

REGIONAL NOTIFICATION CENTERS

Underground Service Alert of Northern California and Nevada: 811
www.usanorth811.org

Serves the following counties in Northern California:

Alameda, Alpine, Amador, Butte, Calaveras, Colusa, Contra Costa, Del Norte, El Dorado, Fresno, Glenn, Humboldt, Kern, Kings, Lake, Lassen, Madera, Marin, Mariposa, Mendocino, Merced, Modoc, Mono, Monterey, Napa, Nevada, Placer, Plumas, Sacramento, San Benito, San Francisco, San Joaquin, San Luis Obispo, San Mateo, Santa Clara, Santa Cruz, Shasta, Sierra, Siskiyou, Solano, Sonoma, Stanislaus, Sutter, Tehama, Trinity, Tulare, Tuolumne, Yolo, and Yuba

Serves the entire state of Nevada

Service: Monday–Friday, 6 a.m.–7 p.m., excluding holidays

Underground Service Alert of Southern California—
811
www.digalert.org

Serves the following counties in Southern California:

Imperial, Inyo, Los Angeles, Orange, Riverside, San Bernardino, San Diego, Santa Barbara, and Ventura

Service: Monday–Friday, 6 a.m.–7 p.m., excluding holidays

Chapter 5.

Preservation of Native American Remains

California has one of the largest Native American populations in the United States. With approximately 115 federally recognized tribes and more applying for recognition, California Native American lands include reservations and rancherias in over half of California's counties. Historically, Native American land holdings encompassed the entire state of California.

Several laws provide for the protection and sensitive treatment of these human remains and associated burial goods (Health and Safety Code section 7050.5; Public Resources Code sections 5097.9-5097.991). The intent of the law is to provide protection to Native American burials and associated grave goods from vandalism and inadvertent destruction.

REPORTING REQUIREMENT

In the event of discovery or recognition of any human remains in any location other than a dedicated cemetery, there shall be no further excavation or disturbance of the site or nearby area. Upon the discovery of human remains or burial artifacts at any site other than a dedicated cemetery, the following actions must be taken immediately:

1. Stop work immediately at that site and any nearby area reasonably suspected to have remains and contact the county coroner.

2. The coroner has two working days to examine the remains after being notified by the person responsible for the excavation. If the remains are Native American, the coroner has 24 hours to notify the Native American Heritage Commission.

3. The Native American Heritage Commission will immediately notify the person it believes to be the most likely descendant of the deceased Native American.

4. The most likely descendant has 24 hours to make recommendations to the owner or representative for the treatment and disposition, with proper dignity, of the remains and grave goods.

5. If the owner doesn't accept the descendant's recommendations, the owner or the descendant may request mediation by the Native American Heritage Commission.

6. If mediation fails to provide measures acceptable to the landowner, the landowner or their authorized representative shall reinter the human remains and items associated with Native American burials, with appropriate dignity, and in a location on the property not subject to further subsurface disturbance.

PENALTIES

It is a felony to obtain or possess Native American remains or associated grave goods. (*See Public Resources Code §§5097.94, 5097.98, and 5097.99.*) Any person who knowingly or willfully removes, obtains, or possesses any Native American remains or associated burial artifacts, without authority of law, is guilty of a felony, punishable by imprisonment in state prison.

ADDITIONAL INFORMATION

To learn more about the protection and preservation of Native American burial grounds, human remains, and associated grave goods, contact the Native American Heritage Commission at:

> Native American Heritage Commission
> 1550 Harbor Boulevard, Suite 100
> West Sacramento, CA 95691
> (916) 373-3710
> Email: nahc@nahc.ca.gov
> Website: www.nahc.ca.gov

Chapter 6.

Construction of Wells

LICENSE REQUIRED FOR WATER WELLS

Section 13750.5 of the California Water Code states:

> No person shall undertake to dig, bore, or drill a water well, cathodic protection well, groundwater monitoring well, or geothermal heat exchange well, to deepen or reperforate such a well, or to abandon or destroy such a well, unless the person responsible for that construction, alteration, destruction, or abandonment possesses a C-57 Water Well Contractor's License.

REPORTING REQUIREMENTS

Water Wells, Cathodic Protection Wells, and Monitoring Wells

California Water Code sections 13751 through 13754 require persons who construct, alter (including, but not limited to, drilling, deepening, reperforation, or abandonment), or destroy a water well, cathodic protection well, monitoring well, or geothermal heat exchange well, to file a report of completion, called the "Well Completion Report, DWR 188," with the California Department of Water Resources (DWR) within 60 days after completion of the work. Earlier versions of the form were called "Water Well Driller's Report." These reports are also called "well logs" or "driller's logs."

This requirement also applies to persons who convert—for use as a water well, cathodic protection well, or monitoring well—any oil or gas well originally constructed under the jurisdiction of the California Department of Conservation.

The State of California and other agencies use the information provided by these reports to evaluate groundwater resources, to protect groundwater quality, and to conserve water supplies.

NOTE: Failure to file the Well Completion Report is a misdemeanor (*Water Code §13754*) and constitutes cause for disciplinary action against your contractor license (*Business and Professions Code section 7110*).

How and where to file

Drillers submit their well completion reports to DWR with the Online System of Well Completion Reports (OSWCR). OSWCR users create an account based on their C-57 license that DWR will validate. Upon approval, users will be able to submit Well Completion Reports.

More information is available on the DWR website: www.water.ca.gov

WELL STANDARDS

Standards for construction, modification, rehabilitation, and destruction of water wells, monitoring wells, and cathodic protection wells are published by DWR in Bulletin 74, the California Well Standards. The current Standards are contained in Bulletin 74-81 *Water Well Standards: State of California,* and the draft supplemental Bulletin 74-90 *California Well Standards: Water Wells, Monitoring Wells, Cathodic Protection Wells.*

Counties and other local jurisdictions may have adopted local well ordinances with standards in addition to the statewide standards contained in Bulletin 74-90. The designated local enforcing agency, which is usually the county environmental health department, should be contacted whenever work on a well is being planned to ensure compliance with local ordinances. Many of these local agencies require permits for any work on a well and charge a fee for that permit.

Questions about well standards should be directed to the local enforcing agency or to DWR at (916) 653-5791.

LAW SECTIONS

LAW SECTIONS

SECTION V.

THE DEPARTMENT OF CONSUMER AFFAIRS

Chapter 7.

Laws Governing the Department of Consumer Affairs

The Department of Consumer Affairs includes 40 regulatory entities—among them the Contractors State License Board—which regulate various services and industries in the state. Some of the other boards and bureaus under the department's purview include the Medical Board of California, the Structural Pest Control Board, and the Bureau of Automotive Repair. The department's mission, through its regulatory boards, is "to promote and protect the interests of California consumers by serving as guardian and advocate for their health, safety, privacy, and economic well being; enhancing public participation in regulatory decision-making; promoting legal and ethical standards of professional conduct; identifying marketplace trends so that the Department's programs and policies are contemporary, relevant, and responsive; partnering with business and consumer groups in California and the nation; and working with law enforcement to combat fraud and enforce consumer protection laws vigorously and fairly." The laws governing the department and the CSLB are part of California's Business and Professions Code. What follows are selected sections from the codes that relate, in general or in specifics, to the purpose and function of the department.

BUSINESS & PROFESSIONS CODE

GENERAL PROVISIONS

§ 7.5. "Conviction"; When action by board following establishment of conviction may be taken; Prohibition against denial of licensure; Application of section

(a) A conviction within the meaning of this code means a judgment following a plea or verdict of guilty or a plea of nolo contendere or finding of guilt. Any action which a board is permitted to take following the establishment of a conviction may be taken when the time for appeal has elapsed, or the judgment of conviction has been affirmed on appeal or when an order granting probation is made suspending the imposition of sentence. However, a board may not deny a license to an applicant who is otherwise qualified pursuant to subdivision (b) or (c) of Section 480.

(b) (1) Nothing in this section shall apply to the licensure of persons pursuant to Chapter 4 (commencing with Section 6000) of Division 3.

(2) This section does not in any way modify or otherwise affect the existing authority of the following entities in regard to licensure:

(A) The State Athletic Commission.

(B) The Bureau for Private Postsecondary Education.

(C) The California Horse Racing Board.

(c) Except as provided in subdivision (b), this section controls over and supersedes the definition of conviction contained within individual practice acts under this code.

(d) This section shall become operative on July 1, 2020.

Added Stats 2018 ch 995 § 2 (AB 2138), effective January 1, 2019, operative July 1, 2020.

§ 8. Governing provisions

Unless the context otherwise requires, the general provisions hereinafter set forth shall govern the construction of this code.

Enacted Stats 1937.

§ 9. Effect of headings

Division, part, chapter, article and section headings contained herein shall not be deemed to govern, limit, modify, or in any manner affect the scope, meaning, or intent of the provisions of this code.

Enacted Stats 1937.

§ 10. Authority of deputies

Whenever, by the provisions of this code, a power is granted to a public officer or a duty imposed upon such an officer, the power may be exercised or duty performed by a deputy of the officer or by a person authorized pursuant to law by the officer, unless it is expressly otherwise provided.

Enacted Stats 1937.

§ 12.5. Violation of regulation adopted pursuant to code provision; Issuance of citation

Whenever in any provision of this code authority is granted to issue a citation for a violation of any provision of this code, that authority also includes the authority to issue a citation for the violation of any regulation adopted pursuant to any provision of this code.

Added Stats 1986 ch 1379 § 1.

§ 14.1. Legislative intent

The Legislature hereby declares its intent that the terms "man" or "men" where appropriate shall be deemed "person" or "persons" and any references to the terms "man" or "men" in sections of this code be changed to "person" or "persons" when such code sections are being amended for any purpose. This act is declaratory and not amendatory of existing law.

Added Stats 1976 ch 1171 § 1.

§ 14.2. "Spouse" to include registered domestic partner

"Spouse" includes "registered domestic partner," as required by Section 297.5 of the Family Code.

Added Stats 2016 ch 50 § 1 (SB 1005), effective January 1, 2017.

§ 22. "Board"

"Board," as used in any provision of this code, refers to the board in which the administration of the provision is vested, and unless otherwise expressly provided, shall include "bureau," "commission," "committee," "department," "division," "examining committee," "program," and "agency."

Enacted Stats 1937. Amended Stats 1947 ch 1350 § 1; Stats 1980 ch 676 § 1; Stats 1991 ch 654 § 1 (AB 1893); Stats 1999 ch 656 § 1 (SB 1306); Stats 2004 ch 33 § 1 (AB 1467), effective April 13, 2004; Stats 2010 ch 670 § 1 (AB 2130), effective January 1, 2011.

§ 23.5. "Director"

"Director," unless otherwise defined, refers to the Director of Consumer Affairs.

Wherever the laws of this state refer to the Director of Professional and Vocational Standards, the reference shall be construed to be to the Director of Consumer Affairs.

Added Stats 1939 ch 30 § 2. Amended Stats 1971 ch 716 § 2.

§ 23.6. "Appointing power"

"Appointing power," unless otherwise defined, refers to the Director of Consumer Affairs.

Added Stats 1945 ch 1276 § 1. Amended Stats 1971 ch 716 § 3.

§ 23.7. "License"

Unless otherwise expressly provided, "license" means license, certificate, registration, or other means to engage in a business or profession regulated by this code or referred to in Section 1000 or 3600.

Added Stats 1994 ch 26 § 1 (AB 1807),.effective March 30, 1994.

§ 23.8. "Licensee"

"Licensee" means any person authorized by a license, certificate, registration, or other means to engage in a business or profession regulated by this code or referred to in Sections 1000 and 3600.

Any reference to licentiate in this code shall be deemed to refer to licensee.

Added Stats 1961 ch 2232 § 1. Amended Stats 2019 ch 351, § 1 (AB 496), effective January 1, 2020.

§ 23.9. Licensing eligibility of prison releasees

Notwithstanding any other provision of this code, any individual who, while imprisoned in a state prison or other correctional institution, is trained, in the course of a rehabilitation program approved by the particular licensing agency concerned and provided by the prison or other correctional institution, in a particular skill, occupation, or profession for which a state license, certificate, or other evidence of proficiency is required by this code shall not, when released from the prison or institution, be denied the right to take the next regularly scheduled state examination or any examination thereafter required to obtain the license, certificate, or other evidence of proficiency and shall not be denied such license, certificate, or other evidence of proficiency, because of that individual's imprisonment or the conviction from which the imprisonment resulted, or because the individual obtained the individual's training in prison or in the correctional institution, if the licensing agency, upon recommendation of the Adult Authority or the Department of the Youth Authority, as the case may be, finds that the individual is a fit person to be licensed.

Added Stats 1967 ch 1690 § 1, as B & P C § 23.8. Amended and Renumbered by Stats 1971 ch 582 § 1; Stats 2019 ch 351 § 2 (AB 496), effective January 1, 2020.

§ 26. Rules and regulations regarding building standards

Wherever, pursuant to this code, any state department, officer, board, agency, committee, or commission is authorized to adopt rules and regulations, such rules and regulations which are building standards, as defined in Section 18909 of the Health and Safety Code, shall be adopted pursuant to the provisions of Part 2.5 (commencing with Section 18901) of Division 13 of the Health and Safety Code unless the provisions of Sections 18930, 18933, 18938, 18940, 18943, 18944, and 18945 of the Health and Safety Code are expressly excepted in the provision of this code under which the authority to adopt the specific building standard is delegated. Any building standard adopted in violation of this section shall have no force or effect. Any building standard adopted prior to January 1, 1980, pursuant to this code and not expressly excepted by statute from such provisions of the State Building Standards Law shall remain in effect only until January 1, 1985, or until adopted, amended, or superseded by provisions published in the State Building Standards Code, whichever occurs sooner.

Added Stats 1979 ch 1152 § 1.

§ 27. Information to be provided on internet; entities in department of consumer affairs required to comply

(a) Each entity specified in subdivisions (c), (d), and (e) shall provide on the internet information regarding the status of every license issued by that entity in accordance with the California Public Records Act (Division 10 (commencing with Section 7920.000) of Title 1 of the Government Code) and the Information Practices Act of 1977 (Chapter 1 (commencing with Section 1798) of Title 1.8 of Part 4 of Division 3 of the Civil Code). The public information to be provided on the internet shall include information on suspensions and revocations of licenses issued by the entity and other related enforcement action, including accusations filed pursuant to the Administrative Procedure Act (Chapter 3.5 (commencing with Section 11340) of Part 1 of Division 3 of Title 2 of the Government Code) taken by the entity relative to persons, businesses, or facilities subject to licensure or regulation by the entity. The information may not include personal information, including home telephone number, date of birth, or social security number. Each entity shall disclose a licensee's address of record. However, each entity shall allow a licensee to provide a post office box number or other alternate address, instead of the licensee's home address, as the address of record. This section shall not preclude an entity from also requiring a licensee, who has provided a post office box number or other alternative mailing address as the licensee's address of record, to provide a physical business address or residence address only for the entity's internal administrative use and not for disclosure as the licensee's address of record or disclosure on the internet.

(b) In providing information on the internet, each entity specified in subdivisions (c) and (d) shall comply with the Department of Consumer Affairs' guidelines for access to public records.

(c) Each of the following entities within the Department of Consumer Affairs shall comply with the requirements of this section:

(1) The Board for Professional Engineers, Land Surveyors, and Geologists shall disclose information on its registrants and licensees.

(2) The Bureau of Automotive Repair shall disclose information on its licensees, including automotive repair dealers, smog check stations, smog check inspectors and repair technicians, and vehicle safety systems inspection stations and technicians.

(3) The Bureau of Household Goods and Services shall disclose information on its licensees, registrants, and permitholders.

(4) The Cemetery and Funeral Bureau shall disclose information on its licensees, including cemetery brokers, cemetery salespersons, cemetery managers, crematory managers, cemetery authorities, crematories, cremated remains disposers, embalmers, funeral establishments, and funeral directors.

(5) The Professional Fiduciaries Bureau shall disclose information on its licensees.

(6) The Contractors State License Board shall disclose information on its licensees and registrants in accordance with Chapter 9 (commencing with Section 7000) of Division 3. In addition to information related to licenses as specified in subdivision (a), the board shall also disclose information provided to the board by the Labor Commissioner pursuant to Section 98.9 of the Labor Code.

(7) The Bureau for Private Postsecondary Education shall disclose information on private postsecondary institutions under its jurisdiction, including disclosure of notices to comply issued pursuant to Section 94935 of the Education Code.

(8) The California Board of Accountancy shall disclose information on its licensees and registrants.

(9) The California Architects Board shall disclose information on its licensees, including architects and landscape architects.

(10) The State Athletic Commission shall disclose information on its licensees and registrants.

(11) The State Board of Barbering and Cosmetology shall disclose information on its licensees.

(12) The Acupuncture Board shall disclose information on its licensees.

(13) The Board of Behavioral Sciences shall disclose information on its licensees and registrants.

(14) The Dental Board of California shall disclose information on its licensees.

(15) The California State Board of Optometry shall disclose information on its licensees and registrants.

(16) The Board of Psychology shall disclose information on its licensees, including psychologists and registered psychological associates.

(17) The Veterinary Medical Board shall disclose information on its licensees, registrants, and permitholders.

(d) The State Board of Chiropractic Examiners shall disclose information on its licensees.

(e) The Structural Pest Control Board shall disclose information on its licensees, including applicators, field representatives, and operators in the areas of fumigation, general pest and wood destroying pests and organisms, and wood roof cleaning and treatment.

(f) "Internet" for the purposes of this section has the meaning set forth in paragraph (6) of subdivision (f) of Section 17538.

Section V

Added Stats 1997 ch 661 § 1 (SB 492). Amended Stats 1998 ch 59 § 1 (AB 969); Stats 1999 ch 655 § 1 (SB 1308); Stats 2000 ch 927 § 1 (SB 1889); Stats 2001 ch 159 § 1 (SB 662); Stats 2003 ch 849 § 1 (AB 1418); Stats 2009 ch 308 § 1 (SB 819), effective January 1, 2010, ch 310 § 1.5 (AB 48), effective January 1, 2010; Stats 2011 ch 381 § 2 (SB 146), effective January 1, 2012, ch 712 § 1 (SB 706), effective January 1, 2012; Stats 2014 ch 316 § 1 (SB 1466), effective January 1, 2015; Stats 2015 ch 689 § 1 (AB 266), effective January 1, 2016; Stats 2016 ch 32 § 1 (SB 837), effective June 27, 2016; Stats 2016 ch 489 § 1 (SB 1478), effective January 1, 2017; Stats 2017 ch 429 § 1 (SB 547), effective January 1, 2018. Stats 2018 ch 578 § 1 (SB 1483), effective January 1, 2019. Stats 2018 ch 599 § 1 (AB 3261), effective January 1, 2019. Stats 2018 ch 703 § 1.3 (SB 1491), effective January 1, 2019 (ch 703 prevails); Stats 2019 ch 351 § 4 (AB 496), effective January 1, 2020; Stats 2020 ch 312 § 1 (SB 1474), effective January 1, 2021; Stats 2021 ch 70 § 1 (AB 141), effective July 12, 2021; Stats 2021 ch 188 § 1 (SB 826), effective January 1, 2022; Stats 2021 ch 630 § 1 (AB 1534), effective January 1, 2022; Stats 2021 ch 647 § 1.3 (SB 801), effective January 1, 2022 (ch 647 prevails); Stats 2022 ch 8 § 1 (SB 1380), effective January 1, 2023; Stats 2023 ch 681 § 1 (AB 1263), effective January 1, 2024.

§ 27.5. Update to Licensee or Registrant Legal Name or Gender

(a) (1) Notwithstanding any other law, if a board within the Department of Consumer Affairs receives government-issued documentation, as described in subdivision (b), from a licensee or registrant demonstrating that the licensee's or registrant's legal name or gender has been changed, the board, upon request by the licensee or registrant, shall update the individual's license or registration by replacing references to the former name or gender on the license or registration, as applicable, with references to the current name or gender.

(2) (A) If the board operates an online license verification system, upon request by a licensee or registrant whose name or gender was updated pursuant to paragraph (1), the board shall replace references to the licensee's or registrant's former name or gender with the individual's current name or gender, as applicable, on the publicly viewable information displayed on the internet about the licensee or registrant. The licensee's or registrant's former name or gender, as applicable, shall not be published online.

(B) Notwithstanding any other law, for licensees or registrants subject to subparagraph (A) who were previously subject to an enforcement action referencing the individual's former name or gender, as applicable, the board shall not post enforcement records online, but shall instead post online a statement stating that the individual previously was subject to enforcement action and directing the public to contact the board for more information about the licensee's or registrant's prior enforcement action. The board shall ensure compliance with the California Public Records Act (Division 10 (commencing with Section 7920.000) of Title 1 of the Government Code) in implementing this section, including, but not limited to, responding to a request for records within 10 days from receipt of the request, as specified in Section 7922.535 of the Government Code.

(C) If a public search of the online license verification system is performed using a licensee's or registrant's former name that was replaced pursuant to subparagraph (A), the board shall post an online statement directing the public to contact the board for more information about the licensee or registrant.

(3) If requested by the licensee or registrant, the board shall reissue the license created by the board and conferred upon the licensee or registrant by the board. A board shall not charge a higher fee for reissuing a document with an updated legal name or gender than the fee it regularly charges for reissuing a document with other updated information.

(b) (1) The documentation identified in either of the following is required to demonstrate a legal name change of a licensee or registrant:

(A) A certified court order issued pursuant to a proceeding authorized by subdivision (b) of Section 1277 of the Code of Civil Procedure and a copy of the certificate issued under the Secretary of State's Safe at Home program authorized by Chapter 3.1 (commencing with Section 6205) of Division 7 of Title 1 of the Government Code reflecting the licensee's or registrant's updated name.

(B) A certified court order issued pursuant to a proceeding authorized by Section 1277.5 of the Code of Civil Procedure or Article 7 (commencing with Section 103425) of Chapter 11 of Part 1 of Division 102 of the Health and Safety Code reflecting the licensee's or registrant's updated name.

(2) Any of the following documents are sufficient to demonstrate a gender change of a licensee or registrant:

(A) State-issued driver's license or identification card.

(B) Birth certificate.

(C) Passport.

(D) Social security card.

(E) Court order indicating a gender change from a court of this state, another state, the District of Columbia, any territory of the United States, or any foreign court.

(c) Notwithstanding any other law, all records related to a request by a licensee or registrant for a board to update the individual's license or registration pursuant to this section, including, but not limited to, all documentation described in subdivision (b), are confidential and not subject to public inspection or disclosure.

Added Stats 2023 ch 225 § 1 (SB 372), effective January 1, 2024.

§ 29.5. Additional qualifications for licensure

In addition to other qualifications for licensure prescribed by the various acts of boards under the department, applicants for licensure and licensees renewing their licenses shall also comply with Section 17520 of the Family Code.

Added Stats 1991 ch 542 § 1 (SB 1161). Amended Stats 2003 ch 607 § 1 (SB 1077).

—*See Family Code Section 17520, Compliance with Support Orders by Applicants for Professional Licenses, in Appendix.*

§ 30. Provision of federal employer identification number or social security number by licensee

(a) (1) Notwithstanding any other law, any board, as defined in Section 22, the State Bar of California, and the Department of Real Estate shall, at the time of issuance of the license, require that the applicant provide its federal employer identification number, if the applicant is a partnership, or the applicant's social security number for all other applicants.

(2) (A) In accordance with Section 135.5, a board, as defined in Section 22, the State Bar of California, and the Department of Real Estate shall require either the individual taxpayer identification number or social security number if the applicant is an individual for a license or certificate, as defined in subparagraph (2) of subdivision (e), and for purposes of this subdivision.

(B) In implementing the requirements of subparagraph (A), a licensing board shall not require an individual to disclose either citizenship status or immigration status for purposes of licensure.

(C) A licensing board shall not deny licensure to an otherwise qualified and eligible individual based solely on the individual's citizenship status or immigration status.

(D) The Legislature finds and declares that the requirements of this subdivision are consistent with subsection (d) of Section 1621 of Title 8 of the United States Code.

(b) A licensee failing to provide the federal employer identification number, or the individual taxpayer identification number or social security number shall be reported by the licensing board to the Franchise Tax Board. If the licensee fails to provide that information after notification pursuant to paragraph (1) of subdivision (b) of Section 19528 of the Revenue and Taxation Code, the licensee shall be subject to the penalty provided in paragraph (2) of subdivision (b) of Section 19528 of the Revenue and Taxation Code.

(c) In addition to the penalty specified in subdivision (b), a licensing board shall not process an application for an initial license unless the applicant provides its federal employer identification number, or individual taxpayer identification number or social security number where requested on the application.

(d) A licensing board shall, upon request of the Franchise Tax Board or the Employment Development Department, furnish to the board or the department, as applicable, the following information with respect to every licensee:

(1) Name.

(2) Address or addresses of record.

(3) Federal employer identification number if the licensee is a partnership, or the licensee's individual taxpayer identification number or social security number for all other licensees.

(4) Type of license.

(5) Effective date of license or a renewal.

(6) Expiration date of license.

(7) Whether license is active or inactive, if known.

(8) Whether license is new or a renewal.

(e) For the purposes of this section:

(1) "Licensee" means a person or entity, other than a corporation, authorized by a license, certificate, registration, or other means to engage in a business or profession regulated by this code or referred to in Section 1000 or 3600.

(2) "License" includes a certificate, registration, or any other authorization needed to engage in a business or profession regulated by this code or referred to in Section 1000 or 3600.

(3) "Licensing board" means any board, as defined in Section 22, the State Bar of California, and the Department of Real Estate.

(f) The reports required under this section shall be filed on magnetic media or in other machine-readable form, according to standards furnished by the Franchise Tax Board or the Employment Development Department, as applicable.

(g) Licensing boards shall provide to the Franchise Tax Board or the Employment Development Department the information required by this section at a time that the board or the department, as applicable, may require.

(h) Notwithstanding Division 10 (commencing with Section 7920.000) of Title 1 of the Government Code, a federal employer identification number, individual taxpayer identification number, or social security number furnished pursuant to this section shall not be deemed to be a public record and shall not be open to the public for inspection.

(i) A deputy, agent, clerk, officer, or employee of a licensing board described in subdivision (a), or any former officer or employee or other individual who, in the course of their employment or duty, has or has had access to the information required to be furnished under this section, shall not disclose or make known in any manner that information, except as provided pursuant to this section, to the Franchise Tax Board, the Employment Development Department, the Office of the Chancellor of the California Community Colleges, a collections agency contracted to collect funds owed to the State Bar by licensees pursuant to Sections 6086.10 and 6140.5, or as provided in subdivisions (j) and (k).

(j) It is the intent of the Legislature in enacting this section to utilize the federal employer identification number, individual taxpayer identification number, or social security number for the purpose of establishing the identification of persons affected by state tax laws, for purposes of compliance with Section 17520 of the Family Code, for purposes of measuring employment outcomes of students who participate in career technical education programs offered by the California Community Colleges, and for purposes of collecting funds owed to the State Bar by licensees pursuant to Section 6086.10 and Section 6140.5 and, to that end, the information furnished pursuant to this section shall be used exclusively for those purposes.

(k) If the board utilizes a national examination to issue a license, and if a reciprocity agreement or comity exists between the State of California and the state requesting release of the individual taxpayer identification number or social security number, any deputy, agent, clerk, officer, or employee of any licensing board described in subdivision (a) may release an individual taxpayer identification number or social security number to an examination or licensing entity, only for the purpose of verification of licensure or examination status.

(l) For the purposes of enforcement of Section 17520 of the Family Code, and notwithstanding any other law, a board, as defined in Section 22, the State Bar of California, and the Department of Real Estate shall at the time of issuance of the license require that each licensee provide the individual taxpayer identification number or social security number of each individual listed on the license and any person who qualifies for the license. For the purposes of this subdivision, "licensee" means an entity that is issued a license by any board, as defined in Section 22, the State Bar of California, the Department of Real Estate, and the Department of Motor Vehicles.

(m) The department shall, upon request by the Office of the Chancellor of the California Community Colleges, furnish to the chancellor's office, as applicable, the following information with respect to every licensee:

(1) Name.

(2) Federal employer identification number if the licensee is a partnership, or the licensee's individual taxpayer identification number or social security number for all other licensees.

(3) Date of birth.

(4) Type of license.

(5) Effective date of license or a renewal.

(6) Expiration date of license.

(n) The department shall make available information pursuant to subdivision (m) only to allow the chancellor's office to measure employment outcomes of students who participate in career technical education programs offered by the California Community Colleges and recommend how these programs may be improved. Licensure information made available by the department pursuant to this section shall not be used for any other purpose.

(o) The department may make available information pursuant to subdivision (m) only to the extent that making the information available complies with state and federal privacy laws.

(p) The department may, by agreement, condition or limit the availability of licensure information pursuant to subdivision (m) in order to ensure the security of the information and to protect the privacy rights of the individuals to whom the information pertains.

(q) All of the following apply to the licensure information made available pursuant to subdivision (m):

(1) It shall be limited to only the information necessary to accomplish the purpose authorized in subdivision (n).

(2) It shall not be used in a manner that permits third parties to personally identify the individual or individuals to whom the information pertains.

(3) Except as provided in subdivision (n), it shall not be shared with or transmitted to any other party or entity without the consent of the individual or individuals to whom the information pertains.

(4) It shall be protected by reasonable security procedures and practices appropriate to the nature of the information to protect that information from unauthorized access, destruction, use, modification, or disclosure.

(5) It shall be immediately and securely destroyed when no longer needed for the purpose authorized in subdivision (n).

(r) The department or the chancellor's office may share licensure information with a third party who contracts to perform the function described in subdivision (n), if the third party is required by contract to follow the requirements of this section.

Added Stats 2017 ch 828 § 2 (SB 173), effective January 1, 2018, operative July 1, 2018. Amended Stats 2018 ch 659 § 1 (AB 3249), effective January 1, 2019. Stats 2018 ch 838 § 2.5 (SB 695), effective January 1, 2019 (ch 838 prevails); Stats 2019 ch 351 § 6 (AB 496), effective January 1, 2020; Stats 2021 ch 615 § 2 (AB 474), effective January 1, 2022.

§ 31. Compliance with judgment or order for support upon issuance or renewal of license

(a) As used in this section, "board" means any entity listed in Section 101, the entities referred to in Sections 1000 and 3600, the State Bar, the Department of Real Estate, and any other state agency that issues a license, certificate, or registration authorizing a person to engage in a business or profession.

(b) Each applicant for the issuance or renewal of a license, certificate, registration, or other means to engage in a business or profession regulated by a board who is not in compliance with a judgment or order for support shall be subject to Section 17520 of the Family Code.

(c) "Compliance with a judgment or order for support" has the meaning given in paragraph (4) of subdivision (a) of Section 17520 of the Family Code.

(d) Each licensee or applicant whose name appears on a list of the 500 largest tax delinquencies pursuant to Section 7063 or 19195 of the Revenue and Taxation Code shall be subject to Section 494.5.

(e) Each application for a new license or renewal of a license shall indicate on the application that the law allows the California Department of Tax and Fee Administration and the Franchise Tax Board to share taxpayer information with a board and requires the licensee to pay the licensee's state tax obligation and that the licensee's license may be suspended if the state tax obligation is not paid.

(f) For purposes of this section, "tax obligation" means the tax imposed under, or in accordance with, Part 1 (commencing with Section 6001), Part 1.5 (commencing with Section 7200), Part 1.6 (commencing with Section 7251), Part 1.7 (commencing with Section 7280), Part 10 (commencing with Section 17001), or Part 11 (commencing with Section 23001) of Division 2 of the Revenue and Taxation Code.

Added Stats 1991 ch 110 § 4 (SB 101). Amended Stats 1991 ch 542 § 3 (SB 1161); Stats 2010 ch 328 § 1 (SB 1330), effective January 1, 2011; Stats 2011 ch 455 § 1 (AB 1424), effective January 1, 2012; Stats 2013 ch 352 § 2 (AB 1317), effective September 26, 2013, operative July 1, 2013; Stats 2019 ch 351 § 7 (AB 496), effective January 1, 2020.

§ 35. Provision in rules and regulations for evaluation experience obtained in armed services

It is the policy of this state that, consistent with the provision of high-quality services, persons with skills, knowledge, and experience obtained in the armed services of the United States should be permitted to apply this learning and contribute to the employment needs of the state at the maximum level of responsibility and skill for which they are qualified. To this end, rules and regulations of boards provided for in this code shall provide for methods of evaluating education, training, and experience obtained in the armed services, if applicable to the requirements of the business, occupation, or profession regulated. These rules and regulations shall also specify how this education, training, and experience may be used to meet the licensure requirements for the particular business, occupation, or profession regulated. Each board shall consult with the Department of Veterans Affairs and the Military Department before adopting these rules and regulations. Each board shall perform the duties required by this section within existing budgetary resources of the agency within which the board operates.

Added Stats 1994 ch 987 § 1 (SB 1646), effective September 28, 1994. Amended Stats 1995 ch 91 § 1 (SB 975); Stats 2010 ch 214 § 1 (AB 2783), effective January 1, 2011.

§ 40. State Board of Chiropractic Examiners or Osteopathic Medical Board of California expert consultant agreements

(a) Subject to the standards described in Section 19130 of the Government Code, any board, as defined in Section 22, the State Board of Chiropractic Examiners, or the Osteopathic Medical Board of California may enter into an agreement with an expert consultant to do any of the following:

(1) Provide an expert opinion on enforcement-related matters, including providing testimony at an administrative hearing.

(2) Assist the board as a subject matter expert in examination development, examination validation, or occupational analyses.

(3) Evaluate the mental or physical health of a licensee or an applicant for a license as may be necessary to protect the public health and safety.

(b) An executed contract between a board and an expert consultant shall be exempt from the provisions of Part 2 (commencing with Section 10100) of Division 2 of the Public Contract Code.

(c) Each board shall establish policies and procedures for the selection and use of expert consultants.

(d) Nothing in this section shall be construed to expand the scope of practice of an expert consultant providing services pursuant to this section.

Added Stats 2011 ch 339 § 1 (SB 541), effective September 26, 2011.

DIVISION 1

DEPARTMENT OF CONSUMER AFFAIRS

Chapter 1

The Department

Chapter 2

The Director of Consumer Affairs

Section V

Chapter 3

Funds of the Department

Chapter 4

Consumer Affairs

Article 1

General Provisions and Definitions

Article 2

Director and Employees

Article 3

Powers and Duties

Article 3.6

Uniform Standards Regarding Substance-Abusing Healing Arts Licensees

Chapter 1

The Department

§ 100. Establishment

There is in the state government, in the Business, Consumer Services, and Housing Agency, a Department of Consumer Affairs.

Enacted Stats 1937. Amended Stats 1969 ch 138 § 5; Stats 1971 ch 716 § 4; Stats 1984 ch 144 § 1. See this section as modified in Governor's Reorganization Plan No. 2 § 1 of

2012. Amended Stats 2012 ch 147 § 1 (SB 1039), effective January 1, 2013, operative July 1, 2013 (ch 147 prevails).

§ 101. Composition of department

The department is comprised of the following:
(a) The Dental Board of California.
(b) The Medical Board of California.
(c) The California State Board of Optometry.
(d) The California State Board of Pharmacy.
(e) The Veterinary Medical Board.
(f) The California Board of Accountancy.
(g) The California Architects Board.
(h) The State Board of Barbering and Cosmetology.
(i) The Board for Professional Engineers, Land Surveyors, and Geologists.
(j) The Contractors State License Board.
(k) The Bureau for Private Postsecondary Education.
(l) The Bureau of Household Goods and Services.
(m) The Board of Registered Nursing.
(n) The Board of Behavioral Sciences.
(o) The State Athletic Commission.
(p) The Cemetery and Funeral Bureau.
(q) The Bureau of Security and Investigative Services.
(r) The Court Reporters Board of California.
(s) The Board of Vocational Nursing and Psychiatric Technicians.
(t) The Landscape Architects Technical Committee.
(u) The Division of Investigation.
(v) The Bureau of Automotive Repair.
(w) The Respiratory Care Board of California.
(x) The Acupuncture Board.
(y) The Board of Psychology.
(z) The Podiatric Medical Board of California.
(aa) The Physical Therapy Board of California.
(ab) The Arbitration Review Program.
(ac) The Physician Assistant Board.
(ad) The Speech-Language Pathology and Audiology and Hearing Aid Dispensers Board.
(ae) The California Board of Occupational Therapy.
(af) The Osteopathic Medical Board of California.
(ag) The California Board of Naturopathic Medicine.
(ah) The Dental Hygiene Board of California.
(ai) The Professional Fiduciaries Bureau.
(aj) The State Board of Chiropractic Examiners.
(ak) The Bureau of Real Estate Appraisers.
(al) The Structural Pest Control Board.

(am) Any other boards, offices, or officers subject to its jurisdiction by law.

Added Stats 2017 ch 823 § 4 (SB 173), effective January 1, 2018, operative July 1, 2018. Amended Stats 2018 ch 578 § 2 (SB 1483), effective January 1, 2019; Stats 2018 ch 858 § 1.5 (SB 1482), effective January 1, 2019 (ch 858 prevails); Stats 2019 ch 351 § 8 (AB 496), effective January 1, 2020; Stats 2020 ch 312 § 2 (SB 1474), effective January 1, 2021; Stats 2021 ch 70 § 2 (AB 141), effective July 27, 2021; Stats 2021 ch 630 § 2 (AB 1534), effective January 1, 2022; Stats 2022 ch 414 § 1 (AB 2685), effective January 1, 2023.

§ 101.1. [Section repealed 2011.]

Added Stats 1994 ch 908 § 2 (SB 2036). Amended Stats 1999 ch 983 § 1 (SB 1307). Repealed Stats 2010 ch 670 § 2 (AB 2130), effective January 1, 2011. The repealed section related to legislative intent regarding existing and proposed consumer-related boards.

§ 101.6. Purpose

The boards, bureaus, and commissions in the department are established for the purpose of ensuring that those private businesses and professions deemed to engage in activities which have potential impact upon the public health, safety, and welfare are adequately regulated in order to protect the people of California.

To this end, they establish minimum qualifications and levels of competency and license persons desiring to engage in the occupations they regulate upon determining that such persons possess the requisite skills and qualifications necessary to provide safe and effective services to the public, or register or otherwise certify persons in order to identify practitioners and ensure performance according to set and accepted professional standards. They provide a means for redress of grievances by investigating allegations of unprofessional conduct, incompetence, fraudulent action, or unlawful activity brought to their attention by members of the public and institute disciplinary action against persons licensed or registered under the provisions of this code when such action is warranted. In addition, they conduct periodic checks of licensees, registrants, or otherwise certified persons in order to ensure compliance with the relevant sections of this code.

Added Stats 1980 ch 375 § 1.

§ 101.7. Meetings of boards; Regular and special

(a) Notwithstanding any other provision of law, boards shall meet at least two times each calendar year. Boards shall meet at least once each calendar year in northern California and once each calendar year in southern California in order to facilitate participation by the public and its licensees.

(b) The director has discretion to exempt any board from the requirement in subdivision (a) upon a showing of good cause that the board is not able to meet at least two times in a calendar year.

(c) The director may call for a special meeting of the board when a board is not fulfilling its duties.

(d) An agency within the department that is required to provide a written notice pursuant to subdivision (a) of Section 11125 of the Government Code, may provide that notice by regular mail, email, or by both regular mail and email. An agency shall give a person who requests a notice the option of receiving the notice by regular mail, email, or by both regular mail and email. The agency shall comply with the requester's chosen form or forms of notice.

(e) An agency that plans to webcast a meeting shall include in the meeting notice required pursuant to subdivision (a) of Section 11125 of the Government Code a statement of the board's intent to webcast the meeting. An agency may webcast a meeting even if the agency fails to include that statement of intent in the notice.

Added Stats 2007 ch 354 § 1 (SB 1047), effective January 1, 2008. Amended Stats 2014 ch 395 § 1 (SB 1243), effective January 1, 2015; Stats 2018 ch 571 § 1 (SB 1480), effective January 1, 2019; Stats 2019 ch 351 § 9 (AB 496), effective January 1, 2020.

§ 102. Assumption of duties of board created by initiative

Upon the request of any board regulating, licensing, or controlling any professional or vocational occupation created by an initiative act, the Director of Consumer Affairs may take over the duties of the board under the same conditions and in the same manner as provided in this code for other boards of like character. Such boards shall pay a proportionate cost of the administration of the department on the same basis as is charged other boards included within the department. Upon request from any such board which has adopted the provisions of Chapter 5 (commencing with Section 11500) of Part 1 of Division 3 of Title 2 of the Government Code as rules of procedure in proceedings before it, the director shall assign hearing officers for such proceedings in accordance with Section 110.5.

Enacted Stats 1937. Amended Stats 1945 ch 869 § 1; Stats 1971 ch 716 § 6.

§ 102.3. Interagency agreement to delegate duties of certain repealed boards; Technical committees for regulation of professions under delegated authority; Renewal of agreement

(a) The director may enter into an interagency agreement with an appropriate entity within the Department of Consumer Affairs as provided for in Section 101 to delegate the duties, powers, purposes, responsibilities, and jurisdiction that have been succeeded and vested with the department, of a board, as defined in Section 477, which became inoperative and was repealed in accordance with Chapter 908 of the Statutes of 1994.

(b) (1) Where, pursuant to subdivision (a), an interagency agreement is entered into between the director and that entity, the entity receiving the delegation of authority may establish a technical committee to regulate, as directed by the entity, the profession subject to the authority that has been delegated. The entity may delegate to the technical committee only those powers that it received pursuant to the interagency agreement with the director. The technical committee shall have only those powers that have been delegated to it by the entity.

(2) Where the entity delegates its authority to adopt, amend, or repeal regulations to the technical committee, all regulations adopted, amended, or repealed by the technical committee shall be subject to the review and approval of the entity.

(3) The entity shall not delegate to a technical committee its authority to discipline a licensee who has violated the provisions of the applicable chapter of the Business and Professions Code that is subject to the director's delegation of authority to the entity.

(c) An interagency agreement entered into, pursuant to subdivision (a), shall continue until such time as the licensing program administered by the technical committee has undergone a review by the Assembly Committee on Business and Professions and the Senate Committee on Business, Professions and Economic Development to evaluate and determine whether the licensing program has demonstrated a public need for its continued existence. Thereafter, at the director's discretion, the interagency agreement may be renewed.

Added Stats 1997 ch 475 § 1 (AB 1546). Amended Stats 2004 ch 33 § 2 (AB 1467), effective April 13, 2004; Stats 2019 ch 351 § 10 (AB 496), effective January 1, 2020.

§ 103. Compensation and reimbursement for expenses

Each member of a board, commission, or committee created in the various chapters of Division 2 (commencing with Section 500) and Division 3 (commencing with Section 5000), and in Chapter 2 (commencing with Section 18600) and Chapter 3 (commencing with Section 19000) of Division 8, shall receive the moneys specified in this section when authorized by the respective provisions.

Each such member shall receive a per diem of one hundred dollars ($100) for each day actually spent in the discharge of official duties, and shall be reimbursed for traveling and other expenses necessarily incurred in the performance of official duties.

The payments in each instance shall be made only from the fund from which the expenses of the agency are paid and shall be subject to the availability of money.

Notwithstanding any other provision of law, no public officer or employee shall receive per diem salary compensation for serving on those boards, commissions, or committees on any day when the officer or employee also received compensation for the officer or employee's regular public employment.

Added Stats 1959 ch 1645 § 1. Amended Stats 1978 ch 1141 § 1; Stats 1985 ch 502 § 1; Stats 1987 ch 850 § 1; Stats 1993 ch 1264 § 1 (SB 574); Stats 2019 ch 351 § 11 (AB 496), effective January 1, 2020.

§ 105.5. Tenure of members of boards, etc., within department

Notwithstanding any other provision of this code, each member of a board, commission, examining committee, or other similarly constituted agency within the department shall hold office until the appointment and qualification of that member's successor or until one year shall have elapsed since the expiration of the term for which the member was appointed, whichever first occurs.

Added Stats 1967 ch 524 § 1. Amended Stats 2019 ch 351 § 12 (AB 496), effective January 1, 2020.

§ 106. Removal of board members

The appointing authority has power to remove from office at any time any member of any board appointed by the appointing authority for continued neglect of duties required by law, or for incompetence, or unprofessional or dishonorable conduct. Nothing in this section shall be construed as a limitation or restriction on the power of the appointing authority conferred on the appointing authority by any other provision of law to remove any member of any board.

Enacted Stats 1937. Amended Stats 1945 ch 1276 § 3; Stats 2019 ch 351 § 13 (AB 496), effective January 1, 2020.

§ 106.5. Removal of member of licensing board for disclosure of examination information

Notwithstanding any other provision of law, the Governor may remove from office a member of a board or other licensing entity in the department if it is shown that such member has knowledge of the specific questions to be asked on the licensing entity's next examination and directly or indirectly discloses any such question or questions in advance of or during the examination to any applicant for that examination.

The proceedings for removal shall be conducted in accordance with the provisions of Chapter 5 of Part 1 of Division 3 of Title 2 of the Government Code, and the Governor shall have all the powers granted therein.

Section V

Added Stats 1977 ch 482 § 1.

§ 107. Executive officers

Pursuant to subdivision (e) of Section 4 of Article VII of the California Constitution, each board may appoint a person exempt from civil service, who shall be designated as an executive officer unless the licensing act of the particular board designates the person as a registrar, and may fix that person's salary, with the approval of the Department of Human Resources pursuant to Section 19825 of the Government Code.

Enacted Stats 1937. Amended Stats 1984 ch 47 § 2, effective March 21, 1984; Stats 1987 ch 850 § 2. See this section as modified in Governor's Reorganization Plan No. 1 § 1 of 2011; Amended Stats 2012 ch 665 § 1 (SB 1308), effective January 1, 2013; Stats 2019 ch 351 § 14 (AB 496), effective January 1, 2020; Stats 2020 ch 370 § 1 (SB 1371), effective January 1, 2021.

§ 107.5. Official seals

If any board in the department uses an official seal pursuant to any provision of this code, the seal shall contain the words "State of California" and "Department of Consumer Affairs" in addition to the title of the board, and shall be in a form approved by the director.

Added Stats 1967 ch 1272 § 1. Amended Stats 1971 ch 716 § 7.

§ 108. Status and powers of boards

Each of the boards comprising the department exists as a separate unit, and has the functions of setting standards, holding meetings, and setting dates thereof, preparing and conducting examinations, passing upon applicants, conducting investigations of violations of laws under its jurisdiction, issuing citations and holding hearings for the revocation of licenses, and the imposing of penalties following those hearings, insofar as these powers are given by statute to each respective board.

Enacted Stats 1937. Amended Stats 2008 ch 179 § 1 (SB 1498), effective January 1, 2009.

§ 108.5. Witness fees and expenses

In any investigation, proceeding, or hearing that any board, commission, or officer in the department is empowered to institute, conduct, or hold, any witness appearing at the investigation, proceeding, or hearing whether upon a subpoena or voluntarily, may be paid the sum of twelve dollars ($12) per day for every day in actual attendance at the investigation, proceeding, or hearing and for the witness's actual, necessary, and reasonable expenses and those sums shall be a legal charge against the funds of the respective board, commission, or officer; provided further, that no witness appearing other than at the instance of the board, commission, or officer may be compensated out of the fund.

The board, commission, or officer shall determine the sums due to any witness and enter the amount on its minutes.

Added Stats 1943 ch 1035 § 1. Amended Stats 1957 ch 1908 § 6; Stats 1970 ch 1061 § 1; Stats 2019 ch 351 § 15 (AB 496), effective January 1, 2020.

§ 109. Review of decisions; Investigations

(a) The decisions of any of the boards comprising the department with respect to setting standards, conducting examinations, passing candidates, and revoking licenses, are not subject to review by the director, but are final within the limits provided by this code which are applicable to the particular board, except as provided in this section.

(b) The director may initiate an investigation of any allegations of misconduct in the preparation, administration, or scoring of an examination which is administered by a board, or in the review of qualifications which are a part of the licensing process of any board. A request for investigation shall be made by the director to the Division of Investigation through the chief of the division or to any law enforcement agency in the jurisdiction where the alleged misconduct occurred.

(c) The director may intervene in any matter of any board where an investigation by the Division of Investigation discloses probable cause to believe that the conduct or activity of a board, or its members or employees constitutes a violation of criminal law.

The term "intervene," as used in paragraph (c) of this section may include, but is not limited to, an application for a restraining order or injunctive relief as specified in Section 123.5, or a referral or request for criminal prosecution. For purposes of this section, the director shall be deemed to have standing under Section 123.5 and shall seek representation of the Attorney General, or other appropriate counsel in the event of a conflict in pursuing that action.

Enacted Stats 1937. Amended Stats 1991 ch 1013 § 1 (SB 961).

§ 110. Records and property

The department shall have possession and control of all records, books, papers, offices, equipment, supplies, funds, appropriations, land and other property—real or personal—now or hereafter held for the benefit or use of all of the bodies, offices or officers comprising the department. The title to all property held by any of these bodies, offices or officers for the use and benefit of the state, is vested in the State of California to be held in the possession of the department. Except as authorized by a board, the department shall not have the possession and control of examination questions prior to submission to applicants at scheduled examinations.

Enacted Stats 1937. Amended Stats 1996 ch 829 § 1 (AB 3473).

§ 111. Commissioners on examination

Unless otherwise expressly provided, any board may, with the approval of the appointing power, appoint qualified persons, who shall be designated as commissioners on examination, to give the whole or any portion of any examination. A commissioner on examination need not be a member of the board but shall have the same qualifications as one and shall be subject to the same rules.

Added Stats 1937 ch 474. Amended Stats 1947 ch 1350 § 3; Stats 1978 ch 1161 § 1; Stats 2019 ch 351 § 16 (AB 496), effective January 1, 2020.

§ 112. Publication and sale of directories of authorized persons

Notwithstanding any other provision of this code, no agency in the department, with the exception of the Board for Professional Engineers and Land Surveyors, shall be required to compile, publish, sell, or otherwise distribute a directory. When an agency deems it necessary to compile and publish a directory, the agency shall cooperate with the director in determining its form and content, the time and frequency of its publication, the persons to whom it is to be sold or otherwise distributed, and its price if it is sold. Any agency that requires the approval of the director for the compilation, publication, or distribution of a directory, under the law in effect at the time the amendment made to this section at the 1970 Regular Session of the Legislature becomes effective, shall continue to require that approval. As used in this section, "directory" means a directory, roster, register, or similar compilation of the names of persons who hold a license, certificate, permit, registration, or similar indicia of authority from the agency.

Added Stats 1937 ch 474. Amended Stats 1968 ch 1345 § 1; Stats 1970 ch 475 § 1; Stats 1998 ch 59 § 3 (AB 969).

§ 113. Conferences; Traveling expenses

Upon recommendation of the director, officers, and employees of the department, and the officers, members, and employees of the boards, committees, and commissions comprising it or subject to its jurisdiction may confer, in this state or elsewhere, with officers or employees of this state, its political subdivisions, other states, or the United States, or with other persons, associations, or organizations as may be of assistance to the department, board, committee, or commission in the conduct of its work. The officers, members, and employees shall be entitled to their actual traveling expenses incurred in pursuance hereof, but when these expenses are incurred with respect to travel outside of the state, they shall be subject to the approval of the Governor and the Director of Finance.

Added Stats 1937 ch 474. Amended Stats 1941 ch 885 § 1; Stats 2000 ch 277 § 1 (AB 2697); Stats 2001 ch 159 § 2 (SB 662).

§ 114. Reinstatement of expired license of licensee serving in military

(a) Notwithstanding any other provision of this code, any licensee or registrant of any board, commission, or bureau within the department whose license expired while the licensee or registrant was on active duty as a member of the California National Guard or the United States Armed Forces, may, upon application, reinstate their license or registration without examination or penalty, provided that all of the following requirements are satisfied:

(1) The licensee or registrant's license or registration was valid at the time they entered the California National Guard or the United States Armed Forces.

(2) The application for reinstatement is made while serving in the California National Guard or the United States Armed Forces, or not later than one year from the date of discharge from active service or return to inactive military status.

(3) The application for reinstatement is accompanied by an affidavit showing the date of entrance into the service, whether still in the service, or date of discharge, and the renewal fee for the current renewal period in which the application is filed is paid.

(b) If application for reinstatement is filed more than one year after discharge or return to inactive status, the applicant, in the discretion of the licensing agency, may be required to pass an examination.

(c) If application for reinstatement is filed and the licensing agency determines that the applicant has not actively engaged in the practice of the applicant's profession while on active duty, then the licensing agency may require the applicant to pass an examination.

(d) Unless otherwise specifically provided in this code, any licensee or registrant who, either part time or full time, practices in this state the profession or vocation for which the licensee or registrant is licensed or registered shall be required to maintain their license in good standing even though the licensee or registrant is in military service.

For the purposes in this section, time spent by a licensee in receiving treatment or hospitalization in any veterans' facility during which the licensee is prevented from practicing the licensee's profession or vocation shall be excluded from said period of one year.

Added Stats 1951 ch 185 § 2. Amended Stats 1953 ch 423 § 1; Stats 1961 ch 1253 § 1; Stats 2010 ch 389 § 1 (AB 2500), effective January 1, 2011; Stats 2011 ch 296 § 1 (AB 1023), effective January 1, 2012; Stats 2019 ch 351 § 17 (AB 496), effective January 1, 2020.

§ 114.3. Waiver of fees and requirements for active duty members of armed forces and national guard

(a) Notwithstanding any other law, every board, as defined in Section 22, within the department shall waive the renewal fees, continuing education requirements, and other renewal requirements as determined by the board, if any are applicable, for a licensee or registrant called to active duty as a member of the United States Armed Forces or the California National Guard if all of the following requirements are met:

(1) The licensee or registrant possessed a current and valid license with the board at the time the licensee or registrant was called to active duty.

(2) The renewal requirements are waived only for the period during which the licensee or registrant is on active duty service.

(3) Written documentation that substantiates the licensee or registrant's active duty service is provided to the board.

(b) For purposes of this section, the phrase "called to active duty" shall have the same meaning as "active duty" as defined in Section 101 of Title 10 of the United States Code and shall additionally include individuals who are on active duty in the California National Guard, whether due to proclamation of a state of insurrection pursuant to Section 143 of the Military and Veterans Code or due to a proclamation of a state extreme emergency or when the California National Guard is otherwise on active duty pursuant to Section 146 of the Military and Veterans Code.

(c) (1) Except as specified in paragraph (2), the licensee or registrant shall not engage in any activities requiring a license during the period that the waivers provided by this section are in effect.

(2) If the licensee or registrant will provide services for which the licensee or registrant is licensed while on active duty, the board shall convert the license status to military active and no private practice of any type shall be permitted.

(d) In order to engage in any activities for which the licensee or registrant is licensed once discharged from active duty, the licensee or registrant shall meet all necessary renewal requirements as determined by the board within six months from the licensee's or registrant's date of discharge from active duty service.

(e) After a licensee or registrant receives notice of the licensee or registrant's discharge date, the licensee or registrant shall notify the board of their discharge from active duty within 60 days of receiving their notice of discharge.

(f) A board may adopt regulations to carry out the provisions of this section.

(g) This section shall not apply to any board that has a similar license renewal waiver process statutorily authorized for that board.

Added Stats 2012 ch 742 § 1 (AB 1588), effective January 1, 2013. Amended Stats 2019 ch 351 § 18 (AB 496), effective January 1, 2020; Stats 2022 ch 386 § 1 (SB 1237), effective January 1, 2023.

§ 114.5. Military service; Posting of information on Web site about application of military experience and training towards licensure

(a) Each board shall inquire in every application for licensure if the individual applying for licensure is serving in, or has previously served in, the military.

(b) If a board's governing law authorizes veterans to apply military experience and training towards licensure requirements, that board shall post information on the board's Internet Web site about the ability of veteran applicants to apply military experience and training towards licensure requirements.

Added Stats 2013 ch 693 § 1 (AB 1057), effective January 1, 2014. Amended Stats 2016 ch 174 § 1 (SB 1348), effective January 1, 2017.

§ 115. Applicability of Section 114

The provisions of Section 114 of this code are also applicable to a licensee or registrant whose license or registration was obtained while in the armed services.

Added Stats 1951 ch 1577 § 1.

§ 115.4. Licensure process expedited for honorably discharged veterans of Armed Forces

(a) Notwithstanding any other law, on and after July 1, 2016, a board within the department shall expedite, and may assist, the initial licensure process for an applicant who supplies satisfactory evidence to the board that the applicant has served as an active duty member of the Armed Forces of the United States and was honorably discharged.

(b) Notwithstanding any other law, on and after July 1, 2024, a board within the department shall expedite, and may assist, the initial licensure process for an applicant who supplies satisfactory evidence to the board that the applicant is an active duty member of a regular component of the Armed Forces of the United States enrolled in the United States Department of Defense SkillBridge program as

Section V

authorized under Section 1143(e) of Title 10 of the United States Code.

(c) A board may adopt regulations necessary to administer this section in accordance with the provisions of Chapter 3.5 (commencing with Section 11340) of Part 1 of Division 3 of Title 2 of the Government Code.

(d) For purposes of this section, the term "applicant" refers to an applicant for an individual license and does not refer to applicants for business or entity licenses.

Added Stats 2014 ch 657 § 1 (SB 1226), effective January 1, 2015. Amended Stats 2024 Ch 481 § 1 (SB 1451), effective September 22, 2024.

§ 115.5. Board required to expedite licensure process for certain applicants; Adoption of regulations [Repealed]

Added Stats 2012 ch 399 § 1 (AB 1904), effective January 1, 2013. Amended Stats 2019 ch 351 § 19 (AB 496), effective January 1, 2020; Stat 2021 ch 367 § 1 (SB 607), effective September 28, 2021; Repealed July 1, 2022.

§ 115.5. Requirements for expedited licensure process

(a) A board within the department shall expedite the licensure process and waive the licensure application fee and the initial or original license fee charged by the board for an applicant who meets both of the following requirements:

(1) Supplies evidence satisfactory to the board that the applicant is married to, or in a domestic partnership or other legal union with, an active duty member of the Armed Forces of the United States who is assigned to a duty station in this state under official active duty military orders.

(2) Holds a current license in another state, district, or territory of the United States in the profession or vocation for which the applicant seeks a license from the board.

(b) A board may adopt regulations necessary to administer this section.

(c) For purposes of this section, the term "applicant" refers to an applicant for an individual license and does not refer to applicants for business or entity licenses.

Added Stats 2012 ch 399 § 1 (AB 1904), effective January 1, 2013. Amended Stats 2019 ch 351 § 19 (AB 496), effective January 1, 2020; Stat 2021 ch 367 § 1 (SB 607), effective September 28, 2021; Repealed July 1, 2022; Stat 2021 ch 367 § 2 (SB 607), operative July 1, 2021. Amended Stats 2024 Ch 481 § 2 (SB 1451), effective September 22, 2024.

§ 115.6. [Section repealed 2023.]

Added Stats 2021 ch 639 § 1 (AB 107), effective January 1, 2022. Repealed effective July 1, 2023.

§ 115.6. Temporary licensure process for spouses of active duty members of Armed Forces

(a) (1) Except as provided in subdivision (j), a board within the department shall, after appropriate investigation, issue a temporary license to practice a profession or vocation to an applicant who meets the requirements set forth in subdivisions (c) and (d).

(2) Revenues from fees for temporary licenses issued by the California Board of Accountancy shall be credited to the Accountancy Fund in accordance with Section 5132.

(b) The board may conduct an investigation of an applicant for purposes of denying or revoking a temporary license issued pursuant to this section. This investigation may include a criminal background check.

(c) An applicant seeking a temporary license pursuant to this section shall meet the following requirements:

(1) The applicant shall supply evidence satisfactory to the board that the applicant is married to, or in a domestic partnership or other legal union with, an active duty member of the Armed Forces of the United States who is assigned to a duty station in this state under official active duty military orders.

(2) The applicant shall hold a current, active, and unrestricted license that confers upon the applicant the authority to practice, in another state, district, or territory of the United States, the profession or vocation within the same scope for which the applicant seeks a temporary license from the board.

(3) The applicant shall submit an application to the board that shall include a signed affidavit attesting to the fact that the applicant meets all of the requirements for the temporary license, and that the information submitted in the application is accurate, to the best of the applicant's knowledge. The application shall also include written verification from the applicant's original licensing jurisdiction stating that the applicant's license is in good standing in that jurisdiction.

(4) The applicant shall not have committed an act in any jurisdiction that would have constituted grounds for denial, suspension, or revocation of the license under this code at the time the act was committed. A violation of this paragraph may be grounds for the denial or revocation of a temporary license issued by the board.

(5) The applicant shall not have been disciplined by a licensing entity in another jurisdiction and shall not be the subject of an unresolved complaint, review procedure, or disciplinary proceeding conducted by a licensing entity in another jurisdiction.

(6) (A) The applicant shall, upon request by a board, furnish a full set of fingerprints for purposes of conducting a criminal background check.

(B) The board shall request a fingerprint-based criminal history information check from the Department of Justice in accordance with subdivision (u) of Section 11105 of the Penal Code and the Department of Justice shall furnish state or federal criminal history information in accordance with subdivision (p) of Section 11105 of the Penal Code.

(d) The applicant shall pass a California law and ethics examination if otherwise required by the board for the profession or vocation for which the applicant seeks licensure.

(e) Except as specified in subdivision (g), a board shall issue a temporary license pursuant to this section within 30 days of receiving documentation that the applicant has met the requirements specified in subdivisions (c) and (d) if the results of the criminal background check do not show grounds for denial.

(f) (1) A temporary license issued pursuant to this section may be immediately terminated upon a finding that the temporary licenseholder failed to meet any of the requirements described in subdivision (c) or (d) or provided substantively inaccurate information that would affect the person's eligibility for temporary licensure. Upon termination of the temporary license, the board shall issue a notice of termination that shall require the temporary licenseholder to immediately cease the practice of the licensed profession upon receipt.

(2) Notwithstanding any other law, if, after notice and an opportunity to be heard, a board finds that a temporary licenseholder engaged in unprofessional conduct or any other act that is a cause for discipline by the board, the board shall revoke the temporary license.

(g) An applicant seeking a temporary license as a civil engineer, geotechnical engineer, structural engineer, land surveyor, professional geologist, professional geophysicist, certified engineering geologist, or certified hydrogeologist pursuant to this section shall successfully pass the appropriate California-specific examination or examinations required for licensure in those respective professions by the Board for Professional Engineers, Land Surveyors, and Geologists. The board shall issue a temporary license pursuant to this subdivision within 30 days of receiving documentation that the applicant has met the requirements specified in this subdivision and subdivisions (c) and (d) if the results of the criminal background check do not show grounds for denial.

(h) A temporary license issued pursuant to this section is nonrenewable and shall expire 12 months after issuance, upon issuance or denial of a standard license, upon issuance or denial of a license by endorsement, or upon issuance or denial of an expedited license pursuant to Section 115.5, whichever occurs first.

(i) A board shall submit to the department for approval, if necessary to implement this section, draft regulations necessary to administer this section. These regulations shall be adopted pursuant to the Administrative Procedure Act (Chapter 3.5 (commencing with Section 11340) of Part 1 of Division 3 of Title 2 of the Government Code).

(j) (1) This section shall not apply to a board that has a process in place by which an out-of-state licensed applicant in good standing who is married to, or in a domestic partnership or other legal union with, an active duty member of the Armed Forces of the United States is able to receive expedited, temporary authorization to practice while meeting state-specific requirements for a period of at least one year or is able to receive an expedited license by endorsement with no additional requirements superseding those described in subdivisions (c) and (d).

(2) This section shall apply only to the extent that it does not amend an initiative or violate constitutional requirements.

(k) An applicant for a temporary license pursuant to this section shall not be required to provide, and no board shall collect, a fee for the application or issuance of a temporary license.

(*l*) For purposes of this section, the term "applicant" refers to an applicant for an individual license and does not refer to applicants for business or entity licenses.

Added Stats 2021 ch 639 § 2 (AB 107), operative July 1, 2023. Amended Stats 2024 Ch 481 § 3 (SB 1451), effective September 22, 2024.

§ 115.8. Annual report on military, veteran, and spouse Licensure

The Department of Consumer Affairs shall compile information on military and spouse licensure into an annual report for the Legislature, which shall be submitted in conformance with Section 9795 of the Government Code. The report shall include all of the following for each license type of each board:

(a) The number of applications for a temporary license submitted by military spouses per fiscal year, pursuant to Section 115.6.

(b) The number of applications for expedited licenses received from honorably discharged military members and military spouses pursuant to Sections 115.4 and 115.5.

(c) The number of licenses issued and denied per fiscal year pursuant to Sections 115.4, 115.5, and 115.6.

(d) The number of licenses issued pursuant to Section 115.6 that were suspended or revoked per fiscal year.

(e) The number of applications for waived renewal fees received and granted pursuant to Section 114.3 per fiscal year.

(f) The average length of time between application and issuance of licenses pursuant to Sections 115.4, 115.5, and 115.6.

Added Stats 2021 ch 639 § 3 (AB 107), effective January 1, 2022; Amended Stats 2023 ch 510 § 1 (SB 887), effective January 1, 2024.

§ 115.9. Publishing information on licensing options available to military spouses

The department and each board within the department shall publish information pertinent to all licensing options available to military spouses on the home page of the internet website of the department or board, as applicable, including, but not limited to, the following:

(a) The process for expediting applications for military spouses.

(b) The availability of temporary licensure, the requirements for obtaining a temporary license, and length of time a temporary license is active.

(c) The requirements for full, permanent licensure by endorsement or credential for out-of-state applicants.

Added Stats 2021 ch 639 § 4 (AB 107), effective January 1, 2022.

§ 115.10. Servicemember spouse with professional license; registration requirements

(a) For purposes of this section, the following definitions apply:

(1) "Applicant" means a servicemember or a spouse of a servicemember.

(2) "Board" means an entity described in Section 101.

(3) "Professional license" means an individual professional license and does not include a business or entity license.

(4) "Registering authority" means a board or the Department of Real Estate, as applicable.

(5) "Spouse" means an individual who is married to, or who is in a domestic partnership or other legal union with, a military servicemember.

(b) Notwithstanding any other law, a registering authority shall register an applicant who satisfies all of the following requirements:

(1) The applicant holds a professional license in good standing in another state, district, or territory of the United States that confers on the applicant the authority to practice a profession or vocation within a similar scope of practice as that regulated by the registering authority.

(2) The applicant relocated to this state because of military orders for military service within this state and the applicant submits to the registering authority a copy of the military orders.

(3) The applicant performed at least one activity within the scope and under the authority of their professional license during the two years immediately preceding the relocation to this state.

(4) For an applicant who is licensed within the same professional discipline in more than one jurisdiction, both of the following:

(A) The applicant maintains each license in good standing.

(B) The applicant submits to the registering authority written verification from, or documentation printed from an online licensing system for, each jurisdiction that the applicant's license is in good standing in the jurisdiction.

(5) The applicant submits to the registering authority written verification from, or documentation printed from an online licensing system for, the applicant's original licensing jurisdiction that the applicant's license is in good standing in that jurisdiction.

(6) For an applicant that is a spouse, the applicant submits evidence to the registering authority that the applicant is married to, or in a domestic partnership or other legal union with, a servicemember who is subject to military orders described in paragraph (2).

(7) The applicant submits to the registering authority their California address of record and an affidavit attesting to both of the following:

(A) The applicant meets all of the requirements for registration under this section.

(B) The information submitted to the registering authority pursuant to this section is accurate to the best of the applicant's knowledge.

(c) (1) The registering authority shall register an applicant within 30 days of receiving all applicable documentation described in subdivision (b).

(2) The registering authority shall not register an applicant who fails to provide all applicable documentation described in subdivision (b) and shall deem the applicant's request for registration incomplete.

(d) For each person registered pursuant to this section, the registering authority shall post all of the following on the registering authority's internet website:

(1) The person's name.

(2) The person's California address of record.

(3) The person's registration status.

(4) The state name and license number of each license from each original licensing jurisdiction.

(e) A person registered pursuant to this section shall be deemed to be a licensee of the registering authority for purposes of the laws administered by that registering authority relating to standards of practice, discipline, and continuing education for the duration of the military orders described in paragraph (2) of subdivision (b), and the registration shall expire when those military orders expire.

(f) A registering authority may take appropriate enforcement action against a person registered pursuant to this section, including, but not limited to, revoking or suspending the registration of a person who does not meet the requirements of subdivision (b) or the laws applicable to licensees pursuant to subdivision (e).

(g) A registering authority shall not collect or require a fee for registration pursuant to this section.

Section V

(h) A registering authority may develop and publish guidance to implement this section.

Added Stats 2023 ch 196 § 1 (SB 143), effective September 13, 2023.

§ 118. Effect of withdrawal of application; Effect of suspension, forfeiture, etc., of license

(a) The withdrawal of an application for a license after it has been filed with a board in the department shall not, unless the board has consented in writing to such withdrawal, deprive the board of its authority to institute or continue a proceeding against the applicant for the denial of the license upon any ground provided by law or to enter an order denying the license upon any such ground.

(b) The suspension, expiration, or forfeiture by operation of law of a license issued by a board in the department, or its suspension, forfeiture, or cancellation by order of the board or by order of a court of law, or its surrender without the written consent of the board, shall not, during any period in which it may be renewed, restored, reissued, or reinstated, deprive the board of its authority to institute or continue a disciplinary proceeding against the licensee upon any ground provided by law or to enter an order suspending or revoking the license or otherwise taking disciplinary action against the licensee on any such ground.

(c) As used in this section, "board" includes an individual who is authorized by any provision of this code to issue, suspend, or revoke a license, and "license" includes "certificate," "registration," and "permit."

Added Stats 1961 ch 1079 § 1.

§ 119. Misdemeanors pertaining to use of licenses

Any person who does any of the following is guilty of a misdemeanor:

(a) Displays or causes or permits to be displayed or has in the person's possession either of the following:

(1) A canceled, revoked, suspended, or fraudulently altered license.

(2) A fictitious license or any document simulating a license or purporting to be or have been issued as a license.

(b) Lends the person's license to any other person or knowingly permits the use thereof by another.

(c) Displays or represents any license not issued to the person as being the person's license.

(d) Fails or refuses to surrender to the issuing authority upon its lawful written demand any license, registration, permit, or certificate which has been suspended, revoked, or canceled.

(e) Knowingly permits any unlawful use of a license issued to the person.

(f) Photographs, photostats, duplicates, manufactures, or in any way reproduces any license or facsimile thereof in a manner that it could be mistaken for a valid license, or displays or has in the person's possession any such photograph, photostat, duplicate, reproduction, or facsimile unless authorized by this code.

(g) Buys or receives a fraudulent, forged, or counterfeited license knowing that it is fraudulent, forged, or counterfeited. For purposes of this subdivision, "fraudulent" means containing any misrepresentation of fact.

As used in this section, "license" includes "certificate," "permit," "authority," and "registration" or any other indicia giving authorization to engage in a business or profession regulated by this code or referred to in Section 1000 or 3600.

Added Stats 1965 ch 1083 § 1. Amended Stats 1990 ch 350 § 1 (SB 2084) (ch 1207 prevails), ch 1207 § 1 (AB 3242); Stats 1994 ch 1206 § 1 (SB 1775); Stats 2000 ch 568 § 1 (AB 2888); Stats 2019 ch 351 § 22 (AB 496), effective January 1, 2020.

§ 121. Practice during period between renewal and receipt of evidence of renewal

No licensee who has complied with the provisions of this code relating to the renewal of the licensee's license prior to expiration of such license shall be deemed to be engaged illegally in the practice of the licensee's business or profession during any period between such renewal and receipt of evidence of such renewal which may occur due to delay not the fault of the applicant.

As used in this section, "license" includes "certificate," "permit," "authorization," and "registration," or any other indicia giving authorization, by any agency, board, bureau, commission, committee, or entity within the Department of Consumer Affairs, to engage in a business or profession regulated by this code or by the board referred to in the Chiropractic Act or the Osteopathic Act.

Added Stats 1979 ch 77 § 1. Amended Stats 2019 ch 351 § 24 (AB 496), effective January 1, 2020.

§ 121.5. Application of fees to licenses or registrations lawfully inactivated

Except as otherwise provided in this code, the application of delinquency fees or accrued and unpaid renewal fees for the renewal of expired licenses or registrations shall not apply to licenses or registrations that have lawfully been designated as inactive or retired.

Added Stats 2001 ch 435 § 1 (SB 349).

§ 122. Fee for issuance of duplicate certificate

Except as otherwise provided by law, the department and each of the boards, bureaus, committees, and commissions within the department may charge a fee for the processing and issuance of a duplicate copy of any certificate of licensure or other form evidencing licensure or renewal of licensure. The fee shall be in an amount sufficient to cover all costs incident to the issuance of the duplicate certificate or other form but shall not exceed twenty-five dollars ($25).

Added Stats 1986 ch 951 § 1.

§ 123. Conduct constituting subversion of licensing examination; Penalties and damages

It is a misdemeanor for any person to engage in any conduct which subverts or attempts to subvert any licensing examination or the administration of an examination, including, but not limited to:

(a) Conduct which violates the security of the examination materials; removing from the examination room any examination materials without authorization; the unauthorized reproduction by any means of any portion of the actual licensing examination; aiding by any means the unauthorized reproduction of any portion of the actual licensing examination; paying or using professional or paid examination-takers for the purpose of reconstructing any portion of the licensing examination; obtaining examination questions or other examination material, except by specific authorization either before, during, or after an examination; or using or purporting to use any examination questions or materials which were improperly removed or taken from any examination for the purpose of instructing or preparing any applicant for examination; or selling, distributing, buying, receiving, or having unauthorized possession of any portion of a future, current, or previously administered licensing examination.

(b) Communicating with any other examinee during the administration of a licensing examination; copying answers from another examinee or permitting one's answers to be copied by another examinee; having in one's possession during the administration of the licensing examination any books, equipment, notes, written or printed materials, or data of any kind, other than the examination materials distributed, or otherwise authorized to be in one's possession during the examination; or impersonating any examinee or having an impersonator take the licensing examination on one's behalf.

Nothing in this section shall preclude prosecution under the authority provided for in any other provision of law.

In addition to any other penalties, a person found guilty of violating this section, shall be liable for the actual damages sustained by the agency administering the examination not to exceed ten thousand dollars ($10,000) and the costs of litigation.

(c) If any provision of this section or the application thereof to any person or circumstances is held invalid, that invalidity shall not affect other provisions or applications of the section that can be given effect without the invalid provision or application, and to this end the provisions of this section are severable.

Added Stats 1989 ch 1022 § 1. Amended Stats 1991 ch 647 § 1 (SB 879).

§ 123.5. Enjoining violations

Whenever any person has engaged, or is about to engage, in any acts or practices which constitute, or will constitute, a violation of Section 123, the superior court in and for the county wherein the acts or practices take place, or are about to take place, may issue an injunction, or other appropriate order, restraining such conduct on application of a board, the Attorney General or the district attorney of the county.

The proceedings under this section shall be governed by Chapter 3 (commencing with Section 525) of Title 7 of Part 2 of the Code of Civil Procedure.

The remedy provided for by this section shall be in addition to, and not a limitation on, the authority provided for in any other provision of law.

Added Stats 1983 ch 95 § 2, as B & P C § 497. Amended and Renumbered by Stats 1989 ch 1022 § 4.

§ 124. Manner of notice

Notwithstanding subdivision (c) of Section 11505 of the Government Code, whenever written notice, including a notice, order, or document served pursuant to Chapter 3.5 (commencing with Section 11340), Chapter 4 (commencing with Section 11370), or Chapter 5 (commencing with Section 11500), of Part 1 of Division 3 of Title 2 of the Government Code, is required to be given by any board in the department, the notice may be given by regular mail addressed to the last known address of the licensee or by personal service, at the option of the board.

Added Stats 1961 ch 1253 § 2. Amended Stats 1994 ch 26 § 4 (AB 1807), effective March 30, 1994; Stats 1995 ch 938 § 1 (SB 523), operative July 1, 1997; Stats 2019 ch 351 § 25 (AB 496), effective January 1, 2020.

§ 125. Misdemeanor offenses by licensees

Any person, licensed under Division 1 (commencing with Section 100), Division 2 (commencing with Section 500), or Division 3 (com-

Section V

mencing with Section 5000) is guilty of a misdemeanor and subject to the disciplinary provisions of this code applicable to them, who conspires with a person not so licensed to violate any provision of this code, or who, with intent to aid or assist that person in violating those provisions does either of the following:

(a) Allows their license to be used by that person.

(b) Acts as their agent or partner.

Added Stats 1949 ch 308 § 1. Amended Stats 1994 ch 1206 § 2 (SB 1775); Stats 2019 ch 351 § 26 (AB 496), effective January 1, 2020.

§ 125.3. Direction to licensee violating licensing act to pay costs of investigation and enforcement

(a) Except as otherwise provided by law, in any order issued in resolution of a disciplinary proceeding before any board within the department or before the Osteopathic Medical Board, upon request of the entity bringing the proceeding, the administrative law judge may direct a licensee found to have committed a violation or violations of the licensing act to pay a sum not to exceed the reasonable costs of the investigation and enforcement of the case.

(b) In the case of a disciplined licensee that is a corporation or a partnership, the order may be made against the licensed corporate entity or licensed partnership.

(c) A certified copy of the actual costs, or a good faith estimate of costs where actual costs are not available, signed by the entity bringing the proceeding or its designated representative shall be prima facie evidence of reasonable costs of investigation and prosecution of the case. The costs shall include the amount of investigative and enforcement costs up to the date of the hearing, including, but not limited to, charges imposed by the Attorney General.

(d) The administrative law judge shall make a proposed finding of the amount of reasonable costs of investigation and prosecution of the case when requested pursuant to subdivision (a). The finding of the administrative law judge with regard to costs shall not be reviewable by the board to increase the cost award. The board may reduce or eliminate the cost award, or remand to the administrative law judge if the proposed decision fails to make a finding on costs requested pursuant to subdivision (a).

(e) If an order for recovery of costs is made and timely payment is not made as directed in the board's decision, the board may enforce the order for repayment in any appropriate court. This right of enforcement shall be in addition to any other rights the board may have as to any licensee to pay costs.

(f) In any action for recovery of costs, proof of the board's decision shall be conclusive proof of the validity of the order of payment and the terms for payment.

(g) (1) Except as provided in paragraph (2), the board shall not renew or reinstate the license of any licensee who has failed to pay all of the costs ordered under this section.

(2) Notwithstanding paragraph (1), the board may, in its discretion, conditionally renew or reinstate for a maximum of one year the license of any licensee who demonstrates financial hardship and who enters into a formal agreement with the board to reimburse the board within that one-year period for the unpaid costs.

(h) All costs recovered under this section shall be considered a reimbursement for costs incurred and shall be deposited in the fund of the board recovering the costs to be available upon appropriation by the Legislature.

(i) Nothing in this section shall preclude a board from including the recovery of the costs of investigation and enforcement of a case in any stipulated settlement.

(j) This section does not apply to any board if a specific statutory provision in that board's licensing act provides for recovery of costs in an administrative disciplinary proceeding.

(k) Notwithstanding the provisions of this section, the Medical Board of California shall not request nor obtain from a physician and surgeon, investigation and prosecution costs for a disciplinary proceeding against the licensee. The board shall ensure that this subdivision is revenue neutral with regard to it and that any loss of revenue or increase in costs resulting from this subdivision is offset by an increase in the amount of the initial license fee and the biennial renewal fee, as provided in subdivision (e) of Section 2435.

Added Stats 1992 ch 1289 § 1 (AB 2743), effective January 1, 1993. Amended Stats 2001 ch 728 § 1 (SB 724); Stats 2005 ch 674 § 2 (SB 231), effective January 1, 2006; Stats 2006 ch 223 § 2 (SB 1438), effective January 1, 2007; Stats 2019 ch 351 § 27 (AB 496), effective January 1, 2020.

§ 125.5. Enjoining violations; Restitution orders

(a) The superior court for the county in which any person has engaged or is about to engage in any act which constitutes a violation of a chapter of this code administered or enforced by a board within the department may, upon a petition filed by the board with the approval of the director, issue an injunction or other appropriate order restraining such conduct. The proceedings under this section shall be governed by Chapter 3 (commencing with Section 525) of Title 7 of Part 2 of the Code of Civil Procedure. As used in this section, "board" includes commission, bureau, division, agency and a medical quality review committee.

(b) The superior court for the county in which any person has engaged in any act which constitutes a violation of a chapter of this code administered or enforced by a board within the department may, upon a petition filed by the board with the approval of the director, order such person to make restitution to persons injured as a result of such violation.

(c) The court may order a person subject to an injunction or restraining order, provided for in subdivision (a) of this section, or subject to an order requiring restitution pursuant to subdivision (b), to reimburse the petitioning board for expenses incurred by the board in its investigation related to its petition.

(d) The remedy provided for by this section shall be in addition to, and not a limitation on, the authority provided for in any other section of this code.

Added Stats 1972 ch 1238 § 1. Amended Stats 1973 ch 632 § 1; Stats 2d Ex Sess 1975 ch 1 § 2; Stats 1982 ch 517 § 1.

§ 125.6. Unlawful discrimination by licensees

(a) (1) With regard to an applicant, every person who holds a license under the provisions of this code is subject to disciplinary action under the disciplinary provisions of this code applicable to that person if, because of any characteristic listed or defined in subdivision (b) or (e) of Section 51 of the Civil Code, the person refuses to perform the licensed activity or aids or incites the refusal to perform that licensed activity by another licensee, or if, because of any characteristic listed or defined in subdivision (b) or (e) of Section 51 of the Civil Code, the person makes any discrimination, or restriction in the performance of the licensed activity.

(2) Nothing in this section shall be interpreted to prevent a physician or health care professional licensed pursuant to Division 2 (commencing with Section 500) from considering any of the characteristics of a patient listed in subdivision (b) or (e) of Section 51 of the Civil Code if that consideration is medically necessary and for the sole purpose of determining the appropriate diagnosis or treatment of the patient.

(3) Nothing in this section shall be interpreted to apply to discrimination by employers with regard to employees or prospective employees, nor shall this section authorize action against any club license issued pursuant to Article 4 (commencing with Section 23425) of Chapter 3 of Division 9 because of discriminatory membership policy.

(4) The presence of architectural barriers to an individual with physical disabilities that conform to applicable state or local building codes and regulations shall not constitute discrimination under this section.

(b) (1) Nothing in this section requires a person licensed pursuant to Division 2 (commencing with Section 500) to permit an individual to participate in, or benefit from, the licensed activity of the licensee where that individual poses a direct threat to the health or safety of others. For this purpose, the term "direct threat" means a significant risk to the health or safety of others that cannot be eliminated by a modification of policies, practices, or procedures or by the provision of auxiliary aids and services.

(2) Nothing in this section requires a person licensed pursuant to Division 2 (commencing with Section 500) to perform a licensed activity for which the person is not qualified to perform.

(c) (1) "Applicant," as used in this section, means a person applying for licensed services provided by a person licensed under this code.

(2) "License," as used in this section, includes "certificate," "permit," "authority," and "registration" or any other indicia giving authorization to engage in a business or profession regulated by this code.

Added Stats 1974 ch 1350 § 1. Amended Stats 1977 ch 293 § 1; Stats 1980 ch 191 § 1; Stats 1992 ch 913 § 2 (AB 1077); Stats 2007 ch 568 § 2 (AB 14), effective January 1, 2008; Stats 2019 ch 351 § 28 (AB 496), effective January 1, 2020.

§ 125.7. Restraining orders

In addition to the remedy provided for in Section 125.5, the superior court for the county in which any licensee licensed under Division 2 (commencing with Section 500), or any initiative act referred to in that division, has engaged or is about to engage in any act that constitutes a violation of a chapter of this code administered or enforced by a board referred to in Division 2 (commencing with Section 500), may, upon a petition filed by the board and accompanied by an affidavit or affidavits in support thereof and a memorandum of points and authorities, issue a temporary restraining order or other appropriate order restraining the licensee from engaging in the business or profession for which the person is licensed or from any part thereof, in accordance with this section.

(a) If the affidavits in support of the petition show that the licensee has engaged or is about to engage in acts or omissions constituting a violation of a chapter of this code and if the court is satisfied that permitting the licensee to continue to engage in the business or profession for which the license was issued will endanger the public health, safety, or welfare, the court may issue an order temporarily restraining the licensee from engaging in the profession for which he or she is licensed.

(b) The order may not be issued without notice to the licensee unless it appears from facts shown by the affidavits that serious injury would result to the public before the matter can be heard on notice.

(c) Except as otherwise specifically provided by this section, proceedings under this section shall be governed by Chapter 3 (commencing with Section 525) of Title 7 of Part 2 of the Code of Civil Procedure.

(d) When a restraining order is issued pursuant to this section, or within a time to be allowed by the superior court, but in any case not more than 30 days after the restraining order is issued, an accusation shall be filed with the board pursuant to Section 11503 of the Government Code or, in the case of a licensee of the State Department of Health Services, with that department pursuant to Section 100171 of the Health and Safety Code. The accusation shall be served upon the licensee as provided by Section 11505 of the Government Code. The licensee shall have all of the rights and privileges available as specified in Chapter 5 (commencing with Section 11500) of Part 1 of Division 3 of Title 2 of the Government Code. However, if the licensee requests a hearing on the accusation, the board shall provide the licensee with a hearing within 30 days of the request and a decision within 15 days of the date the decision is received from the administrative law judge, or the court may nullify the restraining order previously issued. Any restraining order issued pursuant to this section shall be dissolved by operation of law at the time the board's decision is subject to judicial review pursuant to Section 1094.5 of the Code of Civil Procedure.

(e) The remedy provided for in this section shall be in addition to, and not a limitation upon, the authority provided by any other provision of this code.

Added Stats 1977 ch 292 § 1. Amended Stats 1982 ch 517 § 2; Stats 1994 ch 1206 § 3 (SB 1775); Stats 1997 ch 220 § 1 (SB 68), effective August 4, 1997; Stats 1998 ch 878 § 1.5 (SB 2239).

§ 125.8. Temporary order restraining licensee engaged or about to engage in violation of law

In addition to the remedy provided for in Section 125.5, the superior court for the county in which any licensee licensed under Division 3 (commencing with Section 5000) or Chapter 2 (commencing with Section 18600) or Chapter 3 (commencing with Section 19000) of Division 8 has engaged or is about to engage in any act which constitutes a violation of a chapter of this code administered or enforced by a board referred to in Division 3 (commencing with Section 5000) or Chapter 2 (commencing with Section 18600) or Chapter 3 (commencing with Section 19000) of Division 8 may, upon a petition filed by the board and accompanied by an affidavit or affidavits in support thereof and a memorandum of points and authorities, issue a temporary restraining order or other appropriate order restraining the licensee from engaging in the business or profession for which the person is licensed or from any part thereof, in accordance with the provisions of this section.

(a) If the affidavits in support of the petition show that the licensee has engaged or is about to engage in acts or omissions constituting a violation of a chapter of this code and if the court is satisfied that permitting the licensee to continue to engage in the business or profession for which the license was issued will endanger the public health, safety, or welfare, the court may issue an order temporarily restraining the licensee from engaging in the profession for which he is licensed.

(b) Such order may not be issued without notice to the licensee unless it appears from facts shown by the affidavits that serious injury would result to the public before the matter can be heard on notice.

(c) Except as otherwise specifically provided by this section, proceedings under this section shall be governed by Chapter 3 (commencing with Section 525) of Title 7 of Part 2 of the Code of Civil Procedure.

(d) When a restraining order is issued pursuant to this section, or within a time to be allowed by the superior court, but in any case not more than 30 days after the restraining order is issued, an accusation shall be filed with the board pursuant to Section 11503 of the Government Code. The accusation shall be served upon the licensee as provided by Section 11505 of the Government Code. The licensee shall have all of the rights and privileges available as specified in Chapter 5 (commencing with Section 11500) of Part 1 of Division 3 of Title 2 of the Government Code; however, if the licensee requests a hearing on the accusation, the board must provide the licensee with a hearing within 30 days of the request and a decision within 15 days of the date of the conclusion of the hearing, or the court may nullify the restraining order previously issued. Any restraining order issued pursuant to this section shall be dissolved by operation of law at such time the board's decision is subject to judicial review pursuant to Section 1094.5 of the Code of Civil Procedure.

Added Stats 1977 ch 443 § 1. Amended Stats 1982 ch 517 § 3.

§ 125.9. System for issuance of citations to licensees; Contents; Fines

(a) Except with respect to persons regulated under Chapter 11 (commencing with Section 7500), any board, bureau, or commission within the department, the State Board of Chiropractic Examiners, and the Osteopathic Medical Board of California, may establish, by regulation, a system for the issuance to a licensee of a citation which may contain an order of abatement or an order to pay an administrative fine assessed by the board, bureau, or commission where the licensee is in violation of the applicable licensing act or any regulation adopted pursuant thereto.

(b) The system shall contain the following provisions:

(1) Citations shall be in writing and shall describe with particularity the nature of the violation, including specific reference to the provision of law determined to have been violated.

(2) Whenever appropriate, the citation shall contain an order of abatement fixing a reasonable time for abatement of the violation.

(3) In no event shall the administrative fine assessed by the board, bureau, or commission exceed five thousand dollars ($5,000) for each inspection or each investigation made with respect to the violation, or five thousand dollars ($5,000) for each violation or count if the violation involves fraudulent billing submitted to an insurance company, the Medi-Cal program, or Medicare. In assessing a fine, the board, bureau, or commission shall give due consideration to the appropriateness of the amount of the fine with respect to factors such as the gravity of the violation, the good faith of the licensee, and the history of previous violations.

(4) A citation or fine assessment issued pursuant to a citation shall inform the licensee that if the licensee desires a hearing to contest the finding of a violation, that hearing shall be requested by written notice to the board, bureau, or commission within 30 days of the date of issuance of the citation or assessment. If a hearing is not requested pursuant to this section, payment of any fine shall not constitute an admission of the violation charged. Hearings shall be held pursuant to Chapter 5 (commencing with Section 11500) of Part 1 of Division 3 of Title 2 of the Government Code.

(5) Failure of a licensee to pay a fine or comply with an order of abatement, or both, within 30 days of the date of assessment or order, unless the citation is being appealed, may result in disciplinary action being taken by the board, bureau, or commission. Where a citation is not contested and a fine is not paid, the full amount of the assessed fine shall be added to the fee for renewal of the license. A license shall not be renewed without payment of the renewal fee and fine.

(c) The system may contain the following provisions:

(1) A citation may be issued without the assessment of an administrative fine.

(2) Assessment of administrative fines may be limited to only particular violations of the applicable licensing act.

(d) Notwithstanding any other provision of law, if a fine is paid to satisfy an assessment based on the finding of a violation, payment of the fine and compliance with the order of abatement, if applicable, shall be represented as satisfactory resolution of the matter for purposes of public disclosure.

(e) Administrative fines collected pursuant to this section shall be deposited in the special fund of the particular board, bureau, or commission.

Added Stats 1986 ch 1379 § 2. Amended Stats 1987 ch 1088 § 1; Stats 1991 ch 521 § 1 (SB 650); Stats 1995 ch 381 § 4 (AB 910), effective August 4, 1995, ch 708 § 1 (SB 609); Stats 2000 ch 197 § 1 (SB 1636); Stats 2001 ch 309 § 1 (AB 761), ch 728 § 1.2 (SB 724); Stats 2003 ch 788 § 1 (SB 362); Stats 2012 ch 291 § 1 (SB 1077), effective January 1, 2013; Stats 2019 ch 351 § 29 (AB 496), effective January 1, 2020; Stats 2020 ch 312 § 3 (SB 1474), effective January 1, 2021.

§ 126. Submission of reports to Governor

Notwithstanding any other provision of this code, any board, commission, examining committee, or other similarly constituted agency within the department required prior to the effective date of this section to submit reports to the Governor under any provision of this code shall not be required to submit such reports.

Added Stats 1967 ch 660 § 1.

§ 127. Submission of reports to director

Notwithstanding any other provision of this code, the director may require such reports from any board, commission, examining committee, or other similarly constituted agency within the department as the director deems reasonably necessary on any phase of their operations.

Added Stats 1967 ch 660 § 2. Amended Stats 2019 ch 351 § 30 (AB 496), effective January 1, 2020.

§ 128. Sale of equipment, supplies, or services for use in violation of licensing requirements

Notwithstanding any other provision of law, it is a misdemeanor to sell equipment, supplies, or services to any person with knowledge that the equipment, supplies, or services are to be used in the performance of a service or contract in violation of the licensing requirements of this code.

The provisions of this section shall not be applicable to cash sales of less than one hundred dollars ($100).

For the purposes of this section, "person" includes, but is not limited to, a company, partnership, limited liability company, firm, or corporation.

For the purposes of this section, "license" includes certificate or registration.

A violation of this section shall be punishable by a fine of not less than one thousand dollars ($1,000) and by imprisonment in the county jail not exceeding six months.

Added Stats 1971 ch 1052 § 1. Amended Stats 1994 ch 1010 § 1 (SB 2053).

§ 128.5. Reduction of license fees in event of surplus funds

(a) Notwithstanding any other provision of law, if at the end of any fiscal year, an agency within the Department of Consumer Affairs, except the agencies referred to in subdivision (b), has unencumbered funds in an amount that equals or is more than the agency's operating budget for the next two fiscal years, the agency shall reduce license or other fees, whether the license or other fees be fixed by stat-

Section V

ute or may be determined by the agency within limits fixed by statute, during the following fiscal year in an amount that will reduce
any surplus funds of the agency to an amount less than the agency's
operating budget for the next two fiscal years.

(b) Notwithstanding any other provision of law, if at the end of any
fiscal year, the California Architects Board, the Board of Behavioral
Sciences, the Veterinary Medical Board, the Court Reporters Board of
California, the Medical Board of California, the Board of Vocational
Nursing and Psychiatric Technicians, or the Bureau of Security and
Investigative Services has unencumbered funds in an amount that
equals or is more than the agency's operating budget for the next two
fiscal years, the agency shall reduce license or other fees, whether the
license or other fees be fixed by statute or may be determined by the
agency within limits fixed by statute, during the following fiscal year
in an amount that will reduce any surplus funds of the agency to an
amount less than the agency's operating budget for the next two fiscal
years.

Added Stats 1972 ch 938 § 2, effective August 16, 1972, as B & P C § 128. Amended
Stats 1973 ch 863 § 3. Amended and Renumbered by Stats 1978 ch 1161 § 4. Amended
Stats 1987 ch 850 § 3; Stats 1989 ch 886 § 2; Stats 1993 ch 1263 § 2 (AB 936); Stats
1994 ch 26 § 5 (AB 1807), effective March 30, 1994; Stats 1995 ch 60 § 2 (SB 42), effec-
tive July 6, 1995; Stats 1997 ch 759 § 2 (SB 827); Stats 2000 ch 1054 § 1 (SB 1863);
Stats. 2009, Ch. 308 (SB 819).

§ 129. Handling of complaints; Reports to Legislature

(a) As used in this section, "board" means every board, bureau,
commission, committee, and similarly constituted agency in the department that issues licenses.

(b) Each board shall, upon receipt of any complaint respecting an
individual licensed by the board, notify the complainant of the initial
administrative action taken on the complainant's complaint within 10
days of receipt. Each board shall notify the complainant of the final
action taken on the complainant's complaint. There shall be a notification made in every case in which the complainant is known. If the
complaint is not within the jurisdiction of the board or if the board is
unable to dispose satisfactorily of the complaint, the board shall
transmit the complaint together with any evidence or information it
has concerning the complaint to the agency, public or private, whose
authority in the opinion of the board will provide the most effective
means to secure the relief sought. The board shall notify the complainant of this action and of any other means that may be available
to the complainant to secure relief.

(c) The board shall, when the board deems it appropriate, notify the
person against whom the complaint is made of the nature of the complaint, may request appropriate relief for the complainant, and may
meet and confer with the complainant and the licensee in order to

mediate the complaint. Nothing in this subdivision shall be construed as authorizing or requiring any board to set or to modify any fee charged by a licensee.

(d) It shall be the continuing duty of the board to ascertain patterns of complaints and to report on all actions taken with respect to those patterns of complaints to the director and to the Legislature at least once per year. The board shall evaluate those complaints dismissed for lack of jurisdiction or no violation and recommend to the director and to the Legislature at least once per year the statutory changes it deems necessary to implement the board's functions and responsibilities under this section.

(e) It shall be the continuing duty of the board to take whatever action it deems necessary, with the approval of the director, to inform the public of its functions under this section.

(f) Notwithstanding any other law, upon receipt of a child custody evaluation report submitted to a court pursuant to Chapter 6 (commencing with Section 3110) of Part 2 of Division 8 of the Family Code, the board shall notify the noncomplaining party in the underlying custody dispute, who is a subject of that report, of the pending investigation.

Added Stats 1972 ch 1041 § 1. Amended Stats 2014 ch 283 § 1 (AB 1843), effective January 1, 2015; Stats 2019 ch 351 § 31 (AB 496), effective January 1, 2020.

§ 130. Terms of office of agency members

(a) Notwithstanding any other law, the term of office of any member of an agency designated in subdivision (b) shall be for a term of four years expiring on June 1.

(b) Subdivision (a) applies to the following boards or committees:

(1) The Medical Board of California.

(2) The Podiatric Medical Board of California.

(3) The Physical Therapy Board of California.

(4) The Board of Registered Nursing, except as provided in subdivision (c) of Section 2703.

(5) The Board of Vocational Nursing and Psychiatric Technicians.

(6) The California State Board of Optometry.

(7) The California State Board of Pharmacy.

(8) The Veterinary Medical Board.

(9) The California Architects Board.

(10) The Landscape Architect Technical Committee.

(11) The Board for Professional Engineers and Land Surveyors.

(12) The Contractors State License Board.

(13) The Board of Behavioral Sciences.

(14) The Court Reporters Board of California.

(15) The State Athletic Commission.

Section V

(16) The Osteopathic Medical Board of California.
(17) The Respiratory Care Board of California.
(18) The Acupuncture Board.
(19) The Board of Psychology.
(20) The Structural Pest Control Board.

Added Stats 1969 ch 465 § 1. Amended Stats 1971 ch 716 § 8; Stats 1978 ch 1161 § 5; Stats 1983 ch 150 § 2; Stats 1986 ch 655 § 1; Stats 1987 ch 850 § 4; Stats 1989 ch 886 § 3; Stats 1990 ch 1256 § 2 (AB 2649); Stats 1991 ch 359 § 2 (AB 1332); Stats 1994 ch 26 § 6 (AB 1807), effective March 30, 1994, ch 1274 § 1.3 (SB 2039); Stats 1995 ch 60 § 3 (SB 42), effective July 6, 1995; Stats 1997 ch 759 § 3 (SB 827); Stats 1998 ch 59 § 4 (AB 969), ch 970 § 1 (AB 2802), ch 971 § 1 (AB 2721); Stats 2000 ch 1054 § 2 (SB 1863); Stats 2001 ch 159 § 3 (SB 662); Stats 2009–2010 4th Ex Sess ch 18 § 2 (ABX4 20), effective October 23, 2009; Stats 2012 ch 4 § 1 (SB 98), effective February 14, 2012. See this section as modified in Governor's Reorganization Plan No. 2 § 3 of 2012; Amended Stats 2013 ch 352 § 4 (AB 1317), effective September 26, 2013, operative July 1, 2013; Stats 2019 ch 351 § 32 (AB 496), effective January 1, 2020; Stats 2020 ch 312 § 4 (SB 1474), effective January 1, 2021; Stats 2021 ch 630 § 3 (AB 1534), effective January 1, 2022.

§ 131. Maximum number of terms

Notwithstanding any other provision of law, no member of an agency designated in subdivision (b) of Section 130 or member of a board, commission, committee, or similarly constituted agency in the department shall serve more than two consecutive full terms.

Added Stats 1970 ch 1394 § 1, operative July 1, 1971. Amended Stats 1987 ch 850 § 5.

§ 134. Proration of license fees

When the term of any license issued by any agency in the department exceeds one year, initial license fees for licenses which are issued during a current license term shall be prorated on a yearly basis.

Added Stats 1974 ch 743 § 1. Amended Stats 1978 ch 1161 § 6.

§ 135. Reexamination of applicants

No agency in the department shall, on the basis of an applicant's failure to successfully complete prior examinations, impose any additional limitations, restrictions, prerequisites, or requirements on any applicant who wishes to participate in subsequent examinations except that any examining agency which allows an applicant conditional credit for successfully completing a divisible part of an examination may require that an applicant be reexamined in those parts successfully completed if such applicant has not successfully completed all parts of the examination within a required period of time established by the examining agency. Nothing in this section, however, requires the exemption of such applicant from the regular fees and requirements normally associated with examinations.

Added Stats 1974 ch 743 § 2.

§ 135.4. Refugees, asylees, and special immigrant visa holders; professional licensing; initial licensure process

(a) Notwithstanding any other law, a board within the department shall expedite, and may assist, the initial licensure process for an applicant who supplies satisfactory evidence to the board that they have been admitted to the United States as a refugee under Section 1157 of Title 8 of the United States Code, have been granted asylum by the Secretary of Homeland Security or the Attorney General of the United States pursuant to Section 1158 of Title 8 of the United States Code, or they have a special immigrant visa (SIV) that has been granted a status under Section 1244 of Public Law 110-181, under Public Law 109-163, or under Section 602(b) of Title VI of Division F of Public Law 111-8.

(b) Nothing in this section shall be construed as changing existing licensure requirements. A person applying for expedited licensure under subdivision (a) shall meet all applicable statutory and regulatory licensure requirements.

(c) A board may adopt regulations necessary to administer this section.

(d) For purposes of this section, "applicant" refers to an applicant for an individual license and does not refer to applicants for business or entity licenses.

Added Stats 2020 ch 186 § 1 (AB 2113), effective January 1, 2021. Amended Stats 2024 Ch 481 § 4 (SB 1451), effective September 22, 2024.

§ 135.5. Licensure and citizenship or immigration status

(a) The Legislature finds and declares that it is in the best interests of the State of California to provide persons who are not lawfully present in the United States with the state benefits provided by all licensing acts of entities within the department, and therefore enacts this section pursuant to subsection (d) of Section 1621 of Title 8 of the United States Code.

(b) Notwithstanding subdivision (a) of Section 30, and except as required by subdivision (e) of Section 7583.23, no entity within the department shall deny licensure to an applicant based on his or her citizenship status or immigration status.

(c) Every board within the department shall implement all required regulatory or procedural changes necessary to implement this section no later than January 1, 2016. A board may implement the provisions of this section at any time prior to January 1, 2016.

Added Stats 2014 ch 752 § 2 (SB 1159), effective January 1, 2015.

Section V

§ 136. Notification of change of address; Punishment for failure to comply

(a) Each person holding a license, certificate, registration, permit, or other authority to engage in a profession or occupation issued by a board within the department shall notify the issuing board at its principal office of any change in the person's mailing address within 30 days after the change, unless the board has specified by regulations a shorter time period.

(b) Except as otherwise provided by law, failure of a licensee to comply with the requirement in subdivision (a) constitutes grounds for the issuance of a citation and administrative fine, if the board has the authority to issue citations and administrative fines.

Added Stats 1994 ch 26 § 7 (AB 1807), effective March 30, 1994. Amended Stats 2019 ch 351 § 34 (AB 496), effective January 1, 2020.

§ 137. Regulations requiring inclusion of license numbers in advertising, etc.

Any agency within the department may promulgate regulations requiring licensees to include their license numbers in any advertising, soliciting, or other presentments to the public.

However, nothing in this section shall be construed to authorize regulation of any person not a licensee who engages in advertising, solicitation, or who makes any other presentment to the public on behalf of a licensee. Such a person shall incur no liability pursuant to this section for communicating in any advertising, soliciting, or other presentment to the public a licensee's license number exactly as provided by the licensee or for failure to communicate such number if none is provided by the licensee.

Added Stats 1974 ch 743 § 3. Amended Stats 2019 ch 351 § 35 (AB 496), effective January 1, 2020.

§ 138. Notice that practitioner is licensed; Evaluation of licensing examination

Every board in the department, as defined in Section 22, shall initiate the process of adopting regulations on or before June 30, 1999, to require its licensees, as defined in Section 23.8, to provide notice to their clients or customers that the practitioner is licensed by this state. A board shall be exempt from the requirement to adopt regulations pursuant to this section if the board has in place, in statute or regulation, a requirement that provides for consumer notice of a practitioner's status as a licensee of this state.

Added Stats 1998 ch 879 § 1 (SB 2238). Amended Stats 1999 ch 67 § 1 (AB 1105), effective July 6, 1999; Stats 2019 ch 351 § 36 (AB 496), effective January 1, 2020.

§ 139. Policy for examination development and validation, and occupational analysis

(a) The Legislature finds and declares that occupational analyses and examination validation studies are fundamental components of licensure programs. It is the intent of the Legislature that the policy developed by the department pursuant to subdivision (b) be used by the fiscal, policy, and sunset review committees of the Legislature in their annual reviews of these boards, programs, and bureaus.

(b) Notwithstanding any other provision of law, the department shall develop, in consultation with the boards, programs, bureaus, and divisions under its jurisdiction, and the Osteopathic Medical Board of California and the State Board of Chiropractic Examiners, a policy regarding examination development and validation, and occupational analysis. The department shall finalize and distribute this policy by September 30, 1999, to each of the boards, programs, bureaus, and divisions under its jurisdiction and to the Osteopathic Medical Board of California and the State Board of Chiropractic Examiners. This policy shall be submitted in draft form at least 30 days prior to that date to the appropriate fiscal, policy, and sunset review committees of the Legislature for review. This policy shall address, but shall not be limited to, the following issues:

(1) An appropriate schedule for examination validation and occupational analyses, and circumstances under which more frequent reviews are appropriate.

(2) Minimum requirements for psychometrically sound examination validation, examination development, and occupational analyses, including standards for sufficient number of test items.

(3) Standards for review of state and national examinations.

(4) Setting of passing standards.

(5) Appropriate funding sources for examination validations and occupational analyses.

(6) Conditions under which boards, programs, and bureaus should use internal and external entities to conduct these reviews.

(7) Standards for determining appropriate costs of reviews of different types of examinations, measured in terms of hours required.

(8) Conditions under which it is appropriate to fund permanent and limited term positions within a board, program, or bureau to manage these reviews.

(c) Every regulatory board and bureau, as defined in Section 22, and every program and bureau administered by the department, the Osteopathic Medical Board of California, and the State Board of Chiropractic Examiners, shall submit to the director on or before December 1, 1999, and on or before December 1 of each subsequent year, its method for ensuring that every licensing examination administered by or pursuant to contract with the board is subject to periodic evaluation. The evaluation shall include (1) a description of the occupational analysis serving as the basis for the examination; (2) sufficient item analysis data to permit a psychometric evaluation of the items; (3) an assessment of the appropriateness of prerequisites for admittance to the examination; and (4) an estimate of the costs and personnel required to perform these functions. The evaluation shall be revised and a new evaluation submitted to the director whenever, in the judgment of the board, program, or bureau, there is a substantial change in the examination or the prerequisites for admittance to the examination.

(d) The evaluation may be conducted by the board, program, or bureau, the Office of Professional Examination Services of the department, the Osteopathic Medical Board of California, or the State Board of Chiropractic Examiners or pursuant to a contract with a qualified private testing firm. A board, program, or bureau that provides for development or administration of a licensing examination pursuant to contract with a public or private entity may rely on an occupational analysis or item analysis conducted by that entity. The department shall compile this information, along with a schedule specifying when examination validations and occupational analyses shall be performed, and submit it to the appropriate fiscal, policy, and sunset review committees of the Legislature by September 30 of each year. It is the intent of the Legislature that the method specified in this report be consistent with the policy developed by the department pursuant to subdivision (b).

Added Stats 1999 ch 67 § 2 (AB 1105), effective July 6, 1999. Amended Stats. 2009, Ch. 307 (SB 821)

§ 139.5. Quarterly internet website posting requirements

Beginning July 1, 2021, each board, as defined in Section 22, within the department that issues a license shall do both of the following on at least a quarterly basis:

(a) Prominently display on its internet website one of the following:

(1) The current average timeframes for processing initial and renewal license applications.

(2) The combined current average timeframe for processing both initial and renewal license applications.

(b) Prominently display on its internet website one of the following:

(1) The current average timeframes for processing each license type that the board administers.

(2) The combined current average timeframe for processing all license types that the board administers.

Added Stats 2020 ch 131 § 1 (SB 878), effective January 1, 2021.

§ 140. Disciplinary action; Licensee's failure to record cash transactions in payment of employee wages

Any board, as defined in Section 22, which is authorized under this code to take disciplinary action against a person who holds a license may take disciplinary action upon the ground that the licensee has failed to record and preserve for not less than three years, any and all cash transactions involved in the payment of employee wages by a licensee. Failure to make these records available to an authorized representative of the board may be made grounds for disciplinary action. In any action brought and sustained by the board which involves a violation of this section and any regulation adopted thereto, the board may assess the licensee with the actual investigative costs incurred, not to exceed two thousand five hundred dollars ($2,500). Failure to pay those costs may result in revocation of the license. Any moneys collected pursuant to this section shall be deposited in the respective fund of the board.

Added Stats 1984 ch 1490 § 2, effective September 27, 1984.

§ 141. Disciplinary action by foreign jurisdiction; Grounds for disciplinary action by state licensing board

(a) For any licensee holding a license issued by a board under the jurisdiction of the department, a disciplinary action taken by another state, by any agency of the federal government, or by another country for any act substantially related to the practice regulated by the California license, may be a ground for disciplinary action by the respective state licensing board. A certified copy of the record of the disciplinary action taken against the licensee by another state, an agency of the federal government, or another country shall be conclusive evidence of the events related therein.

(b) Nothing in this section shall preclude a board from applying a specific statutory provision in the licensing act administered by that board that provides for discipline based upon a disciplinary action taken against the licensee by another state, an agency of the federal government, or another country.

Added Stats 1994 ch 1275 § 2 (SB 2101).

§ 143. Proof of license as condition of bringing action for collection of compensation

(a) No person engaged in any business or profession for which a license is required under this code governing the department or any board, bureau, commission, committee, or program within the department, may bring or maintain any action, or recover in law or equity in any action, in any court of this state for the collection of compensation for the performance of any act or contract for which a license is required without alleging and proving that he or she was duly licensed at all times during the performance of that act or contract, regardless of the merits of the cause of action brought by the person.

(b) The judicial doctrine of substantial compliance shall not apply to this section.

(c) This section shall not apply to an act or contract that is considered to qualify as lawful practice of a licensed occupation or profession pursuant to Section 121.

Added Stats 1990 ch 1207 § 1.5 (AB 3242).

§ 143.5. Provision in agreements to settle certain causes of action prohibited; Adoption of regulations; Exemptions

(a) No licensee who is regulated by a board, bureau, or program within the Department of Consumer Affairs, nor an entity or person acting as an authorized agent of a licensee, shall include or permit to be included a provision in an agreement to settle a civil dispute, whether the agreement is made before or after the commencement of a civil action, that prohibits the other party in that dispute from contacting, filing a complaint with, or cooperating with the department, board, bureau, or program within the Department of Consumer Affairs that regulates the licensee or that requires the other party to withdraw a complaint from the department, board, bureau, or program within the Department of Consumer Affairs that regulates the licensee. A provision of that nature is void as against public policy, and any licensee who includes or permits to be included a provision of that nature in a settlement agreement is subject to disciplinary action by the board, bureau, or program.

(b) Any board, bureau, or program within the Department of Consumer Affairs that takes disciplinary action against a licensee or licensees based on a complaint or report that has also been the subject of a civil action and that has been settled for monetary damages providing for full and final satisfaction of the parties may not require its licensee or licensees to pay any additional sums to the benefit of any plaintiff in the civil action.

(c) As used in this section, "board" shall have the same meaning as defined in Section 22, and "licensee" means a person who has been granted a license, as that term is defined in Section 23.7.

(d) Notwithstanding any other law, upon granting a petition filed by a licensee or authorized agent of a licensee pursuant to Section 11340.6 of the Government Code, a board, bureau, or program within the Department of Consumer Affairs may, based upon evidence and legal authorities cited in the petition, adopt a regulation that does both of the following:

(1) Identifies a code section or jury instruction in a civil cause of action that has no relevance to the board's, bureau's, or program's en-

forcement responsibilities such that an agreement to settle such a cause of action based on that code section or jury instruction otherwise prohibited under subdivision (a) will not impair the board's, bureau's, or program's duty to protect the public.

(2) Exempts agreements to settle such a cause of action from the requirements of subdivision (a).

(e) This section shall not apply to a licensee subject to Section 2220.7.

Added Stats 2012 ch 561 § 1 (AB 2570), effective January 1, 2013.

§ 144. Requirement of fingerprints for criminal record checks; Applicability

(a) Notwithstanding any other law, an agency designated in subdivision (b) shall require an applicant to furnish to the agency a full set of fingerprints for purposes of conducting criminal history record checks. Any agency designated in subdivision (b) may obtain and receive, at its discretion, criminal history information from the Department of Justice and the United States Federal Bureau of Investigation.

(b) Subdivision (a) applies to the following:

(1) California Board of Accountancy.

(2) State Athletic Commission.

(3) Board of Behavioral Sciences.

(4) Court Reporters Board of California.

(5) Dental Board of California.

(6) California State Board of Pharmacy.

(7) Board of Registered Nursing.

(8) Veterinary Medical Board.

(9) Board of Vocational Nursing and Psychiatric Technicians of the State of California.

(10) Respiratory Care Board of California.

(11) Physical Therapy Board of California.

(12) Physician Assistant Board.

(13) Speech-Language Pathology and Audiology and Hearing Aid Dispensers Board.

(14) Medical Board of California.

(15) California State Board of Optometry.

(16) Acupuncture Board.

(17) Cemetery and Funeral Bureau.

(18) Bureau of Security and Investigative Services.

(19) Division of Investigation.

(20) Board of Psychology.

(21) California Board of Occupational Therapy.

(22) Structural Pest Control Board.

(23) Contractors State License Board.

Section V

(24) Naturopathic Medicine Committee.

(25) Professional Fiduciaries Bureau.

(26) Board for Professional Engineers, Land Surveyors, and Geologists.

(27) Podiatric Medical Board of California.

(28) Osteopathic Medical Board of California.

(29) California Architects Board, beginning January 1, 2021.

(30) Landscape Architects Technical Committee, beginning January 1, 2022.

(31) Bureau of Household Goods and Services with respect to household movers as described in Chapter 3.1 (commencing with Section 19225) of Division 8.

(c) For purposes of paragraph (26) of subdivision (b), the term "applicant" shall be limited to an initial applicant who has never been registered or licensed by the board or to an applicant for a new licensure or registration category.

Added Stats 1997 ch 758 § 2 (SB 1346). Amended Stats 2000 ch 697 § 1.2 (SB 1046), operative January 1, 2001; Stats 2001 ch 159 § 4 (SB 662), Stats 2001 ch 687 § 2 (AB 1409) (ch 687 prevails); Stats 2002 ch 744 § 1 (SB 1953), Stats 2002 ch 825 § 1 (SB 1952); Stats 2003 ch 485 § 2 (SB 907), Stats 2003 ch 789 § 1 (SB 364), Stats 2003 ch 874 § 1 (SB 363); Stats 2004 ch 909 § 1.2 (SB 136), effective September 30, 2004; Stats 2009 ch 308 § 4 (SB 819), effective January 1, 2010; Stats 2011 ch 448 § 1 (SB 543), effective January 1, 2012; Stats 2015 ch 719 § 1 (SB 643), effective January 1, 2016; Stats 2016 ch 32 § 3 (SB 837), effective June 27, 2016; Stats 2017 ch 775 § 3 (SB 798), effective January 1, 2018; Stats 2018 ch 6 § 1 (AB 106), effective March 13, 2018; Stats 2019 ch 351 § 37 (AB 496), effective January 1, 2020; Stats 2019 ch 376 § 1 (SB 608), effective January 1, 2020; Stats 2019 ch 865 § 1.3 (AB 1519), effective January 1, 2020 (ch 865 prevails); Stats 2020 ch 312 § 5 (SB 1474), effective January 1, 2021; Stats 2021 ch 70 § 3 (AB 141), effective July 12, 2021; Stats 2021 ch 188 § 2 (SB 826), effective January 1, 2022; Stats 2021 ch 630 § 4.5 (AB 1534), effective January 1, 2022 (ch 630 prevails).

Chapter 2

The Director of Consumer Affairs

§ 150. Designation

The department is under the control of a civil executive officer who is known as the Director of Consumer Affairs.

Enacted Stats 1937. Amended Stats 1971 ch 716 § 9.

§ 151. Appointment and tenure; Salary and traveling expenses

The director is appointed by the Governor and holds office at the Governor's pleasure. The director shall receive the annual salary provided for by Chapter 6 (commencing with Section 11550) of Part 1 of Division 3 of Title 2 of the Government Code, and the director's necessary traveling expenses.

Enacted Stats 1937. Amended Stats 1943 ch 1029 § 1; Stats 1945 ch 1185 § 2; Stats 1947 ch 1442 § 1; Stats 1951 ch 1613 § 14; Stats 1984 ch 144 § 2, ch 268 § 0.1, effective June 30, 1984; Stats 1985 ch 106 § 1; Stats 2019 ch 351 § 38 (AB 496), effective January 1, 2020.

§ 152. Departmental organization

For the purpose of administration, the reregistration and clerical work of the department is organized by the director, subject to the approval of the Governor, in such manner as the director deems necessary to properly segregate and conduct the work of the department.

Enacted Stats 1937. Amended Stats 2019 ch 351 § 39 (AB 496), effective January 1, 2020; Stats 2020 ch 370 § 2 (SB 1371), effective January 1, 2021.

§ 152.5. Extension of renewal dates

For purposes of distributing the reregistration work of the department uniformly throughout the year as nearly as practicable, the boards in the department may, with the approval of the director, extend by not more than six months the date fixed by law for the renewal of any license, certificate or permit issued by them, except that in such event any renewal fee which may be involved shall be prorated in such manner that no person shall be required to pay a greater or lesser fee than would have been required had the change in renewal dates not occurred.

Added Stats 1959 ch 1707 § 1.

§ 152.6. Establishment of license periods and renewal dates

Notwithstanding any other provision of this code, each board within the department shall, in cooperation with the director, establish such license periods and renewal dates for all licenses in such manner as best to distribute the renewal work of all boards throughout each year and permit the most efficient, and economical use of personnel and equipment. To the extent practicable, provision shall be made for the proration or other adjustment of fees in such manner that no person shall be required to pay a greater or lesser fee than the person would have been required to pay if the change in license periods or renewal dates had not occurred.

As used in this section "license" includes "certificate," "permit," "authority," "registration," and similar indicia of authority to engage in a business or profession, and "board" includes "board," "bureau," "commission," "committee," and an individual who is authorized to renew a license.

Section V

Added Stats 1968 ch 1248 § 1. Amended Stats 2019 ch 351 § 40 (AB 496), effective January 1, 2020.

§ 153. Investigations

The director may investigate the work of the boards in the department and may obtain a copy of all records and full and complete data in all official matters in possession of the boards and their members, officers, or employees, other than examination questions prior to submission to applicants at scheduled examinations.

Enacted Stats 1937. Amended Stats 2019 ch 351 § 41 (AB 496), effective January 1, 2020.

§ 154. Matters relating to employees of boards

Any and all matters relating to employment, tenure or discipline of employees of any board, agency or commission, shall be initiated by said board, agency or commission, but all such actions shall, before reference to the State Personnel Board, receive the approval of the appointing power.

To effect the purposes of Division 1 of this code and each agency of the department, employment of all personnel shall be in accord with Article XXIV of the Constitution, the law and rules and regulations of the State Personnel Board. Each board, agency or commission, shall select its employees from a list of eligibles obtained by the appointing power from the State Personnel Board. The person selected by the board, agency or commission to fill any position or vacancy shall thereafter be reported by the board, agency or commission, to the appointing power.

Enacted Stats 1937. Amended Stats 1945 ch 1276 § 4.

§ 154.5. Legal assistance for experts aiding in investigations of licensees

If a person, not a regular employee of a board under this code, including the Board of Chiropractic Examiners and the Osteopathic Medical Board of California, is hired or under contract to provide expertise to the board in the evaluation of an applicant or the conduct of a licensee, and that person is named as a defendant in a civil action arising out of the evaluation or any opinions rendered, statements made, or testimony given to the board or its representatives, the board shall provide for representation required to defend the defendant in that civil action. The board shall not be liable for any judgment rendered against the person. The Attorney General shall be utilized in the action and his or her services shall be a charge against the board.

Added Stats 1986 ch 1205 § 1, as B & P C § 483. Amended and Renumbered by Stats 1987 ch 850 § 8. Amended Stats 1991 ch 359 § 3 (AB 1332).

§ 155. Employment of investigators; Inspectors as employees or under contract

(a) In accordance with Section 159.5, the director may employ such investigators, inspectors, and deputies as are necessary properly to investigate and prosecute all violations of any law, the enforcement of which is charged to the department or to any board, agency, or commission in the department.

(b) It is the intent of the Legislature that inspectors used by boards, bureaus, or commissions in the department shall not be required to be employees of the Division of Investigation, but may either be employees of, or under contract to, the boards, bureaus, or commissions. Contracts for services shall be consistent with Article 4.5 (commencing with Section 19130) of Chapter 6 of Part 2 of Division 5 of Title 2 of the Government Code. All civil service employees currently employed as inspectors whose functions are transferred as a result of this section shall retain their positions, status, and rights in accordance with Section 19994.10 of the Government Code and the State Civil Service Act (Part 2 (commencing with Section 18500) of Division 5 of Title 2 of the Government Code).

(c) Nothing in this section limits the authority of, or prohibits, investigators in the Division of Investigation in the conduct of inspections or investigations of any licensee, or in the conduct of investigations of any officer or employee of a board or the department at the specific request of the director or his or her designee.

Enacted Stats 1937. Amended Stats 1945 ch 1276 § 5; Stats 1971 ch 716 § 10; Stats 1985 ch 1382 § 1.

§ 156. Contractual authority

(a) The director may, for the department and at the request and with the consent of a board within the department on whose behalf the contract is to be made, enter into contracts pursuant to Chapter 3 (commencing with Section 11250) of Part 1 of Division 3 of Title 2 of the Government Code or Chapter 2 (commencing with Section 10290) of Part 2 of Division 2 of the Public Contract Code for and on behalf of any board within the department.

(b) In accordance with subdivision (a), the director may, in his or her discretion, negotiate and execute contracts for examination purposes, which include provisions that hold harmless a contractor where liability resulting from a contract between a board in the department and the contractor is traceable to the state or its officers, agents, or employees.

(c) The director shall report progress on release 3 entities' transition to a new licensing technology platform to all the appropriate committees of the Legislature by December 31 of each year. Progress reports shall include updated plans and timelines for completing all of the following:

(1) Business process documentation.

(2) Cost benefit analyses of information technology options.

(3) Information technology system development and implementation.

(4) Any other relevant steps needed to meet the IT needs of release 3 entities.

(5) Any other information as the Legislature may request.

Added Stats 1953 ch 864 § 1. Amended Stats 1984 ch 144 § 3; Stats 1988 ch 1448 § 1; Stats 2017 ch 429 § 2 (SB 547), effective January 1, 2018.

§ 156.1. Retention of records by providers of services related to treatment of alcohol or drug impairment

(a) Notwithstanding any other law, individuals or entities contracting with the department or any board within the department for the provision of services relating to the treatment and rehabilitation of licensees impaired by alcohol or dangerous drugs shall retain all records and documents pertaining to those services until such time as these records and documents have been reviewed for audit by the department. These records and documents shall be retained for three years from the date of the last treatment or service rendered to that licensee, after which time the records and documents may be purged and destroyed by the contract vendor. This provision shall supersede any other law relating to the purging or destruction of records pertaining to those treatment and rehabilitation programs.

(b) Unless otherwise expressly provided by statute or regulation, all records and documents pertaining to services for the treatment and rehabilitation of licensees impaired by alcohol or dangerous drugs provided by any contract vendor to the department or to any board within the department shall be kept confidential and are not subject to discovery or subpoena.

(c) With respect to all other contracts for services with the department, or any board within the department other than those set forth in subdivision (a), the director or chief deputy director may request an examination and audit by the department's internal auditor of all performance under the contract. For this purpose, all documents and records of the contract vendor in connection with such performance shall be retained by the vendor for a period of three years after final payment under the contract. Nothing in this section shall affect the authority of the State Auditor to conduct any examination or audit under the terms of Section 8546.7 of the Government Code.

Added Stats 1991 ch 654 § 3 (AB 1893). Amended Stats 2003 ch 107 § 1 (AB 569); Stats 2010 ch 517 § 1 (SB 1172), effective January 1, 2011; Stats 2019 ch 351 § 42 (AB 496), effective January 1, 2020.

§ 156.5. Leases for examination or meeting purposes

The director may negotiate and execute for the department and for its component agencies, rental agreements for short-term hiring of space and furnishings for examination or meeting purposes. The director may, in his or her discretion, negotiate and execute contracts for that space which include provisions which hold harmless the provider of the space where liability resulting from use of the space under the contract is traceable to the state or its officers, agents, or employees. Notwithstanding any other provision of law, the director may, in his or her discretion, advance payments as deposits to reserve and hold examination or meeting space. Any such agreement is subject to the approval of the legal office of the Department of General Services.

Added Stats 1967 ch 1235 § 1. Amended Stats 1988 ch 1448 § 1.5.

§ 157. Expenses in criminal prosecutions and unprofessional conduct proceedings

Expenses incurred by any board or on behalf of any board in any criminal prosecution or unprofessional conduct proceeding constitute proper charges against the funds of the board.

Added Stats 1937 ch 474.

§ 158. Refunds to applicants

With the approval of the Director of Consumer Affairs, the boards and commissions comprising the department or subject to its jurisdiction may make refunds to applicants who are found ineligible to take the examinations or whose credentials are insufficient to entitle them to certificates or licenses.

Notwithstanding any other law, any application fees, license fees, or penalties imposed and collected illegally, by mistake, inadvertence, or error shall be refunded. Claims authorized by the department shall be filed with the State Controller, and the Controller shall draw a warrant against the fund of the agency in payment of the refund.

Added Stats 1937 ch 474. Amended Stats 1945 ch 1378 § 1; Stats 1971 ch 716 § 11; Stats 2019 ch 351 § 43 (AB 496), effective January 1, 2020.

§ 159. Administration of oaths

The members and the executive officer of each board, agency, bureau, division, or commission have power to administer oaths and affirmations in the performance of any business of the board, and to certify to official acts.

Added Stats 1947 ch 1350 § 5.

Section V

§ 159.5. Division of Investigation; Appointments; Health Quality Investigation Unit

(a) (1) There is in the department the Division of Investigation. The division is in the charge of a person with the title of chief of the division.

(2) Except as provided in Section 160, investigators who have the authority of peace officers, as specified in subdivision (a) of Section 160 and in subdivision (a) of Section 830.3 of the Penal Code, shall be in the division and shall be appointed by the director.

(b) (1) There is in the Division of Investigation the Health Quality Investigation Unit. The primary responsibility of the unit is to investigate violations of law or regulation within the jurisdiction of the Medical Board of California, the Podiatric Medical Board of California, the Board of Psychology, the Osteopathic Medical Board of California, the Physician Assistant Board, or any entities under the jurisdiction of the Medical Board of California.

(2) The Medical Board of California shall not be charged an hourly rate for the performance of investigations by the unit.

Added Stats 1971 ch 716 § 12. Amended Stats 1985 ch 1382 § 2; Stats 2010 ch 719 § 2 (SB 856), effective October 19, 2010; Stats 2013 ch 515 § 1 (SB 304), effective January 1, 2014; Stats 2019 ch 351 § 44 (AB 496), effective January 1, 2020.

§ 161. Availability of public records at charge sufficient to pay costs

The department, or any board in the department, may, in accordance with the California Public Records Act (Division 10 (commencing with Section 7920.000) of Title 1 of the Government Code) and the Information Practices Act of 1977 (Chapter 1 (commencing with Section 1798) of Title 1.8 of Part 4 of Division 3 of the Civil Code), make available to the public copies of any part of its respective public records, or compilations, extracts, or summaries of information contained in its public records, at a charge sufficient to pay the actual cost thereof. That charge shall be determined by the director with the approval of the Department of General Services.

Added Stats 1949 ch 704 § 1. Amended Stats 1963 ch 590 § 1; Stats 1965 ch 371 § 9; Stats 2019 ch 351 § 45 (AB 496), effective January 1, 2020; Stats 2021 ch 615 § 3 (AB 474), effective January 1, 2022.

§ 162. Evidentiary effect of certificate of records officer as to license, etc.

The certificate of the officer in charge of the records of any board in the department that any person was or was not on a specified date, or during a specified period of time, licensed, certified or registered under the provisions of law administered by the board, or that the license, certificate or registration of any person was revoked or under suspension, shall be admitted in any court as prima facie evidence of the facts therein recited.

Added Stats 1949 ch 355 § 1.

§ 163. Fee for certification of records, etc.

Except as otherwise expressly provided by law, the department and each board in the department shall charge a fee of two dollars ($2) for the certification of a copy of any record, document, or paper in its custody or for the certification of any document evidencing the content of any such record, document or paper.

Added Stats 1961 ch 1858 § 1. Amended Stats 1963 ch 590 § 2.

§ 163.5. Delinquency fees; Reinstatement fees

Except as otherwise provided by law, the delinquency, penalty, or late fee for any licensee within the Department of Consumer Affairs shall be 50 percent of the renewal fee for such license in effect on the date of the renewal of the license, but not less than twenty-five dollars ($25) nor more than one hundred fifty dollars ($150).

A delinquency, penalty, or late fee shall not be assessed until 30 days have elapsed from the date that the licensing agency mailed a notice of renewal to the licensee at the licensee's last known address of record. The notice shall specify the date for timely renewal, and that failure to renew in a timely fashion shall result in the assessment of a delinquency, penalty, or late fee.

In the event a reinstatement or like fee is charged for the reinstatement of a license, the reinstatement fee shall be 150 percent of the renewal fee for such license in effect on the date of the reinstatement of the license, but not more than twenty-five dollars ($25) in excess of the renewal fee, except that in the event that such a fee is fixed by statute at less than 150 percent of the renewal fee and less than the renewal fee plus twenty-five dollars ($25), the fee so fixed shall be charged.

Added Stats 1974 ch 743 § 4. Amended Stats 1985 ch 587 § 1.

§ 163.6. [Section repealed 1992.]

Added Stats 1985 ch 587 § 2. Inoperative June 30, 1991. Repealed, operative January 1, 1992, by its own terms. The repealed section related to reduction in license renewal fees to offset increase in revenue.

Section V

§ 164. Form and content of license, certificate, permit, or similar indicia of authority

The form and content of any license, certificate, permit, or similar indicia of authority issued by any agency in the department, including any document evidencing renewal of a license, certificate, permit, or similar indicia of authority, shall be determined by the director after consultation with and consideration of the views of the agency concerned.

Added Stats 1971 ch 716 § 15. Amended Stats 1987 ch 850 § 6.

§ 165. Prohibition against submission of fiscal impact analysis relating to pending legislation without prior submission to director for comment

Notwithstanding any other provision of law, no board, bureau, committee, commission, or program in the Department of Consumer Affairs shall submit to the Legislature any fiscal impact analysis relating to legislation pending before the Legislature until the analysis has been submitted to the Director of Consumer Affairs, or his or her designee, for review and comment. The boards, bureaus, committees, commissions, and programs shall include the comments of the director when submitting any fiscal impact analysis to the Legislature. This section shall not be construed to prohibit boards, bureaus, committees, commissions, and programs from responding to direct requests for fiscal data from Members of the Legislature or their staffs. In those instances it shall be the responsibility of boards, bureaus, committees, commissions, and programs to also transmit that information to the director, or his or her designee, within five working days.

Added Stats 1984 ch 268 § 0.2, effective June 30, 1984.

§ 166. Development of guidelines for mandatory continuing education programs

The director shall, by regulation, develop guidelines to prescribe components for mandatory continuing education programs administered by any board within the department.

(a) The guidelines shall be developed to ensure that mandatory continuing education is used as a means to create a more competent licensing population, thereby enhancing public protection. The guidelines shall require mandatory continuing education programs to address, at least, the following:

(1) Course validity.

(2) Occupational relevancy.

(3) Effective presentation.

(4) Actual attendance.

(5) Material assimilation.

(6) Potential for application.

(b) The director shall consider educational principles, and the guidelines shall prescribe mandatory continuing education program formats to include, but not be limited to, the following:

(1) The specified audience.

(2) Identification of what is to be learned.

(3) Clear goals and objectives.

(4) Relevant learning methods (participatory, hands-on, or clinical setting).

(5) Evaluation, focused on the learner and the assessment of the intended learning outcomes (goals and objectives).

(c) Any board within the department that, after January 1, 1993, proposes a mandatory continuing education program for its licensees shall submit the proposed program to the director for review to assure that the program contains all the elements set forth in this section and complies with the guidelines developed by the director.

(d) Any board administering a mandatory continuing education program that proposes to amend its current program shall do so in a manner consistent with this section.

(e) Any board currently administering a mandatory continuing education program shall review the components and requirements of the program to determine the extent to which they are consistent with the guidelines developed under this section. The board shall submit a report of their findings to the director. The report shall identify the similarities and differences of its mandatory continuing education program. The report shall include any board-specific needs to explain the variation from the director's guidelines.

(f) Any board administering a mandatory continuing education program, when accepting hours for credit which are obtained out of state, shall ensure that the course for which credit is given is administered in accordance with the guidelines addressed in subdivision (a).

(g) Nothing in this section or in the guidelines adopted by the director shall be construed to repeal any requirements for continuing education programs set forth in any other provision of this code.

Added Stats 1992 ch 1135 § 2.2 (SB 2044). Amended Stats 1994 ch 146 § 1 (AB 3601).

Section V

Chapter 3

Funds of the Department

§ 200.1. Fund accruals exempt from transfer

(a) Any accruals that occur on or after September 11, 1993, to any funds or accounts within the Professions and Vocations Fund that realize increased revenues to that fund or account as a result of legislation enacted on or after September 11, 1993, and that have not been transferred pursuant to Sections 13.50, 13.60, and 13.70 of the Budget Act of 1993 on the effective date of the act that enacted this section, shall be exempt from the transfers contained in Sections 13.50, 13.60, and 13.70 of the Budget Act of 1993. These funds shall include, but not be limited to, all of the following:

(1) Athletic Commission Fund.

(2) Bureau of Home Furnishings and Thermal Insulation Fund.

(3) Contractors License Fund.

(4) Private Investigator Fund.

(5) Respiratory Care Fund.

(6) Vocational Nursing and Psychiatric Technicians Fund.

(b) Subdivision (a) shall not apply to the Contingent Fund of the Medical Board of California.

Added Stats 1994 ch 26 § 10 (AB 1807), effective March 30, 1994. Amended Stats 1997 ch 759 § 4 (SB 827); Stats 2020 ch 312 § 6 (SB 1474), effective January 1, 2021.

§ 201. Levy for administrative expenses

A charge for the estimated administrative expenses of the department, not to exceed the available balance in any appropriation for any one fiscal year, may be levied in advance on a pro rata share basis against any of the funds of any of the boards, bureaus, commissions, divisions, and agencies, at the discretion of the director and with the approval of the Department of Finance.

Enacted Stats 1937. Amended Stats 1947 ch 1350 § 4; Stats 1965 ch 371 § 10; Stats 1974 ch 1221 § 1.

§ 202.5. Itemized statement of services and changes from Department of Justice

Prior to payment to the Department of Justice of any charges for legal services rendered to any board within the department, the Department of Justice shall submit to the board an itemized statement of the services and charges. The itemized statement shall include detailed information regarding the services performed and the amount of time billed for each of those services.

Added Stats 1994 ch 1273 § 1 (SB 2038).

§ 205. Professions and vocations fund [Repealed]

Added Stats 2015 ch 510 § 2.3 (AB 179), effective January 1, 2016, operative July 1, 2016. Amended Stats 2016 ch 800 § 1 (SB 1196), effective January 1, 2017; Stats 2017 ch 421 § 6 (SB 19), effective January 1, 2018, operative July 1, 2018; Stats 2017 ch 669 § 3.5 (AB 1705), effective January 1, 2018, operative July 1, 2018 (ch 669 prevails); Stats 2019 ch 865 § 2 (AB 1519), effective January 1, 2020, repealed July 1, 2022; Stats 2020 ch 312 § 7 (SB 1474), effective January 1, 2021, repealed July 1, 2022.

§ 205. Professions and vocations fund

(a) There is in the State Treasury the Professions and Vocations Fund. The fund shall consist of the following special funds:

(1) Accountancy Fund.

(2) California Architects Board Fund.

(3) Athletic Commission Fund.

(4) Barbering and Cosmetology Contingent Fund.

(5) Cemetery and Funeral Fund.

(6) Contractors License Fund.

(7) State Dentistry Fund.

(8) Home Furnishings and Thermal Insulation Fund.

(9) California Architects Board-Landscape Architects Fund.

(10) Contingent Fund of the Medical Board of California.

(11) Optometry Fund.

(12) Pharmacy Board Contingent Fund.

(13) Physical Therapy Fund.

(14) Private Security Services Fund.

(15) Professional Engineer's, Land Surveyor's, and Geologist's Fund.

(16) Consumer Affairs Fund.

(17) Behavioral Sciences Fund.

(18) Licensed Midwifery Fund.

(19) Court Reporters' Fund.

(20) Veterinary Medical Board Contingent Fund.

(21) Vocational Nursing and Psychiatric Technicians Fund.

(22) Electronic and Appliance Repair Fund.

(23) Acupuncture Fund.

(24) Physician Assistant Fund.

(25) Board of Podiatric Medicine Fund.

(26) Psychology Fund.

(27) Respiratory Care Fund.

(28) Speech-Language Pathology and Audiology and Hearing Aid Dispensers Fund.

(29) Board of Registered Nursing Fund.

(30) Animal Health Technician Examining Committee Fund.

(31) State Dental Hygiene Fund.

Section V

(32) Structural Pest Control Fund.

(33) Structural Pest Control Education and Enforcement Fund.

(34) Structural Pest Control Research Fund.

(35) Household Movers Fund.

(36) Household Goods and Services Fund.

(b) For accounting and recordkeeping purposes, the Professions and Vocations Fund shall be deemed to be a single special fund, and each of the several special funds therein shall constitute and be deemed to be a separate account in the Professions and Vocations Fund. Each account or fund shall be available for expenditure only for the purposes as are now or may hereafter be provided by law.

(c) This section shall remain in effect only until July 1, 2026, and as of that date is repealed.

Added Stats 2019 ch 865 § 3 (AB 1519), effective January 1, 2020, operative July 1, 2022. Amended Stats 2020 ch 121 § 1 (AB 896), effective September 24, 2020, operative July 1, 2022; Stats 2020 ch 312 § 8.5 (SB 1474), effective January 1, 2021, operative July 1, 2022; Stats 2023 ch 508 § 1 (SB 814), effective January 1, 2024, repealed July 1, 2026.

§ 206. Dishonored check tendered for payment of fine, fee, or penalty

Notwithstanding any other provision of law, any person tendering a check for payment of a fee, fine, or penalty that was subsequently dishonored, shall not be granted a license, or other authority that they were seeking, until the applicant pays the amount outstanding from the dishonored payment together with the applicable fee, including any delinquency fee. The board may require the person whose check was returned unpaid to make payment of all fees by cashier's check or money order.

Added Stats 1994 ch 26 § 12 (AB 1807), effective March 30, 1994.

§ 210. BreEZe system vendor contract

(a) (1) The department may enter into a contract with a vendor for the BreEZe system, the integrated, enterprisewide enforcement case management and licensing system described in the department's strategic plan, no sooner than 30 days after notification in writing to the chairpersons of the Appropriations Committees of each house of the Legislature and the Chairperson of the Joint Legislative Budget Committee.

(2) The amount of BreEZe system vendor contract funds, authorized pursuant to this section, shall be consistent with the project costs approved by the office of the State Chief Information Officer based on its review and approval of the most recent BreEZe Special Project Report

to be submitted by the department prior to contract award at the conclusion of procurement activities.

(3) Paragraph (2) shall apply to all Budget Act items for the department that have an appropriation for the BreEZe system.

(b) (1) If the department enters into a contract with a vendor for the BreEZe system pursuant to subdivision (a), the department shall, by December 31, 2014, submit to the Legislature, the Senate Committee on Business, Professions and Economic Development, the Assembly Committee on Business and Professions, and the budget committees of each house, a report analyzing the workload of licensing personnel employed by boards within the department participating in the BreEZe system.

(2) A report to the Legislature pursuant to this subdivision shall be submitted in compliance with Section 9795 of the Government Code.

(3) This subdivision shall become inoperative on December 1, 2018, pursuant to Section 10231.5 of the Government Code.

(c) (1) Notwithstanding any other provision of law, upon the request of the Department of Consumer Affairs, the Department of Finance may augment the budgets of the boards, bureaus, commissions, committees, programs, and divisions that comprise the Department of Consumer Affairs, as defined in Section 101, for expenditure of non-General Fund moneys to pay BreEZe project costs. The augmentation may be made no sooner than 30 days after notification in writing to the chairpersons of the committees in each house of the Legislature that consider appropriations and the Chairperson of the Joint Legislative Budget Committee, or no sooner than whatever lesser time the chairperson of the joint committee may in each instance determine. The amount of funds augmented pursuant to the authority of this subdivision shall be consistent with project cost increases approved by the Secretary of California Technology based on the secretary's review and approval of the most recent BreEZe Special Project Report to be submitted at the conclusion of procurement activities. This subdivision shall apply to all Budget Act items for the boards, bureaus, commissions, committees, programs, and divisions that comprise the Department of Consumer Affairs, as defined in Section 101, that have an appropriation for the BreEZe system in the Budget Act of 2011.

(2) This subdivision shall become inoperative upon enactment of the Budget Act of 2012.

Added Stats 2010 ch 719 § 4 (SB 856), effective October 19, 2010. Amended Stats 2011 ch 448 § 3 (SB 543), effective January 1, 2012; Stats 2019 ch 351 § 46 (AB 496), effective January 1, 2020.

Section V

Chapter 4

Consumer Affairs

Article 1

General Provisions and Definitions

§ 300. Citation of chapter

This chapter may be cited as the Consumer Affairs Act

Added Stats 1970 ch 1394 § 3, operative July 1, 1971.

§ 301. Declaration of intent

It is the intent of the Legislature and the purpose of this chapter to promote and protect the interests of the people as consumers. The Legislature finds that vigorous representation and protection of consumer interests are essential to the fair and efficient functioning of a free enterprise market economy. The Legislature declares that government advances the interests of consumers by facilitating the proper functioning of the free enterprise market economy through (a) educating and informing the consumer to insure rational consumer choice in the marketplace; (b) protecting the consumer from the sale of goods and services through the use of deceptive methods, acts, or practices which are inimical to the general welfare of consumers; (c) fostering competition; and (d) promoting effective representation of consumers' interests in all branches and levels of government.

Added Stats 1970 ch 1394 § 3, operative July 1, 1971. Amended Stats 1975 ch 1262 § 1.

§ 302. Definitions

As used in this chapter, the following terms have the following meanings:

(a) "Department" means the Department of Consumer Affairs.

(b) "Director" means the Director of the Department of Consumer Affairs.

(c) "Consumer" means any individual who seeks or acquires, by purchase or lease, any goods, services, money, or credit for personal, family, or household purposes.

(d) "Person" means an individual, partnership, corporation, limited liability company, association, or other group, however organized.

(e) "Individual" does not include a partnership, corporation, association, or other group, however organized.

(f) "Division" means the Division of Consumer Services.

(g) "Interests of consumers" is limited to the cost, quality, purity, safety, durability, performance, effectiveness, dependability, availability, and adequacy of choice of goods and services offered or furnished to consumers and the adequacy and accuracy of information relating to consumer goods, services, money, or credit (including labeling, packaging, and advertising of contents, qualities, and terms of sales).

Added Stats 1970 ch 1394 § 3, operative July 1, 1971. Amended Stats 1972 ch 808 § 1; Stats 1975 ch 1262 § 2; Stats 1994 ch 1010 § 2 (SB 2053).

§ 303. Division of Consumer Services; Chief [Repealed]

Added Stats 1972 ch 808 § 2. Amended Stats 2017 ch 561 § 1 (AB 1516), effective January 1, 2018. Repealed Stats 2017 ch 429 § 3 (SB 429), effective January 1, 2018 (ch 429 prevails). The repealed section related to the chief of the Division of Consumer Services.

Article 2

Director and Employees

§ 305. Administration of chapter

The director shall administer and enforce the provisions of this chapter. Every power granted or duty imposed upon the director under this chapter may be exercised or performed in the name of the director by a deputy or assistant director or the chief of the department's Division of Consumer Services, subject to such conditions and limitations as the director may prescribe.

Added Stats 1970 ch 1394 § 3, operative July 1, 1971. Amended Stats 1971 ch 114 § 1, effective June 2, 1971, operative July 1, 1971.

§ 306. Employment matters

The director, in accordance with the State Civil Service Act, may appoint and fix the compensation of such clerical or other personnel as may be necessary to carry out the provisions of this chapter. All such personnel shall perform their respective duties under the supervision and the direction of the director.

Added Stats 1970 ch 1394 § 3, operative July 1, 1971.

§ 307. Experts and consultants

The director may contract for the services of experts and consultants where necessary to carry out the provisions of this chapter and may provide compensation and reimbursement of expenses for such experts and consultants in accordance with state law.

Added Stats 1975 ch 1262 § 3.

Section V

§ 308. Notice of Vacancy of Department Chief or Executive Officer of Any Bureau or Board

The director shall notify the appropriate policy committees of the Legislature within 60 days after the position of chief or executive officer of any bureau or board within the department becomes vacant pursuant to Section 1770 of the Government Code.

Added Stats 2021 ch 376 § 1 (AB 830), effective September 28, 2021.

Article 3

Powers and Duties

§ 310. Director's powers and duties

The director shall have the following powers and it shall be his duty to:

(a) Recommend and propose the enactment of such legislation as necessary to protect and promote the interests of consumers.

(b) Represent the consumer's interests before federal and state legislative hearings and executive commissions.

(c) Assist, advise, and cooperate with federal, state, and local agencies and officials to protect and promote the interests of consumers.

(d) Study, investigate, research, and analyze matters affecting the interests of consumers.

(e) Hold public hearings, subpoena witnesses, take testimony, compel the production of books, papers, documents, and other evidence, and call upon other state agencies for information.

(f) Propose and assist in the creation and development of consumer education programs.

(g) Promote ethical standards of conduct for business and consumers and undertake activities to encourage public responsibility in the production, promotion, sale and lease of consumer goods and services.

(h) Advise the Governor and Legislature on all matters affecting the interests of consumers.

(i) Exercise and perform such other functions, powers and duties as may be deemed appropriate to protect and promote the interests of consumers as directed by the Governor or the Legislature.

(j) Maintain contact and liaison with consumer groups in California and nationally.

Added Stats 1970 ch 1394 § 3, operative July 1, 1971. Amended Stats 1975 ch 1262 § 4.

§ 311. Interdepartmental committee

The director may create an interdepartmental committee to assist and advise him in the implementation of his duties. The members of such committee shall consist of the heads of state departments, or their designees. Members of such committee shall serve without compensation but shall be reimbursed for the expenses actually and necessarily incurred by them in the performance of their duties.

Added Stats 1970 ch 1394 § 3, operative July 1, 1971.

§ 312. Report to Governor and Legislature

The director shall submit to the Governor and the Legislature on or before January 1, 2003, and annually thereafter, a report of programmatic and statistical information regarding the activities of the department and its constituent entities. The report shall include information concerning the director's activities pursuant to Section 326, including the number and general patterns of consumer complaints and the action taken on those complaints.

Added Stats 1970 ch 1394 § 3, operative July 1, 1971. Amended Stats 1975 ch 1262 § 5; Stats 1998 ch 829 § 1 SB 1652); Stats 2002 ch 405 § 3 (AB 2973).

§ 313.2. Adoption of regulations in conformance with Americans with Disabilities Act

The director shall adopt regulations to implement, interpret, and make specific the provisions of the Americans with Disabilities Act (P.L. 101–336), as they relate to the examination process for professional licensing and certification programs under the purview of the department.

Added Stats 1992 ch 1289 § 3 (AB 2743).

§ 313.5. Publication of consumer information bibliography

The director shall periodically publish a bibliography of consumer information available in the department library and elsewhere. Such bibliography shall be sent to subscribers upon payment of a reasonable fee therefor.

Added Stats 1972 ch 1251 § 2. Amended Stats 1975 ch 1262 § 7.

Article 3.6

Uniform Standards Regarding Substance-Abusing Healing Arts Licensees

§ 315.2. Cease practice order

(a) A board, as described in Section 315, shall order a licensee of the board to cease practice if the licensee tests positive for any substance that is prohibited under the terms of the licensee's probation or diversion program.

Section V

(b) An order to cease practice under this section shall not be governed by the provisions of Chapter 5 (commencing with Section 11500) of Part 1 of Division 3 of Title 2 of the Government Code.

(c) A cease practice order under this section shall not constitute disciplinary action.

(d) This section shall have no effect on the Board of Registered Nursing pursuant to Article 3.1 (commencing with Section 2770) of Chapter 6 of Division 2.

Added Stats 2010 ch 517 § 2 (SB 1172), effective January 1, 2011.

§ 315.4. Cease practice order for violation of probation or diversion program

(a) A board, as described in Section 315, may adopt regulations authorizing the board to order a licensee on probation or in a diversion program to cease practice for major violations and when the board orders a licensee to undergo a clinical diagnostic evaluation pursuant to the uniform and specific standards adopted and authorized under Section 315.

(b) An order to cease practice under this section shall not be governed by the provisions of Chapter 5 (commencing with Section 11500) of Part 1 of Division 3 of Title 2 of the Government Code.

(c) A cease practice order under this section shall not constitute disciplinary action.

(d) This section shall have no effect on the Board of Registered Nursing pursuant to Article 3.1 (commencing with Section 2770) of Chapter 6 of Division 2.

Added Stats 2010 ch 517 § 3 (SB 1172), effective January 1, 2011.

Article 4

Representation of Consumers

§ 320. Intervention in administrative or judicial proceedings

Whenever there is pending before any state commission, regulatory agency, department, or other state agency, or any state or federal court or agency, any matter or proceeding which the director finds may affect substantially the interests of consumers within California, the director, or the Attorney General, may intervene in such matter or proceeding in any appropriate manner to represent the interests of consumers. The director, or any officer or employee designated by the director for that purpose, or the Attorney General, may thereafter present to such agency, court, or department, in conformity with the rules of practice and procedure thereof, such evidence and argument as he shall determine to be necessary, for the effective protection of the interests of consumers.

Added Stats 1970 ch 1394 § 3, operative July 1, 1971. Amended Stats 1975 ch 1262 § 8.

§ 321. Commencement of legal proceedings

Whenever it appears to the director that the interests of the consumers of this state are being damaged, or may be damaged, by any person who engaged in, or intends to engage in, any acts or practices in violation of any law of this state, or any federal law, the director or any officer or employee designated by the director, or the Attorney General, may commence legal proceedings in the appropriate forum to enjoin such acts or practices and may seek other appropriate relief on behalf of such consumers.

Added Stats 1975 ch 1262 § 9.

Article 5

Consumer Complaints

§ 325. Actionable complaints

It shall be the duty of the director to receive complaints from consumers concerning (a) unfair methods of competition and unfair or deceptive acts or practices undertaken by any person in the conduct of any trade or commerce; (b) the production, distribution, sale, and lease of any goods and services undertaken by any person which may endanger the public health, safety, or welfare; (c) violations of provisions of this code relating to businesses and professions licensed by any agency of the department, and regulations promulgated pursuant thereto; (d) student concerns related to the Bureau for Private Postsecondary Education's performance of its responsibilities, including concerns that arise related to the Bureau for Private Postsecondary Education's handling of a complaint or its administration of the Student Tuition Recovery Fund, established in Article 14 (commencing with Section 94923) of Chapter 8 of Part 59 of Division 10 of Title 3 of the Education Code; and (e) other matters consistent with the purposes of this chapter, whenever appropriate.

Added Stats 1970 ch 1394 § 3, operative July 1, 1971. Amended Stats 2016 ch 593 § 1 (SB 1192), effective January 1, 2017.

§ 325.3. Consumer complaints on paging services

In addition to the duties prescribed by Section 325, it shall be the duty of the director to receive complaints from consumers concerning services provided by the entities described in paragraph (2) of subdivision (b) of Section 234 of the Public Utilities Code.

Added Stats 1995 ch 357 § 1 (AB 202).

§ 326. Proceedings on receipt of complaint

(a) Upon receipt of any complaint pursuant to Section 325, the director may notify the person against whom the complaint is made of the nature of the complaint and may request appropriate relief for the consumer.

(b) The director shall also transmit any valid complaint to the local, state or federal agency whose authority provides the most effective means to secure the relief.

The director shall, if appropriate, advise the consumer of the action taken on the complaint and of any other means which may be available to the consumer to secure relief.

(c) If the director receives a complaint or receives information from any source indicating a probable violation of any law, rule, or order of any regulatory agency of the state, or if a pattern of complaints from consumers develops, the director shall transmit any complaint he or she considers to be valid to any appropriate law enforcement or regulatory agency and any evidence or information he or she may have concerning the probable violation or pattern of complaints or request the Attorney General to undertake appropriate legal action. It shall be the continuing duty of the director to discern patterns of complaints and to ascertain the nature and extent of action taken with respect to the probable violations or pattern of complaints.

Added Stats 1970 ch 1394 § 3, operative July 1, 1971. Amended Stats 1978 ch 1161 § 8; Stats 1989 ch 1360 § 1.

Article 7
Personal Information and Privacy Protection

§ 350. [Section repealed 2008.]

Added Stats 2000 ch 984 § 1 (SB 129). Amended Stats 2001 ch 159 § 5 (SB 662). Repealed Stats 2007 ch 183 § 1 (SB 90), effective January 1, 2008. The repealed section related to the office of privacy protection.

§ 352. [Section repealed 2008.]

Added Stats 2000 ch 984 § 1 (SB 129). Amended Stats 2004 ch 227 § 1 (SB 1102), effective August 16, 2004, operation contingent. Repealed Stats 2007 ch 183 § 2 (SB 90), effective January 1, 2008. The repealed section related to commencement of activities under the article and funding for such.

Chapter 6

Public Members

§ 450. Qualifications generally

In addition to the qualifications provided in the respective chapters of this code, a public member or a lay member of any board shall not be, nor shall they have been within the period of five years immediately preceding their appointment, any of the following:

(a) An employer, or an officer, director, or substantially full-time representative of an employer or group of employers, of any licensee of a board, except that this subdivision shall not preclude the appointment of a person who maintains infrequent employer status with a licensee, or maintains a client, patient, or customer relationship with a licensee that does not constitute more than 2 percent of the practice or business of the licensee.

(b) A person maintaining a contractual relationship with a licensee of a board that would constitute more than 2 percent of the practice or business of the licensee, or an officer, director, or substantially full-time representative of that person or group of persons.

(c) An employee of a licensee of a board, or a representative of the employee, except that this subdivision shall not preclude the appointment of a person who maintains an infrequent employee relationship or renders professional or related services to a licensee if the employment or service does not constitute more than 2 percent of the employment or practice of the member of the board.

Added Stats 1961 ch 2232 § 2. Amended Stats 2019 ch 351 § 48 (AB 496), effective January 1, 2020.

§ 450.3. Conflicting pecuniary interests

No public member shall either at the time of their appointment or during their tenure in office have any financial interest in any organization subject to regulation by the board, commission, or committee of which they are a member.

Added Stats 1972 ch 1032 § 1. Amended Stats 2019 ch 351 § 49 (AB 496), effective January 1, 2020.

§ 450.4. [Section repealed 2003.]

Added Stats 1976 ch 1188 § 1. Repealed Stats 2003 ch 563 § 1 (AB 827). The repealed section related to expertise required by board members.

§ 450.5. Prior industrial and professional pursuits

A public member, or a lay member, at any time within five years immediately preceding his or her appointment, shall not have been engaged in pursuits which lie within the field of the industry or profession, or have provided representation to the industry or profession, regulated by the board of which he or she is a member, nor shall he or she engage in those pursuits or provide that representation during his or her term of office.

Added Stats 1961 ch 2232 § 2. Amended Stats 2003 ch 563 § 2 (AB 827).

§ 450.6. Age

Notwithstanding any other section of law, a public member may be appointed without regard to age so long as the public member has reached the age of majority prior to appointment.

Added Stats 1976 ch 1188 § 1.3.

§ 451. Delegation of duties

If any board shall as a part of its functions delegate any duty or responsibility to be performed by a single member of such board, such delegation shall not be made solely to any public member or any lay member of the board in any of the following instances:

(a) The actual preparation of, the administration of, and the grading of, examinations.

(b) The inspection or investigation of licentiates, the manner or method of practice or doing business, or their place of practice or business.

Nothing in this section shall be construed as precluding a public member or a lay member from participating in the formation of policy relating to the scope of the activities set forth in subdivisions (a) and (b) or in the approval, disapproval or modification of the action of its individual members, nor preclude such member from participating as a member of a subcommittee consisting of more than one member of the board in the performance of any duty.

Added Stats 1961 ch 2232 § 2.

§ 452. "Board"

"Board," as used in this chapter, includes a board, advisory board, commission, examining committee, committee or other similarly constituted body exercising powers under this code.

Added Stats 1961 ch 2232 § 2. Amended Stats 1976 ch 1188 § 1.5.

Chapter 7

Licensee

§ 460. Powers of local governmental entities

(a) No city or county shall prohibit a person or group of persons, authorized by one of the agencies in the Department of Consumer Affairs by a license, certificate, or other such means to engage in a particular business, from engaging in that business, occupation, or profession or any portion thereof.

(b) No city, county, or city and county shall prohibit a healingarts professional licensed with the state under Division 2 (commencing with Section 500) from engaging in any act or performing any procedure that falls within the professionally recognized scopeof practice of that licensee.

(1) This subdivision shall not be construed to prohibit the enforcement of a local ordinance in effect prior to January 1, 2010, related to any act or procedure that falls within the professionally recognized scope of practice of a healing arts professional licensed under Division 2 (commencing with Section 500).

(2) This subdivision shall not be construed to prevent a city, county, or city and county from adopting or enforcing any local ordinance governing zoning, business licensing, or reasonable health and safety requirements for establishments or businesses of a healing arts professional licensed under Division 2 (commencing with Section500).

(c) Nothing in this section shall prohibit any city, county, or city and county from levying a business license tax solely forrevenue purposes, nor any city or county from levying a license taxsolely for the purpose of covering the cost of regulation.

Added Stats 1967 ch 1095 § 1. Amended Stats 1971 ch 716 § 24; Stats. 2009, Ch. 16.

§ 461. Asking applicant to reveal arrest record prohibited

No public agency, state or local, shall, on an initial application form for any license, certificate or registration, ask for or require the applicant to reveal a record of arrest that did not result in a conviction or a plea of nolo contendere. A violation of this section is a misdemeanor.

This section shall apply in the case of any license, certificate or registration provided for by any law of this state or local government, including, but not limited to, this code, the Corporations Code, the Education Code, and the Insurance Code.

Added Stats 1975 ch 883 § 1.

§ 462. Inactive category of licensure

(a) Any of the boards, bureaus, commissions, or programs within the department may establish, by regulation, a system for an inactive category of licensure for persons who are not actively engaged in the practice of their profession or vocation.

(b) The regulation shall contain the following provisions:

(1) The holder of an inactive license issued pursuant to this section shall not engage in any activity for which a license is required.

(2) An inactive license issued pursuant to this section shall be renewed during the same time period in which an active license is renewed. The holder of an inactive license need not comply with any continuing education requirement for renewal of an active license.

(3) The renewal fee for a license in an active status shall apply also for a renewal of a license in an inactive status, unless a lesser renewal fee is specified by the board.

(4) In order for the holder of an inactive license issued pursuant to this section to restore his or her license to an active status, the holder of an inactive license shall comply with all the following:

(A) Pay the renewal fee.

(B) If the board requires completion of continuing education for renewal of an active license, complete continuing education equivalent to that required for renewal of an active license, unless a different requirement is specified by the board.

(c) This section shall not apply to any healing arts board as specified in Section 701.

Added Stats 1994 ch 26 § 14 (AB 1807), effective March 30, 1994.

§ 464. Retired category of licensure

(a) Any of the boards within the department may establish, by regulation, a system for a retired category of licensure for persons who are not actively engaged in the practice of their profession or vocation.

(b) The regulation shall contain the following:

(1) A retired license shall be issued to a person with either an active license or an inactive license that was not placed on inactive status for disciplinary reasons.

(2) The holder of a retired license issued pursuant to this section shall not engage in any activity for which a license is required, unless the board, by regulation, specifies the criteria for a retired licensee to practice his or her profession or vocation.

(3) The holder of a retired license shall not be required to renew that license.

(4) The board shall establish an appropriate application fee for a retired license to cover the reasonable regulatory cost of issuing a retired license.

(5) In order for the holder of a retired license issued pursuant to this section to restore his or her license to an active status, the holder of that license shall meet all the following:

(A) Pay a fee established by statute or regulation.

(B) Certify, in a manner satisfactory to the board, that he or she has not committed an act or crime constituting grounds for denial of licensure.

(C) Comply with the fingerprint submission requirements established by regulation.

(D) If the board requires completion of continuing education for renewal of an active license, complete continuing education equivalent to that required for renewal of an active license, unless a different requirement is specified by the board.

(E) Complete any other requirements as specified by the board by regulation.

(c) A board may upon its own determination, and shall upon receipt of a complaint from any person, investigate the actions of any licensee, including a person with a license that either restricts or prohibits the practice of that person in his or her profession or vocation, including, but not limited to, a license that is retired, inactive, canceled, revoked, or suspended.

(d) Subdivisions (a) and (b) shall not apply to a board that has other statutory authority to establish a retired license.

Added Stats 2016 ch 473 § 1 (AB 2859), effective January 1, 2017.

Chapter 8

Dispute Resolution Programs

Article 1

Legislative Purpose

§ 465.5. Legislative intent

It is the intent of the Legislature to permit counties to accomplish all of the following:

(a) Encouragement and support of the development and use of alternative dispute resolution techniques.

(b) Encouragement and support of community participation in the development, administration, and oversight of local programs designed to facilitate the informal resolution of disputes among members of the community.

(c) Development of structures for dispute resolution that may serve as models for resolution programs in other communities.

(d) Education of communities with regard to the availability and benefits of alternative dispute resolution techniques.

(e) Encouragement of courts, prosecuting authorities, public defenders, law enforcement agencies, and administrative agencies to work in cooperation with, and to make referrals to, dispute resolution programs.

At the time that the state assumes the responsibility for the funding of California trial courts, consideration shall be given to the Dispute Resolution Advisory Council's evaluation of the effectiveness of alternative dispute resolution programs and the feasibility of the operation of a statewide program of grants, with the intention of funding alternative dispute resolution programs on a statewide basis.

Added Stats 1986 ch 1313 § 1.

Article 3

Establishment and Administration of Programs

§ 467. Dispute Resolution Advisory Council

(a) There is in the Division of Consumer Services of the Department of Consumer Affairs a Dispute Resolution Advisory Council. The advisory council shall complete the duties required by this chapter no later than January 1, 1989.

(b) The advisory council shall consist of seven persons, five of whom shall be appointed by the Governor. One member shall be appointed by the Senate Rules Committee, and one member shall be appointed by the Speaker of the Assembly. At least four of the persons appointed to the advisory council shall be active members of the State Bar of California, and at least four persons appointed to the advisory council shall have a minimum of two years of direct experience in utilizing dispute resolution techniques. The members of the advisory council shall reflect the racial, ethnic, sexual, and geographic diversity of the State of California.

(c) The members of the advisory council shall not receive a salary for their services but shall be reimbursed for their actual and necessary travel and other expenses incurred in the performance of their duties.

Added Stats 1986 ch 1313 § 1. Amended Stats 1987 ch 28 § 1, effective May 28, 1987.

§ 467.1. Contract requirements; County programs

(a) A program funded pursuant to this chapter shall be operated pursuant to contract with the county and shall comply with all of the requirements of this chapter and the rules and regulations of the advisory council.

(b) Counties may establish a program of grants to public entities and nonpartisan nonprofit corporations for the establishment and continuance of programs to be operated under the requirements of this chapter and the standards developed by the advisory council. The board of supervisors of a county in which, because of the county's size, the distribution authorized by Section 470.5 is insufficient to establish a county program may enter into an agreement with the board of supervisors of one or more other such counties to establish a program authorized by this chapter on a regional basis.

Added Stats 1986 ch 1313 § 1. Amended Stats 1987 ch 28 § 2, effective May 28, 1987; Stats 2005 ch 75 § 2 (AB 145), effective July 19, 2005, operative January 1, 2006.

§ 467.2. Eligibility for program funding

A program shall not be eligible for funding under this chapter unless it meets all of the following requirements:

(a) Compliance with this chapter and the applicable rules and regulations of the advisory council.

(b) Provision of neutral persons adequately trained in conflict resolution techniques as required by the rules and regulations promulgated by the advisory council pursuant to Section 471.

(c) Provision of dispute resolution, on a sliding scale basis, and without cost to indigents.

(d) Provision that, upon consent of the parties, a written agreement or an award resolving a dispute will be issued setting out a settlement of the issues involved in the dispute and the future responsibilities of each party.

(e) Provision of neutral procedures applicable equally to all participants without any special benefit or consideration given to persons or entities providing funding for the programs.

(f) Provision that participation in the program is voluntary and that the parties are not coerced to enter dispute resolution.

(g) Provision of alternative dispute resolution is the primary purpose of the program.

(h) Programs operated by counties that receive funding under this chapter shall be operated primarily for the purposes of dispute resolution, consistent with the purposes of this chapter.

Added Stats 1986 ch 1313 § 1.

§ 467.3. Provision of written statement to parties; Contents

Programs funded pursuant to this chapter shall provide persons indicating an intention to utilize the dispute resolution process with a written statement prior to the dispute resolution proceeding, in language easy to read and understand, stating all of the following:

(a) The nature of the dispute.

(b) The nature of the dispute resolution process.

(c) The rights and obligations of the parties, including, but not limited to, all of the following:

(1) The right to call and examine witnesses.

(2) The right of the parties to be accompanied by counsel, who may participate as permitted under the rules and procedures of the program.

(d) The procedures under which the dispute resolution will be conducted.

(e) If the parties enter into arbitration, whether the dispute resolution process will be binding.

Added Stats 1986 ch 1313 § 1.

§ 467.4. Agreements resolving disputes; Enforcement; Admissibility in evidence; Tolling statute of limitations

(a) An agreement resolving a dispute entered into with the assistance of a program shall not be enforceable in a court nor shall it be admissible as evidence in any judicial or administrative proceeding, unless the consent of the parties or the agreement includes a provision that clearly states the intention of the parties that the agreement or any resulting award shall be so enforceable or admissible as evidence.

(b) The parties may agree in writing to toll the applicable statute of limitations during the pendency of the dispute resolution process.

Added Stats 1986 ch 1313 § 1.

§ 467.5. Communications during mediation proceedings

Notwithstanding the express application of Chapter 2 (commencing with Section 1115) of Division 9 of the Evidence Code to mediations, all proceedings conducted by a program funded pursuant to this chapter, including, but not limited to, arbitrations and conciliations, are subject to Chapter 2 (commencing with Section 1115) of Division 9 of the Evidence Code.

Added Stats 1988 ch 188 § 2. Amended Stats 1997 ch 772 § 1 (AB 939).

§ 467.6. Statistical records; Anonymity of parties

Each program shall maintain those statistical records required by Section 471.5, and as may be required by the county. The records shall maintain the confidentiality and anonymity of the parties.

Added Stats 1986 ch 1313 § 1.

§ 467.7. Withdrawal from dispute resolution; Criminal complaints; Waiver of right to counsel

(a) Unless the parties have agreed to a binding award, nothing in this chapter shall be construed to prohibit any person who voluntarily enters the dispute resolution process from revoking his or her consent, withdrawing from dispute resolution, and seeking judicial or administrative redress.

(b) In cases in which a criminal complaint has been filed by a prosecutor, other than for an infraction, the advice of counsel shall be obtained before any dispute resolution process is initiated. Nothing in this subdivision shall be construed to preclude a defendant from knowingly and voluntarily waiving the right to counsel. A defendant who indicates a desire to waive the right to counsel shall be encouraged to consult with the public defender or private counsel before waiving that right.

Added Stats 1986 ch 1313 § 1.

Article 4

Application Procedures

§ 468.1. Selection of programs

Programs shall be selected for funding by a county from the applications submitted therefor.

Added Stats 1986 ch 1313 § 1.

§ 468.2. Applications; Required information

Applications submitted for funding shall include, but need not be limited to, all of the following information:

(a) Evidence of compliance with Sections 467.2, 467.3, and 467.4.

(b) A description of the proposed community area of service, cost of the principal components of operation, and any other characteristics, as determined by rules of the advisory council.

(c) A description of available dispute resolution services and facilities within the defined geographical area.

(d) A description of the applicant's proposed program, by type and purpose, including evidence of community support, the present availability of resources, and the applicant's administrative capability.

(e) A description of existing or planned cooperation between the applicant and local human service and justice system agencies.

(f) A demonstrated effort on the part of the applicant to show the manner in which funds that may be awarded under this program may be coordinated or consolidated with other local, state, or federal funds available for the activities described in Sections 467.2, 467.3, and 467.4.

Section V

(g) An explanation of the methods to be used for selecting and training mediators and other facilitators used in the dispute resolution process.

(h) Such additional information as may be required by the county.

Added Stats 1986 ch 1313 § 1.

§ 468.3. Funding priorities; Criteria

Data supplied by each applicant shall be used to assign relative funding priority on the basis of criteria developed by the advisory council. The criteria may include, but shall not be limited to, all of the following, in addition to the criteria set forth in Section 468.2:

(a) Unit cost, according to the type and scope of the proposed program.

(b) Quality and validity of the program.

(c) Number of participants who may be served.

(d) Administrative capability.

(e) Community support factors.

Added Stats 1986 ch 1313 § 1.

Article 6

Funding

§ 470.1. Acceptance of funds by grant recipients

(a) A grant recipient may accept funds from any public or private source for the purposes of this chapter.

(b) A county and its representatives may inspect, examine, and audit the fiscal affairs of the programs and the projects funded under this chapter.

(c) Programs shall, whenever reasonably possible, make use of public facilities at free or nominal costs.

Added Stats 1986 ch 1313 § 1.

§ 470.2. County's share of funding

A county's share of the funding pursuant to this chapter shall not exceed 50 percent of the approved estimated cost of the program.

Added Stats 1986 ch 1313 § 1.

§ 470.3. [Section repealed 2006.]

Added Stats 1986 ch 1313 § 1. Amended Stats 1987 ch 28 § 3, effective May 28, 1987, ch 1431 § 1; Stats 1992 ch 685 § 2 (SB 1707), effective September 12, 1992; Stats 1998 ch 931 § 1 (SB 2139), effective September 28, 1998. Repealed Stats 2005 ch 75 § 3 (AB 145), effective July 19, 2005, operative January 1, 2006. The repealed section related to fees for support of programs.

§ 470.5. Monthly distributions from filing fees for support of dispute resolution programs

(a) On and after January 1, 2006, as described in Section 68085.1 of the Government Code, the Administrative Office of the Courts shall make monthly distributions from superior court filing fees for the support of dispute resolution programs under this chapter in each county that has acted to establish a program. The amount distributed in each county shall be equal to the following:

(1) From each first paper filing fee collected by the court as provided under Section 70611 or 70612, subdivision (a) of Section 70613, subdivision (a) of Section 70614, or Section 70670 of the Government Code, and each first paper or petition filing fee collected by the court in a probate matter as provided under Section 70650, 70651, 70652, 70653, or 70655 of the Government Code, the same amount as was required to be collected for the support of dispute resolution programs in that county as of December 31, 2005, when a fee was collected for the filing of a first paper in a civil action under Section 26820.4 of the Government Code.

(2) From each first paper filing fee in a limited civil case collected by the court as provided under subdivision (b) of Section 70613 or subdivision (b) of Section 70614 of the Government Code, and each first paper or petition filing fee collected by the court in a probate matter as provided under Section 70654, 70656, or 70658 of the Government Code, the same amount as was required to be collected for the support of dispute resolution programs in that county as of December 31, 2005, when a fee was collected for the filing of a first paper in a civil action under Section 72055 of the Government Code where the amount demanded, excluding attorney's fees and costs, was ten thousand dollars ($10,000) or less.

(b) Distributions under this section shall be used only for the support of dispute resolution programs authorized by this chapter. The county shall deposit the amounts distributed under this section in an account created and maintained for this purpose by the county. Records of these distributions shall be available for inspection by the public upon request.

(c) After January 1, 2006, a county that does not already have a distribution from superior court filing fees under this section and that establishes a dispute resolution program authorized by this chapter may approve a distribution under this section. A county that already has a distribution under this section may change the amount of the distribution. The total amount to be distributed for the support of dispute resolution programs under this section may not exceed eight dollars ($8) per filing fee.

(d) The county may make changes under subdivision (c) to be effective January 1 or July 1 of any year, on and after January 1, 2006. The

Section V

county shall provide the Administrative Office of the Courts with a copy of the action of the board of supervisors that establishes the change at least 15 days before the date that the change goes into effect.

Added Stats 2005 ch 75 § 4 (AB 145), effective July 19, 2005, operative January 1, 2006.

§ 470.6. Carry over of moneys and fees

A county may carry over moneys received from distributions under Section 470.5 and from the fees for the support of dispute resolution programs authorized by this chapter that were added to fees for filing a first paper in a civil action in superior court under the laws in effect before January 1, 2006.

Added Stats 2005 ch 75 § 5 (AB 145), effective July 19, 2005, operative January 1, 2006.

Article 7

Rules and Regulations

§ 471.3. Statewide uniformity with guidelines contained in rules and regulations

The rules and regulations adopted by the advisory council pursuant to Section 471 shall be formulated to promote statewide uniformity with the guidelines contained in those rules and regulations.

Added Stats 1987 ch 28 § 6, effective May 28, 1987.

§ 471.5. Annual provision of statistical data

Each program funded pursuant to this chapter shall annually provide the county with statistical data regarding its operating budget; the number of referrals, categories, or types of cases referred to the program; the number of persons served by the program; the number of disputes resolved; the nature of the disputes resolved; rates of compliance; the number of persons utilizing the process more than once; the duration of and the estimated costs of the hearings conducted by the programs; and any other information that the county may require. The data shall maintain the confidentiality and anonymity of the persons employing the dispute resolution process.

Added Stats 1986 ch 1313 § 1. Amended Stats 1987 ch 56 § 1.

DIVISION 1.2

JOINT COMMITTEE ON BOARDS, COMMISSIONS, AND CONSUMER PROTECTION

Chapter 1

Review of Boards under the Department of Consumer Affairs

§ 473.   [Section repealed 2011.]
§ 473.1.   [Section repealed 2011.]
§ 473.15. [Section repealed 2011.]
§ 473.16. [Section repealed 2011.]
§ 473.17. [Section repealed 2000.]
§ 473.2.   [Section repealed 2011.]
§ 473.3.   [Section repealed 2011.]
§ 473.4.   [Section repealed 2011.]
§ 473.5.   [Section repealed 2011.]
§ 473.6.   [Section repealed 2011.]

§ 473. [Section repealed 2011.]

Added Stats 1994 ch 908 § 5 (SB 2036). Amended Stats 1998 ch 991 § 2 (SB 1980); Stats 2003 ch 874 § 2 (SB 363); Stats 2004 ch 33 § 3 (AB 1467), effective April 13, 2004. Repealed Stats 2010 ch 670 § 3 (AB 2130), effective January 1, 2011. The repealed section related to the establishment of the Joint Committee on Boards, Commissions, and Consumer Protection, powers and duties, designation of staff, and termination of Committee.

§ 473.1. [Section repealed 2011.]

Added Stats 1994 ch 908 § 5 (SB 2036). Amended Stats 1997 ch 78 § 3.5 (AB 71); Stats 2000 ch 393 § 1 (SB 2028); Stats 2002 ch 825 § 2 (SB 1952); Stats 2003 ch 789 § 3 (SB 364); Stats 2009 ch 310 § 5 (AB 48), effective January 1, 2010. Repealed Stats 2010 ch 670 § 3 (AB 2130), effective January 1, 2011. The repealed section related to applicability of chapter "Review of Boards under the Department of Consumer Affairs."

§ 473.15. [Section repealed 2011.]

Added Stats 1997 ch 759 § 6 (SB 827). Amended Stats 2000 ch 199 § 1 (SB 2034); Stats 2002 ch 681 § 1 (SB 1954), ch 1012 § 1.5 (SB 2025), effective September 27, 2002; Stats 2004 ch 33 § 4 (AB 1467), effective April 13, 2004; Stats 2005 ch 659 § 0.5 (SB 248), effective January 1, 2006; Stats 2006 ch 658 § 4 (SB 1476), effective January 1, 2007. Repealed Stats 2010 ch 670 § 3 (AB 2130), effective January 1, 2011. The repealed section related to review of specified boards by committee and legislative intent.

§ 473.16. [Section repealed 2011.]

Added Stats 2005 ch 674 § 3 (SB 231), effective January 1, 2006. Repealed Stats 2010 ch 670 § 3 (AB 2130), effective January 1, 2011. The repealed section related to examination and report of Medical Board of California's composition, initial and biennial fees, and report of findings.

§ 473.17. [Section repealed 2000.]

Added Stats ch 736 § 1 (SB 1981). Repealed Stats 2000 ch 393 § 3 (SB 2028). The repealed section related to review of referral of cases by specified boards to Licensing and Health Quality Enforcement Sections of Attorney General's office.

§ 473.2. [Section repealed 2011.]

Added Stats 1994 ch 908 § 5 (SB 2036). Amended Stats 2000 ch 393 § 4 (SB 2028); Stats 2003 ch 789 § 4 (SB 364); Stats 2004 ch 33 § 5 (AB 1467), effective April 13, 2004. Repealed Stats 2010 ch 670 § 3 (AB 2130), effective January 1, 2011. The repealed section related to submission of analysis and report to committee concerning the board.

§ 473.3. [Section repealed 2011.]

Added Stats 1994 ch 908 § 5 (SB 2036). Amended Stats 1997 ch 78 § 3.7 (AB 71); Stats 2000 ch 393 § 5 (SB 2028); Stats 2001 ch 399 § 1 (AB 1720); Stats 2003 ch 789 § 5 (SB 364); Stats 2004 ch 33 § 6 (AB 1467), effective April 13, 2004. Repealed Stats 2010 ch 670 § 3 (AB 2130), effective January 1, 2011. The repealed section related to public hearings prior to termination, continuation, or reestablishment of any board, the review of the Bureau for Private Postsecondary and Vocational Education and Bureau of Automotive Repair.

§ 473.4. [Section repealed 2011.]

Added Stats 1994 ch 908 § 5 (SB 2036). Amended Stats 2004 ch 33 § 7 (AB 1467), effective April 13, 2004. Repealed Stats 2010 ch 670 § 3 (AB 2130), effective January 1, 2011. The repealed section related to the evaluation of boards and regulatory programs and determination of need for continued existence.

§ 473.5. [Section repealed 2011.]

Added Stats 1994 ch 908 § 5 (SB 2036). Amended Stats 2000 ch 393 § 6 (SB 2028); Stats 2004 ch 33 § 8 (AB 1467), effective April 13, 2004. Repealed Stats 2010 ch 670 § 3 (AB 2130), effective January 1, 2011. The repealed section related to report of findings and preliminary recommendations by Joint Committee on Boards, Commissions, and Consumer Protection.

§ 473.6. [Section repealed 2011.]

Added Stats 1997 ch 759 § 7 (SB 827). Amended Stats 2002 ch 1012 § 2 (SB 2025), effective September 27, 2002; Stats 2004 ch 33 § 9 (AB 1467), effective April 13, 2004, ch 909 § 1.5 (SB 136), effective September 30, 2004. Repealed Stats 2010 ch 670 § 3 (AB 2130), effective January 1, 2011. The repealed section related to the referral of proposals to create new licensure categories, change requirements, or create new licensing board to Joint Committee.

DIVISION 1.5

DENIAL, SUSPENSION AND REVOCATION OF LICENSES

Chapter 1

General Provisions

Chapter 2

Denial of Licenses

Chapter 3

Suspension and Revocation of Licenses

Chapter 4

Public Reprovals

Chapter 1

General Provisions

§ 475. Applicability of division

(a) Notwithstanding any other provisions of this code, the provisions of this division shall govern the denial of licenses on the grounds of:

(1) Knowingly making a false statement of material fact, or knowingly omitting to state a material fact, in an application for a license.

(2) Conviction of a crime.

(3) Commission of any act involving dishonesty, fraud or deceit with the intent to substantially benefit himself or another, or substantially injure another.

(4) Commission of any act which, if done by a licentiate of the business or profession in question, would be grounds for suspension or revocation of license.

(b) Notwithstanding any other provisions of this code, the provisions of this division shall govern the suspension and revocation of licenses on grounds specified in paragraphs (1) and (2) of subdivision (a).

(c) A license shall not be denied, suspended, or revoked on the grounds of a lack of good moral character or any similar ground relating to an applicant's character, reputation, personality, or habits.

Added Stats 1972 ch 903 § 1. Amended Stats 1974 ch 1321 § 1; Stats 1992 ch 1289 § 5 (AB 2743).

§ 476. Exemptions

(a) Except as provided in subdivision (b), nothing in this division shall apply to the licensure or registration of persons pursuant to Chapter 4 (commencing with Section 6000) of Division 3, or pursuant to Division 9 (commencing with Section 23000) or pursuant to Chapter 5 (commencing with Section 19800) of Division 8.

(b) Section 494.5 shall apply to the licensure of persons authorized to practice law pursuant to Chapter 4 (commencing with Section 6000) of Division 3, and the licensure or registration of persons pursuant to Chapter 5 (commencing with Section 19800) of Division 8 or pursuant to Division 9 (commencing with Section 23000).

Added Stats 1972 ch 903 § 1. Amended Stats 1983 ch 721 § 1; Stats 2011 ch 455 § 2 (AB 1424), effective January 1, 2012.

§ 477. "Board"; "License"

As used in this division:

(a) "Board" includes "bureau," "commission," "committee," "department," "division," "examining committee," "program," and "agency."

(b) "License" includes certificate, registration or other means to engage in a business or profession regulated by this code.

Added Stats 1972 ch 903 § 1. Amended Stats 1974 ch 1321 § 2; Stats 1983 ch 95 § 1; Stats 1991 ch 654 § 5 (AB 1893).

§ 478. "Application"; "Material"

(a) As used in this division, "application" includes the original documents or writings filed and any other supporting documents or writings including supporting documents provided or filed contemporaneously, or later, in support of the application whether provided or filed by the applicant or by any other person in support of the application.

(b) As used in this division, "material" includes a statement or omission substantially related to the qualifications, functions, or duties of the business or profession.

Added Stats 1992 ch 1289 § 6 (AB 2743).

Chapter 2

Denial of Licenses

§ 480. Grounds for denial by board; Effect of obtaining certificate of rehabilitation

(a) Notwithstanding any other provision of this code, a board may deny a license regulated by this code on the grounds that the applicant has been convicted of a crime or has been subject to formal discipline only if either of the following conditions are met:

(1) The applicant has been convicted of a crime within the preceding seven years from the date of application that is substantially related to the qualifications, functions, or duties of the business or profession for which the application is made, regardless of whether the applicant was incarcerated for that crime, or the applicant has been convicted of a crime that is substantially related to the qualifications, functions, or duties of the business or profession for which the application is

made and for which the applicant is presently incarcerated or for which the applicant was released from incarceration within the preceding seven years from the date of application. However, the preceding seven-year limitation shall not apply in either of the following situations:

(A) The applicant was convicted of a serious felony, as defined in Section 1192.7 of the Penal Code or a crime for which registration is required pursuant to paragraph (2) or (3) of subdivision (d) of Section 290 of the Penal Code.

(B) The applicant was convicted of a financial crime currently classified as a felony that is directly and adversely related to the fiduciary qualifications, functions, or duties of the business or profession for which the application is made, pursuant to regulations adopted by the board, and for which the applicant is seeking licensure under any of the following:

(i) Chapter 6 (commencing with Section 6500) of Division 3.

(ii) Chapter 9 (commencing with Section 7000) of Division 3.

(iii) Chapter 11.3 (commencing with Section 7512) of Division 3.

(iv) Licensure as a funeral director or cemetery manager under Chapter 12 (commencing with Section 7600) of Division 3.

(v) Division 4 (commencing with Section 10000).

(2) The applicant has been subjected to formal discipline by a licensing board in or outside California within the preceding seven years from the date of application based on professional misconduct that would have been cause for discipline before the board for which the present application is made and that is substantially related to the qualifications, functions, or duties of the business or profession for which the present application is made. However, prior disciplinary action by a licensing board within the preceding seven years shall not be the basis for denial of a license if the basis for that disciplinary action was a conviction that has been dismissed pursuant to Section 1203.4, 1203.4a, 1203.41, 1203.42, or 1203.425 of the Penal Code or a comparable dismissal or expungement.

(b) Notwithstanding any other provision of this code, a person shall not be denied a license on the basis that the person has been convicted of a crime, or on the basis of acts underlying a conviction for a crime, if that person has obtained a certificate of rehabilitation under Chapter 3.5 (commencing with Section 4852.01) of Title 6 of Part 3 of the Penal Code, has been granted clemency or a pardon by a state or federal executive, or has made a showing of rehabilitation pursuant to Section 482.

(c) Notwithstanding any other provision of this code, a person shall not be denied a license on the basis of any conviction, or on the basis of the acts underlying the conviction, that has been dismissed pursuant to Section 1203.4, 1203.4a, 1203.41, 1203.42, or 1203.425 of the Penal Code, or a comparable dismissal or expungement. An applicant who has a conviction that has been dismissed pursuant to Section 1203.4, 1203.4a, 1203.41, or 1203.42 of the Penal Code shall provide proof of the dismissal if it is not reflected on the report furnished by the Department of Justice.

(d) Notwithstanding any other provision of this code, a board shall not deny a license on the basis of an arrest that resulted in a disposition other than a conviction, including an arrest that resulted in an infraction, citation, or a juvenile adjudication.

(e) A board may deny a license regulated by this code on the ground that the applicant knowingly made a false statement of fact that is required to be revealed in the application for the license. A board shall not deny a license based solely on an applicant's failure to disclose a fact that would not have been cause for denial of the license had it been disclosed.

(f) A board shall follow the following procedures in requesting or acting on an applicant's criminal history information:

(1) A board issuing a license pursuant to Chapter 3 (commencing with Section 5500), Chapter 3.5 (commencing with Section 5615), Chapter 10 (commencing with Section 7301), Chapter 20 (commencing with Section 9800), or Chapter 20.3 (commencing with Section 9880), of Division 3, or Chapter 3 (commencing with Section 19000) or Chapter 3.1 (commencing with Section 19225) of Division 8 may require applicants for licensure under those chapters to disclose criminal conviction history on an application for licensure.

(2) Except as provided in paragraph (1), a board shall not require an applicant for licensure to disclose any information or documentation regarding the applicant's criminal history. However, a board may request mitigating information from an applicant regarding the applicant's criminal history for purposes of determining substantial relation or demonstrating evidence of rehabilitation, provided that the applicant is informed that disclosure is voluntary and that the applicant's decision not to disclose any information shall not be a factor in a board's decision to grant or deny an application for licensure.

(3) If a board decides to deny an application for licensure based solely or in part on the applicant's conviction history, the board shall notify the applicant in writing of all of the following:

(A) The denial or disqualification of licensure.

(B) Any existing procedure the board has for the applicant to challenge the decision or to request reconsideration.

(C) That the applicant has the right to appeal the board's decision.

(D) The processes for the applicant to request a copy of the applicant's complete conviction history and question the accuracy or completeness of the record pursuant to Sections 11122 to 11127 of the Penal Code.

(g) (1) For a minimum of three years, each board under this code shall retain application forms and other documents submitted by an applicant, any notice provided to an applicant, all other communications received from and provided to an applicant, and criminal history reports of an applicant.

(2) Each board under this code shall retain the number of applications received for each license and the number of applications requiring inquiries regarding criminal history. In addition, each licensing authority shall retain all of the following information:

(A) The number of applicants with a criminal record who received notice of denial or disqualification of licensure.

(B) The number of applicants with a criminal record who provided evidence of mitigation or rehabilitation.

(C) The number of applicants with a criminal record who appealed any denial or disqualification of licensure.

(D) The final disposition and demographic information, consisting of voluntarily provided information on race or gender, of any applicant described in subparagraph (A), (B), or (C).

(3) (A) Each board under this code shall annually make available to the public through the board's internet website and through a report submitted to the appropriate policy committees of the Legislature deidentified information collected pursuant to this subdivision. Each board shall ensure confidentiality of the individual applicants.

(B) A report pursuant to subparagraph (A) shall be submitted in compliance with Section 9795 of the Government Code.

(h) "Conviction" as used in this section shall have the same meaning as defined in Section 7.5.

(i) This section does not in any way modify or otherwise affect the existing authority of the following entities in regard to licensure:

(1) The State Athletic Commission.

(2) The Bureau for Private Postsecondary Education.

(3) The California Horse Racing Board.

(j) This section shall become operative on July 1, 2020.

Added Stats 2018 ch 995 § 4 (AB 2138), effective January 1, 2019, operative July 1, 2020. Amended Stats 2019 ch 359 § 1 (AB 1521), effective January 1, 2020, operative July 1, 2020; Stats 2019 ch 578 § 2.5 (AB 1076), effective January 1, 2020, operative July 1, 2020 (ch 578 prevails).

§ 480.2. Grounds for denial of license by Bureau for Private Postsecondary Education, State Athletic Commission, and California Horse Racing Board

(a) The Bureau for Private Postsecondary Education, the State Athletic Commission, and the California Horse Racing Board may deny a license regulated by it on the grounds that the applicant has one of the following:

(1) Been convicted of a crime.

(2) Done any act involving dishonesty, fraud, or deceit with the intent to substantially benefit themselves or another, or substantially injure another.

(3) (A) Done any act that if done by a licentiate of the business or profession in question, would be grounds for suspension or revocation of license.

(B) The Bureau for Private Postsecondary Education, the State Athletic Commission, and the California Horse Racing Board may deny a license pursuant to this subdivision only if the crime or act is substantially related to the qualifications, functions, or duties of the business or profession for which the application is made.

(b) Notwithstanding any other provision of this code, a person shall not be denied a license solely on the basis that the person has been convicted of a felony if that person has obtained a certificate of rehabilitation under Chapter 3.5 (commencing with Section 4852.01) of Title 6 of Part 3 of the Penal Code or that the person has been convicted of a misdemeanor if the person has met all applicable requirements of the criteria of rehabilitation developed by the Bureau for Private Postsecondary Education, the State Athletic Commission, and the California Horse Racing Board to evaluate the rehabilitation of a person when considering the denial of a license under paragraph (1) of subdivision (f).

(c) Notwithstanding any other provisions of this code, a person shall not be denied a license by the Bureau for Private Postsecondary Education, the State Athletic Commission, or the California Horse Racing Board solely on the basis of a conviction that has been dismissed pursuant to Section 1203.4, 1203.4a, 1203.41, or 1203.425 of the Penal Code. An applicant who has a conviction that has been dismissed pursuant to Section 1203.4, 1203.4a, or 1203.41 of the Penal Code shall provide proof of the dismissal.

(d) The Bureau for Private Postsecondary Education, the State Athletic Commission, and the California Horse Racing Board may deny a license regulated by it on the ground that the applicant knowingly made a false statement of fact that is required to be revealed in the application for the license.

(e) The Bureau for Private Postsecondary Education, the State Athletic Commission, and the California Horse Racing Board shall develop criteria to aid it, when considering the denial, suspension, or revocation of a license, to determine whether a crime or act is substantially related to the qualifications, functions, or duties of the business or profession it regulates.

(f) (1) The Bureau for Private Postsecondary Education, the State Athletic Commission, and the California Horse Racing Board shall develop criteria to evaluate the rehabilitation of a person either when:

(A) Considering the denial of a license under this section.

Section V

(B) Considering suspension or revocation of a license under Section 490.

(2) The Bureau for Private Postsecondary Education, the State Athletic Commission, and the California Horse Racing Board shall take into account all competent evidence of rehabilitation furnished by the applicant or licensee.

(g) Except as otherwise provided by law, following a hearing requested by an applicant pursuant to subdivision (b) of Section 485, the Bureau for Private Postsecondary Education, the State Athletic Commission, and the California Horse Racing Board may take any of the following actions:

(1) Grant the license effective upon completion of all licensing requirements by the applicant.

(2) Grant the license effective upon completion of all licensing requirements by the applicant, immediately revoke the license, stay the revocation, and impose probationary conditions on the license, which may include suspension.

(3) Deny the license.

(4) Take other action in relation to denying or granting the license as the Bureau for Private Postsecondary Education, the State Athletic Commission, or the California Horse Racing Board, in its discretion, may deem proper.

(h) Notwithstanding any other law, in a proceeding conducted by the Bureau for Private Postsecondary Education, the State Athletic Commission, or the California Horse Racing Board to deny an application for a license or to suspend or revoke a license or otherwise take disciplinary action against a person who holds a license, upon the ground that the applicant or the licensee has been convicted of a crime substantially related to the qualifications, functions, and duties of the licensee in question, the record of conviction of the crime shall be conclusive evidence of the fact that the conviction occurred, but only of that fact, and the Bureau for Private Postsecondary Education, the State Athletic Commission, and the California Horse Racing Board may inquire into the circumstances surrounding the commission of the crime in order to fix the degree of discipline or to determine if the conviction is substantially related to the qualifications, functions, and duties of the licensee in question.

(i) Notwithstanding Section 7.5, a conviction within the meaning of this section means a plea or verdict of guilty or a conviction following a plea of nolo contendere. Any action that the Bureau for Private Postsecondary Education, the State Athletic Commission, or the California Horse Racing Board is permitted to take following the establishment of a conviction may be taken when the time for appeal has elapsed, the judgment of conviction has been affirmed on appeal, or when an order granting probation is made suspending the imposition of sentence, irrespective of a subsequent order under the provisions of Section 1203.4, 1203.4a, 1203.41, or 1203.425 of the Penal Code.

(j) This section shall become operative on July 1, 2020.

Added Stats 2018 ch 995 § 5 (AB 2138), effective January 1, 2019, operative July 1, 2020. Amended Stats 2019 ch 578 § 3 (AB 1076), effective January 1, 2020, operative July 1, 2020.

§ 481. Crime and job-fitness criteria

(a) Each board under this code shall develop criteria to aid it, when considering the denial, suspension, or revocation of a license, to determine whether a crime is substantially related to the qualifications, functions, or duties of the business or profession it regulates.

(b) Criteria for determining whether a crime is substantially related to the qualifications, functions, or duties of the business or profession a board regulates shall include all of the following:

(1) The nature and gravity of the offense.

(2) The number of years elapsed since the date of the offense.

(3) The nature and duties of the profession in which the applicant seeks licensure or in which the licensee is licensed.

(c) A board shall not deny a license based in whole or in part on a conviction without considering evidence of rehabilitation submitted by an applicant pursuant to any process established in the practice act or regulations of the particular board and as directed by Section 482.

(d) Each board shall post on its Internet Web site a summary of the criteria used to consider whether a crime is considered to be substantially related to the qualifications, functions, or duties of the business or profession it regulates consistent with this section.

(e) This section does not in any way modify or otherwise affect the existing authority of the following entities in regard to licensure:

(1) The State Athletic Commission.

(2) The Bureau for Private Postsecondary Education.

(3) The California Horse Racing Board.

(f) This section shall become operative on July 1, 2020.

Added Stats 2018 ch 995 § 7 (AB 2138), effective January 1, 2019, operative July 1, 2020.

§ 482. Rehabilitation criteria

(a) Each board under this code shall develop criteria to evaluate the rehabilitation of a person when doing either of the following:

(1) Considering the denial of a license by the board under Section 480.

(2) Considering suspension or revocation of a license under Section 490.

Section V

(b) Each board shall consider whether an applicant or licensee has made a showing of rehabilitation if either of the following are met:

(1) The applicant or licensee has completed the criminal sentence at issue without a violation of parole or probation.

(2) The board, applying its criteria for rehabilitation, finds that the applicant is rehabilitated.

(c) This section does not in any way modify or otherwise affect the existing authority of the following entities in regard to licensure:

(1) The State Athletic Commission.

(2) The Bureau for Private Postsecondary Education.

(3) The California Horse Racing Board.

(d) This section shall become operative on July 1, 2020.

Added Stats 2018 ch 995 § 9 (AB 2138), effective January 1, 2019, operative July 1, 2020.

§ 484. Attestation to good moral character of applicant

No person applying for licensure under this code shall be required to submit to any licensing board any attestation by other persons to his good moral character.

Added Stats 1972 ch 903 § 1. Amended Stats 1974 ch 1321 § 9.

§ 485. Procedure upon denial

Upon denial of an application for a license under this chapter or Section 496, the board shall do either of the following:

(a) File and serve a statement of issues in accordance with Chapter 5 (commencing with Section 11500) of Part 1 of Division 3 of Title 2 of the Government Code.

(b) Notify the applicant that the application is denied, stating (1) the reason for the denial, and (2) that the applicant has the right to a hearing under Chapter 5 (commencing with Section 11500) of Part 1 of Division 3 of Title 2 of the Government Code if written request for hearing is made within 60 days after service of the notice of denial. Unless written request for hearing is made within the 60-day period, the applicant's right to a hearing is deemed waived.

Service of the notice of denial may be made in the manner authorized for service of summons in civil actions, or by registered mail addressed to the applicant at the latest address filed by the applicant in writing with the board in his or her application or otherwise. Service by mail is complete on the date of mailing.

Added Stats 1972 ch 903 § 1. Amended Stats 1997 ch 758 § 2.3 (SB 1346).

§ 486. Contents of decision or notice

Where the board has denied an application for a license under this chapter or Section 496, it shall, in its decision, or in its notice under subdivision (b) of Section 485, inform the applicant of the following:

(a) The earliest date on which the applicant may reapply for a license which shall be one year from the effective date of the decision, or service of the notice under subdivision (b) of Section 485, unless the board prescribes an earlier date or a later date is prescribed by another statute.

(b) That all competent evidence of rehabilitation presented will be considered upon a reapplication.

Along with the decision, or the notice under subdivision (b) of Section 485, the board shall serve a copy of the criteria relating to rehabilitation formulated under Section 482.

Added Stats 1972 ch 903 § 1. Amended Stats 1974 ch 1321 § 9.5; Stats 1997 ch 758 § 2.4 (SB 1346).

§ 487. Hearing; Time

If a hearing is requested by the applicant, the board shall conduct such hearing within 90 days from the date the hearing is requested unless the applicant shall request or agree in writing to a postponement or continuance of the hearing. Notwithstanding the above, the Office of Administrative Hearings may order, or on a showing of good cause, grant a request for, up to 45 additional days within which to conduct a hearing, except in cases involving alleged examination or licensing fraud, in which cases the period may be up to 180 days. In no case shall more than two such orders be made or requests be granted.

Added Stats 1972 ch 903 § 1. Amended Stats 1974 ch 1321 § 10; Stats 1986 ch 220 § 1, effective June 30, 1986.

§ 488. Hearing request

(a) Except as otherwise provided by law, following a hearing requested by an applicant pursuant to subdivision (b) of Section 485, the board may take any of the following actions:

(1) Grant the license effective upon completion of all licensing requirements by the applicant.

(2) Grant the license effective upon completion of all licensing requirements by the applicant, immediately revoke the license, stay the revocation, and impose probationary conditions on the license, which may include suspension.

(3) Deny the license.

(4) Take other action in relation to denying or granting the license as the board in its discretion may deem proper.

(b) This section does not in any way modify or otherwise affect the existing authority of the following entities in regard to licensure:

(1) The State Athletic Commission.

(2) The Bureau for Private Postsecondary Education.

(3) The California Horse Racing Board.

(c) This section shall become operative on July 1, 2020.

Added Stats 2018 ch 995 § 11 (AB 2138), effective January 1, 2019, operative July 1, 2020.

§ 489. Denial of application without a hearing

Any agency in the department which is authorized by law to deny an application for a license upon the grounds specified in Section 480 or 496, may without a hearing deny an application upon any of those grounds, if within one year previously, and after proceedings conducted in accordance with Chapter 5 (commencing with Section 11500) of Part 1 of Division 3 of Title 2 of the Government Code, that agency has denied an application from the same applicant upon the same ground.

Added Stats 1955 ch 1151 § 1, as B & P C § 116. Amended Stats 1978 ch 1161 § 2. Renumbered by Stats 1989 ch 1104 § 1. Amended Stats 1997 ch 758 § 2.5 (SB 1346).

Chapter 3

Suspension and Revocation of Licenses

§ 490. Grounds for suspension or revocation; Discipline for substantially related crimes; Conviction; Legislative findings

(a) In addition to any other action that a board is permitted to take against a licensee, a board may suspend or revoke a license on the ground that the licensee has been convicted of a crime, if the crime is substantially related to the qualifications, functions, or duties of the business or profession for which the license was issued.

(b) Notwithstanding any other provision of law, a board may exercise any authority to discipline a licensee for conviction of a crime that is independent of the authority granted under subdivision (a) only if the crime is substantially related to the qualifications, functions, or duties of the business or profession for which the licensee's license was issued.

(c) A conviction within the meaning of this section means a plea or verdict of guilty or a conviction following a plea of nolo contendere. An action that a board is permitted to take following the establishment of a conviction may be taken when the time for appeal has elapsed, or the judgment of conviction has been affirmed on appeal, or when an order granting probation is made suspending the imposition of sentence, irrespective of a subsequent order under Section 1203.4 of the Penal Code.

(d) The Legislature hereby finds and declares that the application of this section has been made unclear by the holding in Petropoulos v. Department of Real Estate (2006) 142 Cal.App.4th 554, and that the holding in that case has placed a significant number of statutes and regulations in question, resulting in potential harm to the consumers of California from licensees who have been convicted of crimes. Therefore, the Legislature finds and declares that this section establishes an independent basis for a board to impose discipline upon a licensee, and that the amendments to this section made by Chapter 33 of the Statutes of 2008 do not constitute a change to, but rather are declaratory of, existing law.

Added Stats 1974 ch 1321 § 13. Amended Stats 1979 ch 876 § 3; Stats 1980 ch 548 § 1; Stats 1992 ch 1289 § 7 (AB 2743); Stats 2008 ch 33 § 2 (SB 797) (ch 33 prevails), effective June 23, 2008, ch 179 § 3 (SB 1498), effective January 1, 2009; Stats 2010 ch 328 § 2 (SB 1330), effective January 1, 2011.

§ 490.5. Suspension of license for failure to comply with child support order

A board may suspend a license pursuant to Section 17520 of the Family Code if a licensee is not in compliance with a child support order or judgment.

Added Stats 1994 ch 906 § 1 (AB 923), operative January 1, 1996. Amended Stats 2010 ch 328 § 3 (SB 1330), effective January 1, 2011.

§ 491. Procedure upon suspension or revocation

Upon suspension or revocation of a license by a board on one or more of the grounds specified in Section 490, the board shall:

(a) Send a copy of the provisions of Section 11522 of the Government Code to the ex-licensee.

(b) Send a copy of the criteria relating to rehabilitation formulated under Section 482 to the ex-licensee.

Added Stats 1972 ch 903 § 1. Amended Stats 1974 ch 1321 § 14; Stats 1975 ch 678 § 1.

§ 493. Evidentiary effect of record of conviction of crime substantially related to licensee's qualifications, functions, and duties

(a) Notwithstanding any other law, in a proceeding conducted by a board within the department pursuant to law to deny an application for a license or to suspend or revoke a license or otherwise take disciplinary action against a person who holds a license, upon the ground that the applicant or the licensee has been convicted of a crime substantially related to the qualifications, functions, and duties of the licensee in question, the record of conviction of the crime shall be conclusive evidence of the fact that the conviction occurred, but only of that fact.

(b) (1) Criteria for determining whether a crime is substantially related to the qualifications, functions, or duties of the business or profession the board regulates shall include all of the following:

(A) The nature and gravity of the offense.

(B) The number of years elapsed since the date of the offense.

(C) The nature and duties of the profession.

(2) A board shall not categorically bar an applicant based solely on the type of conviction without considering evidence of rehabilitation.

(c) As used in this section, "license" includes "certificate," "permit," "authority," and "registration."

(d) This section does not in any way modify or otherwise affect the existing authority of the following entities in regard to licensure:

(1) The State Athletic Commission.

(2) The Bureau for Private Postsecondary Education.

(3) The California Horse Racing Board.

(e) This section shall become operative on July 1, 2020.

Added Stats 2018 ch 995 § 13 (AB 2138), effective January 1, 2019, operative July 1, 2020.

§ 494. Interim suspension or restriction order

(a) A board or an administrative law judge sitting alone, as provided in subdivision (h), may, upon petition, issue an interim order suspending any licentiate or imposing license restrictions, including, but not limited to, mandatory biological fluid testing, supervision, or remedial training. The petition shall include affidavits that demonstrate, to the satisfaction of the board, both of the following:

(1) The licentiate has engaged in acts or omissions constituting a violation of this code or has been convicted of a crime substantially related to the licensed activity.

(2) Permitting the licentiate to continue to engage in the licensed activity, or permitting the licentiate to continue in the licensed activity without restrictions, would endanger the public health, safety, or welfare.

(b) No interim order provided for in this section shall be issued without notice to the licentiate unless it appears from the petition and supporting documents that serious injury would result to the public before the matter could be heard on notice.

(c) Except as provided in subdivision (b), the licentiate shall be given at least 15 days' notice of the hearing on the petition for an interim order. The notice shall include documents submitted to the board in support of the petition. If the order was initially issued without notice as provided in subdivision (b), the licentiate shall be entitled to a hearing on the petition within 20 days of the issuance of the interim order without notice. The licentiate shall be given notice of the hearing within two days after issuance of the initial interim order, and shall receive all documents in support of the petition. The failure of the board to provide a hearing within 20 days following the issuance of the interim order without notice, unless the licentiate waives his or her right to the hearing, shall result in the dissolution of the interim order by operation of law.

(d) At the hearing on the petition for an interim order, the licentiate may:

(1) Be represented by counsel.

(2) Have a record made of the proceedings, copies of which shall be available to the licentiate upon payment of costs computed in accordance with the provisions for transcript costs for judicial review contained in Section 11523 of the Government Code.

(3) Present affidavits and other documentary evidence.

(4) Present oral argument.

(e) The board, or an administrative law judge sitting alone as provided in subdivision (h), shall issue a decision on the petition for interim order within five business days following submission of the matter. The standard of proof required to obtain an interim order pursuant to this section shall be a preponderance of the evidence standard. If the interim order was previously issued without notice, the board shall determine whether the order shall remain in effect, be dissolved, or modified.

(f) The board shall file an accusation within 15 days of the issuance of an interim order. In the case of an interim order issued without notice, the time shall run from the date of the order issued after the noticed hearing. If the licentiate files a Notice of Defense, the hearing shall be held within 30 days of the agency's receipt of the Notice of Defense. A decision shall be rendered on the accusation no later than 30 days after submission of the matter. Failure to comply with any of the requirements in this subdivision shall dissolve the interim order by operation of law.

(g) Interim orders shall be subject to judicial review pursuant to Section 1094.5 of the Code of Civil Procedure and shall be heard only in the superior court in and for the Counties of Sacramento, San Francisco, Los Angeles, or San Diego. The review of an interim order shall be limited to a determination of whether the board abused its discretion in the issuance of the interim order. Abuse of discretion is established if the respondent board has not proceeded in the manner required by law, or if the court determines that the interim order is not supported by substantial evidence in light of the whole record.

(h) The board may, in its sole discretion, delegate the hearing on any petition for an interim order to an administrative law judge in the Office of Administrative Hearings. If the board hears the noticed petition itself, an administrative law judge shall preside at the hearing, rule on the admission and exclusion of evidence, and advise the board on matters of law. The board shall exercise all other powers relating to the conduct of the hearing but may delegate any or all of them to the administrative law judge. When the petition has been delegated to an administrative law judge, he or she shall sit alone and exercise all of the powers of the board relating to the conduct of the hearing. A decision issued by an administrative law judge sitting alone shall be final when it is filed with the board. If the administrative law judge issues an interim order without notice, he or she shall preside at the noticed hearing, unless unavailable, in which case another administrative law judge may hear the matter. The decision of the administrative law judge sitting alone on the petition for an interim order is final, subject only to judicial review in accordance with subdivision (g).

(i) Failure to comply with an interim order issued pursuant to subdivision (a) or (b) shall constitute a separate cause for disciplinary action against any licentiate, and may be heard at, and as a part of, the noticed hearing provided for in subdivision (f). Allegations of noncompliance with the interim order may be filed at any time prior to the rendering of a decision on the accusation. Violation of the interim order is established upon proof that the licentiate was on notice of the interim order and its terms, and that the order was in effect at the time of the violation. The finding of a violation of an interim order made at the hearing on the accusation shall be reviewed as a part of any review of a final decision of the agency.

If the interim order issued by the agency provides for anything less than a complete suspension of the licentiate from his or her business or profession, and the licentiate violates the interim order prior to the hearing on the accusation provided for in subdivision (f), the agency may, upon notice to the licentiate and proof of violation, modify or expand the interim order.

(j) A plea or verdict of guilty or a conviction after a plea of nolo contendere is deemed to be a conviction within the meaning of this section. A certified record of the conviction shall be conclusive evidence of the fact that the conviction occurred. A board may take action under this section notwithstanding the fact that an appeal of the conviction may be taken.

(k) The interim orders provided for by this section shall be in addition to, and not a limitation on, the authority to seek injunctive relief provided in any other provision of law.

(l) In the case of a board, a petition for an interim order may be filed by the executive officer. In the case of a bureau or program, a petition may be filed by the chief or program administrator, as the case may be.

(m) "Board," as used in this section, shall include any agency described in Section 22, and any allied health agency within the jurisdiction of the Medical Board of California. Board shall also include the Osteopathic Medical Board of California and the State Board of Chiropractic Examiners. The provisions of this section shall not be applicable to the Medical Board of California, the Board of Podiatric Medicine, or the State Athletic Commission.

Added Stats 1993 ch 840 § 1 (SB 842). Amended Stats 1994 ch 1275 § 4 (SB 2101).

§ 494.5. Agency actions when licensee is on certified list; Definitions; Collection and distribution of certified list information; Timing; Notices; Challenges by applicants and licensees; Release forms; Interagency agreements; Fees; Remedies; Inquiries and disclosure of information; Severability

(a) (1) Except as provided in paragraphs (2), (3), and (4), a state governmental licensing entity shall refuse to issue, reactivate, reinstate, or renew a license and shall suspend a license if a licensee's name is included on a certified list.

(2) The Department of Motor Vehicles shall suspend a license if a licensee's name is included on a certified list. Any reference in this section to the issuance, reactivation, reinstatement, renewal, or denial of a license shall not apply to the Department of Motor Vehicles.

(3) The State Bar of California may recommend to refuse to issue, reactivate, reinstate, or renew a license and may recommend to suspend a license if a licensee's name is included on a certified list. The word "may" shall be substituted for the word "shall" relating to the issuance of a temporary license, refusal to issue, reactivate, reinstate, renew, or suspend a license in this section for licenses under the jurisdiction of the California Supreme Court.

(4) The Department of Alcoholic Beverage Control may refuse to issue, reactivate, reinstate, or renew a license, and may suspend a license, if a licensee's name is included on a certified list.

(b) For purposes of this section:

(1) "Certified list" means either the list provided by the State Board of Equalization or the list provided by the Franchise Tax Board of persons whose names appear on the lists of the 500 largest tax delinquencies pursuant to Section 7063 or 19195 of the Revenue and Taxation Code, as applicable.

(2) "License" includes a certificate, registration, or any other authorization to engage in a profession or occupation issued by a state governmental licensing entity. "License" includes a driver's license

issued pursuant to Chapter 1 (commencing with Section 12500) of Division 6 of the Vehicle Code. "License" excludes a vehicle registration issued pursuant to Division 3 (commencing with Section 4000) of the Vehicle Code.

(3) "Licensee" means an individual authorized by a license to drive a motor vehicle or authorized by a license, certificate, registration, or other authorization to engage in a profession or occupation issued by a state governmental licensing entity.

(4) "State governmental licensing entity" means any entity listed in Section 101, 1000, or 19420, the office of the Attorney General, the Department of Insurance, the Department of Motor Vehicles, the State Bar of California, the Department of Real Estate, and any other state agency, board, or commission that issues a license, certificate, or registration authorizing an individual to engage in a profession or occupation, including any certificate, business or occupational license, or permit or license issued by the Department of Motor Vehicles or the Department of the California Highway Patrol. "State governmental licensing entity" shall not include the Contractors State License Board.

(c) The State Board of Equalization and the Franchise Tax Board shall each submit its respective certified list to every state governmental licensing entity. The certified lists shall include the name, social security number or taxpayer identification number, and the last known address of the persons identified on the certified lists.

(d) Notwithstanding any other law, each state governmental licensing entity shall collect the social security number or the federal taxpayer identification number from all applicants for the purposes of matching the names of the certified lists provided by the State Board of Equalization and the Franchise Tax Board to applicants and licensees.

(e) (1) Each state governmental licensing entity shall determine whether an applicant or licensee is on the most recent certified list provided by the State Board of Equalization and the Franchise Tax Board.

(2) If an applicant or licensee is on either of the certified lists, the state governmental licensing entity shall immediately provide a preliminary notice to the applicant or licensee of the entity's intent to suspend or withhold issuance or renewal of the license. The preliminary notice shall be delivered personally or by mail to the applicant's or licensee's last known mailing address on file with the state governmental licensing entity within 30 days of receipt of the certified list. Service by mail shall be completed in accordance with Section 1013 of the Code of Civil Procedure.

(A) The state governmental licensing entity shall issue a temporary license valid for a period of 90 days to any applicant whose name is on a certified list if the applicant is otherwise eligible for a license.

(B) The 90-day time period for a temporary license shall not be extended. Only one temporary license shall be issued during a regular license term and the term of the temporary license shall coincide with the first 90 days of the regular license term. A license for the full term or the remainder of the license term may be issued or renewed only upon compliance with this section.

(C) In the event that a license is suspended or an application for a license or the renewal of a license is denied pursuant to this section, any funds paid by the applicant or licensee shall not be refunded by the state governmental licensing entity.

(f) (1) A state governmental licensing entity shall refuse to issue or shall suspend a license pursuant to this section no sooner than 90 days and no later than 120 days of the mailing of the preliminary notice described in paragraph (2) of subdivision (e), unless the state governmental licensing entity has received a release pursuant to subdivision (h). The procedures in the administrative adjudication provisions of the Administrative Procedure Act (Chapter 4.5 (commencing with Section 11400) and Chapter 5 (commencing with Section 11500) of Part 1 of Division 3 of Title 2 of the Government Code) shall not apply to the denial or suspension of, or refusal to renew, a license or the issuance of a temporary license pursuant to this section.

(2) Notwithstanding any other law, if a board, bureau, or commission listed in Section 101, other than the Contractors State License Board, fails to take action in accordance with this section, the Department of Consumer Affairs shall issue a temporary license or suspend or refuse to issue, reactivate, reinstate, or renew a license, as appropriate.

(g) Notices shall be developed by each state governmental licensing entity. For an applicant or licensee on the State Board of Equalization's certified list, the notice shall include the address and telephone number of the State Board of Equalization, and shall emphasize the necessity of obtaining a release from the State Board of Equalization as a condition for the issuance, renewal, or continued valid status of a license or licenses. For an applicant or licensee on the Franchise Tax Board's certified list, the notice shall include the address and telephone number of the Franchise Tax Board, and shall emphasize the necessity of obtaining a release from the Franchise Tax Board as a condition for the issuance, renewal, or continued valid status of a license or licenses.

(1) The notice shall inform the applicant that the state governmental licensing entity shall issue a temporary license, as provided in subparagraph (A) of paragraph (2) of subdivision (e), for 90 calendar days if the applicant is otherwise eligible and that upon expiration of that time period, the license will be denied unless the state governmental licensing entity has received a release from the State Board of Equalization or the Franchise Tax Board, whichever is applicable.

Section V

(2) The notice shall inform the licensee that any license suspended under this section will remain suspended until the state governmental licensing entity receives a release along with applications and fees, if applicable, to reinstate the license.

(3) The notice shall also inform the applicant or licensee that if an application is denied or a license is suspended pursuant to this section, any moneys paid by the applicant or licensee shall not be refunded by the state governmental licensing entity. The state governmental licensing entity shall also develop a form that the applicant or licensee shall use to request a release by the State Board of Equalization or the Franchise Tax Board. A copy of this form shall be included with every notice sent pursuant to this subdivision.

(h) If the applicant or licensee wishes to challenge the submission of their name on a certified list, the applicant or licensee shall make a timely written request for release to the State Board of Equalization or the Franchise Tax Board, whichever is applicable. The State Board of Equalization or the Franchise Tax Board shall immediately send a release to the appropriate state governmental licensing entity and the applicant or licensee, if any of the following conditions are met:

(1) The applicant or licensee has complied with the tax obligation, either by payment of the unpaid taxes or entry into an installment payment agreement, as described in Section 6832 or 19008 of the Revenue and Taxation Code, to satisfy the unpaid taxes.

(2) The applicant or licensee has submitted a request for release not later than 45 days after the applicant's or licensee's receipt of a preliminary notice described in paragraph (2) of subdivision (e), but the State Board of Equalization or the Franchise Tax Board, whichever is applicable, will be unable to complete the release review and send notice of its findings to the applicant or licensee and state governmental licensing entity within 45 days after the State Board of Equalization's or the Franchise Tax Board's receipt of the applicant's or licensee's request for release. Whenever a release is granted under this paragraph, and, notwithstanding that release, the applicable license or licenses have been suspended erroneously, the state governmental licensing entity shall reinstate the applicable licenses with retroactive effect back to the date of the erroneous suspension and that suspension shall not be reflected on any license record.

(3) The applicant or licensee is unable to pay the outstanding tax obligation due to a current financial hardship. "Financial hardship" means financial hardship as determined by the State Board of Equalization or the Franchise Tax Board, whichever is applicable, where the applicant or licensee is unable to pay any part of the outstanding liability and the applicant or licensee is unable to qualify for an installment payment arrangement as provided for by Section 6832 or Section 19008 of the Revenue and Taxation Code. In order to establish the existence of a financial hardship, the applicant or licensee

shall submit any information, including information related to reasonable business and personal expenses, requested by the State Board of Equalization or the Franchise Tax Board, whichever is applicable, for purposes of making that determination.

(i) An applicant or licensee is required to act with diligence in responding to notices from the state governmental licensing entity and the State Board of Equalization or the Franchise Tax Board with the recognition that the temporary license will lapse or the license suspension will go into effect after 90 days and that the State Board of Equalization or the Franchise Tax Board must have time to act within that period. An applicant's or licensee's delay in acting, without good cause, which directly results in the inability of the State Board of Equalization or the Franchise Tax Board, whichever is applicable, to complete a review of the applicant's or licensee's request for release shall not constitute the diligence required under this section which would justify the issuance of a release. An applicant or licensee shall have the burden of establishing that they diligently responded to notices from the state governmental licensing entity or the State Board of Equalization or the Franchise Tax Board and that any delay was not without good cause.

(j) The State Board of Equalization or the Franchise Tax Board shall create release forms for use pursuant to this section. When the applicant or licensee has complied with the tax obligation by payment of the unpaid taxes, or entry into an installment payment agreement, or establishing the existence of a current financial hardship as defined in paragraph (3) of subdivision (h), the State Board of Equalization or the Franchise Tax Board, whichever is applicable, shall mail a release form to the applicant or licensee and provide a release to the appropriate state governmental licensing entity. Any state governmental licensing entity that has received a release from the State Board of Equalization and the Franchise Tax Board pursuant to this subdivision shall process the release within five business days of its receipt. If the State Board of Equalization or the Franchise Tax Board determines subsequent to the issuance of a release that the licensee has not complied with their installment payment agreement, the State Board of Equalization or the Franchise Tax Board, whichever is applicable, shall notify the state governmental licensing entity and the licensee in a format prescribed by the State Board of Equalization or the Franchise Tax Board, whichever is applicable, that the licensee is not in compliance and the release shall be rescinded. The State Board of Equalization and the Franchise Tax Board may, when it is economically feasible for the state governmental licensing entity to develop an automated process for complying with this subdivision, notify the state governmental licensing entity in a manner prescribed by the State Board of Equalization or the Franchise Tax Board, whichever is applicable, that the licensee has not complied with the installment payment agreement. Upon receipt of this notice, the state governmental licensing entity shall immediately notify the licensee on a form prescribed by the state governmental licensing entity that the licensee's license will be suspended on a specific date, and this date shall be no longer than 30 days from the date the form is mailed. The licensee shall be further notified that the license will remain suspended until a new release is issued in accordance with this subdivision.

(k) The State Board of Equalization and the Franchise Tax Board may enter into interagency agreements with the state governmental licensing entities necessary to implement this section.

(l) Notwithstanding any other law, a state governmental licensing entity, with the approval of the appropriate department director or governing body, may impose a fee on a licensee whose license has been suspended pursuant to this section. The fee shall not exceed the amount necessary for the state governmental licensing entity to cover its costs in carrying out the provisions of this section. Fees imposed pursuant to this section shall be deposited in the fund in which other fees imposed by the state governmental licensing entity are deposited and shall be available to that entity upon appropriation in the annual Budget Act.

(m) The process described in subdivision (h) shall constitute the sole administrative remedy for contesting the issuance of a temporary license or the denial or suspension of a license under this section.

(n) Any state governmental licensing entity receiving an inquiry as to the licensed status of an applicant or licensee who has had a license denied or suspended under this section or who has been granted a temporary license under this section shall respond that the license was denied or suspended or the temporary license was issued only because the licensee appeared on a list of the 500 largest tax delinquencies pursuant to Section 7063 or 19195 of the Revenue and Taxation Code. Information collected pursuant to this section by any state agency, board, or department shall be subject to the Information Practices Act of 1977 (Chapter 1 (commencing with Section 1798) of Title 1.8 of Part 4 of Division 3 of the Civil Code). Any state governmental licensing entity that discloses on its internet website or other publication that the licensee has had a license denied or suspended under this section or has been granted a temporary license under this section shall prominently disclose, in bold and adjacent to the information regarding the status of the license, that the only reason the license was denied, suspended, or temporarily issued is because the licensee failed to pay taxes.

(o) Any rules and regulations issued pursuant to this section by any state agency, board, or department may be adopted as emergency regulations in accordance with the rulemaking provisions of the Administrative Procedure Act (Chapter 3.5 (commencing with Section

11340) of Part 1 of Division 3 of Title 2 of the Government Code). The adoption of these regulations shall be deemed an emergency and necessary for the immediate preservation of the public peace, health, and safety, or general welfare. The regulations shall become effective immediately upon filing with the Secretary of State.

(p) The State Board of Equalization, the Franchise Tax Board, and state governmental licensing entities, as appropriate, shall adopt regulations as necessary to implement this section.

(q) (1) Neither the state governmental licensing entity, nor any officer, employee, or agent, or former officer, employee, or agent of a state governmental licensing entity, may disclose or use any information obtained from the State Board of Equalization or the Franchise Tax Board, pursuant to this section, except to inform the public of the denial, refusal to renew, or suspension of a license or the issuance of a temporary license pursuant to this section. The release or other use of information received by a state governmental licensing entity pursuant to this section, except as authorized by this section, is punishable as a misdemeanor. This subdivision may not be interpreted to prevent the State Bar of California from filing a request with the Supreme Court of California to suspend a member of the bar pursuant to this section.

(2) A suspension of, or refusal to renew, a license or issuance of a temporary license pursuant to this section does not constitute denial or discipline of a licensee for purposes of any reporting requirements to the National Practitioner Data Bank and shall not be reported to the National Practitioner Data Bank or the Healthcare Integrity and Protection Data Bank.

(3) Upon release from the certified list, the suspension or revocation of the applicant's or licensee's license shall be purged from the state governmental licensing entity's internet website or other publication within three business days. This paragraph shall not apply to the State Bar of California.

(r) If any provision of this section or the application thereof to any person or circumstance is held invalid, that invalidity shall not affect other provisions or applications of this section that can be given effect without the invalid provision or application, and to this end the provisions of this section are severable.

(s) All rights to review afforded by this section to an applicant shall also be afforded to a licensee.

(t) Unless otherwise provided in this section, the policies, practices, and procedures of a state governmental licensing entity with respect to license suspensions under this section shall be the same as those applicable with respect to suspensions pursuant to Section 17520 of the Family Code.

(u) No provision of this section shall be interpreted to allow a court to review and prevent the collection of taxes prior to the payment of those taxes in violation of the California Constitution.

(v) This section shall apply to any licensee whose name appears on a list of the 500 largest tax delinquencies pursuant to Section 7063 or 19195 of the Revenue and Taxation Code on or after July 1, 2012.

Added Stats 2011 ch 455 § 3 (AB 1424), effective January 1, 2012. Amended Stats 2012 ch 327 § 1 (SB 937), effective January 1, 2013; Stats 2020 ch 312 § 9 (SB 1474), effective January 1, 2021.

§ 494.6. Suspension under Labor Code Section 244

(a) A business license regulated by this code may be subject to suspension or revocation if the licensee has been determined by the Labor Commissioner or the court to have violated subdivision (b) of Section 244 of the Labor Code and the court or Labor Commissioner has taken into consideration any harm such suspension or revocation would cause to employees of the licensee, as well as the good faith efforts of the licensee to resolve any alleged violations after receiving notice.

(b) Notwithstanding subdivision (a), a licensee of an agency within the Department of Consumer Affairs who has been found by the Labor Commissioner or the court to have violated subdivision (b) of Section 244 of the Labor Code may be subject to disciplinary action by his or her respective licensing agency.

(c) An employer shall not be subject to suspension or revocation under this section for requiring a prospective or current employee to submit, within three business days of the first day of work for pay, an I-9 Employment Eligibility Verification form.

Added Stats 2013 ch 577 § 1 (SB 666), effective January 1, 2014.

Chapter 4

Public Reprovals

§ 495. Public reproval of licentiate or certificate holder for act constituting grounds for suspension or revocation of license or certificate; Proceedings

Notwithstanding any other provision of law, any entity authorized to issue a license or certificate pursuant to this code may publicly reprove a licentiate or certificate holder thereof, for any act that would constitute grounds to suspend or revoke a license or certificate. Any proceedings for public reproval, public reproval and suspension, or public reproval and revocation shall be conducted in accordance with Chapter 5 (commencing with Section 11500) of Part 1 of Division 3 of Title 2 of the Government Code, or, in the case of a licensee or certificate holder under the jurisdiction of the State Department of Health Services, in accordance with Section 100171 of the Health and Safety Code.

Added Stats 1977 ch 886 § 1. Amended Stats 1997 ch 220 § 2 (SB 68), effective August 4, 1997.

Chapter 5

Examination Security

§ 496. Grounds for denial, suspension, or revocation of license

A board may deny, suspend, revoke, or otherwise restrict a license on the ground that an applicant or licensee has violated Section 123 pertaining to subversion of licensing examinations.

Added Stats 1989 ch 1022 § 3.

§ 498. Fraud, deceit or misrepresentation as grounds for action against license

A board may revoke, suspend, or otherwise restrict a license on the ground that the licensee secured the license by fraud, deceit, or knowing misrepresentation of a material fact or by knowingly omitting to state a material fact.

Added Stats 1992 ch 1289 § 8 (AB 2743).

§ 499. Action against license based on licentiate's actions regarding application of another

A board may revoke, suspend, or otherwise restrict a license on the ground that the licensee, in support of another person's application for license, knowingly made a false statement of a material fact or knowingly omitted to state a material fact to the board regarding the application.

Added Stats 1992 ch 1289 § 9 (AB 2743).

SECTION VI.

THE CONTRACTORS STATE LICENSE BOARD; LICENSE LAW, RULES AND REGULATIONS, AND RELATED LAWS

Chapter 8.

Contractors' State License Law

BUSINESS & PROFESSIONS CODE

DIVISION 3

PROFESSIONS AND VOCATIONS GENERALLY

Chapter 9

Contractors

Article 1

Administration

Article 2

Application of Chapter

Article 3

Exemptions

Section VI

Article 4

Classifications

Article 5

Licensing

Article 6

Records

Article 6.2

Arbitration

Article 6.5

Solar Energy System Restitution Program
[Repealed]

Article 7

Disciplinary Proceedings

Section VI

Article 7.5

Workers' Compensation Insurance Reports

Section VI

Article 11

Asbestos Consultants

Article 12

Prohibitions

Chapter 9.3

Home Inspectors

Chapter 9.4

Home Energy Rating System (HERS) Home Inspections

Section VI

Chapter 9

Contractors

Article 1
Administration

§ 7000. Citation of chapter

This chapter constitutes, and may be cited as, the Contractors State License Law.

Added Stats 1961 ch 1822 § 2. Amended Stats 1984 ch 193 § 1; Stats 2020 ch 312 § 46 (SB 1474), effective January 1, 2021.

§ 7000.2. Requiring contractors to show proof of compliance with local business tax requirements prior to permit issuance; Limit on business taxes

Nothing in this code shall be interpreted to prohibit cities, counties, and cities and counties from requiring contractors to show proof that they are in compliance with local business tax requirements of the entity prior to issuing any city, county, or city and county permit. Nothing in this code shall be interpreted to prohibit cities, counties, and cities and counties from denying the issuance of a permit to a licensed contractor who is not in compliance with local business tax requirements.

Any business tax required or collected as part of this process shall not exceed the amount of the license tax or license fee authorized by Section 37101 of the Government Code or Section 16000 of the Business and Professions Code.

Added Stats 1992 ch 325 § 1 (AB 2710).

§ 7000.5. Contractors' State License Board; Members; Effect of repeal [Repealed effective January 1, 2029]

(a) There is in the Department of Consumer Affairs a Contractors State License Board, which consists of 15 members.

(b) Notwithstanding any other provision of law, the repeal of this section renders the board subject to review by the appropriate policy committees of the Legislature.

(c) This section shall remain in effect only until January 1, 2029, and as of that date is repealed.

Added Stats 1939 ch 37 § 1, as B & P C § 7000. Amended Stats 1961 ch 1821 § 61; Amended and renumbered by Stats 1961 ch 1822 § 3; Amended Stats 1963 ch 1098 § 1;

Stats 1971 ch 716 § 98; Stats 1972 ch 1314 § 1; Stats 1975 ch 1153 § 1; Stats 1982 ch 676 § 40; Stats 1994 ch 908 § 48 (SB 2036); Stats 1997 ch 812 § 1 (SB 857), ch 813 § 1 (SB 825); Stats 1999 ch 656 § 5 (SB 1306); Stats 2000 ch 1005 § 1 (SB 2029); Stats 2002 ch 744 § 2 (SB 1953); Stats 2004 ch 33 § 24 (AB 1467), effective April 13, 2004; Stats 2005 ch 675 § 10 (SB 232), effective January 1, 2006; Stats 2006 ch 658 § 105 (SB 1476), effective January 1, 2007; Stats 2008 ch 385 § 7 (SB 963), effective January 1, 2009; Stats 2010 ch 695 § 37 (SB 294), effective January 1, 2011, repealed January 1, 2012; Stats 2011 ch 448 § 21 (SB 543), effective January 1, 2012, repealed January 1, 2016; Stats 2015 ch 656 § 6 (SB 467), effective January 1, 2016, repealed January 1, 2020. Amended Stats 2019 ch 378 § 1 (SB 610), effective January 1, 2020, repealed January 1, 2024; Stats 2020 ch 312 § 47 (SB 1474), effective January 1, 2021, repealed January 1, 2024; Stats 2022 ch 625 § 15 (SB 1443), effective January 1, 2023, repealed January 1, 2025; Stats 2023 ch 485 § 1 (SB 1455), effective January 1, 2025, repealed January 1, 2025.

§ 7000.6. Priority of board; Protection of the public

Protection of the public shall be the highest priority for the Contractors State License Board in exercising its licensing, regulatory, and disciplinary functions. Whenever the protection of the public is inconsistent with other interests sought to be promoted, the protection of the public shall be paramount.

Added Stats 2002 ch 744 § 3 (SB 1953). Amended Stats 2020 ch 312 § 48 (SB 1474), effective January 1, 2021.

§ 7001. Members of board; Qualifications; Public member

All members of the board, except the public members, shall be contractors actively engaged in the contracting business, have been so engaged for a period of not less than five years preceding the date of their appointment and shall so continue in the contracting business during the term of their office. No one, except a public member, shall be eligible for appointment who does not at the time hold an unexpired license to operate as a contractor.

The public members shall not be licentiates of the board.

Added Stats 1939 ch 37 § 1. Amended Stats 1961 ch 1821 § 62; Stats 1971 ch 716 § 99; Stats 2000 ch 1005 § 2 (SB 2029).

§ 7002. Board members; Kinds of contractors and qualifications; Definitions

(a) One member of the board shall be a general engineering contractor, two members shall be general building contractors, two members shall be specialty contractors, one member shall be a member of a labor organization representing the building trades, one member shall be an active local building official, and eight members shall be public members, one of whom shall be from a statewide senior citizen organization.

(b) No public member shall be a current or former licensee of the board or a close family member of a licensee or be currently or formerly connected with the construction industry or have any financial interest in the business of a licensee of the board. Each public member shall meet all of the requirements for public membership on a board as set forth in Chapter 6 (commencing with Section 450) of Division 1. Notwithstanding the provisions of this subdivision and those of Section 450, a representative of a labor organization shall be eligible for appointment to serve as a public member of the board.

(c) Each contractor member of the board shall be of recognized standing in his or her branch of the contracting business and hold an unexpired license to operate as a contractor. In addition, each contractor member shall, as of the date of his or her appointment, be actively engaged in the contracting business and have been so engaged for a period of not less than five years. Each contractor member shall remain actively engaged in the contracting business during the entire term of his or her membership on the board.

(d) Each member of the board shall be at least 30 years of age and of good character. In addition, each member shall have been a citizen and resident of the State of California for at least five years next preceding his or her appointment.

(e) For the purposes of construing this article, the terms "general engineering contractor," "general building contractor," and "specialty contractor" shall have the meanings given in Article 4 (commencing with Section 7055) of this chapter.

Added Stats 1939 ch 37 § 1. Amended 1941 ch 971 § 1; Stats 1961 ch 1821 § 63; Stats 1963 ch 1098 § 2; Stats 1971 ch 716 § 100; Stats 1972 ch 1314 § 2; Stats 1973 ch 319 § 32; Stats 1975 ch 1153 § 2; Stats 1976 ch 1188 § 39; Stats 1991 ch 1160 § 1 (AB 2190); Stats 1994 ch 279 § 1 (AB 203); Stats 2000 ch 1005 § 3 (SB 2029).

§ 7003. Terms, vacancies, and appointment of successors

Except as otherwise provided, an appointment to fill a vacancy caused by the expiration of the term of office shall be for a term of four years and shall be filled, except for a vacancy in the term of a public member, by a member from the same branch of the contracting business as was the branch of the member whose term has expired. A vacancy in the term of a public member shall be filled by another public member. Each member shall hold office until the appointment and qualification of his or her successor or until the office is deemed to be vacant pursuant to Section 1774 of the Government Code, whichever first occurs.

Vacancies occurring in the membership of the board for any cause shall be filled by appointment for the balance of the unexpired term.

No person shall serve as a member of the board for more than two consecutive terms.

The Governor shall appoint four of the public members, including the public member who is from a statewide senior citizen organization, the local building official, the member of a labor organization representing the building trades, and the five contractor members qualified as provided in Section 7002. The Senate Rules Committee and the Speaker of the Assembly shall each appoint two public members.

Added Stats 1939 ch 37 § 1. Amended Stats 1955 ch 1532 § 1; Stats 1961 ch 1821 § 64; Stats 1963 ch 1098 § 3; Stats 1971 ch 716 § 101; Stats 1972 ch 1314 § 3; Stats 1973 ch 319 § 33; Stats 1975 ch 1153 § 3; Stats 1976 ch 1188 § 40; Stats 1982 ch 676 § 41; Stats 1991 ch 1160 § 2 (AB 2190); Stats 1994 ch 279 § 2 (AB 203); Stats 1999 ch 983 § 5 (SB 1307); Stats 2000 ch 1005 § 4 (SB 2029).

—See Government Code 1774, Vacancies; Appointments and Reappointments by the Governor and Senate, in Appendix.

§ 7005. Removal of members; Grounds

The Governor may remove any member of the board for misconduct, incompetency or neglect of duty.

Added Stats 1939 ch 37 § 1.

§ 7006. Meetings of board; Regular and special

The board shall meet at least once each calendar quarter for the purpose of transacting business as may properly come before it. The board shall make every effort to make all regularly scheduled quarterly meetings of the board available as a webcast when the appropriate resources are available.

Special meetings of the board may be held at times as the board may provide in its bylaws. Four members of the board may call a special meeting at any time.

Added Stats 1939 ch 37 § 1. Amended Stats 2001 ch 728 § 52 (SB 724); Stats 2019 ch 378 § 2 (SB 610), effective January 1, 2020.

§ 7007. Quorum; Notice of meetings

Eight members constitute a quorum at a board meeting.

Due notice of each meeting and the time and place thereof shall be given each member in the manner provided by the bylaws.

Added Stats 1939 ch 37 § 1. Amended Stats 1961 ch 1821 § 65; Stats 1972 ch 1314 § 4; Stats 1975 ch 1153 § 4; Stats 2000 ch 1005 § 5 (SB 2029).

Section VI

§ 7008. Appointment of committees; Making of rules and regulations

The board may appoint such committees and make such rules and regulations as are reasonably necessary to carry out the provisions of this chapter. Such rules and regulations shall be adopted in accordance with the provisions of the Administrative Procedure Act.

Added Stats 1939 ch 37 § 1. Amended Stats 1957 ch 2084 § 20; Stats 1983 ch 891 § 1.

§ 7009. Administration of oaths and taking of proofs

Any member or committee of the board may administer oaths and may take testimony and proofs concerning all matters within the jurisdiction of the board.

Added Stats 1939 ch 37 § 1.

§ 7010. Functions and duties of board

The board is vested with all functions and duties relating to the administration of this chapter, except those functions and duties vested in the director under the provisions of Division I of this code.

Added Stats 1939 ch 37 § 1.

§ 7011. Registrar of contractors [Repealed effective January 1, 2029]

(a) The board, by and with the approval of the director, shall appoint a registrar of contractors and fix the registrar's compensation.

(b) The registrar shall be the executive officer and secretary of the board and shall carry out all of the administrative duties as provided in this chapter and as delegated to the registrar by the board.

(c) For the purpose of administration of this chapter, there may be appointed a deputy registrar, a chief reviewing and hearing officer, and, subject to Section 159.5, other assistants and subordinates as may be necessary.

(d) Appointments shall be made in accordance with the provisions of civil service laws.

(e) This section shall remain in effect only until January 1, 2029, and as of that date is repealed.

Added Stats 1939 ch 37 § 1. Amended Stats 1947 ch 1406 § 1; Stats 1951 ch 1613 § 16; Stats 1963 ch 1587 § 1; Stats 1971 ch 716 § 102; Stats 1994 ch 908 § 49 (SB 2036); Stats 1997 ch 812 § 2 (SB 857), ch 813 § 2 (SB 825); Stats 1999 ch 656 § 6 (SB 1306); Stats 2001 ch 615 § 9 (SB 26), effective October 9, 2001; Stats 2002 ch 744 § 4 (SB 1953); Stats 2005 ch 675 § 11 (SB 232), effective January 1, 2006; Stats 2006 ch 658 § 106 (SB 1476), effective January 1, 2007; Stats 2008 ch 385 § 8 (SB 963), effective January 1, 2009; Stats 2010 ch 695 § 38 (SB 294), effective January 1, 2011, repealed January 1, 2012; Stats 2011 ch 448 § 22 (SB 543), effective January 1, 2012, repealed January 1, 2016; Stats 2015 ch 656 § 7 (SB 467), effective January 1, 2016, repealed January 1, 2020; Stats 2019 ch 378 § 3 (SB 610), effective January 1, 2020, repealed January 1, 2024; Stats 2022 ch 625 § 16 (SB 1443), effective January 1, 2023, repealed January 1, 2025; Stats 2024 ch 485 § 2 (SB 1455), effective January 1, 2025, repealed January 1, 2029.

§ 7011.3. Prohibition against double penalty for same offense

The registrar shall not assess a civil penalty against a licensed contractor who has been assessed a specified civil penalty by the Labor Commissioner under Section 1020 or 1022 of the Labor Code for the same offense.

Added Stats 1982 ch 327 § 5, effective June 30, 1982.

§ 7011.4. Enforcement division for licensing provisions and workers' compensation insurance; Special investigators

(a) Notwithstanding Section 7011, there is in the Contractors State License Board, a separate enforcement division that shall rigorously enforce this chapter prohibiting all forms of unlicensed activity and shall enforce the obligation to secure the payment of valid and current workers' compensation insurance in accordance with Section 3700.5 of the Labor Code.

(b) Persons employed as special investigators of the Contractors State License Board and designated by the Director of Consumer Affairs shall have the authority to issue a written notice to appear in court pursuant to Chapter 5C (commencing with Section 853.5) of Title 3 of Part 2 of the Penal Code. An employee so designated is not a peace officer and does not have the power of arrest.

(c) When participating in the activities of the Joint Enforcement Strike Force on the Underground Economy pursuant to Section 329 of the Unemployment Insurance Code, the enforcement division shall have free access to all places of labor.

Added Stats 1989 ch 1363 § 1. Amended Stats 1994 ch 413 § 1 (SB 1694); Stats 2004 ch 865 § 4 (SB 1914); Stats 2012 ch 85 § 1 (AB 2554), effective January 1, 2013; Stats 2014 ch 392 § 1 (SB 315), effective January 1, 2015; Stats 2015 ch 389 § 2 (SB 560), effective January 1, 2016; Stats 2020 ch 312 § 49 (SB 1474), effective January 1, 2021; Stats 2021 ch 188 § 6 (SB 826), effective January 1, 2022.

—See Government Code Section 11181, Powers in Connection with Investigations and Actions, in Appendix.

§ 7011.5. Investigators as peace officers

Persons employed as investigators of the Special Investigations Unit of the Contractors State License Board and designated by the

Director of Consumer Affairs have the authority of peace officers while engaged in exercising the powers granted or performing the duties imposed upon them in investigating the laws administered by the Contractors State License Board or commencing directly or indirectly any criminal prosecution arising from any investigation conducted under these laws. All persons herein referred to shall be deemed to be acting within the scope of employment with respect to all acts and matters in this section set forth.

Added Stats 1982 ch 1277 § 1. Amended Stats 2020 ch 312 § 50 (SB 1474), effective January 1, 2021.

§ 7011.7. Reviewing and investigating complaints

(a) The registrar shall review and investigate complaints filed in a manner consistent with this chapter and the Budget Act. It is the intent of the Legislature that complaints be reviewed and investigated as promptly as resources allow.

(b) The board shall set as a goal the improvement of its disciplinary system so that an average of no more than six months elapses from the receipt of a complaint to the completion of an investigation.

(c) Notwithstanding subdivision (a), the goal for completing the review and investigation of complaints that, in the opinion of the board, involve complex fraud issues or complex contractual arrangements, should be no more than one year.

Added Stats 1983 ch 1301 § 1, operative January 1, 1984. Amended Stats 1989 ch 1132 § 1, effective September 29, 1989; Stats 2000 ch 1005 § 6 (SB 2029).

§ 7011.8. False complaints against contractors; Penalties

(a) Any person subject to licensure under this chapter who reports to, or causes a complaint to be filed with, the Contractors State License Board that a person licensed by that entity has engaged in professional misconduct, knowing the report or complaint to be false, may be issued a citation by the registrar.

(b) The board may notify the appropriate district attorney or city attorney that a person subject to licensure under this chapter has made or filed what the entity believes to be a false report or complaint against a licensee.

Added Stats 1992 ch 437 § 1 (AB 2966). Amended Stats 2001 ch 745 § 5 (SB 1191), effective October 12, 2001; Stats 2012 ch 661 § 10 (SB 1576), effective January 1, 2013; Stats 2020 ch 312 § 51 (SB 1474), effective January 1, 2021.

§ 7012. Cooperation in enforcement of legislation relating to construction industry; Assistants

The registrar, with the approval of the board and the director, may, when funds are available, cooperate in the enforcement of governmental legislation relating to the construction industry, and, except as provided by Section 159.5, shall appoint such assistants as may be necessary therefor.

Added Stats 1939 ch 37 § 1. Amended Stats 1971 ch 716 § 103.

§ 7013. Review of registrar's acts or decisions by board; Application of section

The board may in its discretion review and sustain or reverse by a majority vote any action or decision of the registrar.

This section shall apply to any action, decision, order, or proceeding of the registrar conducted in accordance with the provisions of Chapter 5 (commencing with Section 11500) of Part 1 of Division 3 of Title 2 of the Government Code.

Added Stats 1939 ch 37 § 1. Amended Stats 1961 ch 941 § 1; Stats 1979 ch 410 § 1.

§ 7013.5. Transcript of witness as evidence

In all application, citation, or disciplinary proceedings pursuant to this chapter and conducted in accordance with the provisions of Chapter 5 (commencing with Section 11500) of Part 1 of Division 3 of Title 2 of the Government Code, the testimony of a witness given in any contested civil or criminal action or special proceeding, in any state or before any governmental body or agency, to which the licensee or person complained against is a party, or in whose behalf the action or proceeding is prosecuted or defended, may be received in evidence, so far as relevant and material to the issues in the proceedings, by means of a duly authenticated transcript of that testimony and without proof of the unavailability of the witness; provided that the registrar may order the production of and testimony by that witness, in lieu of or in addition to receiving a transcript of his or her testimony and may decline to receive in evidence the transcript of testimony, in whole or in part, when it appears that the testimony was given under circumstances that did not require or allow an opportunity for full cross-examination.

Added Stats 2003 ch 607 § 30 (SB 1077).

Section VI

§ 7014. Equipment and records; Procurement

The board may procure equipment and records necessary to carry out the provisions of this chapter.

Added Stats 1939 ch 37 § 1.

§ 7015. Seal of board

The board shall adopt a seal for its own use. The seal shall have the words "Contractors State License Board, State of California, Department of Consumer Affairs," and the care and custody thereof shall be in the hands of the registrar.

Added Stats 1939 ch 37 § 1. Amended Stats 1972 ch 1138 § 1; Stats 2020 ch 312 § 52 (SB 1474), effective January 1, 2021.

§ 7016. Per diem and expenses of members of board

Each member of the board shall receive a per diem and expenses as provided in Section 103.

Added Stats 1959 ch 1645 § 27.

§ 7017.3. Report on complaints and case aging statistics

The Contractors State License Board shall report annually to the Legislature, not later than October 1 of each year, the following statistical information for the prior fiscal year. The following data shall be reported on complaints filed with the board against licensed contractors, registered home improvement salespersons, and unlicensed persons acting as licensees or registrants:

(a) The number of complaints received by the board categorized by source, such as public, trade, profession, government agency, or board-initiated, and by type of complaint, such as licensee or nonlicensee.

(b) The number of complaints closed prior to referral for field investigation, categorized by the reason for the closure, such as settled, referred for mandatory arbitration, or referred for voluntary arbitration.

(c) The number of complaints referred for field investigation categorized by the type of complaint, such as licensee or nonlicensee.

(d) The number of complaints closed after referral for field investigation categorized by the reason for the closure, such as settled, referred for mandatory arbitration, or referred for voluntary arbitration.

(e) For the board's Intake/Mediation Center and the board's Investigation Center closures, respectively, the total number of complaints closed prior to a field investigation per consumer services representative, and the total number of complaints closed after referral for a field investigation per investigator and special investigator. Additionally, the board shall report the total number of complaints closed by other board staff during the year.

(f) The number of complaints pending at the end of the fiscal year grouped in 90-day increments, and the percentage of total complaints pending, represented by the number of complaints in each grouping.

(g) The number of citations issued to licensees categorized by the type of citation such as order of correction only or order of correction and fine, and the number of citations issued to licensees that were vacated or withdrawn.

(h) The number of citations issued to nonlicensees and the number of these citations that were vacated or withdrawn.

(i) The number of complaints referred to a local prosecutor for criminal investigation or prosecution, the number of complaints referred to the Attorney General for the filing of an accusation, and the number of complaints referred to both a local prosecutor and the Attorney General, categorized by type of complaint, such as licensee and nonlicensee.

(j) Actions taken by the board, including, but not limited to, the following:

(1) The number of disciplinary actions categorized by type, such as revocations or suspensions, categorized by whether the disciplinary action resulted from an accusation, failure to comply with a citation, or failure to comply with an arbitration award.

(2) The number of accusations dismissed or withdrawn.

(k) For subdivisions (g) and (j), the number of cases containing violations of Sections 7121 and 7121.5, and paragraph (5) of subdivision (a) of Section 7159.5, categorized by section.

(*l*) The number of interim suspension orders sought, the number of interim suspension orders granted, the number of temporary restraining orders sought, and the number of temporary restraining orders granted.

(m) The amount of cost recovery ordered and the amount collected.

(n) Case aging data, including data for each major stage of the enforcement process, including the following:

(1) The average number of days from the filing of a complaint to its closure by the board's Intake/Mediation Center prior to the referral for an investigation categorized by the type of complaint, such as licensee or nonlicensee.

(2) The average number of days from the referral of a complaint for an investigation to its closure by the Investigation Center categorized by the type of complaint, such as licensee or nonlicensee.

(3) The average number of days from the filing of a complaint to the referral of the completed investigation to the Attorney General.

(4) The average number of days from the referral of a completed investigation to the Attorney General to the filing of an accusation by the Attorney General.

(5) The average number of days from the filing of an accusation to the first hearing date or date of a stipulated settlement.

(6) The average number of days from the receipt of the administrative law judge's proposed decision to the registrar's final decision.

Added Stats 2002 ch 744 § 5 (SB 1953). Amended Stats 2006 ch 106 § 1 (AB 2457), effective January 1, 2007; Stats 2007 ch 130 § 28 (AB 299), effective January 1, 2008; Stats 2020 ch 312 § 53 (SB 1474), effective January 1, 2021; Stats 2021 ch 188 § 7 (SB 826), effective January 1, 2022.

—See Civil Code Section 3097, Preliminary 20-Day Notice (Private Work), in Appendix.

§ 7018. Contractor license search by ZIP Code or geographic location

The board shall maintain the current contractor license check search function on their internet website that permits consumers to search for a licensed contractor by either ZIP Code or geographic location.

Added Stats 2016 ch 270 § 1 (AB 2486), effective January 1, 2017. Amended Stats 2019 ch 378 § 4 (SB 610), effective January 1, 2020.

§ 7019. Contract with licensed professionals for site investigation of consumer complaints

(a) If funding is made available for that purpose, the board may contract with licensed professionals, as appropriate, for the site investigation of consumer complaints.

(b) The board may contract with other professionals, including, but not limited to, interpreters and manufacturer's representatives, whose skills or expertise are required to aid in the investigation or prosecution of a licensee, registrant, applicant for a license or registration, or those subject to licensure or registration by the board.

(c) The registrar shall determine the rate of reimbursement for those individuals providing assistance to the board pursuant to this section. All reports shall be completed on a form prescribed by the registrar.

(d) As used in this section, "licensed professionals" means, but is not limited to, engineers, architects, landscape architects, geologists, and accountants licensed, certificated, or registered pursuant to this division.

Added Stats 1987 ch 1264 § 2, effective September 28, 1987. Amended Stats 1991 ch 1160 § 4 (AB 2190); Stats 2002 ch 1013 § 59 (SB 2026).

§ 7019.1. [Section repealed 2001.]

Added Stats 1997 ch 812 § 2 (SB 857), operative until July 1, 2000. Repealed, operative January 1, 2001, by its own terms. The repealed section related to copy of opinion.

—*See Unemployment Insurance Code Section 329, Joint Enforcement Strike Force on the Underground Economy, in Appendix.*

—*See also Labor Code Section 106, Authority of the Labor Commissioner, in the Appendix.*

§ 7020. Computerized enforcement tracking system for consumer complaints

The board shall maintain a computerized enforcement tracking system for consumer complaints.

Added Stats 1987 ch 1264 § 3, effective September 28, 1987. Amended Stats 1991 ch 1160 § 5 (AB 2190).

§ 7021. Interagency agreement for information to protect the public

The board may enter into an interagency agreement with any other state or local agency the board deems to be in possession of any information relevant to its priority to protect the public described in Section 7000.6.

Added Stats 2016 ch 372 § 1 (SB 465), effective January 1, 2017.

Article 2
Application of Chapter

§ 7025. "Members of the personnel of record"; "Person"; "Qualifying person"; "Qualifying individual"; "Qualifier"

(a) "Members of the personnel of record" as used in this chapter means every person listed in the records of the registrar as then associated with a licensee.

(b) "Person" as used in this chapter includes an individual, a firm, partnership, corporation, limited liability company, federally recognized tribe, association or other organization, or any combination thereof.

(c) "Qualifying person," "qualifying individual," or "qualifier," as used in this chapter, means a person who qualifies for a license pursuant to Section 7068.

Added Stats 1939 ch 37 § 1. Amended Stats 2010 ch 698 § 2 (SB 392), effective January 1, 2011; Stat 2024 ch 485 § 3 (SB 1455), effective 1, 2025.

Section VI

§ 7025.1 Tribal Licensure

(a) As used in this chapter, the following definitions apply:

(1) "Federally recognized tribe" means a tribe located in this state and included on the list published in the Federal Register pursuant to the Federally Recognized Indian Tribe List Act of 1994 (25 U.S.C. Sec. 5131) and includes an entity controlled by and established for the benefit of one or more tribes.

(2) "Participating tribe" means a federally recognized tribe that formally applies for licensure from the board pursuant to Section 7065.

(b) The board shall license a federally recognized tribe that applies for licensure under Section 7065 and is otherwise compliant with the provisions of this chapter for the purpose of engaging in a business regulated by this chapter.

(c) This chapter is not intended to infringe upon or diminish the existing rights, privileges, and immunities of federally recognized tribes as set forth in federal, state, or tribal law, or the jurisdiction of those participating tribes.

(d) This chapter does not confer upon the board, registrar, or director any rights or authority to regulate any activity within the jurisdiction of a participating tribe.

Added Stats 2024 ch 485 § 4 (SB 1455), effective 1, 2025.

§ 7026. "Contractor"; "Roadway"

"Contractor," for the purposes of this chapter, is synonymous with "builder" and, within the meaning of this chapter, a contractor is any person who undertakes to or offers to undertake to, or purports to have the capacity to undertake to, or submits a bid to, or does himself or herself or by or through others, construct, alter, repair, add to, subtract from, improve, move, wreck or demolish any building, highway, road, parking facility, railroad, excavation or other structure, project, development or improvement, or to do any part thereof, including the erection of scaffolding or other structures or works in connection therewith, or the cleaning of grounds or structures in connection therewith, or the preparation and removal of roadway construction zones, lane closures, flagging, or traffic diversions, or the installation, repair, maintenance, or calibration of monitoring equipment for underground storage tanks, and whether or not the performance of work herein described involves the addition to, or fabrication into, any structure, project, development or improvement herein described of any material or article of merchandise. "Contractor" includes subcontractor and specialty contractor. "Roadway" includes, but is not limited to, public or city streets, highways, or any public conveyance.

Added Stats 1939 ch 37 § 1. Amended Stats 1939 ch 1091 § 1; Stats 1941 ch 971 § 2; Stats 1949 ch 90 § 1; Stats 1963 ch 972 § 1; Stats 1969 ch 761 § 1; Stats 1970 ch 340 § 1; Stats 1973 ch 892 § 1; Stats 1977 ch 429 § 1; Stats 1999 ch 708 § 1 (AB 1206); Stats 2001 ch 728 § 53 (SB 724).

§ 7026.1. "Contractor"

(a) The term "contractor" includes all of the following:

(1) Any person not exempt under Section 7053 who maintains or services air-conditioning, heating, or refrigeration equipment that is a fixed part of the structure to which it is attached.

(2) (A) Any person, consultant to an owner-builder, firm, association, organization, partnership, business trust, corporation, or company, who or which undertakes, offers to undertake, purports to have the capacity to undertake, or submits a bid to construct any building or home improvement project, or part thereof.

(B) For purposes of this paragraph, a consultant is a person, other than a public agency or an owner of privately owned real property to be improved, who meets either of the following criteria as it relates to work performed pursuant to a home improvement contract as defined in Section 7151.2:

(i) Provides or oversees a bid for a construction project.

(ii) Arranges for and sets up work schedules for contractors and subcontractors and maintains oversight of a construction project.

(3) A temporary labor service agency that, as the employer, provides employees for the performance of work covered by this chapter. The provisions of this paragraph shall not apply if there is a properly licensed contractor who exercises supervision in accordance with Section 7068.1 and who is directly responsible for the final results of the work. Nothing in this paragraph shall require a qualifying individual, as provided in Section 7068, to be present during the supervision of work covered by this chapter. A contractor requesting the services of a temporary labor service agency shall provide his or her license number to that temporary labor service agency.

(4) Any person not otherwise exempt by this chapter, who performs tree removal, tree pruning, stump removal, or engages in tree or limb cabling or guying. The term contractor does not include a person performing the activities of a nurseryperson who in the normal course of routine work performs incidental pruning of trees, or guying of planted trees and their limbs. The term contractor does not include a gardener who in the normal course of routine work performs incidental pruning of trees measuring less than 15 feet in height after planting.

(5) Any person engaged in the business of drilling, digging, boring, or otherwise constructing, deepening, repairing, reperforating, or abandoning any water well, cathodic protection well, or monitoring well.

(b) The term "contractor" or "consultant" does not include a common interest development manager, as defined in Section 11501, and a common interest development manager is not required to have a contractor's license when performing management services, as defined in subdivision (d) of Section 11500.

Added Stats 1971 ch 1365 § 1. Amended Stats 1991 ch 1160 § 6 (AB 2190); Stats 2003 ch 759 § 1 (AB 544); Stats 2004 ch 183 § 10 (AB 3082); Stats 2012 ch 371 § 1 (AB 2237), effective January 1, 2013; Stats 2013 ch 319 § 6 (SB 822), effective January 1, 2014.

§ 7026.2. Definitions

(a) For the purposes of this chapter, "contractor" includes any person engaged in the business of the construction, installation, alteration, repair, or preparation for moving of a mobilehome or mobilehome accessory buildings and structures upon a site for the purpose of occupancy as a dwelling.

(b) "Contractor" does not include the manufacturer of the mobilehome or mobilehome accessory building or structure if it is constructed at a place other than the site upon which it is installed for the purpose of occupancy as a dwelling, and does not include the manufacturer when the manufacturer is solely performing work in compliance with the manufacturer's warranty. "Contractor" includes the manufacturer if the manufacturer is engaged in onsite construction, alteration, or repair of a mobilehome or mobilehome accessory buildings and structures pursuant to specialized plans, specifications, or models, or any work other than in compliance with the manufacturer's warranty.

(c) "Contractor" does not include a seller of a manufactured home or mobilehome who holds a retail manufactured home or mobilehome dealer's license under Chapter 7 (commencing with Section 18045) of Part 2 of Division 13 of the Health and Safety Code, if the installation of the manufactured home or mobilehome is to be performed by a licensed contractor and the seller certifies that fact in writing to the buyer prior to the performance of the installation. The certification shall include the name, business address, and contractor's license number of the licensed contractor by whom the installation will be performed.

(d) For the purposes of this chapter, the following terms have the following meanings:

(1) "Mobilehome" means a vehicle defined in Section 18008 of the Health and Safety Code.

(2) "Mobilehome accessory building or structure" means a building or structure defined in Section 18008.5 of the Health and Safety Code.

(3) "Manufactured home" means a structure defined in Section 18007 of the Health and Safety Code.

Added Stats 1969 ch 761 § 2 as § 7027. Amended Stats 1970 ch 340 § 2; Stats 1973 ch 892 § 2; Stats 1983 ch 891 § 1.5; Stats 1986 ch 851 § 1. Renumbered by Stats 1991 ch 1160 § 17 (AB 2190).

—See California Water Code Section 13750.5, License Required for Water Wells, in the Appendix.

§ 7026.3. Persons who install or contract for the installation of carpet

For the purpose of this chapter, "contractor" includes any person who installs or contracts for the installation of carpet wherein the carpet is attached to the structure by any conventional method as determined by custom and usage in the trade; except that a seller of installed carpet who holds a retail furniture dealer's license under Chapter 3 (commencing with Section 19000) of Division 8 shall not be required to have a contractor's license if the installation of the carpet is performed by a licensed contractor and the seller so certifies in writing to the buyer prior to the performance of the installation, which certification shall include the name, business address, and contractor's license number of the licensed contractor by whom the installation will be performed.

Added Stats 1991 ch 1160 § 9 (AB 2190).

§ 7026.11. Permissible scope of work for the General Manufactured Housing Contractor (C-47) license classification

Notwithstanding any other provision of law, the permissible scope of work for the General Manufactured Housing Contractor (C-47) license classification set forth in Section 832.47 of Division 8 of Title 16 of the California Code of Regulations shall include manufactured homes, as defined in Section 18007 of the Health and Safety Code, mobilehomes, as defined in Section 18008 of the Health and Safety Code, and multifamily manufactured homes, as defined in Section 18008.7 of the Health and Safety Code.

Added Stats 2007 ch 540 § 1 (SB 538), effective January 1, 2008.

§ 7026.12. Installations of fire protection systems

Except as provided in Section 7026.13, the installation of a fire protection system, excluding an electrical alarm system, shall be performed only by either of the following:

Section VI

(a) A contractor holding a fire protection contractor classification, as defined in the regulations of the board.

(b) An owner-builder of an owner-occupied, single-family dwelling, if not more than two single-family dwellings on the same parcel are constructed within one year, plans are submitted to, and approved by, the city, county, or city and county authority, and the city, county, or city and county authority inspects and approves the installation.

Added Stats 1988 ch 1035 § 1. Amended Stats 1994 ch 185 § 1 (AB 2646); Stats 2013 ch 377 § 1 (AB 433), effective January 1, 2014.

§ 7026.13. [Section repealed 2017.]

Added Stats 2013 ch 377 § 2 (AB 433), effective January 1, 2014, repealed January 1, 2017. The repealed section related to exception for installations of residential fire protection systems.

§ 7027. Advertising as contractor

Any person who advertises or puts out any sign or card or other device that would indicate to the public that he or she is a contractor, or who causes his or her name or business name to be included in a classified advertisement or directory under a classification for construction or work of improvement covered by this chapter is subject to the provisions of this chapter regardless of whether his or her operations as a builder are otherwise exempted.

Added Stats 1957 ch 948 § 1, as B & P C § 7026.6. Amended Stats 1978 ch 771 § 1. Amended and renumbered by Stats 1991 ch 1160 § 12 (AB 2190); Stats 2011 ch 432 § 8 (SB 944), effective January 1, 2012.

§ 7027.1. Advertising by unlicensed person; Penalties

(a) It is a misdemeanor for any person to advertise for construction or work of improvement covered by this chapter unless that person holds a valid license under this chapter in the classification so advertised, except that a licensed building or engineering contractor may advertise as a general contractor.

(b) "Advertise," as used in this section, includes, but not by way of limitation, the issuance of any card, sign, or device to any person, the causing, permitting, or allowing of any sign or marking on or in any building or structure, or in any newspaper, magazine, or by airwave or any electronic transmission, or in any directory under a listing for construction or work of improvement covered by this chapter, with or without any limiting qualifications.

(c) A violation of this section is punishable by a fine of not less than seven hundred dollars ($700) and not more than one thousand dollars

($1,000), which fine shall be in addition to any other punishment imposed for a violation of this section.

(d) If upon investigation, the registrar has probable cause to believe that an unlicensed individual is in violation of this section, the registrar may issue a citation pursuant to Section 7028.7 or 7099.10.

Added Stats 1957 ch 948 § 2, as B & P C § 7026.7. Amended Stats 1978 ch 771 § 2; Stats 1986 ch 518 § 1. Amended and renumbered by Stats 1991 ch 1160 § 13 (AB 2190). Amended Stats 1994 ch 413 § 2 (SB 1694); Stats 1998 ch 599 § 2 (SB 597).

§ 7027.2. Advertising by person not licensed

Notwithstanding any other provision of this chapter, a person who is not licensed pursuant to this chapter may advertise for construction work or a work of improvement covered by this chapter only if the aggregate contract price for labor, material, and all other items on a project or undertaking is less than one thousand dollars ($1,000) and the person states in the advertisement that the person is not licensed under this chapter.

Added Stats 1978 ch 771 § 3, as B & P C § 7026.8. Amended and renumbered Stats 1991 ch 1160 § 14 (AB 2190); Stats 2014 ch 392 § 2 (SB 315), effective January 1, 2015. Amended Stats 2024 ch 240 § 1 (AB 2622), effective January 1, 2025.

§ 7027.3. Penalties for fraudulent use of incorrect license number

Any person, licensed or unlicensed, who willfully and intentionally uses, with intent to defraud, a contractor's license number that does not correspond to the number on a currently valid contractor's license held by that person, is punishable by a fine not exceeding ten thousand dollars ($10,000), or by imprisonment in state prison, or in county jail for not more than one year, or by both that fine and imprisonment. The penalty provided by this section is cumulative to the penalties available under all other laws of this state. If, upon investigation, the registrar has probable cause to believe that an unlicensed individual is in violation of this section, the registrar may issue a citation pursuant to Section 7028.7.

Added Stats 1984 ch 815 § 1, as B & P C § 7026.10. Amended Stats 1987 ch 930 § 1, effective September 22, 1987. Amended and renumbered by Stats 1991 ch 1160 § 15 (AB 2190). Amended Stats 2001 ch 728 § 54 (SB 724).

§ 7027.4. Advertising as insured or bonded; Requirements; Cause for discipline

(a) It is a cause for discipline for any contractor to advertise that he or she is "insured" or has insurance without identifying in the advertisement the type of insurance, including, for example, "commercial general liability insurance" or "workers' compensation insurance" that is carried by the contractor. The contractor may abbreviate the title of the type of insurance.

(b) It is cause for discipline for a contractor to advertise that he or she is "bonded" if the reference is to a contractor's license bond required pursuant to Section 7071.6 or to a disciplinary bond required pursuant to Section 7071.8.

(c) "Advertise," as used in this section, includes, but is not limited to, the issuance of any card, sign, or device to any person, the causing, permitting, or allowing of any sign or marking on or in any building or structure or business vehicle or in any newspaper, magazine, or by airwave or any electronic transmission, or in any directory under a listing for construction or work of improvement covered by this chapter, for the direct or indirect purpose of performing or offering to perform services that require a contractor's license.

Added Stats 2003 ch 607 § 31 (SB 1077).

§ 7027.5. Authority for landscape contractor to design systems or facilities; Prime contract for pool, spa, hot tub, outdoor cooking center, outdoor fireplace, or rainwater capture system; Subcontracting work outside of the field and scope of activities

(a) A landscape contractor working within the classification for which the license is issued may design systems or facilities for work to be performed and supervised by that contractor.

(b) Notwithstanding any other provision of this chapter, a landscape contractor working within the classification for which the license is issued may enter into a prime contract for the construction of any of the following:

(1) A swimming pool, spa, or hot tub, provided that the improvements are included within the landscape project that the landscape contractor is supervising and the construction of any swimming pool, spa, or hot tub is subcontracted to a single licensed contractor holding a Swimming Pool (C-53) classification, as set forth in Section 832.53 of Title 16 of the California Code of Regulations, or performed by the landscape contractor if the landscape contractor also holds a Swimming Pool (C-53) classification. The contractor constructing the swimming pool, spa, or hot tub may subcontract with other appropriately licensed contractors for the completion of individual components of the construction.

(2) An outdoor cooking center, provided that the improvements are included within a residential landscape project that the contractor is supervising. For purposes of this subdivision, "outdoor cooking cen-

ter" means an unenclosed area within a landscape that is used for the cooking or preparation of food or beverages.

(3) An outdoor fireplace, provided that it is included within a residential landscape project that the contractor is supervising and is not attached to a dwelling.

(4) A rainwater capture system, as defined in Section 10573 of the Water Code, used exclusively for landscape irrigation or as a water supply for a fountain, pond, or similar decorative water feature in a landscaping project.

(c) (1) Work performed in connection with a landscape project specified in paragraph (2), (3), or (4) of subdivision (b) that is outside of the field and scope of activities authorized to be performed under the Landscape Contractor (C-27) classification, as set forth in Section 832.27 of Title 16 of the California Code of Regulations, may only be performed by a landscape contractor if the landscape contractor also either holds an appropriate specialty license classification to perform the work or is licensed as a General Building contractor. If the landscape contractor neither holds an appropriate specialty license classification to perform the work nor is licensed as a General Building contractor, the work shall be performed by a Specialty contractor holding the appropriate license classification or by a General Building contractor performing work in accordance with the requirements of subdivision (b) of Section 7057.

(2) Notwithstanding paragraph (1), a landscape contractor performing work under the Landscape Contractor (C-27) classification, as set forth in Section 832.27 of Title 16 of the California Code of Regulations, may design and install all exterior components of a rainwater capture system, as defined in Section 10573 of the Water Code, that are not a part of, or attached to, a structure.

(d) A violation of this section shall be cause for disciplinary action.

(e) Nothing in this section authorizes a landscape contractor to engage in or perform activities that require a license pursuant to the Professional Engineers Act (Chapter 7 (commencing with Section 6700)).

Added Stats 1983 ch 699 § 12. Amended Stats 2003 ch 34 § 1 (AB 341); Stats 2007 ch 107 § 1 (AB 711), effective January 1, 2008; Stats 2008 ch 179 § 17 (SB 1498), effective January 1, 2009; Stats 2012 ch 537 § 1 (AB 1750), effective January 1, 2013.

§ 7028. Engaging in business without license; Fine and punishment; Statute of limitations

(a) Unless exempted from this chapter, it is a misdemeanor for a person to engage in the business of, or act in the capacity of, a contractor within this state under either of the following conditions:

(1) The person is not licensed in accordance with this chapter.

(2) The person performs acts covered by this chapter under a license that is under suspension for failure to pay a civil penalty or to comply with an order of correction, pursuant to Section 7090.1, or for failure to resolve all outstanding final liabilities, pursuant to Section 7145.5.

(b) A first conviction for the offense described in this section is punishable by a fine not exceeding five thousand dollars ($5,000) or by imprisonment in a county jail not exceeding six months, or by both that fine and imprisonment.

(c) If a person has been previously convicted of the offense described in this section, unless the provisions of subdivision (d) are applicable, the court shall impose a fine of 20 percent of the contract price, or 20 percent of the aggregate payments made to, or at the direction of, the unlicensed person, or five thousand dollars ($5,000), whichever is greater, and, unless the sentence prescribed in subdivision (d) is imposed, the person shall be confined in a county jail for not less than 90 days, except in an unusual case where the interests of justice would be served by imposition of a lesser sentence or a fine. If the court imposes only a fine or a jail sentence of less than 90 days for second or subsequent convictions under this section, the court shall state the reasons for its sentencing choice on the record.

(d) A third or subsequent conviction for the offense described in this section is punishable by a fine of not less than five thousand dollars ($5,000) nor more than the greater amount of ten thousand dollars ($10,000) or 20 percent of the contract price, or 20 percent of the aggregate payments made to, or at the direction of, the unlicensed person, and by imprisonment in a county jail for not more than one year or less than 90 days. The penalty provided by this subdivision is cumulative to the penalties available under all other laws of this state.

(e) A person who violates this section is subject to the penalties prescribed in subdivision (d) if the person was named on a license that was previously revoked and, either in fact or under law, was held responsible for any act or omission resulting in the revocation.

(f) If the unlicensed person engaging in the business of or acting in the capacity of a contractor has agreed to furnish materials and labor on an hourly basis, "the contract price" for the purposes of this section means the aggregate sum of the cost of materials and labor furnished and the cost of completing the work to be performed.

(g) Notwithstanding any other law, an indictment for any violation of this section by an unlicensed person shall be found, or information or a complaint shall be filed, within four years from the date of the contract proposal, contract, completion, or abandonment of the work, whichever occurs last.

(h) For any conviction under this section, a person who utilized the services of the unlicensed person is a victim of crime and is eligible, pursuant to subdivision (f) of Section 1202.4 of the Penal Code, for restitution for economic losses, regardless of whether he or she had knowledge that the person was unlicensed.

(i) The changes made to this section by the act adding this subdivision are declaratory of existing law.

Added Stats 1939 ch 37 § 1. Amended Stats 1963 ch 1883 § 1; Stats 1969 ch 1583 § 4; Stats 1972 ch 125 § 1; Stats 1982 ch 607 § 1; Stats 1989 ch 366 § 1; Stats 1995 ch 467 § 1 (SB 1061); Stats 1996 ch 145 § 1 (AB 2958); Stats 2003 ch 706 § 1 (SB 443); Stats 2004 ch 183 § 11 (AB 3082); Stats 2005 ch 205 § 1 (SB 488), effective January 1, 2006; Stats 2008 ch 33 § 13 (SB 797), effective June 23, 2008; Stats 2009 ch 319 § 1 (AB 370), effective January 1, 2010; Stats 2010 ch 328 § 15 (SB 1330), effective January 1, 2011; Stats 2014 ch 392 § 3 (SB 315), effective January 1, 2015.

§ 7028.1. Penalties against uncertified contractors performing asbestos-related work

It is a misdemeanor for any contractor, whether licensed or unlicensed, to perform or engage in asbestos-related work, as defined in Section 6501.8 of the Labor Code, without certification pursuant to Section 7058.5 of this code, or to perform or engage in a removal or remedial action, as defined in subdivision (d) of Section 7058.7, or, unless otherwise exempted by this chapter, to bid for the installation or removal of, or to install or remove, an underground storage tank, without certification pursuant to Section 7058.7. A contractor in violation of this section is subject to one of the following penalties:

(a) Conviction of a first offense is punishable by a fine of not less than one thousand dollars ($1,000) or more than three thousand dollars ($3,000), and by possible revocation or suspension of any contractor's license.

(b) Conviction of a subsequent offense requires a fine of not less than three thousand dollars ($3,000) or more than five thousand dollars ($5,000), or imprisonment in the county jail not exceeding one year, or both the fine and imprisonment, and a mandatory action to suspend or revoke any contractor's license.

Added Stats 1985 ch 1587 § 1, effective October 2, 1985. Amended Stats 1986 ch 1443 § 1, effective September 30, 1986, ch 1451 § 1.4, effective September 30, 1986; Stats 1990 ch 1366 § 1 (SB 2004), effective September 26, 1990; Stats 1991 ch 1160 § 18 (AB 2190); Stats 1993 ch 589 § 10 (AB 2211); Stats 1996 ch 712 § 1 (SB 1557); Stats 2004 ch 865 § 7 (SB 1914).

§ 7028.2. Complaints; Disposition of penalties

A criminal complaint pursuant to this chapter may be brought by the Attorney General or by the district attorney or prosecuting attorney of any city, in any county in the state with jurisdiction over the contractor or employer, by reason of the contractor's or employer's act, or failure to act, within that jurisdiction. Any penalty assessed by the court shall be paid to the office of the prosecutor bringing the complaint.

Added Stats 1985 ch 1587 § 2, effective October 2, 1985. Amended Stats 1986 ch 1451 § 1.5, effective September 30, 1986; Stats 1989 ch 366 § 2; Stats 1998 ch 931 § 8 (SB 2139), effective September 28, 1998.

§ 7028.3. Injunction against violations

In addition to all other remedies, when it appears to the registrar, either upon complaint or otherwise, that a licensee has engaged in, or is engaging in, any act, practice, or transaction which constitutes a violation of this chapter whereby another person may be substantially injured, or that any person, who does not hold a state contractor's license in any classification, has engaged in, or is engaging in, any act, practice, or transaction which constitutes a violation of this chapter, whether or not there is substantial injury, the registrar may, either through the Attorney General or through the district attorney of the county in which the act, practice, or transaction is alleged to have been committed, apply to the superior court of that county or any other county in which such person maintains a place of business or resides, for an injunction restraining such person from acting in the capacity of a contractor without a license in violation of this chapter, or from acting in violation of this chapter when another person may be substantially injured, and, upon a proper showing, a temporary restraining order, a preliminary injunction, or a permanent injunction shall be granted.

Added Stats 1965 ch 942 § 1. Amended Stats 1969 ch 698 § 1, ch 1583 § 7; Stats 1982 ch 517 § 17.

§ 7028.4. Injunction against continuing violation by person not holding state contractor's license

In addition to the remedies set forth in Section 7028.3, on proper showing by (1) a licensed contractor, or an association of contractors, (2) a consumer affected by the violation, (3) a district attorney, or (4) the Attorney General, of a continuing violation of this chapter by a person who does not hold a state contractor's license in any classification, an injunction shall issue by a court specified in Section 7028.3 at the request of any such party, prohibiting such violation. The plaintiff in any such action shall not be required to prove irreparable injury.

Added Stats 1969 ch 1583 § 8. Amended Stats 1971 ch 442 § 1.

§ 7028.5. Specified individuals acting as contractor without license

It is unlawful for a person who is or has been a partner, officer, director, manager, responsible managing employee, responsible managing member, responsible managing manager, or responsible managing officer of, or an individual who is listed in the personnel of record of, a licensed partnership, corporation, limited liability company, firm, association or other organization to individually engage in the business or individually act in the capacity of a contractor within this state without having a license in good standing to so engage or act.

Added Stats 1941 ch 971 § 3. Amended Stats 2010 ch 698 § 3 (SB 392), effective January 1, 2011.

§ 7028.6. Authority to issue citations

The Registrar of Contractors is hereby empowered to issue citations containing orders of abatement and civil penalties against persons acting in the capacity of or engaging in the business of a contractor within this state without having a license in good standing to so act or engage.

Added Stats 1981 ch 1124 § 1. Amended Stats 1998 ch 633 § 1 (SB 2217); Stats 2010 ch 415 § 17 (SB 1491), effective January 1, 2011.

§ 7028.7. Issuance of citation

(a) If upon inspection or investigation, either upon complaint or otherwise, the registrar has probable cause to believe that a person is acting in the capacity of or engaging in the business of a contractor or salesperson within this state without having a license or registration in good standing to so act or engage, and the person is not otherwise exempted from this chapter, the registrar shall issue a citation to that person.

(b) Within 72 hours of receiving notice that a public entity is intending to award, or has awarded, a contract to an unlicensed contractor, the registrar shall give written notice to the public entity that a citation may be issued if a contract is awarded to an unlicensed contractor. If after receiving the written notice from the registrar that the public entity has awarded or awards the contract to an unlicensed contractor, the registrar may issue a citation to the responsible officer or employee of the public entity as specified in Section 7028.15.

(c) Each citation shall be in writing and shall describe with particularity the basis of the citation. Notwithstanding Sections 125.9 and 148, each citation shall contain an order of abatement and an assessment of a civil penalty in an amount not less than two hundred dollars ($200) nor more than fifteen thousand dollars ($15,000).

(d) With the approval of the Contractors State License Board, the registrar shall prescribe procedures for the issuance of a citation under this section. The board shall adopt regulations covering the assessment of a civil penalty that shall give due consideration to the gravity of the violation, and any history of previous violations.

(e) The sanctions authorized under this section shall be separate from, and in addition to, all other remedies either civil or criminal.

Added Stats 1986 ch 995 § 3, operative January 1, 1988. Amended Stats 1990 ch 774 § 1 (SB 1079), effective September 11, 1990; Stats 1991 ch 785 § 1 (AB 800); Stats 1992 ch 606 § 1 (AB 3240); Stats 2001 ch 728 § 55 (SB 724); Stats 2009 ch 307 § 69 (SB 821), effective January 1, 2010; Stats 2010 ch 415 § 18 (SB 1491), effective January 1, 2011; Stats 2020 ch 312 § 54 (SB 1474), effective January 1, 2021.

§ 7028.8. Service of citation

Service of a citation issued under Section 7028.7 may be made by certified mail at the last known business address or residence address of the person cited.

Added Stats 1981 ch 1124 § 3.

§ 7028.9. Limitations period

A citation under Section 7028.7 shall be issued by the registrar within four years after the act or omission that is the basis for the citation or within 18 months after the date of the filing of the complaint with the registrar, whichever is later.

Added Stats 1981 ch 1124 § 4. Amended Stats 1996 ch 145 § 2 (AB 2958); Stats 2010 ch 415 § 19 (SB 1491), effective January 1, 2011.

§ 7028.10. Appeal to registrar

Any person served with a citation under Section 7028.7 may appeal to the registrar within 15 working days after service of the citation with respect to violations alleged, scope of the order of abatement, or amount of civil penalty assessed.

Added Stats 1981 ch 1124 § 5. Amended Stats 1985 ch 1281 § 1.

§ 7028.11. Citation as final order

If within 15 working days after service of the citation, the person cited fails to notify the registrar that he or she intends to appeal the citation, the citation shall be deemed a final order of the registrar and not subject to review by any court or agency. The 15-day period may be extended by the registrar for good cause.

Added Stats 1981 ch 1124 § 6. Amended Stats 1985 ch 1281 § 2.

§ 7028.12. Hearing; Decision

If the person cited under Section 7028.7 timely notifies the registrar that he or she intends to contest the citation, the registrar shall afford an opportunity for a hearing. The registrar shall thereafter issue a decision, based on findings of fact, affirming, modifying, or vacating the citation or directing other appropriate relief. The proceedings under this section shall be conducted in accordance with the provisions of Chapter 5 (commencing with Section 11500) of Part 1 of Division 3 of Title 2 of the Government Code, and the registrar shall have all the powers granted therein.

Added Stats 1981 ch 1124 § 7.

§ 7028.13. Application for court order; Collection of civil penalty; Assignment of rights to civil penalty; Time limit for collection of penalty

(a) After the exhaustion of the review procedures provided for in Sections 7028.10 to 7028.12, inclusive, the registrar may apply to the appropriate superior court for a judgment in the amount of the civil penalty and an order compelling the cited person to comply with the order of abatement. The application, which shall include a certified copy of the final order of the registrar, shall constitute a sufficient showing to warrant the issuance of the judgment and order. If the cited person did not appeal the citation, a certified copy of the citation and proof of service, and a certification that the person cited is not or was not a licensed contractor or applicant for a license at the time of issuance of the citation, shall constitute a sufficient showing to warrant the issuance of the judgment and order.

(b) Notwithstanding any other provision of law, the registrar may delegate the collection of the civil penalty for any citation issued to any person or entity legally authorized to engage in collections. Costs of collection shall be borne by the person cited. The registrar shall not delegate the authority to enforce the order of abatement.

(c) Notwithstanding any other provision of law, the registrar shall have the authority to assign the rights to the civil penalty, or a portion thereof, for adequate consideration. The assignee and the registrar shall have all the rights afforded under the ordinary laws of assignment of rights and delegation of duties. The registrar shall not assign the order of abatement. The assignee may apply to the appropriate superior court for a judgment based upon the assigned rights upon the same evidentiary showing as set forth in subdivision (a).

(d) Notwithstanding any other provision of law, including subdivisions (a) and (b) of Section 340 of the Code of Civil Procedure, the registrar or his or her designee or assignee shall have four years from the date of the final order to collect civil penalties except that the registrar or his or her designee or assignee shall have 10 years from the date of the judgment to enforce civil penalties on citations that have been converted to judgments through the process described in subdivisions (a) and (c).

Added Stats 1981 ch 1124 § 8. Amended Stats 2001 ch 728 § 56 (SB 724); Stats 2005 ch 280 § 2 (SB 1112), effective January 1, 2006.

§ 7028.14. Waiver of part of civil penalty on issuance of license

Notwithstanding any other provision of the law, the registrar may waive part of the civil penalty if the person against whom the civil penalty is assessed satisfactorily completes all the requirements for, and is issued, a contractor's license. Any outstanding injury to the public shall be satisfactorily settled prior to issuance of the license.

Added Stats 1989 ch 1174 § 1.

§ 7028.15. License required to submit bid to public agency; Exceptions

(a) It is a misdemeanor for any person to submit a bid to a public agency in order to engage in the business or act in the capacity of a contractor within this state without having a license therefor, except in any of the following cases:

(1) The person is particularly exempted from this chapter.

(2) The bid is submitted on a state project governed by Section 10164 of the Public Contract Code or on any local agency project governed by Section 20103.5 of the Public Contract Code.

(b) If a person has been previously convicted of the offense described in this section, the court shall impose a fine of 20 percent of the price of the contract under which the unlicensed person performed contracting work, or four thousand five hundred dollars ($4,500), whichever is greater, or imprisonment in the county jail for not less than 10 days nor more than six months, or both.

In the event the person performing the contracting work has agreed to furnish materials and labor on an hourly basis, "the price of the contract" for the purposes of this subdivision means the aggregate sum of the cost of materials and labor furnished and the cost of completing the work to be performed.

(c) This section shall not apply to a joint venture license, as required by Section 7029.1. However, at the time of making a bid as a joint venture, each person submitting the bid shall be subject to this section with respect to his or her individual licensure.

(d) This section shall not affect the right or ability of a licensed architect, land surveyor, or registered professional engineer to form joint ventures with licensed contractors to render services within the scope of their respective practices.

(e) Unless one of the foregoing exceptions applies, a bid submitted to a public agency by a contractor who is not licensed in accordance with this chapter shall be considered nonresponsive and shall be rejected by the public agency. Unless one of the foregoing exceptions applies, a local public agency shall, before awarding a contract or issuing a purchase order, verify that the contractor was properly licensed when the contractor submitted the bid. Notwithstanding any other provision of law, unless one of the foregoing exceptions applies, the registrar may issue a citation to any public officer or employee of a public entity who knowingly awards a contract or issues a purchase order to a contractor who is not licensed pursuant to this chapter. The amount of civil penalties, appeal, and finality of such citations shall be subject to Sections 7028.7 to 7028.13, inclusive. Any contract awarded to, or any purchase order issued to, a contractor who is not licensed pursuant to this chapter is void.

(f) Any compliance or noncompliance with subdivision (e) of this section, as added by Chapter 863 of the Statutes of 1989, shall not invalidate any contract or bid awarded by a public agency during which time that subdivision was in effect.

(g) A public employee or officer shall not be subject to a citation pursuant to this section if the public employee, officer, or employing agency made an inquiry to the board for the purposes of verifying the license status of any person or contractor and the board failed to respond to the inquiry within three business days. For purposes of this section, a telephone response by the board shall be deemed sufficient.

Added Stats 1989 ch 863 § 1. Amended Stats 1990 ch 321 § 1 (SB 929), effective July 16, 1990; Stats 1991 ch 785 § 2 (AB 800); Stats 1992 ch 294 § 1 (AB 2347).

—See Public Contract Code Section 10164, License Required for Award of Contract on State Project; 10262 Payment to Subcontractors, and 20103.5, Public Works Contracts: Bidder or Contract Not Licensed; Penalties, in Appendix.

§ 7028.16. Punishment for engaging in business without license with respect to structures damaged by natural disaster for which state of emergency has been declared

A person who engages in the business or acts in the capacity of a contractor, without having a license therefor, in connection with the offer or performance of repairs or improvements to a residential or nonresidential structure or property, or by adding to, or subtracting from, grounds in connection therewith, for damage or destruction caused by a natural disaster for which a state of emergency is proclaimed by the Governor pursuant to Section 8625 of the Government

Code, or for which an emergency or major disaster is declared by the President of the United States, shall be punished by a fine up to ten thousand dollars ($10,000), or by imprisonment pursuant to subdivision (h) of Section 1170 of the Penal Code for 16 months, or for two or three years, or by both that fine and imprisonment, or by a fine up to one thousand dollars ($1,000), or by imprisonment in a county jail not exceeding one year, or by both that fine and imprisonment. In addition, a person who utilized the services of the unlicensed contractor is a victim of crime regardless of whether that person had knowledge that the contractor was unlicensed.

Added Stats 1st Ex Sess 1989-1990 ch 36 § 3, effective September 22, 1990. Amended Stats 2009 ch 319 § 2 (AB 370), effective January 1, 2010; Stats 2011 ch 15 § 18 (AB 109), effective April 4, 2011, operative October 1, 2011; Stats 2020 ch 364 § 1 (SB 1189), effective January 1, 2021.

—*See Penal Code Sections 670, State of Emergency; Fraud of Owners or Lessees of Residential Structures; Penalties; 667.16, Enhanced Sentence for Fraud in Repairing Natural Disaster Damage; 551, Insurance Fraud, in Appendix.*

§ 7028.17. Failure of unlicensed person to comply with citation; Distribution of fines

(a) The failure of an unlicensed individual to comply with a citation after it is final is a misdemeanor.

(b) Notwithstanding Section 1462.5 or 1463 of the Penal Code or any other provision of law, any fine collected upon conviction in a criminal action brought under this section shall be distributed as follows:

(1) If the action is brought by a district attorney, any fine collected shall be paid to the treasurer of the county in which the judgment was entered to be designated for use by the district attorney.

(2) If the action is brought by a city attorney or city prosecutor, any fine collected shall be paid to the treasurer of the city in which the judgment was entered, to be designated for use by the city attorney.

Added Stats 1988 ch 725 § 1, as B & P C § 7099.85. Amended Stats 1989 ch 366 § 3. Amended and renumbered by Stats 1991 ch 1160 § 30 (AB 2190).

§ 7029. Issuance and suspension of joint venture license

A joint venture license is a license issued to any combination of individuals, corporations, limited liability companies, partnerships, or other joint ventures, each of which holds a current, active license in good standing. A joint venture license may be issued in any classification in which at least one of the entities is licensed. An active joint venture license shall be automatically suspended by operation of law during any period in which any member of the entity does not hold a current, active license in good standing.

Added Stats 1983 ch 891 § 3. Amended Stats 1984 ch 1174 § 1; Stats 2010 ch 698 § 4 (SB 392), effective January 1, 2011.

§ 7029.1. Unlawfully acting in joint venture without license

(a) Except as provided in this section, it is unlawful for any two or more licensees, each of whom has been issued a license to act separately in the capacity of a contractor within this state, to be awarded a contract jointly or otherwise act as a contractor without first having secured a joint venture license in accordance with the provisions of this chapter.

(b) Prior to obtaining a joint venture license, contractors licensed in accordance with this chapter may jointly bid for the performance of work covered by this section. If a combination of licensees submit a bid for the performance of work for which a joint venture license is required, a failure to obtain that license shall not prevent the imposition of any penalty specified by law for the failure of a contractor who submits a bid to enter into a contract pursuant to the bid.

(c) A violation of this section constitutes a cause for disciplinary action.

Added Stats 1983 ch 891 § 4. Amended Stats 1987 ch 930 § 3, effective September 22, 1987; Stats 2003 ch 607 § 32 (SB 1077).

§ 7029.5. Display of name, business address and business license number on commercial vehicles

Every C-36 plumbing contractor, C-45 sign contractor, and C-57 well-drilling contractor licensed under this chapter shall have displayed on each side of each motor vehicle used in his or her business, for which a commercial vehicle registration fee has been paid pursuant to Article 3 (commencing with Section 9400) of Chapter 6 of Division 3 of the Vehicle Code, his or her name, permanent business address, and contractor's license number, all in letters and numerals not less than 1½ inches high.

The identification requirements of this section shall also apply to any drill rig used for the drilling of water wells.

Failure to comply with this section constitutes a cause for disciplinary action.

Added Stats 1972 ch 681 § 1, operative July 1, 1973, as B & P C § 7029.6. Amended and renumbered by Stats 1991 ch 1160 § 20 (AB 2190); Stats 2011 ch 432 § 9 (SB 944), effective January 1, 2012.

Section VI

§ 7029.6. Display of business name and contractors' license number

Except for contractors identified in Section 7029.5, every contractor licensed under this chapter shall have displayed, in or on each motor vehicle used in his or her construction business, for which a commercial vehicle registration fee has been paid pursuant to Article 3 (commencing with Section 9400) of Chapter 6 of Division 3 of the Vehicle Code, his or her business name and contractors' license number in a clearly visible location in print type of at least 72-point font or three-quarters of an inch in height and width.

Added Stats 2003 ch 118 § 1 (AB 1538).

§ 7030. Licensee's statement on contracts; Notice requirements; Exceptions

(a) Except for contractors writing home improvement contracts pursuant to Section 7151.2 and contractors writing service and repair contracts pursuant to Section 7159.10, every person licensed pursuant to this chapter shall include the following statement in at least 10-point type on all written contracts with respect to which the person is a prime contractor:

"Contractors are required by law to be licensed and regulated by the Contractors State License Board which has jurisdiction to investigate complaints against contractors if a complaint regarding a patent act or omission is filed within four years of the date of the alleged violation. A complaint regarding a latent act or omission pertaining to structural defects must be filed within 10 years of the date of the alleged violation. Any questions concerning a contractor may be referred to the Registrar, Contractors State License Board, P.O. Box 26000, Sacramento, CA 95826."

(b) Every person licensed pursuant to this chapter shall include the following statement in at least 12-point type in all home improvement contracts written pursuant to Section 7151.2 and service and repair contracts written pursuant to Section 7159.10:

"Information about the Contractors State License Board (CSLB): CSLB is the state consumer protection agency that licenses and regulates construction contractors.

Contact CSLB for information about the licensed contractor you are considering, including information about disclosable complaints, disciplinary actions and civil judgments that are reported to CSLB.

Use only licensed contractors. If you file a complaint against a licensed contractor within the legal deadline (usually four years), CSLB has authority to investigate the complaint. If you use an unlicensed contractor, CSLB may not be able to help you resolve your complaint. Your only remedy may be in civil court, and you may be liable for damages arising out of any injuries to the unlicensed contractor or the unlicensed contractor's employees.

For more information:

Visit CSLB's internet website at www.cslb.ca.gov

Call CSLB at 800-321-CSLB (2752)

Write CSLB at P.O. Box 26000, Sacramento, CA 95826."

(c) Failure to comply with the notice requirements set forth in subdivision (a) or (b) of this section is cause for disciplinary action.

Added Stats 2005 ch 48 § 5 (SB 1113), effective July 18, 2005, operative January 1, 2006. Amended Stats 2011 ch 432 § 10 (SB 944), effective January 1, 2012; Stats 2020 ch 312 § 55 (SB 1474), effective January 1, 2021.

§ 7030.1. Disclosure

(a) A contractor, who has his or her license suspended or revoked two or more times within an eight-year period, shall disclose either in capital letters in 10-point roman boldface type or in contrasting red print in at least 8-point roman boldface type, in a document provided prior to entering into a contract to perform work on residential property with four or fewer units, any disciplinary license suspension, or license revocation during the last eight years resulting from any violation of this chapter by the contractor, whether or not the suspension or revocation was stayed.

(b) The disclosure notice required by this section may be provided in a bid, estimate, or other document prior to entering into a contract.

(c) A violation of this section is subject to the following penalties:

(1) A penalty of one thousand dollars ($1,000) shall be assessed for the first violation.

(2) A penalty of two thousand five hundred dollars ($2,500) shall be assessed for the second violation.

(3) A penalty of five thousand dollars ($5,000) shall be assessed for a third violation in addition to a one-year suspension of license by operation of law.

(4) A fourth violation shall result in the revocation of license in accordance with this chapter.

Added Stats 1996 ch 282 § 3 (AB 2494).

§ 7030.5. Inclusion of license number in contracts, bids, and advertising

Every person licensed pursuant to this chapter shall include his license number in: (a) all construction contracts; (b) subcontracts and calls for bid; and (c) all forms of advertising, as prescribed by the registrar of contractors, used by such a person.

Added Stats 1972 ch 124 § 1, operative July 1, 1973. Amended Stats 1973 ch 153 § 1, effective July 6, 1973, operative July 1, 1973.

§ 7031. Allegation and proof of license in action on contract; Recovery of compensation paid to unlicensed contractor; Substantial compliance; Exceptions

(a) Except as provided in subdivision (e), no person engaged in the business or acting in the capacity of a contractor, may bring or maintain any action, or recover in law or equity in any action, in any court of this state for the collection of compensation for the performance of any act or contract where a license is required by this chapter without alleging that they were a duly licensed contractor at all times during the performance of that act or contract regardless of the merits of the cause of action brought by the person, except that this prohibition shall not apply to contractors who are each individually licensed under this chapter but who fail to comply with Section 7029.

(b) Except as provided in subdivision (e), a person who utilizes the services of an unlicensed contractor may bring an action in any court of competent jurisdiction in this state to recover all compensation paid to the unlicensed contractor for performance of any act or contract.

(c) A security interest taken to secure any payment for the performance of any act or contract for which a license is required by this chapter is unenforceable if the person performing the act or contract was not a duly licensed contractor at all times during the performance of the act or contract.

(d) If licensure or proper licensure is controverted, then proof of licensure pursuant to this section shall be made by production of a verified certificate of licensure from the Contractors State License Board which establishes that the individual or entity bringing the action was duly licensed in the proper classification of contractors at all times during the performance of any act or contract covered by the action. Nothing in this subdivision shall require any person or entity controverting licensure or proper licensure to produce a verified certificate. When licensure or proper licensure is controverted, the burden of proof to establish licensure or proper licensure shall be on the licensee.

(e) The judicial doctrine of substantial compliance shall not apply under this section where the person who engaged in the business or acted in the capacity of a contractor has never been a duly licensed contractor in this state. However, notwithstanding subdivision (b) of Section 143, the court may determine that there has been substantial compliance with licensure requirements under this section if it is shown at an evidentiary hearing that the person who engaged in the business or acted in the capacity of a contractor (1) had been duly licensed as a contractor in this state prior to the performance of the act or contract, (2) acted reasonably and in good faith to maintain proper licensure, and (3) acted promptly and in good faith to remedy the failure to comply with the licensure requirements upon learning of the failure.

(f) The exceptions to the prohibition against the application of the judicial doctrine of substantial compliance found in subdivision (e) shall apply to all contracts entered into on or after January 1, 1992, and to all actions or arbitrations arising therefrom, except that the amendments to subdivisions (e) and (f) enacted during the 1994 portion of the 1993-94 Regular Session of the Legislature shall not apply to either of the following:

(1) Any legal action or arbitration commenced prior to January 1, 1995, regardless of the date on which the parties entered into the contract.

(2) Any legal action or arbitration commenced on or after January 1, 1995, if the legal action or arbitration was commenced prior to January 1, 1995, and was subsequently dismissed.

Added Stats 1939 ch 37 § 1. Amended Stats 1957 ch 845 § 1; Stats 1961 ch 1325 § 1; Stats 1965 ch 681 § 1; Stats 1989 ch 368 § 1; Stats 1991 ch 632 § 1 (AB 1382); Stats 1992 ch 229 § 1 (AB 2413); Stats 1993 ch 797 § 1 (AB 628); Stats 1994 ch 550 § 1 (SB 1844); Stats 2001 ch 226 § 1 (AB 678); Stats 2003 ch 289 § 1 (AB 1386); Stats 2016 ch 244 § 1 (AB 1793), effective January 1, 2017; Stats 2020 ch 312 § 56 (SB 1474), effective January 1, 2021.

§ 7031.5. Applicant's statement as to license required by city or county permit regulations; Penalty for violation

Each county or city which requires the issuance of a permit as a condition precedent to the construction, alteration, improvement, demolition or repair of any building or structure shall also require that each applicant for such a permit file as a condition precedent to the issuance of a permit a statement which he has prepared and signed stating that the applicant is licensed under the provisions of this chapter, giving the number of the license and stating that it is in full force and effect, or, if the applicant is exempt from the provisions of this chapter, the basis for the alleged exemption.

Any violation of this section by any applicant for a permit shall be subject to a civil penalty of not more than five hundred dollars ($500).

Added Stats 1963 ch 1140 § 1. Amended Stats 1977 ch 1052 § 1.

§ 7032. Construction of chapter; Complaints to registrar against licensees

Nothing in this chapter shall limit the power of a city or county to regulate the quality and character of installations made by contractors through a system of permits and inspections which are designed to secure compliance with and aid in the enforcement of applicable state and local building laws, or to enforce other local laws necessary for the protection of the public health and safety. Nothing in this chapter shall limit the power of a city or county to adopt any system of permits requiring submission to and approval by the city or county of plans and specifications for an installation prior to the commencement of construction of the installation.

Cities or counties may direct complaints to the registrar against licensees based upon determinations by city or county enforcement officers of violations by such licensees of codes the enforcement of which is the responsibility of the complaining city or county. Such complaints shall to the extent determined to be necessary by the registrar be given priority in processing over other complaints.

Nothing contained in this section shall be construed as authorizing a city or county to enact regulations relating to the qualifications necessary to engage in the business of contracting.

Added Stats 1959 ch 1403 § 1, effective July 1, 1959. Amended Stats 1961 ch 198 § 1.

§ 7033. Requirement of filing by licensee or applicant statement as to license, or exemption and proof thereof

Every city or city and county which requires the issuance of a business license as a condition precedent to engaging, within the city or city and county, in a business which is subject to regulation under this chapter, shall require that each licensee and each applicant for issuance or renewal of such license shall file, or have on file, with such city or city and county, a signed statement that such licensee or applicant is licensed under the provisions of this chapter and stating that the license is in full force and effect, or, if such licensee or applicant is exempt from the provisions of this chapter, he shall furnish proof of the facts which entitle him to such exemption.

Added Stats 1965 ch 1082 § 1.

—See *Government Code Section 37101.7, Licensing for Revenue by Cities, in Appendix.*

§ 7034. Insertion of void or unenforceable provisions in contract prohibited

(a) No contractor that is required to be licensed under this chapter shall insert in any contract, or be a party, with a subcontractor that is licensed under this chapter to any contract which contains, a provision, clause, covenant, or agreement which is void or unenforceable under Section 2782 of the Civil Code.

(b) No contractor that is required to be licensed under this chapter shall require a waiver of lien rights from any subcontractor, employee, or supplier in violation of Section 8122 of the Civil Code.

Added Stats 1976 ch 411 § 1. Amended Stats 1979 ch 1013 § 3; Stats 2010 ch 697 § 1 (SB 189), effective January 1, 2011, operative July 1, 2012.

—*See Civil Code Sections 2782 Construction Contracts; Invalidity of Provisions to Indemnify Promissee Against Liability; Exceptions and 2782.6 Exception for Professional Engineer or Geologist; "Hazardous Materials" Defined, in Appendix.*

§ 7035. Subcontractor for specialty contractor

(a) A specialty contractor shall not enter into a contract for the performance of work on the same single project or undertaking with more than one subcontractor in the same license classification as the specialty contractor offering the contract, unless either of the following requirements are satisfied:

(1) The subcontractor employs persons who are classified as employees to perform work in that license classification on the single project or undertaking.

(2) The specialty contractor is a signatory to a bona fide collective bargaining agreement that covers the type of work being performed on the single project or undertaking and addresses the issue of subcontracting or subletting.

(b) A violation of subdivision (a) shall constitute a cause for disciplinary action.

(c) For purposes of this section, the following definitions shall apply:

(1) "Employs persons who are classified as employees" means the subcontractor classifies the individuals as employees rather than as independent contractors for purposes of the Labor Code.

(2) "Specialty contractor" has the same meaning as in Section 7058.

Added Stats 2023 ch 568 § 1 (AB 1204), effective January 1, 2024.

Article 3

Exemptions

§ 7040. United States, State, and subdivisions

(a) This chapter does not apply to an authorized representative of the United States government, the State of California, any federally recognized tribe or participating tribe acting within tribal jurisdiction, or any incorporated town, city, county, irrigation district, reclamation district, or other municipal or political corporation or subdivision of this state when the entity or its representative is acting within the scope of the entity's or representative's official capacity.

(b) Nothing in this section authorizes the entity or its authorized representative thereof either to enter into or authorize a contract with an unlicensed contractor for work that is required by this chapter to be performed by a licensed contractor.

Added Stats 1939 ch 37 § 1. Amended Stats 1986 ch 1230 § 1; Stats 1995 ch 467 § 2 (SB 1061); Stats 2019 ch 378 § 5 (SB 610), effective January 1, 2020; Stats 2024 ch 485 § 5 (SB 1455), effective January 1, 2025.

—*See Public Contract Code Section 6100 License Required for Award of Contract, in Appendix.*

§ 7041. Court officers

This chapter does not apply to officers of a court when they are acting within the scope of their office.

Added Stats 1939 ch 37 § 1.

§ 7042. Public utilities in their own business operations

This chapter does not apply to public utilities operating under the regulation of the State Railroad Commission on construction, maintenance and development work incidental to their own business.

Added Stats 1939 ch 37 § 1.

§ 7042.1. Adoption fees; Deferral, waiver, or reduction

(a) Notwithstanding any other provisions of this chapter, gas heat, or electrical corporations and their subsidiaries that are regulated as public utilities by the Public Utilities Commission shall not conduct work for which a contractor's license is required, except under any one or more of the following conditions:

(1) The work is performed upon the gas, heat, or electrical corporation's properties.

(2) The work is performed through a contract with a contractor or contractors licensed pursuant to this chapter or the work is performed for low-income citizens pursuant to a program authorized by order of the Public Utilities Commission.

(3) The work is undertaken by the gas, heat, or electrical corporation in furtherance of the generation, transmission, or distribution of electricity, gas, or steam, whether within or without the service area of the corporation, if any work performed within a structure and be-

yond a customer's utility meter is necessary to protect the public safety or to avoid interruption of service.

(4) The work is otherwise exempt from the provisions of this chapter.

(5) The work is performed to comply with programs or procedures ordered or authorized by the Public Utilities Commission not inconsistent with the objectives expressed in Chapter 984 of the Statutes of 1983.

(b) For the purposes of this section, the following terms have the following meanings:

(1) "Gas, heat, or electrical corporation properties" means properties which a gas, heat, or electrical corporation owns or leases, or over which it has been granted an easement for utility purposes, or facilities which a gas, heat, or electrical corporation owns or operates for utility purposes.

(2) "Subsidiaries" means subsidiaries of a gas, heat, or electrical corporation regulated as public utilities by the Public Utilities Commission which carry out activities solely for utility purposes.

(c) It is the intention of the Legislature in enacting this section that public utility regulations be clearly based on the principle that the energy conservation industry should be allowed to develop in a competitive manner, as declared in Chapter 984 of the Statutes of 1983.

Added Stats 1984 ch 1136 § 1. Amended Stats 1989 ch 29 § 1.

—*See Labor Code Section 3099 Electrician Competency and Training Standards, in Appendix.*

§ 7042.5. Application of chapter; Underground trenching operations; Cable television corporation defined

This chapter does not apply to public utilities operating under the regulation of the Public Utilities Commission on construction, maintenance, and development work incidental to their own business, or to those activities of a cable television corporation subject to regulation pursuant to Section 768.5 of the Public Utilities Code, except underground trenching by a cable television corporation within the public streets, other than that necessary solely for the connection of its distribution system to, or within the properties of, subscribers or potential subscribers.

As used in this section, a cable television corporation is a corporation or person that transmits television programs by cable to subscribers for a fee.

Added Stats 1983 ch 1230 § 1. Amended Stats 1984 ch 945 § 1.

§ 7043. Oil or gas drilling and operation

This chapter does not apply to any construction, repair or operation incidental to the discovering or producing of petroleum or gas, or the drilling, testing, abandoning or other operation of any petroleum or gas well, when performed by an owner or lessee.

Added Stats 1939 ch 37 § 1.

§ 7044. Property owner making own improvements

(a) This chapter does not apply to any of the following:

(1) An owner who builds or improves a structure on his or her property, provided that both of the following conditions are met:

(A) None of the improvements are intended or offered for sale.

(B) The property owner personally performs all of the work or any work not performed by the owner is performed by the owner's employees with wages as their sole compensation.

(2) An owner who builds or improves a structure on his or her property, provided that both of the following conditions are met:

(A) The owner directly contracts with licensees who are duly licensed to contract for the work of the respective trades involved in completing the project.

(B) For projects involving single-family residential structures, no more than four of these structures are intended or offered for sale in a calendar year. This subparagraph shall not apply if the owner contracts with a general contractor for the construction.

(3) A homeowner improving his or her principal place of residence or appurtenances thereto, provided that all of the following conditions exist:

(A) The work is performed prior to sale.

(B) The homeowner has actually resided in the residence for the 12 months prior to completion of the work.

(C) The homeowner has not availed himself or herself of the exemption in this paragraph on more than two structures more than once during any three-year period.

(4) A nonprofit corporation providing assistance to an owner-builder, as defined in subdivision (a) of Section 50692 of the Health and Safety Code, who is participating in a mutual self-help housing program, as defined in Section 50078 of the Health and Safety Code.

(b) In all actions brought under this chapter, both of the following shall apply:

(1) Except as provided in paragraph (2), proof of the sale or offering for sale of a structure by or for the owner-builder within one year after completion of the structure constitutes a rebuttable presumption

affecting the burden of proof that the structure was undertaken for purposes of sale.

(2) Proof of the sale or offering for sale of five or more structures by the owner-builder within one year after completion constitutes a conclusive presumption that the structures were undertaken for purposes of sale.

Added Stats 1981 ch 1124 § 10. Amended Stats 1988 ch 1035 § 1.3; Stats 2009 ch 307 § 70 (SB 821), effective January 1, 2010; Stats 2016 ch 714 § 1 (SB 944), effective January 1, 2017.

§ 7044.01. Remedies; Violations; Fees and costs

In addition to all other remedies, any licensed contractor or association of contractors, labor organization, consumer affected by the violation, district attorney, or the Attorney General shall be entitled to seek injunctive relief prohibiting any violation of this chapter by an owner-builder who is neither licensed nor exempted from licensure under this chapter. The plaintiff in that action shall not be required to prove irreparable injury and shall be entitled to attorney's fees and all costs incurred in the prosecution of the action, provided the plaintiff is the prevailing party. The defendant in that action shall be entitled to attorney's fees and all costs incurred in the defense against the action, provided the defendant is the prevailing party.

Enacted by Stats. 2009, Ch. 307.

§ 7044.1. Real estate licensee acting within scope of license

This chapter does not apply to a real estate licensee acting within the course and scope of his or her license pursuant to the Real Estate Law (Part 1 (commencing with Section 10000) of Division 4). However, nothing in this section shall authorize a real estate licensee or a property manager to act in the capacity of a contractor unless licensed by the board.

Added Stats 1994 ch 361 § 1 (AB 2636).

§ 7044.2. Inapplicability of chapter

This chapter does not apply to an admitted surety insurer whenever that surety insurer engages a contractor to undertake the completion of a contract on which a performance or completion bond was issued by the surety insurer, provided all actual construction work is performed by duly licensed contractors.

Added Stats 1996 ch 287 § 1 (SB 2002). Amended Stats 1997 ch 17 § 7 (SB 947).

§ 7045. Sale or installation of products not part of structure

This chapter does not apply to the sale or installation of any finished products, materials, or articles of merchandise that do not become a fixed part of the structure, nor shall it apply to a material supplier or manufacturer furnishing finished products, materials, or articles of merchandise who does not install or contract for the installation of those items. The term "finished products" shall not include installed carpets or mobilehomes or mobilehome accessory structures, as defined in Section 7026.2.

This chapter shall apply to the installation of home improvement goods, as defined in Section 7151.

Added Stats 1939 ch 37 § 1. Amended Stats 1961 ch 1585 § 1; Stats 1967 ch 687 § 1; Stats 1969 ch 761 § 3; Stats 1970 ch 340 § 3; Stats 1973 ch 892 § 3; Stats 1979 ch 1012 § 1; Stats 1981 ch 916 § 1; Stats 1991 ch 1160 § 23 (AB 2190); Stats 1993 ch 589 § 11 (AB 2211).

§ 7046. Personal property work; Mobilehome accessory buildings or structures

This chapter does not apply to any construction, alteration, improvement, or repair of personal property. The term "personal property" shall not include mobilehomes or mobilehome accessory structures as defined in Section 7026.2.

Added Stats 1939 ch 37 § 1. Amended Stats 1969 ch 761 § 4; Stats 1970 ch 340 § 4; Stats 1973 ch 892 § 4; Stats 1991 ch 1160 § 24 (AB 2190).

§ 7048. Contracts aggregating less than specified amount; When exemption not applicable

(a) This chapter does not apply to a work or operation on one undertaking or project by one or more contracts, if the aggregate contract price for labor, materials, and all other items, is less than one thousand dollars ($1,000) that work or operation being considered of casual, minor, or inconsequential nature, and the work or operation does not require a building permit.

(b) This section does not apply in a case wherein the work of construction is only a part of a larger or major operation, whether undertaken by the same or a different contractor, or in which a division of the operation is made in contracts of amounts less than one thousand dollars ($1,000) for the purpose of evasion of this chapter or otherwise.

(c) This section does not apply to a person who does either of the following:

(1) Advertises or puts out a sign or card or other device that might indicate to the public that the person is a contractor or that the person is qualified to engage in the business of a contractor.

(2) Employs another person to perform, or assist in performing, the work or operation.

Added Stats 1939 ch 37 § 1. Amended Stats 1945 ch 1361 § 1; Stats 1977 ch 416 § 1; Stats 1986 ch 293 § 1; Stats 1998 ch 633 § 3 (SB 2217); Stats 2004 ch 865 § 8 (SB 1914); Stats 2024 ch 240 § 2 (AB 2622), effective January 1, 2025.

§ 7049. Ditch work and agricultural or fire prevention work

This chapter does not apply to any construction or operation incidental to the construction and repair of irrigation and drainage ditches of regularly constituted irrigation districts, reclamation districts, or to farming, dairying, agriculture, viticulture, horticulture, or stock or poultry raising, or clearing or other work upon the land in rural districts for fire prevention purposes, except when performed by a licensee under this chapter.

The provisions of this chapter do apply to the business of drilling, digging, boring, or otherwise constructing, deepening, repairing, reperforating, or abandoning water wells.

Added Stats 1939 ch 37 § 1. Amended 1959 ch 1691 § 2.

§ 7051. Application of chapter to certain licensees or registrants

This chapter does not apply to a licensed architect or a registered civil or professional engineer acting solely in his or her professional capacity or to a licensed structural pest control operator acting within the scope of his or her license or a licensee operating within the scope of the Geologist and Geophysicist Act.

Added Stats 1949 ch 90 § 4. Amended Stats 1955 ch 1532 § 4; Stats 1994 ch 26 § 206 (AB 1807), effective March 30, 1994.

§ 7052. People furnishing material or supplies

This chapter does not apply to any person who only furnishes materials or supplies without fabricating them into, or consuming them in the performance of, the work of the contractor.

Added Stats 1949 ch 90 § 5.

§ 7053. Employees

Except as provided in Article 10 (commencing with Section 7150), this chapter does not apply to any person who engages in the activities herein regulated as an employee who receives wages as his or her sole compensation, does not customarily engage in an independently established business, and does not have the right to control or discretion as to the manner of performance so as to determine the final results of the work performed.

Added Stats 1949 ch 90 § 6. Amended Stats 1970 ch 227 § 1; Stats 1974 ch 434 § 1; Stats 1982 ch 1427 § 2.

§ 7054. Inapplicability of chapter to licensed alarm company operators

This chapter does not apply to any person who performs work in the installation, maintenance, monitoring, selling, alteration, or servicing of alarm systems, as defined in Section 7590.1, and who holds an alarm company operator's license issued pursuant to Chapter 11.6 (commencing with Section 7590).

Added Stats 1982 ch 1210 § 1. Amended Stats 1991 ch 1160 § 25 (AB 2190); Stats 2018 ch 406 § 2 (SB 904), effective January 1, 2019.

§ 7054.5. Application of licensing provisions to installation of satellite antenna systems on residential structures

The licensing provisions of this chapter do not apply to any person registered under Chapter 20 (commencing with Section 9800) if that person's activities consist only of installing satellite antenna systems on residential structures or property.

Added Stats 1987 ch 422 § 1.

—See Business & Professions Code Sections 7590.1, Definitions; 5537 Licensed Contractor Exemptions from the Architect Act 5537.2 Exemptions and 6737.5, Exemptions for the Provisions of the Engineers Act, in Appendix.

Article 4
Classifications

§ 7055. Branches of contracting business

For the purpose of classification, the contracting business includes any or all of the following branches:
(a) General engineering contracting.
(b) (1) General building contracting.
(2) Residential remodeling contracting.
(c) Specialty contracting.

Added Stats 1945 ch 1159 § 1. Amended Stats 2020 ch 364 § 2 (SB 1189), effective January 1, 2021.

§ 7056. General engineering contractor

A general engineering contractor is a contractor whose principal contracting business is in connection with fixed works requiring specialized engineering knowledge and skill, including the following divisions or subjects: irrigation, drainage, water power, water supply, flood control, inland waterways, harbors, docks and wharves, shipyards and ports, dams and hydroelectric projects, levees, river control and reclamation works, railroads, highways, streets and roads, tunnels, airports and airways, sewers and sewage disposal plants and systems, waste reduction plants, bridges, overpasses, underpasses and other similar works, pipelines and other systems for the transmission of petroleum and other liquid or gaseous substances, parks, playgrounds and other recreational works, refineries, chemical plants and similar industrial plants requiring specialized engineering knowledge and skill, powerhouses, powerplants and other utility plants and installations, mines and metallurgical plants, land leveling and earthmoving projects, excavating, grading, trenching, paving and surfacing work and cement and concrete works in connection with the above-mentioned fixed works.

Added Stats 1945 ch 1159 § 2. Amended Stats 1951 ch 1606 § 1; Stats 2011 ch 296 § 12 (AB 1023), effective January 1, 2012.

§ 7057. General building contractor

(a) Except as provided in this section, a general building contractor is a contractor whose principal contracting business is in connection with any structure built, being built, or to be built, for the support, shelter, and enclosure of persons, animals, chattels, or movable property of any kind, requiring in its construction the use of at least two unrelated building trades or crafts, or to do or superintend the whole or any part thereof.

This does not include anyone who merely furnishes materials or supplies under Section 7045 without fabricating them into, or consuming them in the performance of, the work of the general building contractor.

(b) A general building contractor may take a prime contract or a subcontract for a framing or carpentry project. However, a general building contractor shall not take a prime contract for any project involving trades other than framing or carpentry unless the prime contract requires at least two unrelated building trades or crafts other than framing or carpentry, or unless the general building contractor holds the appropriate license classification or subcontracts with an appropriately licensed contractor to perform the work. A general building contractor shall not take a subcontract involving trades other than framing or carpentry, unless the subcontract requires at least two unrelated trades or crafts other than framing or carpentry, or unless the general building contractor holds the appropriate license classification. The general building contractor shall not count framing or carpentry in calculating the two unrelated trades necessary in order for the general building contractor to be able to take a prime contract or subcontract for a project involving other trades.

(c) A general building contractor shall not contract for any project that includes a fire protection system as provided for in Section 7026.12 or 7026.13, or the "C-57" Well Drilling classification as provided for in Section 13750.5 of the Water Code, unless the general building contractor holds the appropriate license classification, or subcontracts with the appropriately licensed contractor.

Added Stats 1945 ch 1159 § 3. Amended Stats 1997 ch 812 § 2 (SB 857); Stats 2002 ch 1013 § 60 (SB 2026); Stats 2013 ch 377 § 3 (AB 433), effective January 1, 2014.

§ 7057.5. Residential remodeling contractor

(a) A residential remodeling contractor is a contractor whose principal contracting business is in connection with any project to make improvements to, on, or in an existing residential wood frame structure, and the project requires the use of at least three unrelated building trades or crafts for a single contract.

(b) (1) A residential remodeling contractor may take a prime contract for trades or crafts which may include, but is not limited to, the following:

(A) Drywall.

(B) Finish carpentry.

(C) Flooring.

(D) Insulation.

(E) Painting.

(F) Plastering.

(G) Roof repair.

(H) Siding.

(I) Tiling.

(J) Installing, repairing, or replacing electrical fixtures, such as dimmers, fans, lights, outlets, and switches.

(K) Installing, repairing, or replacing plumbing fixtures, such as faucets, sinks, toilets, and tubs.

(L) Installing, repairing, or replacing mechanical fixtures, such as air filters, air delivery and return grills, and preassembled exhaust fans.

(2) A residential remodeling contractor shall not take a contract unless the contract includes three or more unrelated trades or crafts.

(3) Subject to the limit described in paragraph (2), a residential remodeling contractor may self-perform its contract or may subcontract any of the trades or crafts to appropriately licensed subcontractor or subcontractors.

(c) A residential remodeling contractor shall conduct its contracting activity in accordance with the following restrictions:

(1) A residential remodeling contractor shall not contract for a project that includes the following trades or crafts unless the contractor holds the appropriate license classification or subcontracts with an appropriately licensed contractor:

(A) C-16 Fire Protection.

(B) C-22 Asbestos Abatement.

(C) C-57 Well Drilling.

(2) A residential remodeling contractor shall not contract to make structural changes to load bearing portions of an existing structure, including, but not limited to, footings, foundations, load bearing walls, partitions, and roof structures.

(3) (A) The residential remodeling contractor shall not contract to install, replace, substantially alter, or extend electrical, mechanical, or plumbing systems or their component parts, or the mechanisms or devices that are part of those systems, unless the residential remodeling contractor holds the appropriate license classification or subcontracts with an appropriately licensed contractor.

(B) The residential remodeling contractor may contract to make minor alterations to existing electrical, mechanical, or plumbing systems to effectuate the purpose of installing, repairing, or replacing electrical, mechanical and plumbing fixtures, provided that the contract requires the use of at least three unrelated building trades or crafts.

(C) The board may adopt regulations to further define what activity constitutes the minor alterations described in subparagraph (B), and to further define the electrical, mechanical, or plumbing systems, or their component parts, or the mechanisms or devices that are part of those systems, that are subject to the restriction described in subparagraph (A).

(d) This contractor classification may be cited as the B-2 Residential Remodeling Contractor.

Added Stats 2020 ch 364 § 3 (SB 1189), effective January 1, 2021.

§ 7058. "Specialty contractor"

(a) A specialty contractor is a contractor whose operations involve the performance of construction work requiring special skill and

Section VI

whose principal contracting business involves the use of specialized building trades or crafts.

(b) A specialty contractor includes a contractor whose operations include the business of servicing or testing fire extinguishing systems.

(c) A specialty contractor includes a contractor whose operations are concerned with the installation and laying of carpets, linoleum, and resilient floor covering.

(d) A specialty contractor includes a contractor whose operations are concerned with preparing or removing roadway construction zones, lane closures, flagging, or traffic diversions on roadways, including, but not limited to, public streets, highways, or any public conveyance.

Added Stats 1945 ch 1159 § 4. Amended Stats 1959 ch 2175 § 1; Stats 1963 ch 1320 § 1; Stats 1967 ch 687 § 2; Stats 1985 ch 253 § 1; Stats 1991 ch 1160 § 26 (AB 2190); Stats 1999 ch 708 § 2 (AB 1206); Stats 2007 ch 354 § 15 (SB 1047), effective January 1, 2008.

§ 7058.1. [Section repealed 2002.]

Added Stats 1999 ch 708 § 3 (AB 1206). Repealed Stats 2002 ch 1013 § 61 (SB 2026). The repealed section related to requirements for exemption from testing.

§ 7058.5. Classification or certification of contractors performing asbestos-related work

A contractor shall not engage in asbestos-related work, as defined in Section 6501.8 of the Labor Code, that involves 100 square feet or more of surface area of asbestos containing materials, unless the contractor holds a C-22 Asbestos Abatement classification or the qualifier for the license passes an asbestos certification examination. Additional updated asbestos certification examinations may be required based on new health and safety information. The decision on whether to require an updated certification examination shall be made by the Contractors State License Board, in consultation with the Division of Occupational Safety and Health in the Department of Industrial Relations and the Division of Environmental and Occupational Disease Control in the State Department of Public Health.

No asbestos certification examination shall be required for contractors involved with the installation, maintenance, and repair of asbestos cement pipe or sheets, vinyl asbestos floor materials, or asbestos bituminous or resinous materials.

"Asbestos," as used in this section, has the same meaning as defined in Section 6501.7 of the Labor Code.

(b) The Contractors State License Board shall make available to all applicants, either on the board's internet website or, if requested, in hard copy, a booklet containing information relative to handling and disposal of asbestos, together with an open book examination concerning asbestos-related work. All applicants for an initial contractor license shall complete the open book examination and, prior to the issuance of a contractor's license, submit it to the board electronically or by mail if the applicant elects to use the hard-copy format.

Added Stats 1985 ch 1587 § 3, effective October 2, 1985. Amended Stats 1986 ch 1451 § 2, effective September 30, 1986; Stats 1987 ch 930 § 4, effective September 22, 1987; Stats 1991 ch 1160 § 27 (AB 2190); Stats 2010 ch 415 § 20 (SB 1491), effective January 1, 2011; Stat 2021 ch 188 § 8 (SB 826), effective January 1, 2022.

§ 7058.6. Registration with Division of Occupational Safety and Health as condition of asbestos certification; Certification examination; Proof of current registration

(a) The board shall not issue an asbestos certification, as required by Section 7058.5, unless the contractor is registered with the Division of Occupational Safety and Health of the Department of Industrial Relations pursuant to Section 6501.5 of the Labor Code. The board may issue an asbestos certification to a contractor who is not registered, provided the contractor in a written statement acknowledges that they do not perform asbestos-related work. The board shall notify both the division and the contractor, in writing, of the contractor's passage of the certification examination, for the purpose of allowing the contractor to satisfy the requirement of paragraph (1) of subdivision (a) of Section 6501.5 of the Labor Code. The contractor shall register with the division within 90 days from the date the contractor is notified of the passage of the certification examination. The board may require a reexamination if the contractor fails to register within 90 days following issuance of the notification. Applicable test fees shall be paid for any reexamination required under this section.

(b) Any contractor who is certified to engage in asbestos-related work shall present proof of current registration with the division pursuant to Section 6501.5 of the Labor Code upon application for renewal of the contractor's license, if the contractor engages in asbestos-related work, as defined in Section 6501.8 of the Labor Code.

(c) A contractor who is not certified pursuant to this section may bid on and contract to perform a project involving asbestos-related work as long as the asbestos-related work is performed by a contractor who holds the C-22 Asbestos Abatement classification or is certified and registered pursuant to this section and Section 6501.5 of the Labor Code.

(d) The board shall obtain and periodically update the list of contractors certified to engage in asbestos-related work who are registered pursuant to Section 6501.5 of the Labor Code.

Section VI

Added Stats 1988 ch 1003 § 1.5, operative July 1, 1989. Amended Stats 1995 ch 467 § 3 (SB 1061); Stats 2011 ch 432 § 11 (SB 944), effective January 1, 2012; Stats 2021 ch 188 § 9 (SB 826), effective January 1, 2022.

§ 7058.7. Hazardous substance certification examination

(a) No contractor may engage in a removal or remedial action, as defined in subdivision (d), unless the qualifier for the license has passed an approved hazardous substance certification examination.

(b) (1) The Contractors State License Board, the Division of Occupational Safety and Health of the Department of Industrial Relations, and the Department of Toxic Substances Control shall jointly select an advisory committee, which shall be composed of two representatives of hazardous substance removal workers in California, two general engineering contractors in California, and two representatives of insurance companies in California who shall be selected by the Insurance Commissioner.

(2) The Contractors State License Board shall develop a written test for the certification of contractors engaged in hazardous substance removal or remedial action, in consultation with the Division of Occupational Safety and Health, the State Water Resources Control Board, the Department of Toxic Substances Control, and the advisory committee.

(c) The Contractors State License Board may require additional updated approved hazardous substance certification examinations of licensees currently certified based on new public or occupational health and safety information. The Contractors State License Board, in consultation with the Department of Toxic Substances Control and the State Water Resources Control Board, shall approve other initial and updated hazardous substance certification examinations and determine whether to require an updated certification examination of all current certificate holders.

(d) For purposes of this section "removal or remedial action" has the same meaning as found in Part 2 (commencing with Section 78000) of Division 45 of the Health and Safety Code, if the action requires the contractor to dig into the surface of the earth and remove the dug material and the action is at a site listed pursuant to Article 5 (commencing with Section 78760) of Chapter 4 of Part 2 of Division 45 of the Health and Safety Code or any other site listed as a hazardous substance release site by the Department of Toxic Substances Control or a site listed on the National Priorities List compiled pursuant to the Comprehensive Environmental Response, Compensation, and Liability Act of 1980 (42 U.S.C. Sec. 9601 et seq.). "Removal or remedial action" does not include asbestos-related work, as defined in Section 6501.8 of the Labor Code, or work related to a hazardous substance spill on a highway.

(e) (1) A contractor may not install or remove an underground storage tank, unless the contractor has passed the hazardous substance certification examination developed pursuant to this section.

(2) A contractor who is not certified may bid on or contract for the installation or removal of an underground tank, if the work is performed by a contractor who is certified pursuant to this section.

(3) For purposes of this subdivision, "underground storage tank" has the same meaning as defined in subdivision (y) of Section 25281 of the Health and Safety Code.

Added Stats 1986 ch 1443 § 2, effective September 30, 1986. Amended Stats 1990 ch 1366 § 2 (SB 2004), effective September 26, 1990; Stats 1992 ch 1289 § 42.5 (AB 2743), ch 1290 § 1 (AB 3188), effective September 30, 1992; Stats 1993 ch 168 § 1 (AB 427); Stats 2002 ch 999 § 1 (AB 2481); Stats 2020 ch 312 § 57 (SB 1474), effective January 1, 2021; Stats 2022 ch 258 § 1 (AB 2327), effective January 1, 2023, operative effective 1/1/2024.

—See Health and Safety Code Section 25281 Definitions in Appendix.

—See Labor Code Sections 6501.5 Asbestos Certification, 6501.7 Asbestos: Definitions and 6501.8 Asbestos-Related Work Containing Construction Material, in Appendix.

—See also Health and Safety Code Sections 25914 Asbestos and Hazardous Removal Contracts Intent, 25914.1 Definitions, 25914.2 Need for Separate Contract; Emergency Conditions and 25914.3 Certification Requirements: Bids, in Appendix

§ 7058.8. Information to public regarding removal or encapsulation of asbestos-containing materials

The board shall make available to the public upon request information about contracting for the removal or encapsulation of asbestos-containing materials in a building including all of the following:

(a) Steps to take when contracting with a company to remove asbestos.

(b) Existing laws and regulations pertaining to asbestos-related work in California.

(c) Basic health information as contained in the United States Environmental Protection Agency publication, "Guidance for Controlling Asbestos-Containing Materials in Buildings."

(d) A current list of contractors who are certified pursuant to Section 7058.5 to engage in asbestos-related work and who are registered pursuant to Section 6501.5 of the Labor Code.

Added Stats 1988 ch 1003 § 2, operative July 1, 1989. Amended Stats 2011 ch 432 § 12 (SB 944), effective January 1, 2012.

§ 7059. Rules and regulations affecting classification of contractors; Contracts involving two or more crafts; Public works contracts

(a) The board may adopt reasonably necessary rules and regulations to effect the classification of contractors in a manner consistent with established usage and procedure as found in the construction business, and may limit the field and scope of the operations of a licensed contractor to those in which they are classified and qualified to engage, as defined by Sections 7055, 7056, 7057, and 7058. A licensee may make application for classification and be classified in more than one classification if the licensee meets the qualifications prescribed by the board for such additional classification or classifications. The application shall be in a form as prescribed by the registrar and shall be accompanied by the application fee fixed by this chapter. No license fee shall be charged for an additional classification or classifications.

Nothing contained in this section shall prohibit a specialty contractor from taking and executing a contract involving the use of two or more crafts or trades, if the performance of the work in the crafts or trades, other than in which they are licensed, is incidental and supplemental to the performance of the work in the craft for which the specialty contractor is licensed.

(b) (1) In public works contracts, as defined in Section 1101 of the Public Contract Code, the awarding authority shall determine the license classification necessary to bid and perform the project, in accordance with the classifications prescribed by this article and as set forth in Division 8 of Title 16 of the California Code of Regulations. In no case shall the awarding authority award a prime contract to a specialty contractor whose classification constitutes less than a majority of the project. When a specialty contractor is authorized to bid a project, all work to be performed outside of their license specialty, except work authorized by subdivision (a), shall be performed by a licensed subcontractor in compliance with the Subletting and Subcontracting Fair Practices Act (Chapter 4 (commencing with Section 4100) of Part 1 of Division 2 of the Public Contract Code).

(2) Nothing contained in this subdivision shall be construed as authorizing an awarding authority to enact regulations relating to the qualifications necessary to engage in the business of contracting.

(3) Nothing contained in this subdivision shall deprive the registrar of the authority to investigate complaints and commence disciplinary proceedings for violations of this chapter.

Added Stats 1939 ch 37 § 1. Amended Stats 1941 ch 971 § 9; Stats 1945 ch 1159 § 5; Stats 1957 ch 2084 § 21; Stats 1966 ch 4 § 1; Stats 1983 ch 891 § 5; Stats 1987 ch 485 § 1; Stats 2024 ch 485 § 6 (SB 1455), effective January 1, 2025.

§ 7059.1. Misleading or incompatible use of name styles

(a) A licensee shall not use any business name that indicates the licensee is qualified to perform work in classifications other than those issued for that license, or any business name that is incompatible with the type of business entity licensed.

(b) A licensee shall not conduct business under more than one name for each license. Nothing in this section shall prevent a licensee from obtaining a business name change as otherwise provided by this chapter.

Added Stats 1983 ch 891 § 6. Amended Stats 2001 ch 728 § 57 (SB 724).

Article 5
Licensing

§ 7065. Investigation, classification, and examinations

(a) Under rules and regulations adopted by the board and approved by the director, the registrar shall investigate, classify, and qualify applicants for contractors' licenses by written examination. This examination shall include questions designed to show that the applicant has the necessary degree of knowledge required by Section 7068 and shall include pertinent questions relating to the laws of this state and the contracting business and trade.

(b) (1) Contractors' licenses are to be issued to individual owners, partnerships, corporations, limited liability companies, and participating tribes, in accordance with this chapter.

(A) Every person who is an officer, member, responsible manager, or director of a corporation or limited liability company seeking licensure under this chapter shall be listed on the application as a member of the personnel of record.

(B) Every person who is a member of a partnership seeking licensure under this chapter shall be listed on the application as a member of the personnel record.

(2) A corporation or limited liability company, whether foreign or domestic, seeking licensure under this chapter shall provide its identification number issued by the Secretary of State.

(3) A tribal business, including a corporation organized or chartered by a federally recognized tribe pursuant to tribally enacted laws or to Section 17 of the federal Act of June 18, 1934, popularly known as the "Indian Reorganization Act," shall provide verification of its status as a tribal business. Verification may include, but is not limited to, the following:

(A) Enacted resolution ratifying the charter pursuant to Section 17 of the Indian Reorganization Act.

(B) Enacted resolution authorizing the tribally chartered corporation under tribally enacted laws.

(C) Articles of incorporation or by-laws.

(D) A current list of federally recognized tribes or directory of tribal leadership published under the Federally Recognized Indian Tribe List Act of 1994 (25 U.S.C. Sec. 5131) or on the internet website of the United States Bureau of Indian Affairs.

(c) An applicant shall qualify for licensure in accordance with this subdivision as follows:

(1) An individual owner may qualify by examination for a contractor's license upon the appearance of the owner or a qualifying individual appearing as a responsible managing employee on behalf of the owner.

(2) A partnership may qualify by examination for a contractor's license upon the appearance of a partner or a qualifying individual appearing as a responsible managing employee on behalf of the partnership.

(3) A corporation or participating tribe may qualify by examination for a contractor's license upon the appearance of a qualifying individual appearing either as a responsible managing officer or a responsible managing employee on behalf of the corporation.

(4) A limited liability company may qualify by examination for a contractor's license upon the appearance of a qualifying individual appearing as a responsible managing officer, a responsible managing manager, a responsible managing member, or a responsible managing employee on behalf of the company.

(d) No examination shall be required of a qualifying individual if, within the five-year period immediately preceding the application for licensure, the qualifying individual has either personally passed the written examination for the same classification being applied for, or has served as the qualifying individual for a licensee whose license was in good standing at any time during the five-year period immediately preceding the application for licensure and in the same classification being applied for.

(e) The registrar may contract with a public or private organization to conduct or administer the examination. The registrar may also contract with a public or private organization for materials or services related to the examination.

Added Stats 1939 ch 37 § 1. Amended Stats 1979 ch 1013 § 4; Stats 1980 ch 138 § 1, effective May 30, 1980; Stats 1981 ch 1122 § 1; Stats 1982 ch 378 § 1, ch 1347 § 2; Stats 1989 ch 350 § 1; Stats 2010 ch 698 § 5 (SB 392), effective January 1, 2011; Stats 2011 ch 296 § 13 (AB 1023), effective January 1, 2012; Stats 2020 ch 295 § 1 (AB 3087), effective January 1, 2021; Stat 2024 ch 485 § 7 (SB 1455), effective January 1, 2025.

—*See Government Code Section 12944, Discrimination by "Licensing Board," in Appendix.*

§ 7065.01. Examination not required for limited specialty license classification

Notwithstanding Section 7065, no trade examination shall be required of an applicant for the limited specialty license classification.

Added Stats 2002 ch 311 § 2 (AB 264).

§ 7065.05. Review and revision of examination contents

The board shall periodically review and, if needed, revise the contents of qualifying examinations to insure that the examination questions are timely and relevant to the business of contracting. The board shall, in addition, construct and conduct examinations in such a manner as to preclude the possibility of any applicant having prior knowledge of any specific examination question.

Added Stats 1979 ch 1013 § 5. Amended Stats 2000 ch 1005 § 8 (SB 2029); Stats 2005 ch 280 § 3 (SB 1112), effective January 1, 2006.

§ 7065.06. Revision to landscaping contractor examination

(a) Before the board revises the examination for a landscaping contractor (C-27), the board shall confer with the Department of Water Resources and the California Landscape Contractors Association to determine whether any updates or revisions to the examination are needed to reflect new and emerging landscape irrigation efficiency practices.

(b) The board shall ensure that the examination includes questions that are specific to water use efficiency and sustainable practices to help ensure that the state's water efficiency needs identified in the California Water Plan, described in Section 10004 of the Water Code, are sufficiently supported.

(c) The board shall ensure that the reference study material for the examination continues to include the most current version of the Model Water Efficient Landscape Ordinance (23 Cal. Code Regs. 490, et seq.) and shall add other collateral material specific to water use efficiency and sustainability.

Added Stats 2018 ch 867 § 2 (AB 2371), effective January 1, 2019.

§ 7065.1. Waiver of examination

Notwithstanding Section 7065, the registrar may waive the examination for a contractor's license under any of the following circumstances:

Section VI

(a) The qualifying individual has, for five of the seven years immediately preceding the application for licensure, been listed on the official records of the board as a member of the personnel of any licensee who held a license, which was active and in good standing, in the same classification being applied for, and who during the period listed on the license has been actively engaged in a licensee's construction activities in the same classification within which the applicant applies for a license.

(b) The qualifying individual is an immediate member of the family of a licensee whose individual license was active and in good standing for five of the seven years immediately preceding the application for licensure, and the qualifying individual is able to show all of the following:

(1) The qualifying individual has been actively engaged in the licensee's business for five of the seven years immediately preceding the application for licensure.

(2) The license is required to continue the existing family business in the event of the absence or death of the licensee.

(3) An application is made for a new license in the same classifications in which the licensee is or was licensed.

(c) The qualifying individual is an employee of a corporation or a limited liability company seeking to replace its former qualifying individual and has been employed by that corporation or limited liability company under the following conditions:

(1) For five of the seven years immediately preceding the application for licensure, the qualifying individual has been continually employed by the corporation or limited liability company in a supervisory capacity in the same classifications being applied for.

(2) For five of the seven years immediately preceding the application for licensure, the corporation or limited liability company has held an active license in good standing in the same classifications being applied for.

(3) The corporation or limited liability company has not requested a waiver under this subdivision within the past five years.

For purposes of this section, employees of a corporation or limited liability company shall include, but not be limited to, the officers of a corporation and the officers and managers of a limited liability company.

Added Stats 1981 ch 1122 § 3. Amended Stats 1982 ch 378 § 2; Stats 1986 ch 27 § 1; Stats 1990 ch 1456 § 1 (SB 2476); Stats 1992 ch 746 § 1 (AB 2424); Stats 2010 ch 698 § 6 (SB 392), effective January 1, 2011.

§ 7065.2. Waiver of examination

Notwithstanding Section 7065, the registrar may waive the examination for a contractor's license if the applicant has previously held a valid contractor's license in this state and has been acting in the capacity of a contractor for the United States government in a position exempt from licensure under this chapter.

Added Stats 1987 ch 630 § 1.

§ 7065.3. Additional classification without examination under specified conditions

Notwithstanding Section 7065, upon a conclusive showing by a licensee that he or she possesses experience satisfactory to the registrar in the classification applied for, an additional classification may be added, without further examination, under all of the following conditions:

(a) For five of the seven years immediately preceding the application, the qualifying individual of the licensee has been listed as a member of the personnel of any licensee whose license was active and in good standing, and who during the period listed on a license was actively engaged in the licensee's construction activities.

(b) The qualifying individual for the applicant has had within the last 10 years immediately preceding the filing of the application, not less than four years experience as a journeyman, foreman, supervising employee, or contractor in the classification within which the licensee intends to engage in the additional classification as a contractor.

(c) The application is, as determined by the registrar, for a classification that is closely related to the classification or classifications in which the licensee is licensed, or the qualifying individual is associated with a licensed general engineering contractor or licensed general building contractor and is applying for a classification that is a significant component of the licensed contractor's construction business as determined by the registrar. This section shall not apply to an applicant who is licensed solely within the limited-specialty classifications.

Pursuant to Section 7065, the registrar shall conduct a comprehensive investigation of no less than 3 percent of applications filed under this section to ensure that the applicants met the experience requirements of this section.

Added Stats 1990 ch 1456 § 3 (SB 2476). Amended Stats 2013 ch 319 § 7 (SB 822), effective January 1, 2014.

§ 7065.4. Reciprocity

The registrar may accept the qualifications of an applicant who is licensed as a contractor in a similar classification in another state if that state accepts the qualifications of a contractor licensed in this state for purposes of licensure in that other state, and if the board ascertains, on a case-by-case basis, that the professional qualifications and conditions of good standing for licensure and continued licensure are at least the same or greater in that state as in California. The registrar may waive the trade examination for that applicant if the applicant provides written certification from that other state in which he or she is licensed, that the applicant's license has been in good standing for the previous five years.

Added Stats 1990 ch 1326 § 2 (AB 3480), effective September 25, 1990.

§ 7065.5. Minor not to be licensed unless guardian appointed

No license shall be issued to a minor, nor to any partnership a partner of which is a minor, nor to any corporation any officer, director or responsible managing employee of which is a minor, nor to any limited liability company any officer, manager, or responsible managing employee of which is a minor, nor to any other kind of business organization in which a minor holds a responsible official position, unless the minor shall first have had a guardian appointed by a court of competent jurisdiction.

Added Stats 1941 ch 971 § 10. Amended Stats 2010 ch 698 § 7 (SB 392), effective January 1, 2011.

§ 7066. Application; Form and contents; Fee

To obtain an original license, an applicant shall submit to the registrar an application in writing containing the statement that the applicant desires the issuance of a license under the terms of this chapter.

The application shall be made on a form prescribed by the registrar in accordance with the rules and regulations adopted by the board and shall be accompanied by the fee fixed by this chapter.

Added Stats 1939 ch 37 § 1.

§ 7066.5. Blank forms

Any person may obtain blank license application forms from the board or may cause to be printed forms used by or approved by the Registrar of Contractors.

Added Stats 1984 ch 1252 § 1. Amended Stats 2011 ch 432 § 13 (SB 944), effective January 1, 2012.

§ 7067.5. [Section repealed 2016.]

Added Stats 1965 ch 636 § 1. Amended Stats 1969 ch 735 § 1; Stats 1974 ch 435 § 1; Stats 1979 ch 1013 § 6. Repealed Stats 2015 ch 656 § 8 (SB 467), effective January 1, 2016. The repealed section related to financial solvency, requirements to license applicants, and financial statements of licensees.

§ 7067.6. Application form; Signatures required

(a) Every application form for an original license, for renewal thereof, for reinstatement or for reissuance, including both active and inactive licenses, shall be signed by both the applicant and by the person qualifying on behalf of an individual or firm as referred to in Section 7068.1.

(b) (1) Notwithstanding any other law, the board may implement a system that provides for the electronic transmission of an application described in subdivision (a) and the acceptance of a digital or electronic signature as part of the filing of those applications.

(2) The board by regulation may specify the form and manner of these transmissions and acceptances, including, but not limited to, the adoption of any protocols necessary to ensure the validity and security of any information, signature, data, or document transmitted electronically or digitally. Upon the effective date of the regulations, the electronic submission of an initial license application or a renewal application, including a digital or electronic signature, shall satisfy the requirements of this article.

Added Stats 1963 ch 1016 § 1. Amended Stats 2015 ch 281 § 1 (SB 561), effective January 1, 2016.

§ 7068. Qualifications

(a) The board shall require an applicant to show the degree of knowledge and experience in the classification applied for, and the general knowledge of the building, safety, health, and lien laws of the state and of the administrative principles of the contracting business that the board deems necessary for the safety and protection of the public.

(b) An applicant shall qualify in regard to their experience and knowledge in one of the following ways:

(1) If an individual, they shall qualify by personal appearance or by the appearance of their responsible managing employee who is qualified for the same license classification as the classification being applied for.

(2) If a partnership or a limited partnership, it shall qualify by the appearance of a general partner or by the appearance of a responsible managing employee who is qualified for the same license classification as the classification being applied for.

(3) If a corporation, or any other combination or organization, it shall qualify by the appearance of a responsible managing officer or responsible managing employee who is qualified for the same license classification as the classification being applied for.

(4) If a limited liability company, it shall qualify by the appearance of a responsible managing officer, a responsible managing manager, responsible managing member, or a responsible managing employee who is qualified for the same license classification as the classification being applied for.

(c) (1) For purposes of this chapter, "a responsible managing employee" means an individual who is a bona fide employee of the applicant and is actively engaged in the classification of work for which that responsible managing employee is the qualifying person on behalf of the applicant.

(2) For purposes of this subdivision, the following definitions apply:

(A) "Bona fide employee of the applicant" means an employee who is permanently employed by the applicant.

(B) "Actively engaged" means working 32 hours per week, or 80 percent of the total hours per week that the applicant's business is in operation, whichever is less.

(d) The board shall, in addition, require an applicant who qualifies by means of a responsible managing employee under either paragraph (1) or (2) of subdivision (b) to show their general knowledge of the building, safety, health, and lien laws of the state and of the administrative principles of the contracting business as the board deems necessary for the safety and protection of the public.

(e) Except in accordance with Section 7068.1, no person qualifying on behalf of an individual or firm under paragraph (1), (2), (3), or (4) of subdivision (b) shall hold any other active contractor's license while acting in the capacity of a qualifying individual pursuant to this section.

(f) At the time of application for renewal of a license, the current qualifying individual shall file a statement with the registrar, on a form prescribed by the registrar, verifying their capacity as a qualifying individual to the licensee.

(g) Statements made by or on behalf of an applicant as to the applicant's experience in the classification applied for shall be verified by a qualified and responsible person. In addition, the registrar shall, as specified by board regulation, randomly review a percentage of such statements for their veracity.

(h) The registrar shall review experience gained by applicants from other states to determine whether all of that experience was gained in a lawful manner in that state.

Added Stats 1939 ch 37 § 1. Amended Stats 1941 ch 971 § 11; Stats 1957 ch 720 § 1; Stats 1959 ch 407 § 1; Stats 1963 ch 1017 § 1; Stats 1967 ch 1368 § 1; Stats 1979 ch 1013 § 7; Stats 1980 ch 138 § 2, effective May 30, 1980; Stats 1986 ch 995 § 4; Stats 1989 ch 1174 § 2; Stats 1991 ch 1160 § 28 (AB 2190); Stats 2004 ch 865 § 9 (SB 1914); Stats 2010 ch 698 § 8 (SB 392), effective January 1, 2011; Stats 2021 ch 376 § 5 (AB 830), effective September 28, 2021.

—*See Unemployment Code Section 1095, Permissible Uses for EDD Data, in Appendix.*

§ 7068.1. Duty of individual qualifying on behalf of another; Acting as qualifying individual for additional person or firm; Violation as cause for disciplinary action and misdemeanor

(a) The person qualifying on behalf of an individual or firm under paragraph (1), (2), (3), or (4) of subdivision (b) of Section 7068 shall be responsible for exercising supervision and control of their employer's or principal's construction operations to secure compliance with this chapter and the rules and regulations of the board. This person shall not act in the capacity of the qualifying person for an additional individual or firm unless one of the following conditions exists:

(1) There is a common ownership of at least 20 percent of the equity of each individual or firm for which the person acts in a qualifying capacity.

(2) The additional firm is a subsidiary of or a joint venture with the first. "Subsidiary," as used in this subdivision, means any firm at least 20 percent of the equity of which is owned by the other firm.

(3) With respect to a firm under paragraph (2), (3), or (4) of subdivision (b) of Section 7068, the majority of the partners, officers, or managers are the same.

(b) Notwithstanding paragraphs (1) to (3), inclusive, of subdivision (a), a qualifying individual may act as the qualifier for no more than three firms in any one-year period.

(c) The following definitions shall apply for purposes of this section:

(1) "Firm" means a partnership, a limited partnership, a corporation, a limited liability company, or any other combination or organization described in Section 7068.

(2) "Person" is limited to natural persons, notwithstanding the definition of "person" in Section 7025.

(3) "Supervision and control" means direct supervision or control or monitoring and being available to assist others to whom direct supervision and control has been delegated.

(4) "Direct supervision or control" means any of the following:

(A) Supervising construction operations.

(B) Managing construction activities by making technical and administrative decisions.

(C) Checking jobs for proper workmanship.

(D) Supervision on construction sites.

(d) The board shall require every applicant or licensee qualifying by the appearance of a qualifying individual to submit detailed information on the qualifying individual's duties and responsibilities for supervision and control of the applicant's construction operations.

(e) Violation of this section shall constitute a cause for disciplinary action and shall be punishable as a misdemeanor by imprisonment in a county jail not to exceed six months, by a fine of not less than three thousand dollars ($3,000), but not to exceed five thousand dollars ($5,000), or by both the fine and imprisonment.

Added Stats 1959 ch 407 § 2. Amended Stats 1961 ch 1777 § 1; Stats 1963 ch 1016 § 2; Stats 1967 ch 1368 § 2; Stats 1979 ch 1013 § 8; Stats 1991 ch 145 § 1 (AB 425); Stats 2006 ch 106 § 2 (AB 2457), effective January 1, 2007; Stats 2010 ch 698 § 9 (SB 392), effective January 1, 2011; Stats 2011 ch 296 § 14 (AB 1023), effective January 1, 2012; Stats 2013 ch 180 § 1 (SB 262), effective January 1, 2014; Stats 2021 ch 376 § 6 (AB 830), effective September 28, 2021; Stats 2024 ch 485 § 8 (SB 1455), effective January 1, 2025.

§ 7068.2. Disassociation of responsible managing officer; Notice; Replacement; Petition of licensee; Failure to notify registrar

(a) If the responsible managing officer, responsible managing employee, responsible managing member, or responsible managing manager disassociates from the licensed entity, the licensee or the qualifier shall notify the registrar in writing within 90 days after the date of disassociation. The licensee shall have 90 days after the date of disassociation in which to replace the qualifier. Upon failure to replace the qualifier within 90 days after the date of disassociation, the license shall be automatically suspended or the classification removed at the end of the 90 days.

(b) To replace a responsible managing officer, responsible managing employee, responsible managing member, or responsible managing manager, the licensee shall file an application as prescribed by the registrar, accompanied by the fee fixed by this chapter, designating an individual to qualify as required by this chapter.

(c) Upon failure of the licensee or the qualifier to notify the registrar of the disassociation of the qualifier within 90 days after the date of disassociation, the license shall be automatically suspended or the classification removed and the qualifier removed from the license effective the date the written notification is received at the board's headquarters office.

(d) The person qualifying on behalf of a licensee under Section 7068 shall be responsible for the licensee's construction operations until the date of disassociation or the date the board receives the written notification of disassociation, whichever is later.

(e) (1) Upon a showing of good cause by the licensee, the registrar may review and accept a petition for one 90-day extension to replace the qualifier immediately following the initial 90-day period described in subdivision (a) only under one or more of the following circumstances:

(A) If the licensee is disputing the date of disassociation.

(B) If the responsible managing officer, employee, member, or manager has died.

(C) If there has been a delay in processing the application to replace the qualifier that is out of the applicant's control and it is the responsibility of the board or another state or federal agency that is relied upon in the application process.

(2) This petition shall be received within 90 days after the date of disassociation or death or delay. The petition shall only be considered if an application to replace the qualifier as prescribed by the registrar is on file with the board. Under the circumstances described in subparagraphs (A) and (B) of paragraph (1), the licensee shall have no more than a total of 180 days after the date of disassociation or death in which to replace the qualifier.

(f) Failure of the licensee or the qualifier to notify the registrar of the qualifier's disassociation within 90 days after the date of disassociation shall constitute grounds for disciplinary action.

Added Stats 1983 ch 891 § 9. Amended Stats 1984 ch 1174 § 3; Stats 1987 ch 930 § 5, effective September 22, 1987; Stats 2010 ch 698 § 10 (SB 392), effective January 1, 2011; Stats 2011 ch 168 § 1 (AB 1091), effective January 1, 2012; Stats 2012 ch 162 § 2 (SB 1171), effective January 1, 2013.

§ 7068.5. Taking qualifying examination on behalf of applicant for contractor's license; Misdemeanor

It is a misdemeanor for any person other than the examinee named in the application to take the qualifying examination on behalf of an applicant for a contractor's license.

Added Stats 1961 ch 491 § 1.

§ 7068.7. Obtaining examination for another; Misdemeanor

Any person who obtains and provides for another the qualifying examination, or any part thereof, when not authorized to do so, is guilty of a misdemeanor.

Added Stats 1979 ch 1013 § 9.

§ 7069. Grounds for denial of license; Fingerprints of applicants; Criminal history and subsequent arrest information

(a) An applicant, and each officer, director, partner, manager, associate, and responsible managing employee thereof, shall not have committed acts or crimes that are grounds for denial of licensure under Section 480.

(b) As part of an application for a contractor's license, the board shall require an applicant to furnish a full set of fingerprints for purposes of conducting a criminal history record check. Fingerprints furnished pursuant to this subdivision shall be submitted in an electronic format if readily available. Requests for alternative methods of furnishing fingerprints are subject to the approval of the registrar. The board shall use the fingerprints furnished by an applicant to obtain criminal history information on the applicant from the Department of Justice and the United States Federal Bureau of Investigation, and the board may obtain any subsequent arrest information that is available.

Added Stats 1939 ch 37 § 1. Amended Stats 1941 ch 971 § 12; Stats 1955 ch 1547 § 1; Stats 1978 ch 1161 § 362; Stats 2002 ch 744 § 6 (SB 1953); Stats 2003 ch 874 § 20 (SB 363); Stats 2004 ch 909 § 27.3 (SB 136), effective September 30, 2004; Stats 2007 ch 240 § 1 (AB 936), effective January 1, 2008; Stats 2010 ch 698 § 11 (SB 392), effective January 1, 2011.

§ 7069.1. Arrest of licensee or home improvement salesperson

(a) Upon notification of an arrest of a member of the personnel of a licensee or a home improvement salesperson, the registrar, by first-class mail to the last official address of record, may require the arrestee to provide proof of the disposition of the matter.

(b) The proof required by this section shall be satisfactory for carrying out the purposes of this chapter, and at the registrar's discretion may include, but is not limited to, certified court documents, certified court orders, or sentencing documents. Any proof required by this section shall be received by the registrar within 90 days of the date of the disposition, or within 90 days of the registrar's demand for information if that date is later.

(c) Failure to comply with the provisions of this section constitutes cause for disciplinary action.

Added Stats 2004 ch 586 § 1 (AB 2216).

§ 7070. Showing that no license was refused or revoked

An applicant shall show that he or she has never been denied a license or had a license revoked for reasons that would preclude the granting of the license applied for. Where the board has denied an application for license under this chapter or Chapter 2 (commencing with Section 480) of Division 1.5, it shall, in its decision, or in its notice under subdivision (b) of Section 485, inform the applicant of the earliest date that the applicant may reapply for a license, which shall be one year from the effective date of the decision or service of notice under subdivision (b) of Section 485, unless the board prescribes an earlier date.

Added Stats 1939 ch 37 § 1. Amended Stats 1997 ch 334 § 1 (SB 299).

§ 7071. Refusal to corporation, partnership, or limited liability company for member's lack of qualifications

No license shall be issued to a corporation, partnership, limited liability company, or other combination or organization if a responsible officer or director of the corporation, or other combination or organization, or a partner of the partnership, or a manager or officer of the limited liability company, or any member of an organization seeking licensure under this chapter does not meet the qualifications required of an applicant other than those qualifications relating to knowledge and experience.

Added Stats 1939 ch 37 § 1. Amended Stats 1955 ch 1267 § 1; Stats 2010 ch 698 § 12 (SB 392), effective January 1, 2011; Stats 2011 ch 296 § 15 (AB 1023), effective January 1, 2012.

§ 7071.3. Entry into armed forces by licensee; Designation of manager to act for such entrant; Renewal fee and duration of license

Notwithstanding any other provision of this code, the holder of a current valid license under this chapter who has entered or enters the armed forces of the United States may designate a responsible managing person or persons to act for him while in the armed forces and until one year after his discharge therefrom, after which time the authority to so act for the licensee shall terminate. The renewal fee shall be paid for any such licensee so designating others to act for him.

Any license shall remain in full force and effect for 30 days after the entrance of the licensee into the armed forces, but he shall prior to the expiration of such 30-day period provide the registrar with the name or names of the persons so designated to conduct his business. The registrar may qualify such persons in any manner he may adopt. Persons so designated shall not have committed acts or crimes constituting grounds for denial of licensure under Section 480.

Persons so designated committing any of the acts or crimes constituting grounds for denial of licensure under Section 480 shall be removed from the business of such licensee after a hearing as provided in this chapter.

Added Stats 1945 ch 452 § 1, effective May 24, 1945. Amended Stats 1961 ch 1636 § 1, operative October 1, 1962; Stats 1978 ch 1161 § 363.

§ 7071.4. Licensee; Bond

(a) Each person licensed under the provisions of this chapter and subject to any of the bonding provisions of this article shall maintain the requisite bond as executed by an admitted surety insurer or as deposited with the registrar pursuant to paragraph (1) of subdivision (a) of Section 995.710 of the Code of Civil Procedure in the appropriate amount. Notwithstanding Article 7 (commencing with Section 995.710) of Chapter 2 of Title 14 of Part 2 of the Code of Civil Procedure, no other method of deposit, including, but not limited to, a certificate of deposit, shall satisfy a bond requirement under this article.

(b) All existing alternatives in lieu of a bond currently filed with the registrar shall be replaced for a surety bond or the deposit prescribed by paragraph (1) of subdivision (a) of Section 995.710 of the Code of Civil Procedure by January 1, 2020.

(c) (1) If the board is notified, in writing, of a civil action against the deposit authorized under this section, the deposit or any portion thereof shall not be released for any purpose, except as determined by the court.

(2) If any deposit authorized under this section is insufficient to pay, in full, all claims that have been adjudicated under any action filed in accordance with this section, the amount of the deposit shall be distributed to all claimants in proportion to the amount of their respective claims.

(d) Notwithstanding subdivision (a), this section shall not apply to the bond equivalents described in Section 7159.5 of this chapter.

(e) (1) This section shall be operative on and after January 1, 2019, upon which date the registrar shall thereafter no longer accept alternatives in lieu of a bond, other than as provided in this section.

(2) Notwithstanding any other law, in order to comply with the bonding provisions of this article, a person shall only be required to provide information consistent with the requirements for an applicant under Section 30.

(f) All alternatives in lieu of a bond filed with the registrar before January 1, 2019, and any lawful money or cashier's check deposited pursuant to paragraph (1) of subdivision (a) of Section 995.710 of the Code of Civil Procedure after January 1, 2019, shall be subject to the following limitations periods:

(1) Any action, other than an action to recover wages or fringe benefits, against a deposit given in lieu of a contractor's bond or bond of a

qualifying individual filed by an active licensee shall be brought within three years after the expiration of the license period during which the act or omission occurred, or within three years of the date the license of the active licensee was inactivated, canceled, or revoked by the board, whichever occurs first.

(2) Any action, other than an action to recover wages or fringe benefits, against a deposit given in lieu of a disciplinary bond filed by an active licensee pursuant to Section 7071.8 shall be brought within three years after the expiration of the license period during which the act or omission occurred, or within three years of the date the license of the active licensee was inactivated, canceled, or revoked by the board, or within three years after the last date for which a deposit given in lieu of a disciplinary bond filed pursuant to Section 7071.8 was required, whichever date is first.

(3) A claim to recover wages or fringe benefits shall be brought within six months from the date that the wage or fringe benefit delinquencies were discovered, but in no event shall a civil action thereon be brought later than two years from the date the wage or fringe benefit contributions were due.

(g) In any case in which a claim is filed against an alternative given in lieu of a bond filed with the registrar before January 1, 2019, or deposited with the registrar pursuant to subdivision (a), by any employee or by an employee organization on behalf of an employee, concerning wages or fringe benefits based upon the employee's employment, claims for the nonpayment shall be filed with the Labor Commissioner. The Labor Commissioner shall, pursuant to the authority vested by Section 96.5 of the Labor Code, conduct hearings to determine whether or not the wages or fringe benefits should be paid to the complainant. Upon a finding by the commissioner that the wages or fringe benefits should be paid to the complainant, the commissioner shall notify the registrar of the findings. The registrar shall not make payment from the deposit on the basis of findings by the commissioner for a period of 10 days following determination of the findings. If, within the period, the complainant or the contractor files written notice with the registrar and the commissioner of an intention to seek judicial review of the findings pursuant to Section 11523 of the Government Code, the registrar shall not make payment if an action is actually filed, except as determined by the court. If, thereafter, no action is filed within 60 days following determination of findings by the commissioner, the registrar shall make payment from the deposit to the complainant.

(h) Legal fees may not be charged by the board against any alternative given in lieu of a bond filed with the registrar before January 1, 2019, or deposited with the registrar pursuant to subdivision (a).

Added Stats 2018 ch 925 § 1 (AB 3126), effective January 1, 2019. Amended Stats 2020 ch 312 § 58 (SB 1474), effective January 1, 2021.

§ 7071.5. Contractor's bond

The contractor's bond required by this article shall be executed by an admitted surety in favor of the State of California, in a form acceptable to the registrar and filed with the registrar by the licensee or applicant. The contractor's bond shall be for the benefit of the following:

(a) A homeowner contracting for home improvement upon the homeowner's personal family residence damaged as a result of a violation of this chapter by the licensee.

(b) A property owner contracting for the construction of a single-family dwelling who is damaged as a result of a violation of this chapter by the licensee. That property owner shall only recover under this subdivision if the single-family dwelling is not intended for sale or offered for sale at the time the damages were incurred.

(c) A person damaged as a result of a willful and deliberate violation of this chapter by the licensee, or by the fraud of the licensee in the execution or performance of a construction contract.

(d) An employee of the licensee damaged by the licensee's failure to pay wages.

(e) A person or entity, including a laborer described in subdivision (b) of Section 8024 of the Civil Code, to which a portion of the compensation of an employee of a licensee is paid by agreement with that employee or the collective bargaining agent of that employee, damaged as the result of the licensee's failure to pay fringe benefits for its employees, including, but not limited to, employer payments described in Section 1773.1 of the Labor Code and regulations thereunder (without regard to whether the work was performed on a private or public work). Damage to a person or entity under this subdivision is limited to actual employer payments required to be made on behalf of employees of the licensee, as part of the overall compensation of those employees, which the licensee fails to pay.

Added Stats 1967 ch 1604 § 6, operative July 1, 1969. Amended Stats 1979 ch 1013 § 10, ch 1138 § 1.5; Stats 1980 ch 27 § 1.5, effective March 5, 1980; Stats 1982 ch 517 § 18; Stats 1999 ch 795 § 1 (SB 914); Stats 2008 ch 157 § 1 (SB 1432), effective January 1, 2009; Stats 2010 ch 697 § 2 (SB 189), effective January 1, 2011, operative July 1, 2012.

—See Code of Civil Procedure, Bond and Undertaking Law Sections 995.010 to 996.560 in Appendix.

§ 7071.6. [Section repealed 2023.]

Added Stats 2002 ch 1123 § 2 (SB 1919), operative January 1, 2004. Amended Stats 2005 ch 280 § 4 (SB 1112), effective January 1, 2006; Stats 2007 ch 354 § 16 (SB 1047), effective January 1, 2008; Stats 2015 ch 656 § 9 (SB 467), effective January 1, 2016; Stats 2019 ch 378 § 6 (SB 610), effective January 1, 2020; Stats 2021 ch 367 § 16 (SB 607), repealed January 1, 2023.

§ 7071.6. Bond as condition precedent to license

(a) The board shall require as a condition precedent to the issuance, reinstatement, reactivation, renewal, or continued maintenance of a license, that the applicant or licensee file or have on file a contractor's bond in the sum of twenty-five thousand dollars ($25,000).

(b) Excluding the claims brought by the beneficiaries specified in subdivision (a) of Section 7071.5, the aggregate liability of a surety on claims brought against a bond required by this section shall not exceed the sum of seven thousand five hundred dollars ($7,500). The bond proceeds in excess of seven thousand five hundred dollars ($7,500) shall be reserved exclusively for the claims of the beneficiaries specified in subdivision (a) of Section 7071.5. However, nothing in this section shall be construed so as to prevent any beneficiary specified in subdivision (a) of Section 7071.5 from claiming or recovering the full measure of the bond required by this section.

(c) A bond shall not be required of a holder of a license that has been inactivated on the official records of the board during the period the license is inactive.

(d) Notwithstanding any other law, as a condition precedent to licensure, the board may require an applicant to post a contractor's bond in twice the amount required pursuant to subdivision (a) until the time that the license is renewed, under the following conditions:

(1) The applicant has either been convicted of a violation of Section 7028 or has been cited pursuant to Section 7028.7.

(2) If the applicant has been cited pursuant to Section 7028.7, the citation has been reduced to a final order of the registrar.

(3) The violation of Section 7028, or the basis for the citation issued pursuant to Section 7028.7, constituted a substantial injury to the public.

(e) This section shall become operative on January 1, 2023.

Added Stats 2002 ch 1123 § 2 (SB 1919), operative January 1, 2004. Amended Stats 2005 ch 280 § 4 (SB 1112), effective January 1, 2006; Stats 2007 ch 354 § 16 (SB 1047), effective January 1, 2008; Stats 2015 ch 656 § 9 (SB 467), effective January 1, 2016; Stats 2019 ch 378 § 6 (SB 610), effective January 1, 2020; Stats 2021 ch 367 § 16 (SB 607), repealed January 1, 2023; Stats 2021 ch 367 § 16 (SB 607), operative January 1, 2023.

§ 7071.6.5. Surety bond as condition precedent to license

(a) The board shall require, as a condition precedent to the issuance, reissuance, reinstatement, reactivation, renewal, or continued valid use of a limited liability company license, that the applicant or licensee file or have on file a surety bond in the sum of one hundred thousand dollars ($100,000).

(b) The bond required by this section shall be executed by an admitted surety in favor of the State of California, in a form acceptable to the registrar and filed with the registrar, electronically or otherwise, by the applicant or licensee.

(c) The bond required by this section shall be for the benefit of any employee damaged by his or her employer's failure to pay wages, interest on wages, or fringe benefits and is intended to serve as an additional safeguard for workers employed by or contracted to work for a limited liability company.

(d) If an applicant or licensee subject to subdivision (a) is also a party to a collective bargaining agreement, the bond required by this section shall also cover, in addition to the coverage described in subdivision (c), welfare fund contributions, pension fund contributions, and apprentice program contributions.

(e) The bond required by this section shall not be applicable to a licensee whose license has been inactivated on the official records of the board during the period the license is inactive.

Added Stats 2010 ch 698 § 13 (SB 392), effective January 1, 2011.

§ 7071.7. Acceptance of bond as of effective date; Retroactive reinstatement of license

(a) Except as provided in subdivision (b), the registrar shall accept a bond required by Section 7071.6, 7071.6.5, 7071.8, or 7071.9 as of the effective date shown on the bond, if the bond is received by the registrar within 90 days after that date, and shall reinstate the license to which the bond pertains, if otherwise eligible, retroactive to the effective date of the bond.

(b) Notwithstanding subdivision (a), the registrar shall accept a bond as of the effective date shown on the bond, even if the bond is not received by the registrar within 90 days after that date, upon a showing by the licensee, on a form acceptable to the registrar, that the failure to have a bond on file was due to circumstances beyond the control of the licensee. The registrar shall reinstate the license to which the bond pertains, if otherwise eligible, retroactive to the effective date of the bond.

Added Stats 1986 ch 27 § 2. Amended Stats 2010 ch 698 § 14 (SB 392), effective January 1, 2011.

§ 7071.8. [Section repealed 2023.]

Added 1941 ch 882 § 1, as B & P C § 7071.5. Amended Stats 1961 ch 1125 § 1; Stats 1963 ch 1972 § 1; Stats 1965 ch 1022 § 1, ch 1025 § 1. Amended and renumbered Stats 1967 ch 1604 § 1, operative July 1, 1969. Amended Stats 1968 ch 482 § 2, operative July 1, 1969; Stats 1974 ch 434 § 2; Stats 1982 ch 517 § 20; Stats 1986 ch 79 § 1; Stats 1992 ch 294 § 2 (AB 2347); Stats 1994 ch 192 § 1 (AB 3475); Stats 2010 ch 698 § 15 (SB 392), effective January 1, 2011; Stats 2021 ch 367 § 18 (SB 607), repealed effective January 1, 2023.

§ 7071.8. Bond required for restoration of suspended or revoked license

(a) This section applies to an application for a license, for renewal or restoration of a license, an application to change officers or members of a corporation or a limited liability company, or for continued valid use of a license which has been disciplined, whether or not the disciplinary action has been stayed, made by any of the following persons or firms:

(1) A person whose license has been suspended or revoked as a result of disciplinary action, or a person who was a qualifying individual for a licensee at any time during which cause for disciplinary action occurred resulting in suspension or revocation of the licensee's license, whether or not the qualifying individual had knowledge or participated in the prohibited act or omission.

(2) A person who was an officer, director, manager, partner, or member of the personnel of record of a licensee at any time during which cause for disciplinary action occurred resulting in suspension or revocation of the licensee's license and who had knowledge of or participated in the act or omission which was the cause for the disciplinary action.

(3) A partnership, corporation, limited liability company, firm, or association of which an existing or new officer, director, manager, partner, qualifying person, or member of the personnel of record has had a license suspended or revoked as a result of disciplinary action.

(4) A partnership, corporation, limited liability company, firm, or association of which a member of the personnel of record, including, but not limited to, an officer, director, manager, partner, or qualifying person was, likewise, a manager, officer, director, or partner of a licensee at any time during which cause for disciplinary action occurred resulting in suspension or revocation of the license, and who had knowledge of or participated in the act or omission which was the cause for the disciplinary action.

(b) The board shall require as a condition precedent to the issuance, reissuance, renewal, or restoration of a license to the applicant, or to the approval of an application to change officers of a corporation or a limited liability company, or removal of suspension, or to the continued valid use of a license which has been suspended or revoked, but which suspension or revocation has been stayed, that the applicant or licensee file or have on file a contractor's bond in a sum to be fixed by the registrar based upon the seriousness of the violation, but which sum shall not be less than twenty-five thousand dollars ($25,000) nor more than 10 times that amount required by Section 7071.6.

(c) The bond is in addition to, may not be combined with, and does not replace any other type of bond required by this chapter. The bond shall remain on file with the registrar for a period of at least two years and for any additional time that the registrar determines. The bond period shall run only while the license is current, active, and in good standing, and shall be extended until the license has been current, active, and in good standing for the required period. Each applicant or licensee shall be required to file only one disciplinary contractor's bond of the type described in this section for each application or license subject to this bond requirement.

(d) This section shall become operative on January 1, 2023.

Added 1941 ch 882 § 1, as B & P C § 7071.5. Amended Stats 1961 ch 1125 § 1; Stats 1963 ch 1972 § 1; Stats 1965 ch 1022 § 1, ch 1025 § 1. Amended and renumbered Stats 1967 ch 1604 § 1, operative July 1, 1969. Amended Stats 1968 ch 482 § 2, operative July 1, 1969; Stats 1974 ch 434 § 2; Stats 1982 ch 517 § 20; Stats 1986 ch 79 § 1; Stats 1992 ch 294 § 2 (AB 2347); Stats 1994 ch 192 § 1 (AB 3475); Stats 2010 ch 698 § 15 (SB 392), effective January 1, 2011; Stats 2021 ch 367 § 18 (SB 607), repealed effective January 1, 2023; Stats 2021 ch 367 § 18 (SB 607), operative January 1, 2023.

§ 7071.9. [Section repealed 2023.]

Added Stats 1967 ch 1604 § 7, operative July 1, 1970. Amended Stats 1968 ch 482 § 3, operative July 1, 1970; Stats 1971 ch 669 § 2; Stats 1972 ch 7 § 2, effective February 29, 1972, operative March 4, 1972; Stats 1973 ch 319 § 36, Stats 1979 ch 1013 § 12; Stats 1980 ch 27 § 3, effective March 5, 1980; Stats 1982 ch 517 § 21; Stats 1986 ch 27 § 3; Stats 1993 ch 1264 § 6.4 (SB 574); Stats 2004 ch 865 § 10 (SB 1914); Stats 2007 ch 354 § 17 (SB 1047), effective January 1, 2008; Stats 2010 ch 698 § 16 (SB 392), effective January 1, 2011; Stat. 2021 ch 367 § 20 (SB 607) Repealed January 1, 2023.

§ 7071.9. Requirement of qualifying individual's bond as condition precedent to license

(a) (1) If the qualifying individual, as referred to in Sections 7068 and 7068.1, is neither the proprietor, a general partner, nor a joint licensee, the qualifying individual shall file or have on file a qualifying individual's bond as provided in Section 7071.10 in the sum of twenty-five thousand dollars ($25,000). This bond is in addition to, and shall not be combined with, any contractor's bond required by Sections 7071.5 to 7071.8, inclusive, and is required for the issuance, reinstatement, reactivation, or continued valid use of a license.

(2) This subdivision shall not apply to a federally recognized tribe or a participating tribe.

(b) Excluding the claims brought by the beneficiaries specified in paragraph (1) of subdivision (a) of Section 7071.10, the aggregate liability of a surety on claims brought against the bond required by this section shall not exceed the sum of seven thousand five hundred dollars ($7,500). The bond proceeds in excess of seven thousand five hundred dollars ($7,500) shall be reserved exclusively for the claims of the beneficiaries specified in paragraph (1) of subdivision (a) of Section 7071.10. However, nothing in this section shall be construed to prevent any beneficiary specified in paragraph (1) of subdivision (a) of Section 7071.10 from claiming or recovering the full measure of the bond required by this section. This bond is in addition to, and shall not be combined with, any contractor's bond required by Sections 7071.5 to 7071.8, inclusive, and is required for the issuance, reinstatement, reactivation, or continued valid use of a license.

(c) The responsible managing officer of a corporation shall not be required to file or have on file a qualifying individual's bond, if the responsible managing officer owns 10 percent or more of the voting stock of the corporation and certifies to that fact on a form prescribed by the registrar.

(d) The qualifying individual for a limited liability company shall not be required to file or have on file a qualifying individual's bond if the qualifying individual owns at least a 10-percent membership interest in the limited liability company and certifies to that fact on a form prescribed by the registrar.

Added Stats 1967 ch 1604 § 7, operative July 1, 1970. Amended Stats 1968 ch 482 § 3, operative July 1, 1970; Stats 1971 ch 669 § 2; Stats 1972 ch 7 § 2, effective February 29, 1972, operative March 4, 1972; Stats 1973 ch 319 § 36, Stats 1979 ch 1013 § 12; Stats 1980 ch 27 § 3, effective March 5, 1980; Stats 1982 ch 517 § 21; Stats 1986 ch 27 § 3; Stats 1993 ch 1264 § 6.4 (SB 574); Stats 2004 ch 865 § 10 (SB 1914); Stats 2007 ch 354 § 17 (SB 1047), effective January 1, 2008; Stats 2010 ch 698 § 16 (SB 392), effective January 1, 2011; Stat. 2021 ch 367 § 20 (SB 607) Repealed January 1, 2023; Stat. 2021 ch 367 § 21 (SB 607) Operative January 1, 2023.

§ 7071.10. Qualifying individual's bond

The qualifying individual's bond required by this article shall be executed by an admitted surety insurer in favor of the State of California, in a form acceptable to the registrar and filed with the registrar by the qualifying individual. The qualifying individual's bond shall not be required in addition to the contractor's bond when, as set forth under paragraph (1) of subdivision (b) of Section 7068, the individual proprietor has qualified for the license by his or her personal appearance, or the qualifier is a general partner as set forth under paragraph (2) of subdivision (b) of Section 7068. The qualifying individual's bond shall be for the benefit of the following persons:

(a) A homeowner contracting for home improvement upon the homeowner's personal family residence damaged as a result of a violation of this chapter by the licensee.

(b) A property owner contracting for the construction of a single-family dwelling who is damaged as a result of a violation of this chapter by the licensee. That property owner shall only recover under this subdivision if the single-family dwelling is not intended for sale or offered for sale at the time the damages were incurred.

(c) A person damaged as a result of a willful and deliberate violation of this chapter by the licensee, or by the fraud of the licensee in the execution or performance of a construction contract.

(d) An employee of the licensee damaged by the licensee's failure to pay wages.

(e) A person or entity, including a laborer described in subdivision (b) of Section 8024 of the Civil Code, to which a portion of the compensation of an employee of a licensee is paid by agreement with that employee or the collective bargaining agent of that employee, that is damaged as the result of the licensee's failure to pay fringe benefits for its employees including, but not limited to, employer payments described in Section 1773.1 of the Labor Code and regulations adopted thereunder (without regard to whether the work was performed on a public or private work). Damage to a person or entity under this subdivision is limited to employer payments required to be made on behalf of employees of the licensee, as part of the overall compensation of those employees, which the licensee fails to pay.

Added Stats 1967 ch 1604 § 8, operative July 1, 1969. Amended Stats 1968 ch 482 § 4, operative July 1, 1969; Stats 1979 ch 1013 § 13, ch 1138 § 2.5; Stats 1982 ch 517 § 22; Stats 1999 ch 795 § 2 (SB 914); Stats 2008 ch 157 § 2 (SB 1432), effective January 1, 2009; Stats 2010 ch 697 § 3 (SB 189), effective January 1, 2011, operative July 1, 2012.

§ 7071.11. Aggregate liability of surety on claim for wages and benefits; Renewal of license contingent on satisfaction of claims and debts; Limitations periods; Notice of payment; Protest of settlement; Accord; Legal fees not to be charged

(a) The aggregate liability of a surety on a claim for wages and fringe benefits brought against a bond required by this article, other than a bond required by Section 7071.8, shall not exceed the sum of four thousand dollars ($4,000). If a bond required by this article is insufficient to pay all claims in full, the sum of the bond shall be distributed to all claimants in proportion to the amount of their respective claims.

(b) No license may be renewed, reissued, or reinstated while a judgment or admitted claim in excess of the amount of the bond remains unsatisfied.

(c) Except for claims covered by subdivision (d), any action against a bond required under this article, excluding the judgment bond specified under Section 7071.17, shall be brought in accordance with the following:

(1) Within two years after the expiration of the license period during which the act or omission occurred. The provisions of this paragraph shall be applicable only if the license has not been inactivated, canceled, or revoked during the license period for which the bond was posted and accepted by the registrar as specified under Section 7071.7.

(2) If the license has been inactivated, canceled, or revoked, an action shall be brought within two years of the date the license of the active licensee would have expired had the license not been inactivated, canceled, or revoked. For the provisions of this paragraph to be applicable, the act or omission for which the action is filed must have occurred prior to the date the license was inactivated, canceled, or revoked.

(3) An action against a disciplinary bond filed by an active licensee pursuant to Section 7071.8 shall be brought in accordance with the provisions of paragraph (1) or (2), as applicable, or within two years after the last date for which a disciplinary bond filed pursuant to Section 7071.8 was required, whichever date is first.

(d) A claim to recover wages or fringe benefits shall be brought within six months from the date that the wage or fringe benefit delinquencies were discovered, but in no event shall a civil action thereon be brought later than two years from the date the wage or fringe benefit contributions were due.

(e) Whenever the surety makes payment on a claim against a bond required by this article, whether or not payment is made through a court action or otherwise, the surety shall, within 30 days of the payment, provide notice to the registrar. The notice required by this subdivision shall provide the following information by declaration on a form prescribed by the registrar:

(1) The name and license number of the contractor.

(2) The surety bond number.

(3) The amount of payment.

(4) The statutory basis upon which the claim is made.

(5) The names of the person or persons to whom payments have been made.

(6) Whether or not the payments were the result of a good faith action by the surety.

The notice shall also clearly indicate whether or not the licensee filed a protest in accordance with this section.

(f) Prior to the settlement of a claim through a good faith payment by the surety, a licensee shall have not less than 15 days in which to provide a written protest. This protest shall instruct the surety not to make payment from the bond on the licensee's account upon the specific grounds that the claim is opposed by the licensee, and provide the surety a specific and reasonable basis for the licensee's opposition to payment.

(1) Whenever a licensee files a protest in accordance with this subdivision, the board shall investigate the matter and file disciplinary action as set forth under this chapter if there is evidence that the surety has sustained a loss as the result of a good faith payment made for the purpose of mitigating any damages incurred by any person or entity covered under Section 7071.5.

(2) A licensee that fails to file a protest as specified in this subdivision shall have 90 days from the date of notification by the board to submit proof of payment of the actual amount owed to the surety and, if applicable, proof of payment of any judgment or admitted claim in excess of the amount of the bond or, by operation of law, the license shall be suspended at the end of the 90 days. A license suspension pursuant to this subdivision shall be disclosed indefinitely as a failure to settle outstanding final liabilities in violation of this chapter. The disclosure specified by this subdivision shall also be applicable to all licenses covered by the provisions of subdivision (g).

(g) During any period in which a surety remains unreimbursed for a loss or expense sustained on a bond issued pursuant to this article, the license for which the bond was issued, and any other license on which any member of the licensee's personnel of record has also been listed, may not be renewed, reissued, or reinstated while the licensee was subject to suspension or disciplinary action under this section.

(h) The licensee may provide the board with a notarized copy of an accord, reached with the surety to satisfy the debt in lieu of full payment. By operation of law, failure to abide by the accord shall result in the automatic suspension of a license to which this section applies. A license that is suspended for failure to abide by the accord may only be renewed or reinstated when proof of satisfaction of all debts is made.

(i) Legal fees may not be charged against the bond by the board.

Added Stats 1963 ch 1972 § 2, as B & P C § 7071.6. Amended Stats 1965 ch 1022 § 2. Amended and renumbered by Stats 1967 ch 1604 § 2, operative July 1, 1969. Amended Stats 1968 ch 482 § 5, operative July 1, 1969; Stats 1972 ch 7 § 3, effective February 29, 1972, operative March 4, 1972; Stats 1974 ch 201 § 1; Stats 1977 ch 280 § 1, effective July 7, 1977; Stats 1979 ch 1013 § 14, ch 1138 § 3.5; Stats 1980 ch 27 § 3.5, effective March 5, 1980; Stats 1982 ch 517 § 23; Stats 1986 ch 1353 § 1, operative July 1, 1987; Stats 1990 ch 1326 § 3 (AB 3480), effective September 25, 1990; Stats 1993 ch 1264 § 7 (SB 574); Stats 1999 ch 795 § 3 (SB 914); Stats 2001 ch 728 § 58 (SB 724); Stats 2002 ch 311 § 3 (AB 264); Stats 2004 ch 865 § 11 (SB 1914); Stats 2005 ch 280 § 5 (SB 1112), effective January 1, 2006; Stats 2008 ch 157 § 3 (SB 1432), effective January 1, 2009; Stats 2010 ch 698 § 17 (SB 392), effective January 1, 2011.

—*See Code of Civil Procedure, Bond and Undertaking Law Sections 995.010 to 996.560 in Appendix.*

§ 7071.12. [Section repealed 2019.]

Added Stats 1982 ch 517 § 24.5. Amended Stats 2005 ch 280 § 6 (SB 1112), effective January 1, 2006. Repealed Stats 2018 ch 925 § 2 (AB 3126), effective January 1, 2019.

§ 7071.13. Reference to bond in advertising, soliciting, or other presentments as ground for suspension of license

Any reference by a contractor in his advertising, soliciting, or other presentments to the public to any bond required to be filed pursuant to this chapter is a ground for the suspension of the license of such contractor.

Added Stats 1963 ch 1972 § 4, as B & P C § 7071.8. Renumbered Stats 1967 ch 1604 § 4, operative July 1, 1969.

§ 7071.14. Prohibited discrimination in denying license bond; Liability for damages

No licensee or applicant for a license under this chapter shall be denied a contractor's license bond solely because of his race, religious creed, color, national origin, ancestry, or sex. Whoever denies a contractor's license bond solely on the grounds specified herein is liable for each and every such offense for the actual damages, and two hundred fifty dollars ($250) in addition thereto, suffered by the licensee or applicant for a license.

Added Stats 1971 ch 669 § 4.

§ 7071.15. Revocation or suspension of license for failure to maintain bond

If a licensee fails to maintain a sufficient bond required by this article, the license is subject to suspension or revocation pursuant to Section 996.020 of the Code of Civil Procedure.

Added Stats 1983 ch 18 § 1.5, effective April 21, 1983.

Section VI

§ 7071.17. Bond required where applicant or licensee has unsatisfied final judgment for failure to pay contractor, subcontractor, consumer, materials supplier, or employee; Notice of unsatisfied final judgments; Suspension for noncompliance; Reinstatement; Disqualification from serving as personnel of record for other licensee; Disciplinary action

(a) Notwithstanding any other provision of law, the board shall require, as a condition precedent to accepting an application for licensure, renewal, reinstatement, or to change officers or other personnel of record, that an applicant, previously found to have failed or refused to pay a contractor, subcontractor, consumer, materials supplier, or employee based on an unsatisfied final judgment, file or have on file with the board a bond sufficient to guarantee payment of an amount equal to the unsatisfied final judgment or judgments. The applicant shall have 90 days from the date of notification by the board to file the bond or the application shall become void and the applicant shall reapply for issuance, reinstatement, or reactivation of a license. The board may not issue, reinstate, or reactivate a license until the bond is filed with the board. The bond required by this section is in addition to the contractor's bond. The bond shall be on file for a minimum of one year, after which the bond may be removed by submitting proof of satisfaction of all debts. The applicant may provide the board with a notarized copy of any accord, reached with any individual holding an unsatisfied final judgment, to satisfy a debt in lieu of filing the bond. The board shall include on the license application for issuance, reinstatement, or reactivation, a statement, to be made under penalty of perjury, as to whether there are any unsatisfied judgments against the applicant on behalf of contractors, subcontractors, consumers, materials suppliers, or the applicant's employees. Notwithstanding any other provision of law, if it is found that the applicant falsified the statement then the license will be retroactively suspended to the date of issuance and the license will stay suspended until the bond, satisfaction of judgment, or notarized copy of any accord applicable under this section is filed.

(b) (1) Notwithstanding any other provision of law, all licensees shall notify the registrar in writing of any unsatisfied final judgment imposed on the licensee. If the licensee fails to notify the registrar in writing within 90 days, the license shall be automatically suspended on the date that the registrar is informed, or is made aware of the unsatisfied final judgment.

(2) The suspension shall not be removed until proof of satisfaction of the judgment, or in lieu thereof, a notarized copy of an accord is submitted to the registrar.

(3) If the licensee notifies the registrar in writing within 90 days of the imposition of any unsatisfied final judgment, the licensee shall, as a condition to the continual maintenance of the license, file or have on file with the board a bond sufficient to guarantee payment of an amount equal to all unsatisfied judgments applicable under this section.

(4) The licensee has 90 days from the date of notification by the board to file the bond or at the end of the 90 days the license shall be automatically suspended. In lieu of filing the bond required by this section, the licensee may provide the board with a notarized copy of any accord reached with any individual holding an unsatisfied final judgment.

(c) By operation of law, failure to maintain the bond or failure to abide by the accord shall result in the automatic suspension of any license to which this section applies.

(d) A license that is suspended for failure to comply with the provisions of this section can only be reinstated when proof of satisfaction of all debts is made, or when a notarized copy of an accord has been filed as set forth under this section.

(e) This section applies only with respect to an unsatisfied final judgment that is substantially related to the construction activities of a licensee licensed under this chapter, or to the qualifications, functions, or duties of the license.

(f) Except as otherwise provided, this section does not apply to an applicant or licensee when the financial obligation covered by this section has been discharged in a bankruptcy proceeding.

(g) Except as otherwise provided, the bond shall remain in full force in the amount posted until the entire debt is satisfied. If, at the time of renewal, the licensee submits proof of partial satisfaction of the financial obligations covered by this section, the board may authorize the bond to be reduced to the amount of the unsatisfied portion of the outstanding judgment. When the licensee submits proof of satisfaction of all debts, the bond requirement may be removed.

(h) The board shall take the actions required by this section upon notification by any party having knowledge of the outstanding judgment upon a showing of proof of the judgment.

(i) For the purposes of this section, the term "judgment" also includes any final arbitration award where the time to file a petition for a trial de novo or a petition to vacate or correct the arbitration award has expired, and no petition is pending.

(j) (1) If a judgment is entered against a licensee or any personnel of record of a licensee, then a qualifying person or personnel of record of the licensee at the time of the activities on which the judgment is based shall be automatically prohibited from serving as a qualifying individual or other personnel of record on any license until the judgment is satisfied.

(2) The prohibition described in paragraph (1) shall cause the license of any other existing renewable licensed entity with any of the same personnel of record as the judgment debtor licensee or with any of the same judgment debtor personnel to be suspended until the license of the judgment debtor is reinstated, the judgment is satisfied, or until those same personnel of record disassociate themselves from the renewable licensed entity.

(k) For purposes of this section, lawful money or cashier's check deposited pursuant to paragraph (1) of subdivision (a) of Section 995.710 of the Code of Civil Procedure, may be submitted in lieu of the bond.

(l) Notwithstanding subdivision (f), the failure of a licensee to notify the registrar of an unsatisfied final judgment in accordance with this section is cause for disciplinary action.

Added Stats 1995 ch 467 § 6 (SB 1061). Amended Stats 1997 ch 469 § 1 (AB 772); Stats 2003 ch 363 § 1 (AB 1382); Stats 2010 ch 698 § 18 (SB 392), effective January 1, 2011; Stats 2017 ch 506 § 1 (AB 1278), effective January 1, 2018; Stats 2018 ch 925 § 3 (AB 3126), effective January 1, 2019; Stats 2019 ch 378 § 7 (SB 610), effective January 1, 2020; Stats 2020 ch 370 § 10 (SB 1371), effective January 1, 2021.

—*See Code of Civil Procedure Section 116.220 Jurisdiction of Small Claims Court, in Appendix.*

—*See Code of Civil Procedure, Bond and Undertaking Law Sections 995.010 to 996.560 in Appendix.*

§ 7071.18. Report to registrar of convictions; Study of judgments, arbitration awards, settlements for construction defects in rental residential units; Contents of study

(a) Notwithstanding any other law, a licensee shall report to the registrar in writing the occurrence of any of the following within 90 days after the licensee obtains knowledge of the event:

(1) The conviction of the licensee for any felony.

(2) The conviction of the licensee for any other crime that is substantially related to the qualifications, functions, and duties of a licensed contractor.

(b) (1) The board shall consult with licensees, consumers, and other interested stakeholders in order to prepare a study of judgments, arbitration awards, and settlements that were the result of claims for construction defects for rental residential units and, by January 1, 2018, shall report to the Legislature the results of this study to determine if the board's ability to protect the public as described in Section 7000.6 would be enhanced by regulations requiring licensees to report judgments, arbitration awards, or settlement payments of those claims. Participation by licensees and consumers shall be voluntary. The study shall include, but not be limited to, criteria used by insurers or others to differentiate between settlements that are for nuisance value and those that are not, whether settlement information or other information can help identify licensees who may be subject to an enforcement action, if there is a way to separate subcontractors from general contractors when identifying licensees who may be subject to an enforcement action, whether reporting should be limited to settlements resulting from construction defects that resulted in death or injury, the practice of other boards within the department, and any other criteria considered reasonable by the board. The board shall submit the report to the Legislature in accordance with Section 9795 of the Government Code.

(2) Records or documents obtained by the board during the course of implementing this subdivision that are exempt from public disclosure under the California Public Records Act (Chapter 3.5 (commencing with Section 6250) of Division 7 of Title 1 of the Government Code) shall remain exempt from disclosure pursuant to that act.

Added Stats 2016 ch 372 § 2 (SB 465), effective January 1, 2017.

§ 7071.19. Insurance as condition precedent to license; Aggregate limit of liability; Compliance with financial security requirements; Duties of registrar

(a) As a condition of the issuance, reinstatement, reactivation, or continued valid use of a license under this chapter, in addition to any bond required under this article, a limited liability company shall, in accordance with this section, maintain a policy or policies of insurance against liability imposed on or against it by law for damages arising out of claims based upon acts, errors, or omissions arising out of the contracting services it provides.

(b) The total aggregate limit of liability under the policy or policies of insurance required under this section shall be as follows:

(1) For a limited liability company licensee with five or fewer persons listed on the members of the personnel of record, the aggregate limit shall not be less than one million dollars ($1,000,000).

(2) For a limited liability company licensee with more than five persons listed on the members of the personnel of record, an additional one hundred thousand dollars ($100,000) of insurance shall be obtained for each person listed on the personnel of record of the licensee except that the maximum amount of insurance is not required to exceed five million dollars ($5,000,000) in any one designated period,

less amounts paid in defending, settling, or discharging claims as set forth under this section.

(c) The policy or policies required by this section may be issued on a claims-made or occurrence basis, and shall cover: (1) in the case of a claims-made policy, claims initially asserted in the designated period, and (2) in the case of an occurrence policy, occurrences during the designated period. For purposes of this section, "designated period" means a policy year or any other period designated in the policy that is not greater than 12 months. Any policy or policies secured to satisfy the requirements of this section shall be written by an insurer or insurers duly licensed by this state or an eligible surplus line insurer, with the insurance procured pursuant to Section 1765.1 of the Insurance Code, and may be in a form reasonably available in the commercial insurance market and may be subject to those terms, conditions, exclusions, and endorsements that are typically contained in those policies. A policy or policies of insurance maintained pursuant to this section may be subject to a deductible or self-insured retention.

(d) The impairment or exhaustion of the aggregate limit of liability by amounts paid under any policy in connection with the settlement, discharge, or defense of claims applicable to a designated period shall not require the licensee to acquire additional insurance coverage for that designated period. However, the aggregate limit of liability coverage (coverage limit) required by this section shall be reinstated by not later than the commencement date of the next designated period, and the license of any licensee that fails to comply with this provision shall be suspended by operation of law until the date that the licensee complies with the coverage limit requirements of this section. In addition, the amount to which any coverage limit is depleted may be reported on the license record.

(e) Upon the dissolution and winding up of the company, the company shall, with respect to any insurance policy or policies then maintained pursuant to this section, maintain or obtain an extended reporting period endorsement or equivalent provision in the maximum total aggregate limit of liability required to comply with this section for a minimum of three years if reasonably available from the insurer.

(f) Prior to the issuance, reinstatement, or reactivation of a limited liability company license as provided under this chapter, the applicant or licensee shall, in the manner prescribed by the registrar, submit the information and documentation required by this section and requested by the registrar, demonstrating compliance with the financial security requirements specified by this section.

(g) For any insurance policy secured by a licensee in satisfaction of this section, a Certificate of Liability Insurance, signed by an authorized agent or employee of the insurer, shall be submitted electronically or otherwise to the registrar. The insurer issuing the certificate, or, in the case of a surplus line policy, the surplus line broker, shall report to the registrar the following information for any policy required under this section: name, license number, policy number, dates that coverage is scheduled to commence and lapse, the date and amount of any payment of claims, and cancellation date if applicable.

(h) Upon the issuance, reinstatement, or reactivation of a license under this section, the registrar may post the following information to the licensee's license record on the Internet:

(1) The name of the insurer or insurers providing the liability policy or policies submitted by the licensee for the most recent designated period.

(2) Any policy numbers and the sum of the aggregate limit of liability provided by each.

Added Stats 2010 ch 698 § 19 (SB 392), effective January 1, 2011. Amended Stats 2013 ch 114 § 1 (AB 1236), effective January 1, 2014.

§ 7071.20. Licensee; Reporting requirement

(a) A licensee shall report to the registrar in writing within 90 days after the licensee has knowledge of any civil action resulting in a final judgment, executed settlement agreement, or final arbitration award in which the licensee is named as a defendant or cross-defendant, filed on or after January 1, 2019, that meets all of the following criteria:

(1) The action alleges fraud, deceit, negligence, breach of contract or express or implied warranty, misrepresentation, incompetence, recklessness, wrongful death, or strict liability by the act or omission of a licensee while acting in the capacity of a contractor, whether as a general contractor or as a specialty contractor.

(2) The amount or value of the judgment, settlement payment, or arbitration award for which the licensee is named as a defendant or cross-defendant, is one million dollars ($1,000,000) or greater, not including investigative costs or prior repairs performed by the licensee.

(3) The action is the result of a claim for damages to a property or person that allegedly resulted in a failure or condition that creates a substantial risk of a failure in the load bearing portions of a multifamily rental residential structure.

(4) The action is the result of a claim for damages to a property or person that was allegedly caused by a licensee's construction, repair, alteration to, subtraction from, improvement of, moving, wrecking, or demolishing of, any part of a multifamily rental residential structure, either personally or by or through others.

(5) The action, if a civil action, has been designated by a court of competent jurisdiction as a "complex case" pursuant to rules 3.400 to 3.403, inclusive, of the California Rules of Court because it involves a claim of construction defect or insurance coverage arising out of a construction defect claim, pursuant to paragraph (2) or (7) of subdivision (c) of Rule 3.400 of the California Rules of Court.

(b) This section shall not apply to residential construction subject to any part of Title 7 (commencing with Section 895) of Part 2 of Division 2 of the Civil Code.

(c) In an action that meets the criteria of this section, in which more than one contractor is named as a defendant or cross-defendant, all contractors who are apportioned any liability either by the court or pursuant to an agreement between parties, shall report the action pursuant to subdivision (a). This subdivision does not apply to a contractor who is named as a defendant or cross-defendant, but is assigned liability of less than fifteen thousand dollars ($15,000) in the action.

(d) The reports required by this section shall be signed by the licensee and shall set forth the license number of the licensee and the facts that constitute the reportable event. If the reportable event involves the action of a court, the report shall also set forth the following:

(1) The title of the matter.

(2) The court or agency name.

(3) The docket number.

(4) The claim or file number.

(5) The date on which the reportable event occurred.

(e) (1) The registrar or a designee shall review the reports required by this section. The registrar or designee shall return the report to the licensee and take no further action if, upon review, the registrar or a designee finds any of the following:

(A) The facts of the reportable event would not substantiate an allegation that a licensee has violated this chapter.

(B) There are reasonable grounds to believe that the public interest is sufficiently served by the existing resolution or disposition of the reportable event as reached by the parties to the action or by the court.

(C) Disciplinary action is unnecessary.

(2) Any report returned to a licensee pursuant to this subdivision shall be deemed to be a complaint resolved in favor of the licensee and the facts underlying the event as reported by the licensee shall not be subject to further review by the board, except upon receipt of an independent complaint involving the same underlying facts.

(3) If additional information is necessary to make the determination required by paragraph (1), the registrar or designee shall keep and regard the report as a complaint that shall be subject to Sections 7090

and 7091. The disclosure of any complaint referred to investigation pursuant to this section shall comply with the public disclosure provisions of Section 7124.6.

(f) Failure of a licensee to report to the registrar in the time and manner required by this section shall be grounds for disciplinary action. Criminal penalties shall not be imposed for a violation of this section.

(g) Except as provided in paragraphs (1) and (2) of subdivision (e), nothing in this section is intended to limit the registrar's authority on his or her motion, or upon the verified written complaint of another, to investigate the actions of a contractor as specified in Section 7090.

Added Stats 2018 ch 514 § 1 (SB 1465), effective January 1, 2019.

§ 7071.21. Licensee insurer; Reporting requirement

(a) An insurer providing a licensee commercial general liability insurance, construction defect insurance, or professional liability insurance shall report to the registrar within 30 days of all or a portion of the insurer's payment of a civil action judgment, settlement payment, or arbitration award, that meets all of the requirements of Section 7071.20, against the licensee all of the following:

(1) The name and license number of the licensee.

(2) The claim or file number.

(3) The amount or value of the judgment, settlement payment, or arbitration award.

(4) The amount paid by the insurer.

(5) The identity of the payee.

(b) (1) The registrar or a designee shall review the reports required by this section. The registrar or designee shall return the report to the licensee and take no further action if, upon review, the registrar or a designee finds any of the following:

(A) The facts of the reportable event would not substantiate an allegation that a licensee has violated this chapter.

(B) There are reasonable grounds to believe that the public interest is sufficiently served by the existing resolution or disposition of the reportable event as reached by the parties to the action or by the court.

(C) Disciplinary action is unnecessary.

(2) Any report returned to a licensee pursuant to this subdivision shall be deemed to be a complaint resolved in favor of the licensee and the facts underlying the event as reported by the licensee shall not be subject to further review by the board, except upon receipt of an independent complaint involving the same underlying facts.

(3) If additional information is necessary to make the determination required by paragraph (1), the registrar or designee shall keep and

regard the report as a complaint that shall be subject to Sections 7090 and 7091. The disclosure of any complaint referred to investigation pursuant to this section shall comply with the public disclosure provisions of Section 7124.6.

(c) Except as provided in paragraphs (1) and (2) of subdivision (b), nothing in this section is intended to limit the registrar's authority on his or her motion, or upon the verified written complaint of another, to investigate the actions of a contractor as specified in Section 7090.

Added Stats 2018 ch 514 § 2 (SB 1465), effective January 1, 2019.

§ 7071.22. Licensee reports; Not confidentiality violation

(a) Sections 7071.20 and 7071.21 shall apply if a party to the civil action, judgment, settlement payment, or arbitration award is or was a licensee, as defined in Section 7096, or was a member of the personnel of the record, a person, or a qualifying person, as those terms are defined in Section 7025.

(b) Notwithstanding any other law, a licensee or person providing a report to the registrar pursuant to Section 7071.20 or 7071.21 shall not be considered to have violated a confidential settlement agreement or other confidential agreement.

(c) The board may adopt regulations to further the purposes of Sections 7071.20 and 7071.21, specifically with regard to the reporting requirements of those sections.

Added Stats 2018 ch 514 § 3 (SB 1465), effective January 1, 2019.

§ 7072. Issuance of license

Following receipt of the application fee and an application furnishing complete information in the manner required by the registrar, and after such examination and investigation as he may require, the registrar, within 15 days after approval of the application, shall notify the applicant that a license may be issued to him on payment of the initial license fee provided in Article 8 (commencing at Section 7135), and, when the initial license fee is paid, shall issue a license to him permitting him to engage in business as a contractor under the terms of this chapter.

Added Stats 1939 ch 37 § 1. Amended Stats 1961 ch 1636 § 3, operative October 1, 1962; Stats 1970 ch 340 § 5.

§ 7072.5. Issuance of pocket card

(a) Upon the issuance of a license, a plasticized pocket card of a size, design, and content as may be determined by the registrar shall be issued at no cost to each licensee, or to the partners, managers, officers, or responsible managing officers of licensees licensed as other than individuals, which card shall be evidence that the licensee is duly licensed pursuant to this chapter. All cards issued shall be surrendered upon the suspension, revocation, or denial of renewal of the license, and shall be mailed or delivered to the board within five days of the suspension, revocation, or denial.

(b) When a person to whom a card is issued terminates his or her position, office, or association with a licensee that is licensed as other than an individual, that person shall surrender his or her card to the licensee and within five days thereafter the card shall be mailed or delivered by the licensee to the board for cancellation.

Added Stats 1988 ch 1495 § 1. Amended Stats 2006 ch 106 § 3 (AB 2457), effective January 1, 2007; Stats 2010 ch 698 § 20 (SB 392), effective January 1, 2011.

§ 7073. Grounds and procedures for denial of application; Rehabilitation and reapplication; Probationary license in lieu of denial

(a) The registrar may deny any application for a license or supplemental classification where the applicant has failed to comply with any rule or regulation adopted pursuant to this chapter or where there are grounds for denial under Section 480. Procedures for denial of an application shall be conducted in accordance with Section 485.

(b) When the board has denied an application for a license on grounds that the applicant has committed a crime substantially related to qualifications, functions, or duties of a contractor, it shall, in its decision or in its notice under subdivision (b) of Section 485, inform the applicant of the earliest date on which the applicant may reapply for a license. The board shall develop criteria, similar to the criteria developed to evaluate rehabilitation, to establish the earliest date on which the applicant may reapply. The date set by the registrar shall not be more than five years from the effective date of the decision or service of notice under subdivision (b) of Section 485.

(c) The board shall inform an applicant that all competent evidence of rehabilitation shall be considered upon reapplication.

(d) Along with the decision or notice under subdivision (b) of Section 485, the board shall serve a copy of the criteria for rehabilitation formulated under Section 482.

(e) In lieu of denying licensure as authorized under this section, the registrar may issue an applicant a probationary license with terms and conditions. During the probationary period, if information is brought to the attention of the registrar regarding any act or omission of the licensee constituting grounds for discipline or denial of licensure for which the registrar determines that revocation of the probationary license would be proper, the registrar shall notify the applicant to show cause within 30 days why the probationary license should not be revoked. The proceedings shall be conducted in accordance with the provisions of Chapter 5 (commencing with Section 11500) of Part 1 of Division 3 of Title 2 of the Government Code, and the registrar shall have all the powers granted therein. A probationary license shall not be renewed during any period in which any proceeding brought pursuant to this section is pending.

Added Stats 1983 ch 891 § 11. Amended Stats 2004 ch 586 § 2 (AB 2216); Stats 2005 ch 280 § 7 (SB 1112), effective January 1, 2006.

§ 7074. When application becomes void; Disposition of application; Fee for reapplication

(a) Except as otherwise provided by this section, an application for an original license, for an additional classification, or for a change of qualifier shall become void when:

(1) The applicant or the examinee for the applicant has failed to achieve a passing grade in the qualifying examination within 18 months after the application has been deemed acceptable by the board.

(2) The applicant for an original license, after having been notified to do so, fails to pay the initial license fee within 90 days from the date of the notice.

(3) The applicant, after having been notified to do so, fails to file within 90 days from the date of the notice any bond or lawful money or cashier's check deposited pursuant to paragraph (1) of subdivision (a) of Section 995.710 of the Code of Civil Procedure or other documents that may be required for issuance or granting pursuant to this chapter.

(4) After filing, the applicant withdraws the application.

(5) The applicant fails to return the application rejected by the board for insufficiency or incompleteness within 90 days from the date of original notice or rejection.

(6) The application is denied after disciplinary proceedings conducted in accordance with the provisions of this code.

(b) The void date on an application may be extended up to 90 days or one examination may be rescheduled without a fee upon documented evidence by the applicant that the failure to complete the application process or to appear for an examination was due to a medical emergency or other circumstance beyond the control of the applicant.

(c) An application voided pursuant to this section shall remain in the possession of the registrar for the period as he or she deems necessary and shall not be returned to the applicant. Any reapplication for a license shall be accompanied by the fee fixed by this chapter.

Added Stats 1983 ch 891 § 13. Amended Stats 2001 ch 728 § 59 (SB 724); Stats 2016 ch 634 § 4 (SB 1479), effective January 1, 2017. Stats 2018 ch 925 § 4 (AB 3126), effective January 1, 2019.

§ 7075. Display of license

The license shall be displayed in the licensee's main office or chief place of business. Satisfactory evidence of the possession of a license and the current renewal thereof shall be provided by the licensee upon demand.

Added Stats 1939 ch 37 § 1. Amended Stats 1961 ch 1636 § 4, operative October 1, 1962; Stats 1963 ch 1016 § 3; Stats 1971 ch 716 § 104; Stats 1990 ch 1326 § 4 (AB 3480), effective September 25, 1990.

§ 7075.1. Nontransferability of license

(a) No license, regardless of type or classification, shall be transferable to any other person or entity under any circumstances.

(b) A license number may be reissued after cancellation, revocation, suspension, or expiration beyond the renewal period specified in Section 7141, only under the following circumstances:

(1) To an individual upon application.

(2) To a partnership upon application if there is no change in the partners or partnership structure.

(3) To a corporation upon application if there is no change in the status of the corporation as registered with the Secretary of State.

(4) To a limited liability company upon application if there is no change in the status of the company as registered with the Secretary of State.

(c) A license number may be reissued or reassigned to a different entity only under the following conditions:

(1) To a corporation when the parent corporation has merged or created a subsidiary, the subsidiary has merged into the parent corporation, or the corporation has changed its filing status with the Secretary of State from a domestic corporation to a foreign corporation or from a foreign corporation to a domestic corporation, and the new entity is being formed to continue the business of the formerly licensed corporation.

(2) To a limited liability company when the parent limited liability company has merged or created a subsidiary, the subsidiary has merged into the parent limited liability company, or the limited liability company has changed its filing status with the Secretary of State from a domestic limited liability company to a foreign limited liability company or from a foreign limited liability company to a domestic limited liability company, and the new entity is being formed to continue the business of the formerly licensed limited liability company.

(3) To an individual when the individual is an immediate family member of a licensed individual who is deceased or absent and the license is required to continue an existing family contracting business.

(4) To a corporation or limited liability company when created by immediate members of an individual licensee's family to continue an existing deceased or absent individual licensee's contracting business.

(5) To a corporation or limited liability company when the corporation or limited liability company is formed by an individual licensee and the individual licensee maintains ownership directly or indirectly of shares or membership interests evidencing more than 50 percent of the voting power.

(6) To a limited liability company that is formed by a corporation to continue the business of the corporation subsequent to the cancellation of the corporate entity's license, provided the personnel listed for each entity are the same.

(d) For purposes of this section, an immediate family member of a deceased or absent licensed individual is either a spouse, father, mother, brother, sister, son, daughter, stepson, stepdaughter, grandson, granddaughter, son-in-law, or daughter-in-law.

Added Stats 1990 ch 1326 § 4.5 (AB 3480), effective September 25, 1990. Amended Stats 1992 ch 746 § 2 (AB 2424); Stats 2010 ch 698 § 21 (SB 392), effective January 1, 2011; Stats 2017 ch 573 § 29 (SB 800), effective January 1, 2018.

§ 7076. Events resulting in cancellation of license; Continuance of license

(a) An individual license shall be canceled upon the death of a person licensed as an individual. An immediate member of the family of the deceased licensee may request a continuance of the license to complete projects in progress and undertake new work for a reasonable amount of time to be determined by rules of the board. The request for a continuance must be made in writing and received at the board's headquarters office within 90 days after the death. Approval of the continuance of an individual license may be contingent upon meeting the bond requirements of Sections 7071.5 and 7071.6 within 90 days of notification by the board of that requirement. The immediate member of the family must apply for and obtain his or her own license to continue contracting after the continuance expires.

(b) A partnership license shall be canceled upon the death of a general partner. The remaining partner or partners shall notify the registrar in writing within 90 days of the death of a general partner. Failure to notify the registrar within 90 days of the death is grounds for disciplinary action.

The remaining general partner or partners may request a continuance of the license to complete projects in progress and undertake new work for a reasonable amount of time to be determined by rules of the board. The request for a continuance must be made in writing and received at the board's headquarters office within 90 days after the death. The remaining general partner or partners must apply for and obtain a new license to continue contracting after the continuance expires.

(c) A partnership license shall be canceled upon the disassociation of a general partner or upon the dissolution of the partnership. The disassociating partner or the remaining partner or partners shall notify the registrar in writing within 90 days of the disassociation of a general partner or dissolution of the partnership. Failure to notify the registrar of the disassociation or dissolution within 90 days shall cause the license to be canceled effective the date the written notification is received at the board's headquarters office. Failure to notify the registrar within 90 days of the disassociation or dissolution is grounds for disciplinary action. The remaining general partner or partners may request a continuance of the license to complete projects contracted for or in progress prior to the date of disassociation or dissolution for a reasonable length of time to be determined by rules of the board. The request for a continuance must be made in writing and received at the board's headquarters office within 90 days after the disassociation or dissolution. The remaining general partner or partners must apply for and obtain a new license to undertake new work and to continue contracting after the continuance expires.

(d) The general partner or partners shall notify the registrar in writing within 90 days of the death of a limited partner. Failure to notify the registrar within 90 days of the death is grounds for disciplinary action.

The death of a limited partner will not affect the partnership license unless the partnership license has only one limited partner. In this case, the license will be canceled upon the death of the limited partner unless a new limited partner is added to the license within 90 days of the death.

If the license is canceled, the remaining general partner or partners may request a continuance of the license to complete projects in progress and to undertake new work for a reasonable amount of time to be determined by rules of the board. The request for a continuance must be made in writing and received at the board's headquarters office within 90 days after the death. The remaining general partner or partners must apply for and obtain a new license to continue contracting after the continuance expires.

(e) The general partner or partners shall notify the registrar in writing within 90 days of the disassociation of a limited partner.

Section VI

Failure to notify the registrar of the disassociation, within 90 days, shall cause the disassociation to be effective the date the written notification is received at the board's headquarters office. Failure to notify the registrar within 90 days of the disassociation is grounds for disciplinary action.

The disassociation of a limited partner will not affect the partnership license unless the partnership license has only one limited partner. In this case, the license will be canceled upon the disassociation of the limited partner unless a new limited partner is added to the license within 90 days of the disassociation. If the license is canceled, the remaining general partner or partners may request a continuance of the license to complete projects contracted for or in progress prior to the date of disassociation for a reasonable amount of time to be determined by rules of the board. The request for a continuance must be made in writing and received at the board's headquarters office within 90 days after the disassociation. The remaining general partner or partners must apply for and obtain a new license to undertake new work and to continue contracting after the continuance expires.

(f) A joint venture license shall be canceled upon the cancellation, revocation, or disassociation of any of its entity licenses or upon the dissolution of the joint venture. The registrar shall be notified in writing within 90 days of the disassociation of a joint venture entity or dissolution of the joint venture. Failure to notify the registrar of the disassociation or dissolution within 90 days shall cause the license to be canceled effective the date the written notification is received at the board's headquarters office. Failure to notify the registrar within 90 days of the disassociation or dissolution is grounds for disciplinary action.

Any remaining entity or entities may request a continuance of the license to complete projects contracted for or in progress prior to the date of disassociation or dissolution for a reasonable amount of time to be determined by rules of the board. The request for a continuance must be made in writing and received at the board's headquarters office within 90 days of the disassociation or dissolution. The remaining entity or entities must apply for and obtain a new license to undertake new work and to continue contracting after the continuance expires.

(g) Any individual, partnership, or joint venture license continued in accordance with this section is subject to all other provisions of this chapter.

(h) A corporation license shall be canceled upon the corporation's dissolution, merger, or surrender of its right to do business in this state. The corporation or participating tribe shall notify the registrar in writing within 90 days of the dissolution, merger, or surrender. Failure to notify the registrar of the dissolution, merger, or surrender within 90 days shall cause the license to be canceled effective the date written notification is received at the board's headquarters office. If the corporation or participating tribe fails to notify the board of the dissolution, merger, or surrender, the corporation license shall be canceled 60 days after the board's discovery when researching the relevant corporate records. Failure to notify the registrar within 90 days of the dissolution, merger, or surrender is grounds for disciplinary action.

(i) A limited liability company license shall be canceled upon the company's dissolution, merger, or surrender of its right to do business in this state. The limited liability company shall notify the registrar in writing within 90 days of the dissolution, merger, or surrender. Failure to notify the registrar of the dissolution, merger, or surrender within 90 days shall cause the license to be canceled effective the date written notification is received at the board's headquarters office. If the limited liability company fails to notify the board of the dissolution, merger, or surrender, the limited liability company license shall be canceled 60 days after the board's discovery when researching the records of the Secretary of State. Failure to notify the registrar within 90 days of the dissolution, merger, or surrender is grounds for disciplinary action.

(j) The registrar shall review and accept the petition of a licensee who disputes the date of cancellation upon a showing of good cause. This petition shall be received within 90 days of the board's official notice of cancellation.

Added Stats 1995 ch 467 § 8 (SB 1061). Amended Stats 2010 ch 698 § 22 (SB 392), effective January 1, 2011; Stats 2012 ch 661 § 11 (SB 1576), effective January 1, 2013; Stats 2024 ch 485 § 10 (SB 1455), effective January 1, 2025.

§ 7076.1. Voluntary surrender of license

Upon the voluntary surrender of a license by a licensee, the registrar shall order the license canceled. Cancellation will be effected upon receipt of the request by the registrar. No refund will be made of any fee which a licensee may have paid prior to the surrender of the license.

To reinstate a canceled license the licensee must pay all of the fees and meet all of the qualifications and requirements set forth in this chapter for obtaining an original license.

Added Stats 1975 ch 329 § 1.

§ 7076.2. Suspension for failure to be registered and in good standing after notice; Personal liability

(a) Notwithstanding any other provision of law, the failure of a contractor licensed to do business as a corporation or limited liability company in this state to be registered and in good standing with the Secretary of State after notice from the registrar shall result in the automatic suspension of the license by operation of law. The registrar shall notify the licensee in writing of its failure to be registered and in good standing with the Secretary of State and that the licensee shall be suspended 30 days from the date of the notice if the licensee does not provide proof satisfactory to the registrar that it is properly registered and in good standing with the Secretary of State. Reinstatement may be made at any time following the suspension by providing proof satisfactory to the registrar that the license is properly registered and in good standing.

(b) Where the license of a limited liability company is suspended pursuant to subdivision (a), each person within the company identified in Section 7028.5 shall be personally liable up to one million dollars ($1,000,000) each for damages resulting to third parties in connection with the company's performance, during the period of suspension, of any act or contract where a license is required by this chapter. This personal liability shall not apply where there has been substantial compliance with the licensure requirements, as described in subdivision (e) of Section 7031.

(c) This section shall not apply to a federally recognized tribe or a participating tribe.

Added Stats 1995 ch 467 § 9 (SB 1061). Amended Stats 2010 ch 698 § 23 (SB 392), effective January 1, 2011; Stats 2024 ch 485 § 11 (SB 1455), effective January 1, 2025.

§ 7076.5. Inactive license certificate; Reinstatement; Holder not entitled to practice

(a) A contractor may inactivate his or her license by submitting a form prescribed by the registrar accompanied by the current active license certificate. When the current license certificate has been lost, the licensee shall pay the fee prescribed by law to replace the license certificate. Upon receipt of an acceptable application to inactivate, the registrar shall issue an inactive license certificate to the contractor. The holder of an inactive license shall not be entitled to practice as a contractor until his or her license is reactivated.

(b) Any licensed contractor who is not engaged in work or activities which require a contractor's license may apply for an inactive license.

(c) Inactive licenses shall be valid for a period of four years from their due date.

(d) During the period that an existing license is inactive, no bonding requirement pursuant to Section 7071.6, 7071.8 or 7071.9 or qualifier requirement pursuant to Section 7068 shall apply. An applicant for license having met the qualifications for issuance may request that the license be issued inactive unless the applicant is subject to the provisions of Section 7071.8.

(e) The board shall not refund any of the renewal fee which a licensee may have paid prior to the inactivation of his or her license.

(f) An inactive license shall be renewed on each established renewal date by submitting the renewal application and paying the inactive renewal fee.

(g) An inactive license may be reactivated by submitting an application acceptable to the registrar, by paying the full renewal fee for an active license and by fulfilling all other requirements of this chapter. No examination shall be required to reactivate an inactive license.

(h) The inactive status of a license shall not bar any disciplinary action by the board against a licensee for any of the causes stated in this chapter.

Added Stats 1983 ch 891 § 18. Amended Stats 1987 ch 875 § 1.

§ 7077. Original license probationary; Revocation

Every original license, except an additional classification issued pursuant to Section 7059, shall be a probationary license until such time as the license is renewed. If information is brought to the attention of the registrar, during such probationary period, regarding any act or omission of the licensee constituting grounds for denial, revocation, or suspension of an application or license, such that, in the registrar's discretion, it would be proper to revoke the probationary license, the registrar shall forthwith notify the applicant to show cause within not more than 30 days, why the probationary license should not be revoked. The proceedings shall be conducted in accordance with the provisions of Chapter 5 (commencing with Section 11500) of Part 1 of Division 3 of Title 2 of the Government Code, and the registrar shall have all the powers granted therein. A probationary license shall not be renewed during the pendency of any proceedings brought pursuant to this section.

Added Stats 1979 ch 1013 § 15.

Article 6
Records

§ 7080.5. Public posting following acceptance of application

When an application has been accepted by the registrar, the name and address of the applicant, every classification for which the applicant has applied, and the names and titles of all personnel who have signed the application shall be publicly posted by the registrar, on the day following acceptance, in the office of the Contractors State License Board in Sacramento.

Added Stats 1984 ch 1252 § 2. Amended Stats 2020 ch 312 § 59 (SB 1474), effective January 1, 2021.

§ 7081. List of contractors

Whenever funds are available for the purpose, the registrar shall publish a list of the names and addresses of contractors, registered under this chapter and of the licenses issued, suspended or revoked, and such further information with respect to this chapter and its administration as he deems proper.

He may furnish the lists to such public works and building departments, public officials or public bodies, and other persons interested in or allied with the building and construction industry in this or any other State as he deems advisable and, at such intervals as he deems necessary whenever funds are available.

Copies of the lists may also be furnished by the registrar upon request to any firm or individual upon payment of a reasonable fee fixed by the registrar.

Added Stats 1939 ch 37 § 1.

§ 7082. Publication and distribution of information of industry

Whenever funds are available for the purpose, the registrar may publish and disseminate to licentiates of the board, and public officials or other persons interested in or allied with the building and construction industry, such information with relation to the administration and enforcement of this chapter as he deems necessary to carry out its purposes.

Added Stats 1939 ch 37 § 1.

§ 7083. Notification by licensees of changes in recorded information

(a) Notwithstanding any other law, licensees shall notify the registrar, on a form prescribed by the registrar, in writing within 90 days of any change to information recorded under this chapter. This notification requirement shall include, but not be limited to, changes in business address, personnel, business name, qualifying individual bond exemption pursuant to Section 7071.9, or exemption to qualify multiple licenses pursuant to Section 7068.1.

(b) Failure of the licensee to notify the registrar of any change to information within 90 days shall cause the change to be effective the date the written notification is received at the board's headquarters office.

(c) Failure to notify the registrar of the changes within the 90 days is grounds for disciplinary action.

Added Stats 1983 ch 891 § 21. Amended Stats 1984 ch 1174 § 5; Stats 1986 ch 27 § 4; Stats 1990 ch 1326 § 7 (AB 3480), effective September 25, 1990; Stats 2004 ch 865 § 12 (SB 1914); Stats 2015 ch 430 § 5 (AB 181), effective January 1, 2016.

§ 7083.1. Notification of registrar of change of address of licensee whose license is expired, suspended, or cancelled

A licensee whose license is expired or suspended, and is renewable under Section 7141, or whose license is canceled, shall notify the registrar in writing of a change of address of record within 90 days, and shall maintain a current address of record during the five-year period immediately following the expiration or cancellation of the license.

Added Stats 1987 ch 930 § 6, effective September 22, 1987. Amended Stats 2007 ch 240 § 2 (AB 936), effective January 1, 2008.

§ 7083.2. Report of valid email address

(a) An applicant for licensure or registration that has a valid email address shall report to the board that email address at the time of application.

(b) A registrant or licensee that has a valid email address shall report that email address to the board at the time of renewal.

(c) To protect the privacy of applicants, registrants, and licensees, the email address provided to the board pursuant to subdivisions (a) and (b) shall not be considered a public record and shall not be disclosed pursuant to Section 27 or pursuant to a request under the California Public Records Act (Division 10 (commencing with Section 7920.000) of Title 1 of the Government Code), unless required by an order of a court of competent jurisdiction.

(d) Information sent from an email account of the board to a valid email address provided by an applicant, registrant, or licensee is presumed to have been delivered to the email address provided.

(e) For the purposes of this section, "valid email address" means an email address at which the applicant, registrant, or licensee is currently receiving email at the time the application, registration, or license renewal is submitted to the board.

Added Stats 2023 ch 153 § 1 (SB 630), effective January 1, 2024.

Article 6.2
Arbitration

§ 7085. Referral to arbitration; Conditions

(a) After investigating any verified complaint alleging a violation of Section 7107, 7109, 7110, 7113, 7119, or 7120, and any complaint arising from a contract involving works of improvement and finding a possible violation, the registrar may, with the concurrence of both the licensee and the complainant, refer the alleged violation, and any dispute between the licensee and the complainant arising thereunder, to arbitration pursuant to this article, provided the registrar finds that:

(1) There is evidence that the complainant has suffered or is likely to suffer material damages as a result of a violation of Section 7107, 7109, 7110, 7113, 7119, or 7120, and any complaint arising from a contract involving works of improvement.

(2) There are reasonable grounds for the registrar to believe that the public interest would be better served by arbitration than by disciplinary action.

(3) The licensee does not have a history of repeated or similar violations.

(4) The licensee was in good standing at the time of the alleged violation.

(5) The licensee does not have any outstanding disciplinary actions filed against him or her.

(6) The parties have not previously agreed to private arbitration of the dispute pursuant to contract or otherwise.

(7) The parties have been advised of the provisions of Section 2855 of the Civil Code.

For the purposes of paragraph (1), "material damages" means damages greater than the amount of the bond required under subdivision (a) of Section 7071.6, but less than fifty thousand dollars ($50,000).

(b) In all cases in which a possible violation of the sections set forth in paragraph (1) of subdivision (a) exists and the contract price, or the demand for damages is equal to or less than the amount of the bond required under Section 7071.6, but, regardless of the contract price, the complaint shall be referred to arbitration, utilizing the criteria set forth in paragraphs (2) to (6), inclusive, of subdivision (a).

Added Stats 1979 ch 1013 § 16. Amended Stats 1987 ch 1311 § 1, effective September 28, 1987; Stats 1989 ch 1132 § 2, effective September 29, 1989; Stats 1992 ch 597 § 1 (AB 497); Stats 1998 ch 492 § 1 (SB 1792); Stats 2002 ch 312 § 1 (AB 728); Stats 2004 ch 865 § 13 (SB 1914); Stats 2005 ch 280 § 8 (SB 1112), effective January 1, 2006.

§ 7085.2. Arbitrator's award deemed award of registrar

An arbitrator may render an award and that award shall be deemed to be an order of the registrar.

Added Stats 1987 ch 1311 § 2, effective September 28, 1987.

§ 7085.3. Notice; Consequences of election; Right to retain counsel; Agreement to arbitrate

Once the registrar determines that arbitration pursuant to subdivision (a) of Section 7085 would be a suitable means of resolving the dispute, the registrar shall notify the complainant and the licensee of this decision. The registrar shall also notify the complainant of the consequences of selecting administrative arbitration over judicial remedies and advise the parties of their rights to retain counsel at their own expense. The registrar shall forward an "agreement to arbitrate" to the complainant and the licensee. This agreement shall be returned to the registrar within 30 calendar days of the date that the agreement is mailed by the registrar. The return of this agreement by the parties shall authorize the registrar to proceed with administrative arbitration.

Added Stats 1979 ch 1013 § 16. Amended Stats 1987 ch 1311 § 3, effective September 28, 1987; Stats 1989 ch 1132 § 3, effective September 29, 1989.

§ 7085.4. Referral of agreement to arbitrate to arbitrator or arbitration association; Notification of complainant and licensee

(a) For cases that the registrar determines to refer to arbitration under subdivision (a) of Section 7085, once the complainant and the licensee authorize the registrar to proceed with administrative arbitration, the registrar shall refer the agreement to arbitrate to an arbitrator or an arbitration association approved by the board.

Section VI

(b) Once the registrar determines that a complaint must be referred to arbitration pursuant to subdivision (b) of Section 7085, the registrar shall notify the complainant and the licensee of that decision. The registrar shall inform the parties of the consequences of administrative arbitration over judicial remedies and shall advise the parties of their right to retain counsel at their own expense if they so choose. The registrar shall forward a notice to arbitrate to the complainant and the licensee. This notice shall be returned to the registrar within 30 calendar days of the date that the notice is mailed by the registrar. The complainant's failure to return an executed copy of the notice shall result in the closure of the complaint.

Notwithstanding Section 7085.5, a licensee's failure to return an executed copy of the notice shall not prohibit the registrar from referring the dispute to arbitration or bar the registrar from issuing an order enforcing any award resulting therefrom, pursuant to Section 7085.6, whether the award resulted from a contested hearing or a noncontested hearing.

Added Stats 1979 ch 1013 § 16. Amended Stats 1987 ch 1311 § 4, effective September 28, 1987; Stats 1989 ch 1132 § 4, effective September 29, 1989.

§ 7085.5. Rules of conduct for arbitrations; court procedure and exclusion of liability

Arbitrations of disputes arising out of cases filed with or by the board shall be conducted in accordance with the following rules:

(a) All "agreements to arbitrate" shall include the names, addresses, and telephone numbers of the parties to the dispute, the issue in dispute, and the amount in dollars or any other remedy sought. The appropriate fee shall be paid by the board from the Contractors License Fund.

(b) (1) The board or appointed arbitration association shall appoint an arbitrator in the following manner: immediately after the filing of the agreement to arbitrate, the board or appointed arbitration association shall submit simultaneously to each party to the dispute, an identical list of names of persons chosen from the panel. Each party to the dispute shall have seven days from the mailing date in which to cross off any names to which it objects, number the remaining names to indicate the order of preference, and return the list to the board or appointed arbitration association. If a party does not return the list within the time specified, all persons named in the list are acceptable. From among the persons who have been approved on both lists, and in accordance with the designated order of mutual preference, the board or appointed arbitration association shall appoint an arbitrator to serve. If the parties fail to agree on any of the parties named, if acceptable arbitrators are unable to act, or if, for any other reason, the appointment cannot be made from the submitted lists, the board or appointed arbitration association shall have the power to make the appointment from among other members of the panel without the submission of any additional lists. Each dispute shall be heard and determined by one arbitrator unless the board or appointed arbitration association, in its discretion, directs that a greater number of arbitrators be appointed.

(2) In all cases in which a complaint has been referred to arbitration pursuant to subdivision (b) of Section 7085, the board or the appointed arbitration association shall have the power to appoint an arbitrator to hear the matter.

(3) The board shall adopt regulations setting minimum qualification standards for listed arbitrators based upon relevant training, experience, and performance.

(c) No person shall serve as an arbitrator in any arbitration in which that person has any financial or personal interest in the result of the arbitration. Prior to accepting an appointment, the prospective arbitrator shall disclose any circumstances likely to prevent a prompt hearing or to create a presumption of bias. Upon receipt of that information, the board or appointed arbitration association shall immediately replace the arbitrator or communicate the information to the parties for their comments. Thereafter, the board or appointed arbitration association shall determine whether the arbitrator should be disqualified and shall inform the parties of its decision, which shall be conclusive.

(d) The board or appointed arbitration association may appoint another arbitrator if a vacancy occurs, or if an appointed arbitrator is unable to serve in a timely manner.

(e) (1) The board or appointed arbitration association shall provide the parties with a list of the times and dates, and locations of the hearing to be held. The parties shall notify the arbitrator, within seven calendar days of the mailing of the list, of the times and dates convenient to each party. If the parties fail to respond to the arbitrator within the seven-day period, the arbitrator shall fix the time, place, and location of the hearing. An arbitrator may, at the arbitrator's sole discretion, make an inspection of the construction site which is the subject of the arbitration. The arbitrator shall notify the parties of the time and date set for the inspection. Any party who so desires may be present at the inspection.

(2) The board or appointed arbitration association shall fix the time, place, and location of the hearing for all cases referred to arbitration pursuant to subdivision (b) of Section 7085. An arbitrator may, at the arbitrator's sole discretion, make an inspection of the construction site which is the subject of the arbitration. The arbitrator shall notify

Section VI

the parties of the time and date set for the inspection. Any party who desires may be present at the inspection.

(f) Any person having a direct interest in the arbitration is entitled to attend the hearing. The arbitrator shall otherwise have the power to require the exclusion of any witness, other than a party or other essential person, during the testimony of any other witness. It shall be discretionary with the arbitrator to determine the propriety of the attendance of any other person.

(g) Hearings shall be adjourned by the arbitrator only for good cause.

(h) A record is not required to be taken of the proceedings. However, any party to the proceeding may have a record made at its own expense. The parties may make appropriate notes of the proceedings.

(i) The hearing shall be conducted by the arbitrator in any manner which will permit full and expeditious presentation of the case by both parties. Consistent with the expedited nature of arbitration, the arbitrator shall establish the extent of, and schedule for, the production of relevant documents and other information, the identification of any witnesses to be called, and a schedule for any hearings to elicit facts solely within the knowledge of one party. The complaining party shall present its claims, proofs, and witnesses, who shall submit to questions or other examination. The defending party shall then present its defenses, proofs, and witnesses, who shall submit to questions or other examination. The arbitrator has discretion to vary this procedure but shall afford full and equal opportunity to the parties for the presentation of any material or relevant proofs.

(j) The arbitration may proceed in the absence of any party who, after due notice, fails to be present. The arbitrator shall require the attending party to submit supporting evidence in order to make an award. An award for the attending party shall not be based solely on the fact that the other party has failed to appear at the arbitration hearing.

(k) The arbitrator shall be the sole judge of the relevancy and materiality of the evidence offered and conformity to legal rules of evidence shall not be required.

(l) The arbitrator may receive and consider documentary evidence. Documents to be considered by the arbitrator may be submitted prior to the hearing. However, a copy shall be simultaneously transmitted to all other parties and to the board or appointed arbitration association for transmittal to the arbitrator or board appointed arbitrator.

(m) The arbitrator shall specifically inquire of the parties whether they have any further proofs to offer or witnesses to be heard. Upon receiving negative replies, the arbitrator shall declare the hearing closed and minutes thereof shall be recorded. If briefs are to be filed, the hearing shall be declared closed as of the final date set by the arbitrator for the receipt of briefs. If documents are to be filed as requested by the arbitrator and the date set for their receipt is later than that set for the receipt of briefs, the later date shall be the date of closing the hearings. The time limit within which the arbitrator is required to make the award shall commence to run, in the absence of other agreements by the parties, upon the closing of the hearings.

(n) The hearing may be reopened on the arbitrator's own motion.

(o) Any party who proceeds with the arbitration after knowledge that any provision or requirement of these rules has not been complied with, and who fails to state their objections to the arbitrator in writing, within 10 calendar days of close of hearing, shall be deemed to have waived their right to object.

(p) (1) Except as provided in paragraph (2), any papers or process necessary or proper for the initiation or continuation of an arbitration under these rules and for any court action in connection therewith, or for the entry of judgment on an award made thereunder, may be served upon any party (A) by regular mail addressed to that party or their attorney at the party's last known address, or (B) by personal service.

(2) Notwithstanding paragraph (1), in all cases referred to arbitration pursuant to subdivision (b) of Section 7085 in which the contractor fails or refuses to return an executed copy of the notice to arbitrate within the time specified, any papers or process specified in paragraph (1) to be sent to the contractor, including the notice of hearing, shall be mailed by certified mail to the contractor's address of record.

(q) The award shall be made promptly by the arbitrator, and unless otherwise agreed by the parties, no later than 30 calendar days from the date of closing the hearing, closing a reopened hearing, or if oral hearing has been waived, from the date of transmitting the final statements and proofs to the arbitrator.

The arbitrator may for good cause extend any period of time established by these rules, except the time for making the award. The arbitrator shall notify the parties of any extension and the reason therefor.

(r) (1) The arbitrator may grant any remedy or relief that the arbitrator deems just and equitable and within the scope of the board's referral and the requirements of the board. The arbitrator, in their sole discretion, may award costs or expenses.

(2) The amendments made in paragraph (1) during the 2003-04 Regular Session shall not be interpreted to prevent an arbitrator from awarding a complainant all direct costs and expenses for the completion or repair of the project.

(s) The award shall become final 30 calendar days from the date the arbitration award is issued. The arbitrator, upon written application of a party to the arbitration, may correct the award upon the following grounds:

(1) There was an evident miscalculation of figures or an evident mistake in the description of any person, things, or property referred to in the award.

(2) There is any other clerical error in the award, not affecting the merits of the controversy.

An application for correction of the award shall be made within 10 calendar days of the date of service of the award by serving a copy of the application on the arbitrator, and all other parties to the arbitration. Any party to the arbitration may make a written objection to the application for correction by serving a copy of the written objection on the arbitrator, the board, and all other parties to the arbitration, within 10 calendar days of the date of service of the application for correction.

The arbitrator shall either deny the application or correct the award within 30 calendar days of the date of service of the original award by mailing a copy of the denial or correction to all parties to the arbitration. Any appeal from the denial or correction shall be filed with a court of competent jurisdiction and a true copy thereof shall be filed with the arbitrator or appointed arbitration association within 30 calendar days after the award has become final. The award shall be in writing, and shall be signed by the arbitrator or a majority of them. If no appeal is filed within the 30-calendar day period, it shall become a final order of the registrar.

(t) Service of the award by certified mail shall be effective if a certified letter containing the award, or a true copy thereof, is mailed by the arbitrator or arbitration association to each party or to a party's attorney of record at their last known address, address of record, or by personally serving any party. Service may be proved in the manner authorized in civil actions.

(u) The board shall pay the expenses of one expert witness appointed by the board when the services of an expert witness are requested by either party involved in arbitration pursuant to this article and the case involves workmanship issues that are itemized in the complaint and have not been repaired or replaced. Parties who choose to present the findings of another expert witness as evidence shall pay for those services. Payment for expert witnesses appointed by the board shall be limited to the expert witness costs for inspection of the problem at the construction site, preparation of the expert witness' report, and expert witness fees for appearing or testifying at a hearing. All requests for payment to an expert witness shall be submitted on a form that has been approved by the registrar. All requests for payment to an expert witness shall be reviewed and approved by the board prior to payment. The registrar shall advise the parties that names of industry experts may be obtained by requesting this information from the registrar.

(v) The arbitrator shall interpret and apply these rules insofar as they relate to their powers and duties.

(w) The following shall apply as to court procedure and exclusion of liability:

(1) The board, the appointed arbitration association, or any arbitrator in a proceeding under these rules is not a necessary party in judicial proceedings relating to the arbitration.

(2) Parties to these rules shall be deemed to have consented that judgment upon the arbitration award may be entered in any federal or state court having jurisdiction thereof.

(3) The board, the appointed arbitration association, or any arbitrator is not liable to any party for any act or omission in connection with any arbitration conducted under these rules.

Added Stats 1987 ch 1311 § 5, effective September 28, 1987. Amended Stats 1988 ch 160 § 3; Stats 1989 ch 1132 § 5, effective September 29, 1989; Stats 1998 ch 492 § 2 (SB 1792); Stats 2003 ch 363 § 2 (AB 1382); Stats 2020 ch 312 § 60 (SB 1474), effective January 1, 2021.

§ 7085.6. Failure to comply with award as grounds for automatic suspension; Appeal; Reinstatement; Delay in revocation for good cause; Dissociation from other licensee

(a)(1) The failure of a licensee to comply with an arbitration award rendered under this article shall result in the automatic suspension of a license by operation of law.

(2) The registrar shall notify the licensee by certified mail of the failure to comply with the arbitrator's award, and that the license shall be automatically suspended 30 calendar days from the date of that notice.

(3) The licensee may appeal the suspension for noncompliance within 15 calendar days after service of the notice by written notice to the registrar.

(4) Reinstatement may be made at any time following the suspension by complying with the arbitrator's award and the final order of the registrar. If no reinstatement of the license is made within 90 days of the date of the automatic suspension, the license and any other contractor's license issued to the licensee shall be automatically revoked by operation of law for a period to be determined by the registrar pursuant to Section 7102.

(5) The registrar may delay, for good cause, the revocation of a contractor's license for failure to comply with the arbitration award. The delay in the revocation of the license shall not exceed one year. When seeking a delay of the revocation of his or her license, a licensee shall

apply to the registrar in writing prior to the date of the revocation of the licensee's license by operation of law and state the reasons that establish good cause for the delay. The registrar's power to grant a delay of the revocation shall expire upon the effective date of the revocation of the licensee's license by operation of law.

(b) The licensee shall be automatically prohibited from serving as an officer, director, associate, partner, manager, or qualifying individual of another licensee, for the period determined by the registrar and the employment, election, or association of that person by another licensee shall constitute grounds for disciplinary action. A qualifier disassociated pursuant to this section shall be replaced within 90 days from the date of disassociation. Upon failure to replace the qualifier within 90 days of the disassociation, the license of the other licensee shall be automatically suspended or the qualifier's classification removed at the end of the 90 days.

Added Stats 1979 ch 1013 § 16. Amended Stats 1987 ch 1311 § 6, effective September 28, 1987; Stats 1988 ch 1619 § 2, effective September 30, 1988; Stats 2003 ch 363 § 3 (AB 1382); Stats 2010 ch 698 § 24 (SB 392), effective January 1, 2011.

§ 7085.7. Enforcement of award

A complainant may enforce an arbitrator's award in accordance with Chapter 2 (commencing with Section 1285) of Title 9 of Part 3 of the Code of Civil Procedure.

Added Stats 1987 ch 1311 § 8, effective September 28, 1987.

§ 7085.9. Disclosure to public of complaint referred to arbitration

Notwithstanding any other provision of law, a complaint referred to arbitration pursuant to Section 7085 is not subject to disclosure to the public until such time as an investigation into an alleged violation of Section 7085.6 has been initiated by the registrar.

Added Stats 1988 ch 1035 § 2.

Article 6.5
Solar Energy System Restitution Program
[Repealed]

§ 7086. Administration upon appropriation [Repealed]
Added Stats 2021 ch 77 § 1 (AB 137), effective July 16, 2021, repealed June 30, 2024.

§ 7086.1. Definitions [Repealed]

Added Stats 2021 ch 77 § 1 (AB 137), effective July 16, 2021, repealed June 30, 2024.

§ 7086.2. Scope of article [Repealed]

Added Stats 2021 ch 77 § 1 (AB 137), effective July 16, 2021, repealed June 30, 2024.

§ 7086.3. Awards limited to eligible claimants [Repealed]

Added Stats 2021 ch 77 § 1 (AB 137), effective July 16, 2021, repealed June 30, 2024.

§ 7086.4. Eligilbity criteria [Repealed]

Added Stats 2021 ch 77 § 1 (AB 137), effective July 16, 2021, repealed June 30, 2024.

§ 7086.5. Exceptions to ineligibility under Section § 7086.4 [Repealed]

Added Stats 2021 ch 77 § 1 (AB 137), effective July 16, 2021, repealed June 30, 2024.

§ 7086.6. "Solar Energy System Restitution Program Claim" form; Additional information; Denial [Repealed]

Added Stats 2021 ch 77 § 1 (AB 137), effective July 16, 2021, repealed June 30, 2024.

§ 7086.7. Documentation required for payment [Repealed]

Added Stats 2021 ch 77 § 1 (AB 137), effective July 16, 2021, repealed June 30, 2024.

§ 7086.8. Payment limitations; Expenditures [Repealed]

Added Stats 2021 ch 77 § 1 (AB 137), effective July 16, 2021, repealed June 30, 2024.

§ 7086.9. Approval and disbursement timelines; Annual accounting statement [Repealed]

Added Stats 2021 ch 77 § 1 (AB 137), effective July 16, 2021, repealed June 30, 2024.

§ 7086.10. Notice of licensee subject of program payment [Repealed]

Added Stats 2021 ch 77 § 1 (AB 137), effective July 16, 2021, repealed June 30, 2024. Amended Stats 2022 ch 11 § 38 (SB 1495), effective January 1, 2023.

§ 7086.11. Repeal of article [Repealed]

Added Stats 2021 ch 77 § 1 (AB 137), effective July 16, 2021, repealed June 30, 2024.

Article 7
Disciplinary Proceedings

§ 7090. Investigation, suspension, revocation; Construction without permit as violation; Burden of proof

The registrar may upon his or her own motion and shall upon the verified complaint in writing of any person, investigate the actions of any applicant, contractor, or home improvement salesperson within the state and may deny the licensure or the renewal of licensure of, or cite, temporarily suspend, or permanently revoke any license or registration if the applicant, licensee, or registrant, is guilty of or commits any one or more of the acts or omissions constituting causes for disciplinary action.

The registrar may proceed to take disciplinary action as in this article provided against an applicant or a person licensed or registered under the provisions of this chapter even though the grounds or cause for such disciplinary action arose upon projects or while the applicant, licensee, or registrant was acting in a capacity or under circumstances or facts which, under the provisions of Sections 7044, 7045, 7046, and 7048, would otherwise exempt the person or his or her operations from the provisions of this chapter.

Notwithstanding any provision of this chapter, if the registrar finds that any contractor licensed or registered under the provisions of this chapter has willfully and deliberately violated any state or local law relating to the issuance of building permits, other than failure to obtain a county or city permit for repair, maintenance, and adjustment of equipment where such repair, maintenance, or adjustment is valued at less than five hundred dollars ($500) for labor or materials, or where the repair of a part or component part of mechanical equipment consists of replacing such part or component part of mechanical equipment in need of repair with the identical part or component part, the registrar shall take disciplinary action against the contractor's license in accordance with this chapter.

For the purpose of this section, there shall be a rebuttable presumption affecting the burden of proof that construction performed without a permit is a willful and deliberate violation.

For the purposes of this section, with respect to administrative proceedings or hearings to suspend or revoke a contractor's license, the registrar at all times shall have the burden of proof to establish by clear and convincing evidence that he or she is entitled to the relief sought in the petition.

Added Stats 1939 ch 37 § 1. Amended Stats 1941 ch 971 § 15; Stats 1972 ch 1138 § 3.5; Stats 1974 ch 717 § 1; Stats 1975 ch 772 § 1; Stats 1984 ch 1174 § 6; Stats 1997 ch 334 § 2 (SB 299); Stats 2010 ch 698 § 25 (SB 392), effective January 1, 2011.

§ 7090.1. Automatic suspension of license for failure to pay civil penalty or comply with order of correction; Contest of determination; Reinstatement; Delay in revocation for good cause; Dissociation from other licensee

(a)(1) Notwithstanding any other provisions of law, the failure to pay a civil penalty, or to comply with an order of correction or an order to pay a specified sum to an injured party in lieu of correction once the order has become final, shall result in the automatic suspension of a license by operation of law 30 days after noncompliance with the terms of the order.

(2) The registrar shall notify the licensee in writing of the failure to comply with the final order and that the license shall be suspended 30 days from the date of the notice.

(3) The licensee may contest the determination of noncompliance within 15 days after service of the notice, by written notice to the registrar. Upon receipt of the written notice, the registrar may reconsider the determination and after reconsideration may affirm or set aside the suspension.

(4) Reinstatement may be made at any time following the suspension by complying with the final order of the citation. If no reinstatement of the license is made within 90 days of the date of the automatic suspension, the cited license and any other contractors' license issued to the licensee shall be automatically revoked by operation of law for a period to be determined by the registrar pursuant to Section 7102.

(5) The registrar may delay, for good cause, the revocation of a contractor's license for failure to comply with the final order of the citation. The delay in the revocation of the license shall not exceed one year. When seeking a delay of the revocation of his or her license, a licensee shall apply to the registrar in writing prior to the date of the revocation of the licensee's license by operation of law and state the reasons that establish good cause for the delay. The registrar's power to grant a delay of the revocation shall expire upon the effective date of the revocation of the licensee's license by operation of law.

(b) The cited licensee shall also be automatically prohibited from serving as an officer, director, associate, partner, manager, or qualifying individual of another licensee, for the period determined by the registrar, and the employment, election, or association of that person by a licensee shall constitute grounds for disciplinary action. A qualifier disassociated pursuant to this section shall be replaced within 90 days of the date of disassociation. Upon failure to replace the qualifier within 90 days of the prohibition, the license of the other licensee shall be automatically suspended or the qualifier's classification removed at the end of the 90 days.

Added Stats 1984 ch 1174 § 7. Amended Stats 1986 ch 27 § 5; Stats 1987 ch 831 § 1; Stats 1988 ch 1619 § 3, effective September 30, 1988; Stats 2003 ch 363 § 4 (AB 1382); Stats 2004 ch 865 § 14 (SB 1914); Stats 2010 ch 698 § 26 (SB 392), effective January 1, 2011.

§ 7090.5. Effect of correction of condition caused by fraudulent act

In the event a licensee commits a fraudulent act which is a ground for disciplinary action under Section 7116 of this article, the correction of any condition resulting from such act shall not in and of itself preclude the registrar from taking disciplinary action under this article.

If the registrar finds a licensee has engaged in repeated acts which would be grounds for disciplinary action under this article, and if by correction of conditions resulting from those acts the licensee avoided disciplinary action as to each individual act, the correction of those conditions shall not in and of itself preclude the registrar from taking disciplinary action under this article.

Added Stats 1953 ch 576 § 1. Amended Stats 1978 ch 985 § 1.

§ 7091. Filing complaints and disciplinary actions

(a) (1) A complaint against a licensee alleging commission of any patent acts or omissions that may be grounds for legal action shall be filed in writing with the registrar within four years after the act or omission alleged as the ground for the disciplinary action.

(2) A disciplinary action against a licensee relevant to this subdivision shall be filed or a referral to the arbitration program outlined in Section 7085 shall be referred within four years after the patent act or omission alleged as the ground for disciplinary action or arbitration or within 18 months from the date of the filing of the complaint with the registrar, whichever is later.

(b) (1) A complaint against a licensee alleging commission of any latent acts or omissions that may be grounds for legal action pursuant to subdivision (a) of Section 7109 regarding structural defects, as defined by regulation, shall be filed in writing with the registrar within 10 years after the act or omission alleged as the ground for the disciplinary action.

(2) A disciplinary action against a licensee relevant to this subdivision shall be filed within 10 years after the latent act or omission al-

leged as the ground for disciplinary action or within 18 months from the date of the filing of the complaint with the registrar, whichever is later. As used in this subdivision "latent act or omission" means an act or omission that is not apparent by reasonable inspection.

(c) A disciplinary action alleging a violation of Section 7112 shall be filed within two years after the discovery by the registrar or by the board of the alleged facts constituting the fraud or misrepresentation prohibited by the section.

(d) With respect to a licensee who has been convicted of a crime and, as a result of that conviction is subject to discipline under Section 7123, the disciplinary action shall be filed within two years after the discovery of the conviction by the registrar or by the board.

(e) A disciplinary action regarding an alleged breach of an express, written warranty issued by the contractor shall be filed not later than 18 months from the expiration of the warranty.

(f) The proceedings under this article shall be conducted in accordance with the provisions of Chapter 5 (commencing with Section 11500) of Part 1 of Division 3 of Title 2 of the Government Code, and the registrar shall have all the powers granted therein.

(g) Nothing in this section shall be construed to affect the liability of a surety or the period of limitations prescribed by law for the commencement of actions against a surety or lawful money or cashier's check deposited pursuant to paragraph (1) of subdivision (a) of Section 995.710 of the Code of Civil Procedure.

Added Stats 1939 ch 37 § 1. Amended Stats 1945 ch 886 § 2; Stats 1955 ch 1532 § 5; Stats 1963 ch 1258 § 1; Stats 1980 ch 865 § 1, ch 1210 § 2; Stats 1987 ch 1264 § 5, effective September 28, 1987; Stats 1994 ch 1135 § 2 (AB 3302); Stats 2001 ch 728 § 60 (SB 724); Stats 2002 ch 312 § 3 (AB 728); Stats 2007 ch 85 § 1 (AB 243), effective January 1, 2008; Stats 2018 ch 925 § 5 (AB 3126), effective January 1, 2019.

§ 7095. Decision of registrar; specific terms and conditions

(a) The decision may:

(1) Provide for the immediate complete suspension by the licensee of all operations as a contractor during the period fixed by the decision.

(2) Permit the licensee to complete any or all contracts shown by competent evidence taken at the hearing to be then uncompleted.

(3) Impose upon the licensee compliance with such specific terms and conditions as may be just in connection with the licensee's operations as a contractor disclosed at the hearing and may further provide that until those terms and conditions are complied with no application for restoration of the suspended or revoked license shall be accepted by the registrar.

(4) (A) Provide for the stay of execution of the decision pending completion of specified terms and conditions of probation.

(B) Failure to fully comply with the terms and conditions of probation set pursuant to subparagraph (A) may result in automatic termination of the stay of execution without further notice. If a stay of execution is terminated pursuant to this subparagraph, the decision shall be considered a disciplinary action within the meaning of this chapter.

(b) The specific terms and conditions imposed pursuant to paragraph (3) or (4) of subdivision (a) may include, but are not limited to, any of the following:

(1) Payment of restitution to persons injured as a result of the violation.

(2) Payment of the costs of investigation and enforcement pursuant to Section 125.3.

(3) Enrollment in, and completion of, specified administrative or trade-specific coursework.

(4) Successful completion of the board's law and business examination or trade examination, as appropriate.

(5) Any further terms and conditions as are set forth for specified violations in the board's disciplinary guidelines in Section 871 of Title 16 of the California Code of Regulations.

Added Stats 1939 ch 37 § 1; Amended Stats 2023 ch 153 § 2 (SB 630), effective January 1, 2024.

§ 7096. "Licensee"

For the purposes of this chapter, the term "licensee" shall include an individual, partnership, corporation, limited liability company, joint venture, or any combination or organization licensed under this chapter, and shall also include any named responsible managing officer, responsible managing manager, responsible managing member, or personnel of that licentiate whose appearance has qualified the licentiate under the provisions of Section 7068.

Added Stats 1957 ch 1712 § 1. Amended Stats 1995 ch 467 § 10 (SB 1061); Stats 2010 ch 698 § 27 (SB 392), effective January 1, 2011.

§ 7097. Suspension of additional license issued following suspension of any license

Notwithstanding the provisions of Sections 7121 and 7122, when any license has been suspended by a decision of the registrar pursuant to an accusation or pursuant to subdivision (b) of Section 7071.17, Section 7085.6 or 7090.1, any additional license issued under this chapter in the name of the licensee or for which the licensee furnished qualifying experience and appearance under the provisions of Section 7068, may be suspended by the registrar without further notice.

Added Stats 1957 ch 1712 § 2. Amended Stats 1995 ch 467 § 11 (SB 1061).

§ 7098. Revocation of additional license issued following revocation of license

Notwithstanding the provisions of Sections 7121 and 7122, when any license has been revoked under the provisions of this chapter, any additional license issued under this chapter in the name of the licensee or for which the licensee furnished qualifying experience and appearance under the provisions of Section 7068, may be revoked by the registrar without further notice.

Added Stats 1957 ch 1712 § 3. Amended Stats 1995 ch 467 § 12 (SB 1061).

§ 7099. Citation

If, upon investigation, the registrar has probable cause to believe that a licensee, or an applicant for a license under this chapter, has committed any acts or omissions which are grounds for denial, revocation, or suspension of license, he or she may, in lieu of proceeding pursuant to this article, issue a citation to the licensee or applicant. Each citation shall be in writing and shall describe with particularity the nature of the violation, including a reference to the provisions alleged to have been violated. In addition, each citation may contain an order of correction fixing a reasonable time for correction of the violation or an order, against the licensee only, for payment of a specified sum to an injured party in lieu of correction, and may contain an assessment of a civil penalty.

Added Stats 1979 ch 1013 § 17. Amended Stats 1983 ch 891 § 22; Stats 1984 ch 606 § 1; Stats 1985 ch 1281 § 3; Stats 1986 ch 27 § 6; Stats 1987 ch 930 § 7, effective September 22, 1987.

§ 7099.1. Regulations for order of correction

The board shall promulgate regulations covering the formulation of an order of correction which gives due consideration to the time required to correct and the practical feasibility of correction.

Added Stats 1979 ch 1013 § 18.

Section VI

§ 7099.2. Regulations for assessment of civil penalties; Factors; Maximum amount; Letter of admonishment

(a) The board shall promulgate regulations covering the assessment of civil penalties under this article that give due consideration to the appropriateness of the penalty with respect to the following factors:

(1) The gravity of the violation.

(2) The good faith of the licensee or applicant for licensure being charged.

(3) The history of previous violations.

(b) Notwithstanding Section 125.9, and except as otherwise provided by this chapter, a civil penalty shall not be assessed in an amount greater than eight thousand dollars ($8,000). Notwithstanding Section 125.9, a civil penalty not to exceed thirty thousand dollars ($30,000) may be assessed for a violation of Section 7110, 7114, 7118, or 7125.4

Added Stats 1979 ch 1013 § 19. Amended Stats 1984 ch 606 § 1.5; Stats 1992 ch 606 § 2 (AB 3240); Stats 1996 ch 282 § 4 (AB 2494); Stats 2003 ch 363 § 5 (AB 1382); Stats 2010 ch 415 § 21 (SB 1491), effective January 1, 2011; Stats 2017 ch 308 § 2 (SB 486), effective January 1, 2018; Stats 2020 ch 312 § 61 (SB 1474), effective January 1, 2021; Stats 2021 ch 94 § 1 (AB 569), effective January 1, 2022; Stats 2022 ch 757 § 1 (AB 1747),effective January 1, 2023.

§ 7099.3. Appeal to registrar

Any licensee or applicant for licensure served with a citation pursuant to Section 7099, may appeal to the registrar within 15 working days from service of the citation with respect to violations alleged by the registrar, correction periods, amount of penalties, and the reasonableness of the change required by the registrar to correct the condition.

Added Stats 1979 ch 1013 § 20. Amended Stats 1983 ch 891 § 23; Stats 1984 ch 606 § 2.

§ 7099.4. Time to contest citation

If within 15 working days from service of the citation issued by the registrar, the licensee or applicant for licensure fails to notify the registrar that he or she intends to contest the citation, the citation shall be deemed a final order of the registrar and not be subject to review by any court or agency. The 15-day period may be extended by the registrar for cause.

Added Stats 1979 ch 1013 § 21. Amended Stats 1983 ch 891 § 24; Stats 1984 ch 606 § 3.

§ 7099.5. Hearing

If a licensee or applicant for licensure notifies the registrar that he or she intends to contest a citation issued under Section 7099, the registrar shall afford an opportunity for a hearing. The registrar shall thereafter issue a decision, based on findings of fact, affirming, modifying, or vacating the citation or penalty, or directing other appropriate relief. The proceedings under this section shall be conducted in accordance with the provisions of Chapter 5 (commencing with Section 11500) of Part 1 of Division 3 of Title 2 of the Government Code, and the registrar shall have all the powers granted therein.

Added Stats 1979 ch 1013 § 22. Amended Stats 1984 ch 606 § 4.

§ 7099.6. Failure to comply with citation as ground for denial, suspension, or revocation of license

(a) The failure of a licensee to comply with a citation after it is final is a ground for suspension or revocation of license.

(b) The failure of an applicant for licensure to comply with a citation after it is final is a ground for denial of license.

Added Stats 1979 ch 1013 § 23. Amended Stats 1984 ch 606 § 5; Stats 1986 ch 1205 § 2.

§ 7099.7. Bond exempt from payment of civil penalty

No order for payment of a civil penalty shall be made against any bond required pursuant to Sections 7071.5 to 7071.8.

Added Stats 1979 ch 1013 § 24.

§ 7099.8. Request for administrative hearing; Request for informal citation conference; Informal citation conference procedures

(a) Notwithstanding any other law, if a person cited pursuant to Section 7028.7 or 7099 wishes to contest the citation, that person shall, within 15 days after service of the citation, file in writing a request for an administrative hearing as provided pursuant to Section 7028.12 or 7099.5.

(b) (1) In addition to, or instead of, requesting an administrative hearing pursuant to subdivision (a), the person cited pursuant to Section 7028.7 or 7099 may, within 15 days after service of the citation, contest the citation by submitting a written request for an informal citation conference to the chief of the enforcement division or a designee.

(2) Upon receipt of a written request for an informal citation conference, the chief of the enforcement division or a designee shall, within

60 days of the request, hold an informal citation conference with the person requesting the conference. The cited person may be accompanied and represented by an attorney or other authorized representative.

(3) If an informal citation conference is held, the request for an administrative hearing shall be deemed withdrawn and the chief of the enforcement division, or a designee, may affirm, modify, or dismiss the citation at the conclusion of the informal citation conference. If so affirmed or modified, the citation originally issued shall be considered withdrawn and an affirmed or modified citation, including reasons for the decision, shall be issued. The affirmed or modified citation shall be mailed to the cited person and that person's counsel, if any, within 10 days of the date of the informal citation conference.

(4) If a cited person wishes to contest a citation affirmed or modified pursuant to paragraph (3), the person shall, within 30 days after service of the modified or affirmed citation, contest the affirmed or modified citation by submitting a written request for an administrative hearing to the chief of the enforcement division or a designee. An informal citation conference shall not be held for affirmed or modified citations.

(c) The citation conference is informal and shall not be subject to the Administrative Procedure Act (Chapter 4.5 (commencing with Section 11400) of, or Chapter 5 (commencing with Section 11500) of Part 1 of, Division 3 of Title 2 of the Government Code).

Added Stats 2018 ch 110 § 1 (SB 1042), effective January 1, 2019. Amended Stats 2019 ch 497 § 12 (AB 991), effective January 1, 2020.

§ 7099.9. Letter of admonishment

(a) If, upon investigation, the registrar has probable cause to believe that a licensee, registrant, or applicant has committed acts or omissions that are grounds for denial, suspension, or revocation of a license or registration, the registrar, or their designee, may issue a letter of admonishment to an applicant, licensee, or registrant in lieu of issuing a citation. Nothing in this article shall in any way limit the registrar's discretionary authority or ability to issue a letter of admonishment as prescribed by this subdivision.

(b) The letter of admonishment shall be in writing and shall describe in detail the nature and facts of the violation, including a reference to the statutes or regulations violated. The letter of admonishment shall inform the licensee, registrant, or applicant that within 30 days of service of the letter of admonishment the licensee, registrant, or applicant may do either of the following:

(1) Submit a written request for an office conference to the registrar to contest the letter of admonishment. Upon a timely request, the reg-

istrar, or their designee, shall hold an office conference with the licensee, registrant, or applicant and, if applicable, their legal counsel or authorized representative.

(A) No individual other than the legal counsel or authorized representative of the licensee, registrant, or applicant may accompany the licensee, registrant, or applicant to the office conference.

(B) Prior to or at the office conference, the licensee, registrant, or applicant may submit to the registrar declarations and documents pertinent to the subject matter of the letter of admonishment.

(C) The office conference is intended to be informal and shall not be subject to the Administrative Procedure Act (Chapter 4.5 (commencing with Section 11400) or Chapter 5 (commencing with Section 11500) of Part 1 of Division 3 of Title 2 of the Government Code).

(D) After the office conference, the registrar, or their designee, may affirm, modify, or withdraw the letter of admonishment. Within 14 calendar days from the date of the office conference, the registrar, or their designee, shall personally serve or send the written decision by certified mail to the licensee's, registrant's, or applicant's address of record. This decision shall be deemed the final administrative decision concerning the letter of admonishment.

(E) Judicial review of the decision may be had by filing a petition for a writ of mandate in accordance with the provisions of Section 1094.5 of the Code of Civil Procedure within 30 days after the date the decision was personally served or sent by certified mail. The judicial review shall extend to the question of whether or not there was a prejudicial abuse of discretion in the issuance of the letter of admonishment or in the decision after the office conference.

(2) Comply with the letter of admonishment and, if required, submit a written corrective action plan to the registrar documenting compliance. If an office conference is not requested pursuant to this section, compliance with the letter of admonishment shall not constitute an admission of the violation noted in the letter of admonishment.

(c) The letter of admonishment shall be served upon the licensee, registrant, or applicant personally or by certified mail at their address of record with the board. If the licensee, registrant, or applicant is served by certified mail, service shall be effective upon deposit in the United States mail.

(d) The licensee, registrant, or applicant shall maintain and have readily available a copy of the letter of admonishment and corrective action plan, if any, for at least one year from the date of issuance of the letter of admonishment.

(e) Nothing in this subdivision shall in any way limit the board's authority or ability to do either of the following:

(1) Issue a citation pursuant to Section 125.9, 148, or 7099.

(2) Institute disciplinary proceedings pursuant to this article.

(f) The issuance of a letter of admonishment shall not be construed as a disciplinary action or discipline for purposes of licensure or the reporting of discipline for licensure.

(g) The board shall not issue a letter of admonishment when any one of the following factors is present:

(1) The licensee, registrant, or applicant was unlicensed at the time of the violation.

(2) The licensee, registrant, or applicant has a history of the same or similar violations.

(3) The violation resulted in financial harm to another.

(4) The victim is an elder or dependent adult as defined in Section 368 of the Penal Code.

(5) The violation is related to the repair of damage caused by a natural disaster.

(h) The board may adopt regulations to further define the circumstances under which a letter of admonishment may be issued.

Added Stats 2020 ch 312 § 62 (SB 1474), effective January 1, 2021; Stats 2021 ch 94 § 1 (AB 569), effective January 1, 2022.

§ 7099.10. Citation; Hearing; Disconnection of telephone service

(a) If, upon investigation, the registrar has probable cause to believe that a licensee, an applicant for a license, or an unlicensed individual acting in the capacity of a contractor who is not otherwise exempted from the provisions of this chapter, has violated Section 7027.1 by advertising for construction or work of improvement covered by this chapter in an alphabetical or classified directory, without being properly licensed, the registrar may issue a citation under Section 7099 containing an order of correction which requires the violator to cease the unlawful advertising and to notify the telephone company furnishing services to the violator to disconnect the telephone service furnished to any telephone number contained in the unlawful advertising, and that subsequent calls to that number shall not be referred by the telephone company to any new telephone number obtained by that person.

(b) If the person to whom a citation is issued under subdivision (a) notifies the registrar that he or she intends to contest the citation, the registrar shall afford an opportunity for a hearing, as specified in Section 7099.5, within 90 days after receiving the notification.

(c) If the person to whom a citation and order of correction is issued under subdivision (a) fails to comply with the order of correction after the order is final, the registrar shall inform the Public Utilities Commission of the violation, and the Public Utilities Commission shall require the telephone corporation furnishing services to that person to disconnect the telephone service furnished to any telephone number contained in the unlawful advertising.

(d) The good faith compliance by a telephone corporation with an order of the Public Utilities Commission to terminate service issued pursuant to this section shall constitute a complete defense to any civil or criminal action brought against the telephone corporation arising from the termination of service.

Added Stats 1986 ch 518 § 2. Amended Stats 1991 ch 1160 § 32 (AB 2190); Stats 1992 ch 294 § 3 (AB 2347).

§ 7099.11. Advertising to promote services for asbestos removal; Notice to comply; Citation

(a) No person shall advertise, as that term is defined in Section 7027.1, to promote his or her services for the removal of asbestos unless he or she is certified to engage in asbestos-related work pursuant to Section 7058.5, and registered for that purpose pursuant to Section 6501.5 of the Labor Code. Each advertisement shall include that person's certification and registration numbers and shall use the same name under which that person is certified and registered.

(b) The registrar shall issue a notice to comply with the order of correction provisions of subdivision (a) of Section 7099.10, to any person who is certified and registered, as described in subdivision (a), and who fails to include in any advertisement his or her certification and registration numbers.

(c) The registrar shall issue a citation pursuant to Section 7099 to any person who fails to comply with the notice required by subdivision (b), or who advertises to promote his or her services for the removal of asbestos but does not possess valid certification and registration numbers as required by subdivision (a), or who fails to use in that advertisement the same name under which he or she is certified and registered.

Citations shall be issued and conducted pursuant to Sections 7099 to 7099.10, inclusive.

Added Stats 1988 ch 1003 § 1, operative July 1, 1989, as § 7030.6. Amended and renumbered by Stats 1991 ch 1160 § 22 (AB 2190). Amended Stats 1992 ch 294 § 4 (AB 2347).

§ 7100. Continuance of business pending review

In any proceeding for review by a court, the court may in its discretion, upon the filing of a proper bond by the licensee in an amount to be fixed by the court, but not less than one thousand dollars ($1,000) or an amount the court finds is sufficient to protect the public, which-

Section VI

ever is greater, guaranteeing the compliance by the licensee with specific conditions imposed upon him by the registrar's decision, if any, permit the licensee to continue to do business as a contractor pending entry of judgment by the court in the case. There shall be no stay of the registrar's decision pending an appeal or review of any such proceeding unless the appellant or applicant for review shall file a bond in all respects conditioned as, and similar to, the bond required to stay the effect of the registrar's decision in the first instance.

Added Stats 1939 ch 37 § 1. Amended Stats 1945 ch 886 § 3; Stats 1949 ch 753 § 1; Stats 1979 ch 1013 § 27.

§ 7102. Reinstatement or reissuance of license

After suspension of a license upon any of the grounds set forth in this chapter, the registrar may reinstate the license upon proof of compliance by the contractor with all provisions of the decision as to reinstatement or, in the absence of a decision or any provisions of reinstatement, in the sound discretion of the registrar.

After revocation of a license upon any of the grounds set forth in this chapter, the license shall not be reinstated or reissued and a license shall not be issued to any member of the personnel of the revoked licensee found to have had knowledge of or participated in the acts or omissions constituting grounds for revocation, within a minimum period of one year and a maximum period of five years after the final decision of revocation and then only on proper showing that all loss caused by the act or omission for which the license was revoked has been fully satisfied and that all conditions imposed by the decision of revocation have been complied with.

The board shall promulgate regulations covering the criteria to be considered when extending the minimum one-year period. The criteria shall give due consideration to the appropriateness of the extension of time with respect to the following factors:

(a) The gravity of the violation.

(b) The history of previous violations.

(c) Criminal convictions.

When any loss has been reduced to a monetary obligation or debt, however, the satisfaction of the monetary obligation or debt as a prerequisite for the issuance, reissuance, or reinstatement of a license shall not be required to the extent the monetary obligation or debt was discharged in a bankruptcy proceeding. However, any nonmonetary condition not discharged in a bankruptcy proceeding shall be complied with prior to the issuance, the reissuance, or reinstatement of the license.

Added Stats 1939 ch 37 § 1. Amended Stats 1961 ch 1635 § 5, operative October 1, 1962; Stats 1975 ch 818 § 1; Stats 1983 ch 891 § 25; Stats 1987 ch 831 § 2; Stats 1995 ch 467 § 13 (SB 1061); Stats 2006 ch 123 § 1 (AB 2658), effective January 1, 2007.

§ 7103. Effect of disciplinary action by another state

The revocation, suspension, or other disciplinary action of a license to act as a contractor by another state shall constitute grounds for disciplinary action in this state if the individual is a licensee, or applies for a license, in this state. A certified copy of the revocation, suspension, or other disciplinary action by the other state is conclusive evidence of that action.

Added Stats 1994 ch 1135 § 2 (AB 3302).

§ 7104. Notice to complainant of resolution of complaint

When the board resolves a complaint, the board shall notify the complainant in writing of its action and the reasons for taking that action. The board shall provide the same notice in writing to the contractor provided that the contractor is licensed and the notification would not jeopardize an action or investigation that involves the contractor.

Added Stats 1994 ch 1135 § 4 (AB 3302).

§ 7106. Revocation or suspension of license incident to court action

The suspension or revocation of license as in this chapter provided may also be embraced in any action otherwise proper in any court involving the licensee's performance of his legal obligation as a contractor.

Added Stats 1939 ch 37 § 1.

§ 7106.5. Effect of expiration, cancellation, forfeiture, revocation, or suspension of license on jurisdiction of registrar

The expiration, cancellation, forfeiture, revocation, or suspension of a license by operation of law or by order or decision of the registrar or a court of law, or the voluntary surrender of a license by a licensee, shall not deprive the registrar of jurisdiction to proceed with any investigation of or action or disciplinary proceeding against the license, or to render a decision suspending or revoking the license.

Section VI

Added Stats 1941 ch 971 § 16. Amended Stats 1961 ch 1636 § 6, operative October 1, 1962; Stats 2002 ch 1013 § 61.3 (SB 2026); Stats 2012 ch 85 § 2 (AB 2554), effective January 1, 2013.

§ 7107. Abandonment of contract

Abandonment without legal excuse of any construction project or operation engaged in or undertaken by the licensee as a contractor constitutes a cause for disciplinary action.

Added Stats 1939 ch 37 § 1.

§ 7108. Diversion or misapplication of funds or property

Diversion of funds or property received for prosecution or completion of a specific construction project or operation, or for a specified purpose in the prosecution or completion of any construction project or operation, or failure substantially to account for the application or use of such funds or property on the construction project or operation for which such funds or property were received constitutes a cause for disciplinary action.

Added Stats 1939 ch 37 § 1. Amended Stats 1959 ch 97 § 1.

—*See Penal Code Section 484b, Wrongful Diversion of Public Funds, a Public Offense, in Appendix.*

§ 7108.5. Failure to pay subcontractors

(a) A prime contractor or subcontractor shall pay to any subcontractor, not later than seven days after receipt of each progress payment, unless otherwise agreed to in writing, the respective amounts allowed the contractor on account of the work performed by the subcontractors, to the extent of each subcontractor's interest therein. In the event that there is a good faith dispute over all or any portion of the amount due on a progress payment from the prime contractor or subcontractor to a subcontractor, the prime contractor or subcontractor may withhold no more than 150 percent of the disputed amount.

(b) Any violation of this section shall constitute a cause for disciplinary action and shall subject the licensee to a penalty, payable to the subcontractor, of 2 percent of the amount due per month for every month that payment is not made.

(c) In any action for the collection of funds wrongfully withheld, the prevailing party shall be entitled to his or her attorney's fees and costs.

(d) The sanctions authorized under this section shall be separate from, and in addition to, all other remedies, either civil, administrative, or criminal.

(e) This section applies to all private works of improvement and to all public works of improvement, except where Section 10262 of the Public Contract Code applies.

Added Stats 2009 ch 307 § 73 (SB 821), effective January 1, 2010. Amended Stats 2010 ch 328 § 16 (SB 1330), effective January 1, 2011; Stats 2011 ch 700 § 1 (SB 293), effective January 1, 2012.

—*See Public Contract Code Section 10262, in the Appendix.*

§ 7108.6. Failure to pay transportation charges submitted by dump truck carrier

A licensed contractor is required to pay all transportation charges submitted by a duly authorized motor carrier of property in dump truck equipment by the 20th day following the last day of the calendar month in which the transportation was performed, if the charges, including all necessary documentation, are submitted by the fifth day following the last day of the calendar month in which the transportation was performed. The payment shall be made unless otherwise agreed to in writing by the contractor and by the duly authorized motor carrier of property in dump truck equipment. In the event that there is a good faith dispute over a portion of the charges claimed, the contractor may withhold payment of up to 150 percent of the disputed amount or an amount otherwise agreed to by the parties. A violation of this section constitutes a cause for disciplinary action under Section 7120 and shall also subject the contractor licensee to a penalty, payable to the carrier, of 2 percent of the amount due per month for every month that payment is outstanding. In an action for the collection of moneys not paid in accordance with this section, the prevailing party shall be entitled to his or her attorney's fees and costs.

This section applies to all private works of improvement and to all public works of improvement.

Added Stats 1984 ch 1494 § 1. Amended Stats 1995 ch 37 § 1 (AB 311); Stats 1996 ch 712 § 3 (SB 1557).

§ 7109. Departure from accepted trade standards; Departure from plans or specifications

(a) A willful departure in any material respect from accepted trade standards for good and workmanlike construction constitutes a cause for disciplinary action, unless the departure was in accordance with plans and specifications prepared by or under the direct supervision of an architect.

(b) A willful departure from or disregard of plans or specifications in any material respect, which is prejudicial to another, without the consent of the owner or his or her duly authorized representative and without the consent of the person entitled to have the particular construction project or operation completed in accordance with such plans or specifications, constitutes a cause for disciplinary action.

Added Stats 1939 ch 37 § 1. Amended Stats 1963 ch 1611 § 1; Stats 1988 ch 1619 § 4, effective September 30, 1988.

—*See Business & Professions Code Section 8556 Removal and Replacement of Pest Damage Areas; Application of Wood Preservatives: Contracting for Performance of Soil Treatment Pest Control Work, in Appendix.*

§ 7109.5. Violation of safety provisions

(a) Violation of any safety provision in, or authorized by, Article 12 (commencing with Section 3420) of Group 3 of Subchapter 7 of Chapter 4 of Division 1 of Title 8 of the California Code of Regulations constitutes a cause for disciplinary action without regard to whether death or serious injury to an employee resulted from the violation.

(b) Violation of any safety provision in, or authorized by, Division 5 (commencing with Section 6300) of the Labor Code resulting in death or serious injury to an employee constitutes a cause for disciplinary action.

Added Stats 1963 ch 1083 § 2. Amended Stats 2020 ch 128 § 1 (AB 2210), effective January 1, 2021.

§ 7110. Disregard or violation of statutes

Willful or deliberate disregard and violation of the building laws of the state, or of any political subdivision thereof, or of any of the following references to or provisions of law, constitutes a cause for disciplinary action against a licensee:

(a) Section 8550 or 8556.

(b) Sections 1689.5 to 1689.15, inclusive, of the Civil Code.

(c) The safety laws or labor laws or compensation insurance laws or Unemployment Insurance Code of the state.

(d) The Subletting and Subcontracting Fair Practices Act (Chapter 4 (commencing with Section 4100) of Part 1 of Division 2 of the Public Contract Code).

(e) Any provision of the Health and Safety Code or Water Code, relating to the digging, boring, or drilling of water wells.

(f) Any provision of Article 2 (commencing with Section 4216) of Chapter 3.1 of Division 5 of Title 1 of the Government Code.

(g) Section 374.3 of the Penal Code or any substantially similar law or ordinance that is promulgated by a local government agency as defined in Section 82041 of the Government Code.

(h) Any state or local law relating to the issuance of building permits.

Added Stats 2021 ch 46 § 2 (AB 246), effective January 1, 2022. Amended Stats 2022 ch 757 § 2 (AB 1747), effective January 1, 2023.

—*See Public Contract Code Sections 4107 and 4110.*

§ 7110.1. Requiring or causing execution of release

The requiring of an execution of release of any claim or the causing of the execution of any such release in violation of Section 206.5 of the Labor Code is a cause for disciplinary action.

Added Stats 1959 ch 1066 § 2.

—*See Labor Code Section 206.5, Violation: Release of Claim for Wages, in Appendix.*

§ 7110.5. Initiation of action against contractor after receipt of Labor Commissioner's finding of willful violation of Labor Code or transmission of citations.

Upon receipt of a certified copy of the Labor Commissioner's finding of a willful or deliberate violation of the Labor Code by a licensee, pursuant to Section 98.9 of the Labor Code, or upon transmission to the Contractors' State License Board of copies of any citations or other actions taken by the Division of Occupational Safety and Health pursuant to Article 12 (commencing with Section 3420) of Group 3 of Subchapter 7 of Chapter 4 of Division 1 of Title 8 of the Code of California Regulations, the registrar shall initiate disciplinary action against the licensee within 18 months from the date of the registrar's receipt of the violation.

Added Stats 1978 ch 1247 § 1. Amended Stats 2005 ch 280 § 9 (SB 1112), effective January 1, 2006; Stats 2014 ch 392 § 4 (SB 315), effective January 1, 2015; Stats 2020 ch 128 § 2 (AB 2210), effective January 1, 2021.

§ 7111. Failure to make and keep records for inspection; Disciplinary action

(a) Failure to make and keep records showing all contracts, documents, records, receipts, and disbursements by a licensee of all of his or her transactions as a contractor, and failure to have those records available for inspection by the registrar or his or her duly authorized representative for a period of not less than five years after completion of any construction project or operation to which the records refer, or refusal by a licensee to comply with a written request of the registrar to make the records available for inspection constitutes a cause for disciplinary action.

(b) Failure of a licensee, applicant, or registrant subject to the provisions of this chapter, who without lawful excuse, delays, obstructs, or refuses to comply with a written request of the registrar or designee for information or records, to provide that information or make available those records, when the information or records are required in the attempt to discharge any duty of the registrar, constitutes a cause for disciplinary action.

Added Stats 1939 ch 37 § 1. Amended Stats 1959 ch 98 § 1; Stats 1988 ch 1035 § 3; Stats 1991 ch 1160 § 33 (AB 2190).

§ 7111.1. Failure to respond to request to cooperate in investigation of complaint

The failure of, or refusal by, a licensee to respond to a written request of the registrar to cooperate in the investigation of a complaint against that licensee constitutes a cause for disciplinary action.

Added Stats 1984 ch 1174 § 8.

§ 7112. Omission or misrepresentation of material fact by applicant

Omission or misrepresentation of a material fact by an applicant or a licensee in obtaining, or renewing a license, or in adding a classification to an existing license constitutes a cause for disciplinary action.

Added Stats 1939 ch 37 § 1. Amended Stats 2001 ch 728 § 61 (SB 724).

§ 7112.1. Expungement of classification due to omission or misrepresentation

Any classification that has been added to an existing license record as a result of an applicant or licensee omitting or misrepresenting a material fact shall be expunged from the license record pursuant to a final order of the registrar evidencing a violation of Section 7112.

Added Stats 2001 ch 728 § 62 (SB 724).

§ 7113. Failure to complete project for contract price

Failure in a material respect on the part of a licensee to complete any construction project or operation for the price stated in the contract for such construction project or operation or in any modification of such contract constitutes a cause for disciplinary action.

Added Stats 1939 ch 37 § 1.

§ 7113.5. Avoidance or settlement of obligations for less than full amount

The avoidance or settlement by a licensee for less than the full amount of the lawful obligations of the licensee incurred as a contractor, whether by (a) composition, arrangement, or reorganization with creditors under state law, (b) composition, arrangement, or reorganization with creditors under any agreement or understanding, (c) receivership as provided in Chapter 5 (commencing at Section 564) of Title 7 of Part 2 of the Code of Civil Procedure, (d) assignment for the benefit of creditors, (e) trusteeship, or (f) dissolution, constitutes a cause for disciplinary action.

This section shall not apply to an individual settlement of the obligation of a licensee by the licensee with a creditor that is not a part of or in connection with a settlement with other creditors of the licensee.

No disciplinary action shall be commenced against a licensee for discharge of or settling in bankruptcy under federal law, the licensee's lawful obligations incurred as a contractor for less than the full amount of the obligations, so long as the licensee satisfies all of those lawful obligations, to the extent the obligations are not discharged under federal law.

Added Stats 1959 ch 1361 § 1. Amended Stats 1961 ch 1636 § 7, operative October 1, 1962; Stats 1963 ch 991 § 1; Stats 1975 ch 818 § 2; Stats 1980 ch 135 § 1; Stats 2006 ch 123 § 2 (AB 2658), effective January 1, 2007; Stats 2009. Ch. 500 (AB 1059).

§ 7114. Aiding, abetting, or conspiring with unlicensed person to evade law

(a) Aiding or abetting an unlicensed person to evade the provisions of this chapter or combining or conspiring with an unlicensed person, or allowing one's license to be used by an unlicensed person, or acting as agent or partner or associate, or otherwise, of an unlicensed person with the intent to evade the provisions of this chapter constitutes a cause for disciplinary action.

(b) A licensee who is found by the registrar to have violated subdivision (a) shall, in accordance with the provisions of this article, be subject to the registrar's authority to order payment of a specified sum to an injured party, including, but not limited to, payment for any injury resulting from the acts of the unlicensed person.

Added Stats 1939 ch 37 § 1. Amended Stats 1975 ch 329 § 2; Stats 2007 ch 299 § 1 (SB 354), effective January 1, 2008; Stats 2013 ch 319 § 8 (SB 822), effective January 1, 2014.

Section VI

§ 7114.1. False certification of qualifications

Any licensee whose signature appears on a falsified certificate in support of an examinee's experience qualifications, or otherwise certifying to false or misleading experience claims by an applicant, which have been submitted to obtain a contractor's license shall be subject to disciplinary action.

Added Stats 1983 ch 891 § 26.

§ 7114.2. Administrative remedies authorized for misuse of contractor license

Any licensed or unlicensed person who commits any act prohibited by Section 119 is subject to the administrative remedies authorized by this chapter. Unless otherwise expressly provided, the remedies authorized under this section shall be separate from, and in addition to, all other available remedies, whether civil or criminal.

Added Stats 2013 ch 163 § 1 (SB 261), effective January 1, 2014.

§ 7115. Material failure to comply with chapter, rules, or regulations

Failure in any material respect to comply with the provisions of this chapter, or any rule or regulation adopted pursuant to this chapter, or to comply with the provisions of Section 7106 of the Public Contract Code, constitutes a cause for disciplinary action.

Added Stats 1939 ch 37 § 1. Amended Stats 1983 ch 891 § 27; Stats 1984 ch 1174 § 9; Stats 1990 ch 485 § 1 (SB 2290); Stats 1991 ch 1160 § 34 (AB 2190).

§ 7116. Wilful or fraudulent act injuring another

The doing of any wilful or fraudulent act by the licensee as a contractor in consequence of which another is substantially injured constitutes a cause for disciplinary action.

Added Stats 1939 ch 37 § 1.

§ 7116.5. Causes for discipline

It is a cause for discipline for a licensee to do any of the following:

(a) Engage in any conduct that subverts or attempts to subvert an investigation of the board.

(b) Threaten or harass any person or licensee for providing evidence in any possible or actual disciplinary action, arbitration, or other legal action.

(c) Discharge an employee primarily because of the employee's attempt to comply with or aid in compliance with the provisions of this chapter.

Added Stats 2003 ch 607 § 33 (SB 1077).

§ 7117. Acting as contractor under unlicensed name or personnel

Acting in the capacity of a contractor under any license issued hereunder except: (a) in the name of the licensee as set forth upon the license, or (b) in accordance with the personnel of the licensee as set forth in the application for such license, or as later changed as provided in this chapter, constitutes a cause for disciplinary action.

Added Stats 1939 ch 37 § 1.

§ 7117.5. Acting as contractor under inactive or suspended license

(a) Acting in the capacity of a contractor under any license which has been made inactive, as provided in Section 7076.5, constitutes a cause for disciplinary action.

(b) Acting in the capacity of a contractor under any license that has been suspended for any reason constitutes a cause for disciplinary action.

(c) Acting in the capacity of a contractor under any license that has expired constitutes a cause for disciplinary action if the license is subject to renewal pursuant to Section 7141. The actions authorized under this section shall be separate from, and in addition to, all other remedies either civil or criminal.

Added Stats 1961 ch 2099 § 2. Amended Stats 1984 ch 1174 § 10; Stats 1995 ch 467 § 15 (SB 1061).

§ 7117.6. Acting as contractor in unauthorized classification

Acting in the capacity of a contractor in a classification other than that currently held by the licensee constitutes a cause for disciplinary action.

Added Stats 1983 ch 891 § 28.

§ 7118. Entering into contract with unlicensed contractor

Entering into a contract with a contractor while such contractor is not licensed as provided in this chapter constitutes a cause for disciplinary action.

Added Stats 1939 ch 37 § 1. Amended Stats 1975 ch 329 § 3.

§ 7118.4. Asbestos inspections; Disclosure requirements

(a) If a contractor has made an inspection for the purpose of determining the presence of asbestos or the need for related remedial action with knowledge that the report has been required by a person as a condition of making a loan of money secured by the property, or is required by a public entity as a condition of issuing a permit concerning the property, the contractor shall disclose orally and in writing if it is owned or has any common ownership, or any financial relationship whatsoever, including, but not limited to, commissions or referral fees, with an entity in the business of performing the corrective work.

(b) This section does not prohibit a contractor that has contracted to perform corrective work after the report of another company has indicated the presence of asbestos or the need for related remedial action from making its own inspection prior to performing that corrective work or from making an inspection to determine whether the corrective measures were successful and, if not, thereafter performing additional corrective work.

(c) A violation of this section is grounds for disciplinary action.

(d) A violation of this section is a misdemeanor punishable by a fine of not less than three thousand dollars ($3,000) and not more than five thousand dollars ($5,000), or by imprisonment in the county jail for not more than one year, or both.

(e) For the purpose of this section, "asbestos" has the meaning set forth in Section 6501.7 of the Labor Code.

Added Stats 1988 ch 1491 § 1.

§ 7118.5. Sanctions against contractor hiring uncertified person to perform asbestos-related work

Any contractor, applicant for licensure, or person required to be licensed, who, either knowingly or negligently, or by reason of a failure to inquire, enters into a contract with another person who is required to be, and is not, certified pursuant to Section 7058.5 to engage in asbestos-related work, as defined in Section 6501.8 of the Labor Code, is subject to the following penalties:

(a) Conviction of a first offense is an infraction punishable by a fine of not less than one thousand dollars ($1,000) or more than three thousand dollars ($3,000), and by possible revocation or suspension of any contractor's license.

(b) Conviction of a subsequent offense is a misdemeanor requiring revocation or suspension of any contractor's license, and a fine of not less than three thousand dollars ($3,000) or more than five thousand dollars ($5,000), or imprisonment in the county jail for not more than one year, or both the fine and imprisonment.

Added Stats 1988 ch 1003 § 4, operative July 1, 1989. Amended Stats 1991 ch 1160 § 35 (AB 2190).

§ 7118.6. Sanctions for contracting with uncertified person to perform removal or remedial action

Any contractor who, either knowingly or negligently, or by reason of a failure to inquire, enters into a contract with another person who is required to be, and is not certified pursuant to Section 7058.7 to engage in a removal or remedial action, as defined in Section 7058.7, is subject to the following penalties:

(a) Conviction of a first offense is an infraction punishable by a fine of not less than one thousand dollars ($1,000) or more than three thousand dollars ($3,000), and by possible revocation or suspension of any contractor's license.

(b) Conviction of a subsequent offense is a misdemeanor requiring revocation or suspension of any contractor's license, and a fine of not less than three thousand dollars ($3,000) or more than five thousand dollars ($5,000), or imprisonment in the county jail for not more than one year, or both the fine and imprisonment.

Added Stats 1986 ch 1443 § 3, effective September 30, 1986. Amended Stats 1991 ch 1160 § 36 (AB 2190).

§ 7119. Failure to prosecute work diligently

Wilful failure or refusal without legal excuse on the part of a licensee as a contractor to prosecute a construction project or operation with reasonable diligence causing material injury to another constitutes a cause for disciplinary action.

Added Stats 1939 ch 37 § 1.

§ 7120. Failure to pay for materials or services; False denial of liability

Wilful or deliberate failure by any licensee or agent or officer thereof to pay any moneys, when due for any materials or services rendered in connection with his operations as a contractor, when he has the capacity to pay or when he has received sufficient funds therefor as payment for the particular construction work, project, or operation for which the services or materials were rendered or purchased constitutes a cause for disciplinary action, as does the false denial of any such amount due or the validity of the claim thereof with intent to secure for himself, his employer, or other person, any discount upon such indebtedness or with intent to hinder, delay, or defraud the person to whom such indebtedness is due.

Added Stats 1939 ch 37 § 1.

§ 7121. Participation in certain acts as disqualification from employment, election or association by licensee; Disciplinary action

A person who has been denied a license for a reason other than failure to document sufficient satisfactory experience for a supplemental classification for an existing license, or who has had his or her license revoked, or whose license is under suspension, or who has failed to renew his or her license while it was under suspension, or who has been a partner, officer, director, manager, or associate of any partnership, corporation, limited liability company, firm, or association whose application for a license has been denied for a reason other than failure to document sufficient satisfactory experience for a supplemental classification for an existing license, or whose license has been revoked, or whose license is under suspension, or who has failed to renew a license while it was under suspension, and while acting as a partner, officer, director, manager, or associate had knowledge of or participated in any of the prohibited acts for which the license was denied, suspended, or revoked, shall be prohibited from serving as an officer, director, associate, partner, manager, qualifying individual, or member of the personnel of record of a licensee, and the employment, election, or association of this type of person by a licensee in any capacity other than as a nonsupervising bona fide employee shall constitute grounds for disciplinary action.

Added Stats 1941 ch 971 § 18. Amended Stats 1983 ch 891 § 29; Stats 2003 ch 363 § 6 (AB 1382); Stats 2004 ch 865 § 15 (SB 1914); Stats 2010 ch 698 § 28 (SB 392), effective January 1, 2011.

§ 7121.1. Responsibility of disassociated partner, officer, director, manager, or associate for compliance with citation

Notwithstanding any other provision of this chapter, the disassociation of a partner, officer, director, manager, or associate from the license of a partnership, corporation, limited liability company, firm, or association whose license has been cited pursuant to Section 7099 shall not relieve the partner, officer, director, manager, or associate from responsibility for complying with the citation if he or she had knowledge of, or participated in, any of the prohibited acts for which the citation was issued. Section 7121 shall apply to a partner, officer, director, manager, or associate of a licensee that fails to comply with a citation after it is final.

Added Stats 1994 ch 192 § 2 (AB 3475). Amended Stats 2010 ch 698 § 29 (SB 392), effective January 1, 2011.

§ 7121.5. Effect of participation by qualifying individual in acts for which license suspended, revoked, or not renewed

A person who was the qualifying individual on a revoked license, or of a license under suspension, or of a license that was not renewed while it was under suspension, shall be prohibited from serving as an officer, director, associate, partner, manager, or qualifying individual of a licensee, whether or not the individual had knowledge of or participated in the prohibited acts or omissions for which the license was revoked, or suspended, and the employment, election, or association of that person by a licensee shall constitute grounds for disciplinary action.

Added Stats 1983 ch 891 § 30. Amended Stats 2010 ch 698 § 30 (SB 392), effective January 1, 2011.

§ 7121.6. Restricted activities for specified individuals

(a) An individual who meets all of the following criteria shall not perform any act regulated under this chapter for or on behalf of a licensee, other than as a bona fide nonsupervising employee:

(1) The individual was listed as an officer, director, owner, manager, partner, or associate of a license that was revoked.

(2) The individual had knowledge of or participated in any act or omission for which the license was revoked.

(3) The individual is not eligible for reinstatement for licensure under Section 7102.

(b) An individual who meets all of the following criteria shall not perform any act regulated under this chapter for or on behalf of a licensee, other than as a bona fide nonsupervising employee:

(1) The individual furnished the qualifications for licensure, as set forth under Section 7068, and that license was revoked.

(2) The individual served in the capacity of the qualifying individual during the commission or omission of any of the acts that resulted in the revocation of the license, whether or not he or she had knowledge of or participated in those acts.

(3) The individual is not eligible for reinstatement for licensure under Section 7102.

(c) A violation of this section is a misdemeanor punishable by a fine of not less than four thousand five hundred dollars ($4,500), by imprisonment in a county jail for not less than 90 days nor more than one year, or by both the fine and imprisonment. The penalty provided by this subdivision is cumulative to the penalties available under other laws of this state.

(d) Notwithstanding any other provision of law to the contrary, an indictment for any violation of this section shall be found or an information or complaint filed within four years from the performance of any act that is prohibited under this section.

Added Stats 2006 ch 171 § 1 (AB 2897), effective January 1, 2007. Amended Stats 2010 ch 698 § 31 (SB 392), effective January 1, 2011.

§ 7121.65. Notification of license revocation required

Prior to becoming employed in any capacity by an entity that is subject to licensure under this chapter, an individual who is described in subdivision (a) or (b) of Section 7121.6 shall provide the prospective employer with written notice of the license revocation.

Added Stats 2006 ch 171 § 2 (AB 2897), effective January 1, 2007.

§ 7121.7. Employment of individuals with revoked licenses

(a) A qualifying individual, officer, partner, or other person named on a license shall not knowingly employ an individual who is described in subdivision (a) or (b) of Section 7121.6, except as a bona fide nonsupervising employee.

(b) A violation of this section is a misdemeanor punishable by a fine of not less than four thousand five hundred dollars ($4,500), by imprisonment in a county jail for not less than 30 days nor more than one year, or by both the fine and imprisonment.

(c) Notwithstanding any other provision of law to the contrary, an indictment for any violation of this section shall be found or an information or complaint filed within four years from the performance of any act that is prohibited under this section.

Added Stats 2006 ch 171 § 3 (AB 2897), effective January 1, 2007.

§ 7121.8. "Bona fide nonsupervising employee"

For purposes of this article, "bona fide nonsupervising employee" means a person who is exempt from the provisions of this chapter under Section 7053, and who does not otherwise meet the test of an independent contractor, as set forth under Section 2750.5 of the Labor Code.

Added Stats 2006 ch 171 § 4 (AB 2897), effective January 1, 2007.

§ 7122. When act or omission of individual or business entity constitutes cause for disciplinary action against licensee

The performance by an individual, partnership, corporation, limited liability company, firm, or association of an act or omission constituting a cause for disciplinary action, likewise constitutes a cause for disciplinary action against a licensee other than the individual qualifying on behalf of the individual or entity, if the licensee was a partner, officer, director, manager, or associate of that individual, partnership, corporation, limited liability company, firm, or association at the time the act or omission occurred, and had knowledge of or participated in the prohibited act or omission.

Added Stats 1947 ch 1285. Amended Stats 1959 ch 407 § 5; Stats 2010 ch 698 § 32 (SB 392), effective January 1, 2011.

§ 7122.1. Responsibility of disassociated qualifying individual for compliance with citation; Applicability of § 7122.5

Notwithstanding Section 7068.2 or any other provision of this chapter, the disassociation of a qualifying individual from a license after the act or omission has occurred that resulted in a citation pursuant to Section 7099 shall not relieve the qualifying individual from responsibility for complying with the citation. Section 7122.5 shall apply to a qualifying individual of a licensee that fails to comply with a citation after it is final.

Added Stats 1994 ch 192 § 3 (AB 3475). Amended Stats 2003 ch 363 § 7 (AB 1382); Stats 2010 ch 698 § 33 (SB 392), effective January 1, 2011.

§ 7122.2. Responsibility for compliance with arbitration award following disassociation

(a) Notwithstanding Section 7068.2 or any other provisions of this chapter, the disassociation of a qualifying individual from a license that has been referred to arbitration pursuant to Section 7085 shall not relieve the qualifying individual from the responsibility of complying with an arbitration award rendered as a result of acts or omissions committed while acting as the qualifying individual for the license as provided under Sections 7068 and 7068.1.

(b) Section 7122.5 shall apply to a qualifying individual of a licensee that fails to comply with an arbitration award once it is rendered.

Added Stats 2002 ch 312 § 4 (AB 728). Amended Stats 2005 ch 385 § 1 (AB 316), effective January 1, 2006; Stats 2010 ch 698 § 34 (SB 392), effective January 1, 2011.

§ 7122.5. Immateriality of licensee's knowledge or participation

The performance by an individual, partnership, corporation, limited liability company, firm, or association of an act or omission constituting a cause for disciplinary action, likewise constitutes a cause for disciplinary action against a licensee who at the time that the act or omission occurred was the qualifying individual of that individual, partnership, corporation, limited liability company, firm, or association, whether or not he or she had knowledge of or participated in the prohibited act or omission.

Added Stats 1959 ch 407 § 6. Amended Stats 2010 ch 698 § 35 (SB 392), effective January 1, 2011.

§ 7123. Criminal conviction as cause for discipline

A conviction of a crime substantially related to the qualifications, functions and duties of a contractor constitutes a cause for disciplinary action. The record of the conviction shall be conclusive evidence thereof.

Added Stats 1955 ch 1532 § 2. Amended Stats 1978 ch 1161 § 365.

§ 7123.5. Disciplinary action for violation of overpricing following emergency or major disaster

If a contractor is convicted of violating Section 396 of the Penal Code or any substantially similar local ordinance in connection with the sale, or offer for sale, of repair or reconstruction services, as defined in Section 396 of the Penal Code, the Contractors State License Board shall take disciplinary action against the contractor, which shall include a suspension of at least six months or the permanent revocation of the contractor's license.

Added Stats 1993–94 1st Ex Sess ch 52 § 1 (AB 36 X), effective November 30, 1994. Amended Stats 2020 ch 312 § 63 (SB 1474), effective January 1, 2021.

—*See Penal Code Section 396, Unlawful Price Increase Following a Declared State of Emergency, in Appendix.*

§ 7124. What constitutes conviction; When license may be ordered suspended or revoked, or issuance refused

A plea or verdict of guilty or a conviction following a plea of nolo contendere is deemed to be a conviction within the meaning of this article. The board may order the license suspended or revoked, or may decline to issue a license, when the time for appeal has elapsed, or the judgment of conviction has been affirmed on appeal or when an order granting probation is made suspending the imposition of sentence, irrespective of a subsequent order under the provisions of Section 1203.4 of the Penal Code allowing such person to withdraw his plea of guilty and to enter a plea of not guilty, or setting aside the verdict of guilty, or dismissing the accusation, information or indictment.

Added Stats 1955 ch 1532 § 3.

§ 7124.5. [Section repealed 2004.]

Added Stats 1979 ch 188 § 2, effective June 29, 1979. Repealed Stats 2004 ch 865 § 16 (SB 1914). The repealed section related to public disclosure of complaints against licensees.

§ 7124.6. Public access to complaints against licensees; Disclaimer; Limitations of disclosure

(a) The registrar shall make available to members of the public the date, nature, and status of all complaints on file against a licensee that do either of the following:

(1) Have been referred for accusation.

(2) Have been referred for investigation after a determination by board enforcement staff that a probable violation has occurred, and have been reviewed by a supervisor, and regard allegations that if proven would present a risk of harm to the public and would be appropriate for suspension or revocation of the contractor's license or criminal prosecution.

(b) The board shall create a disclaimer that shall accompany the disclosure of a complaint that shall state that the complaint is an allegation. The disclaimer may also contain any other information the board determines would be relevant to a person evaluating the complaint.

(c)(1) A complaint resolved in favor of the contractor shall not be subject to disclosure.

(2) A complaint resolved by issuance of a letter of admonishment pursuant to Section 7099.9 shall not be deemed resolved in favor of the contractor for the purposes of this section. A letter of admonishment issued to a licensee shall be disclosed for a period of either one year or two years from the date of service described in subdivision (c) of Section 7099.9. For the limited purposes of this paragraph, the determination regarding the one- or two-year disclosure shall be made based on the factors enumerated in subdivision (a) of Section 7099.2.

(d) Except as described in subdivision (e), the registrar shall make available to members of the public the date, nature, and disposition of all legal actions.

(e) Disclosure of legal actions shall be limited as follows:

(1) (A) Citations shall be disclosed from the date of issuance and for five years after the date of compliance if no additional disciplinary actions have been filed against the licensee during the five-year period. If additional disciplinary actions were filed against the licensee during the five-year period, all disciplinary actions shall be disclosed for as long as the most recent disciplinary action is subject to disclosure under this section. At the end of the specified time period, those citations shall no longer be disclosed.

(B) Any disclosure pursuant to this paragraph shall also appear on the license record of any other license that includes a qualifier that is listed as one of the members of personnel of record of the license that was issued the citation.

(C) The disclosure described in subparagraph (B) shall be for the period of disclosure of the citation.

(2) Accusations that result in suspension, stayed suspension, or stayed revocation of the contractor's license shall be disclosed from the date the accusation is filed and for seven years after the accusation has been settled, including the terms and conditions of probation if no additional disciplinary actions have been filed against the licensee during the seven-year period. If additional disciplinary actions were filed against the licensee during the seven-year period, all disciplinary actions shall be posted for as long as the most recent disciplinary action is subject to disclosure under this section. At the end of the specified time period, those accusations shall no longer be disclosed.

(3) All revocations that are not stayed shall be disclosed indefinitely from the effective date of the revocation.

Added Stats 2001 ch 494 § 2 (SB 135), operative July 1, 2002. Amended Stats 2003 ch 607 § 34 (SB 1077); Stats 2016 § 1 (SB 1209), effective January 1, 2017. Stats 2017 ch 308 § 3 (SB 486), effective January 1, 2018; Stats 2019 ch 378 § 8 (SB 610), effective January 1, 2020; Stats 2021 ch 3188 § 10 (SB 826), effective January 1, 2022; Stats 2022 ch 293 § 1 (AB 2916).

Article 7.5

Workers' Compensation Insurance Reports

§ 7125. Reports to registrar; Exemptions [Repealed effective January 1, 2028]

(a) Except as provided in subdivision (b), the board shall require as a condition precedent to the issuance, reinstatement, reactivation, renewal, or continued maintenance of a license, that the applicant or licensee have on file at all times a current and valid Certificate of Workers' Compensation Insurance or Certification of Self-Insurance in the applicant's or licensee's business name. A Certificate of Workers' Compensation Insurance shall be issued and filed, electronically or otherwise, by an insurer duly licensed to write workers' compensation insurance in this state. A Certification of Self-Insurance shall be issued and filed by the Director of Industrial Relations. If reciprocity conditions exist, as provided in Section 3600.5 of the Labor Code, the registrar shall require the information deemed necessary to ensure compliance with this section.

(b) This section does not apply to an applicant or licensee who meets both of the following conditions:

(1) Has no employees provided that the applicant or licensee files a statement with the board on a form prescribed by the registrar before the issuance, reinstatement, reactivation, or continued maintenance of a license, certifying that the applicant or licensee does not employ any person in any manner so as to become subject to the workers' compensation laws of California or is not otherwise required to provide for workers' compensation insurance coverage under California law.

(2) Does not hold a C-8 license, as defined in Section 832.08 of Title 16 of the California Code of Regulations, a C-20 license, as defined in Section 832.20 of Title 16 of the California Code of Regulations, a C-22 license, as defined in Section 832.22 of Title 16 of the California Code of Regulations, a C-39 license, as defined in Section 832.39 of Title 16 of the California Code of Regulations, or a D-49 license, a subcategory of a C-61 license, as defined in Section 832.61 of Title 16 of the California Code of Regulations.

(c) This section does not apply to an applicant or licensee organized as a joint venture pursuant to Section 7029 that has no employees, provided that the applicant or licensee files the statement prescribed by subparagraph (1) of subdivision (b).

(d) A Certificate of Workers' Compensation Insurance, Certification of Self-Insurance, or exemption certificate is not required of a holder of a license that has been inactivated on the official records of the board during the period the license is inactive.

(e) (1) The insurer, including the State Compensation Insurance Fund, shall report to the registrar the following information for any policy required under this section: name, license number, policy number, dates that coverage is scheduled to commence and lapse, and cancellation date if applicable.

(2) A workers' compensation insurer shall also report to the registrar a licensee whose workers' compensation insurance policy is canceled by the insurer if all of the following conditions are met:

(A) The insurer has completed a premium audit or investigation.

(B) A material misrepresentation has been made by the insured that results in financial harm to the insurer.

(C) No reimbursement has been paid by the insured to the insurer.

(3) Willful or deliberate disregard and violation of workers' compensation insurance laws constitutes a cause for disciplinary action by the registrar against the licensee.

(f) (1) For any license that, on January 1, 2013, is active and includes a C-39 classification in addition to any other classification, the registrar shall, in lieu of the automatic license suspension otherwise required under this article, remove the C-39 classification from the license unless a valid Certificate of Workers' Compensation Insurance or Certification of Self-Insurance is received by the registrar.

(2) For any licensee whose license, after January 1, 2013, is active and has had the C-39 classification removed as provided in paragraph (1), and who is found by the registrar to have employees and to lack a valid Certificate of Workers' Compensation Insurance or Certification of Self-Insurance, that license shall be automatically suspended as required under this article.

(g) (1) For any licensee whose license, after July 1, 2023, is active and includes a C-8, C-20, C-22, or D-49 classification, in addition to any other classification, the registrar shall, in lieu of the automatic license suspension

otherwise required under this article, remove the C-8, C-20, C-22, or D-49 classification from the license unless a valid Certificate of Workers' Compensation Insurance or Certification of Self-Insurance is received by the registrar.

(2) For any licensee whose license, after July 1, 2023, is active and has had the C-8, C-20, C-22, or D-49 classification removed, as provided in paragraph (1), and who is found by the registrar to have employees and to lack a valid Certificate of Workers' Compensation Insurance or Certification of Self-Insurance, that license shall be automatically suspended as required under this article.

(h) The information reported pursuant to paragraph (2) of subdivision (e) shall be confidential, and shall be exempt from disclosure under the California Public Records Act (Division 10 (commencing with Section 7920.000) of Title 1 of the Government Code).

(i) This section shall remain in effect only until January 1, 2028, and as of that date is repealed, unless a later enacted statute that is enacted before January 1, 2028, deletes or extends that date.

Added Stats 1943 ch 132 § 1. Amended Stats 1990 ch 1386 § 3 (AB 2282); Stats 1991 ch 1160 § 38 (AB 2190); Stats 1995 ch 467 § 16 (SB 1061); Stats 1996 ch 331 § 1 (AB 3355); Stats 2002 ch 311 § 4 (AB 264); Stats 2006 ch 38 § 1 (AB 881), effective January 1, 2007, repealed January 1, 2011; Stats 2010 ch 423 § 1 (AB 2305), effective January 1, 2011, repealed January 1, 2013; Stats 2011 ch 686 § 1 (AB 878), effective January 1, 2012, repealed January 1, 2013; Stats 2012 ch 389 § 1 (AB 2219), effective January 1, 2013; Stat 2022 ch 978 § 1 (SB 216), effective January 1, 2023, repealed effective

January 1, 2026; Stat 2024 ch 485 § 12 (SB 1455), effective January 1, 2025, repealed effective January 1, 2028.

§ 7125. Reports to registrar; Exemptions [Operative effective January 1, 2028]

(a) Except as provided in subdivision (b), the board shall require as a condition precedent to the issuance, reinstatement, reactivation, renewal, or continued maintenance of a license, that the applicant or licensee have on file at all times a current and valid Certificate of Workers' Compensation Insurance or Certification of Self-Insurance in the applicant's or licensee's business name. A Certificate of Workers' Compensation Insurance shall be issued and filed, electronically or otherwise, by an insurer duly licensed to write workers' compensation insurance in this state. A Certification of Self-Insurance shall be issued and filed by the Director of Industrial Relations. If reciprocity conditions exist, as provided in Section 3600.5 of the Labor Code, the registrar shall require the information deemed necessary to ensure compliance with this section.

(b) This section does not apply to an applicant or licensee organized as a joint venture pursuant to Section 7029 that has no employees, provided that the applicant or licensee files a statement with the board on a form prescribed by the registrar before the issuance, reinstatement, reactivation, or continued maintenance of a license, certifying that the applicant or licensee does not employ any person in any manner so as to become subject to the workers' compensation laws of California or is not otherwise required to provide for workers' compensation insurance coverage under California law.

(c) A Certificate of Workers' Compensation Insurance or Certification of Self-Insurance is not required of a holder of a license that has been inactivated on the official records of the board during the period the license is inactive.

(d) (1) The insurer, including the State Compensation Insurance Fund, shall report to the registrar the following information for any policy required

under this section: name, license number, policy number, dates that coverage is scheduled to commence and lapse, and cancellation date if applicable.

(2) A workers' compensation insurer shall also report to the registrar a licensee whose workers' compensation insurance policy is canceled by the insurer if all of the following conditions are met:

(A) The insurer has completed a premium audit or investigation.

(B) A material misrepresentation has been made by the insured that results in financial harm to the insurer.

(C) Reimbursement has not been paid by the insured to the insurer.

(3) Willful or deliberate disregard and violation of workers' compensation insurance laws constitutes a cause for disciplinary action by the registrar against the licensee.

(e) The information reported pursuant to paragraph (2) of subdivision (d) shall be confidential, and shall be exempt from disclosure under the California Public Records Act (Division 10 (commencing with Section 7920.000) of Title 1 of the Government Code).

(f) This section shall become operative on January 1, 2028.

Added Stats 1943 ch 132 § 1. Amended Stats 1990 ch 1386 § 3 (AB 2282); Stats 1991 ch 1160 § 38 (AB 2190); Stats 1995 ch 467 § 16 (SB 1061); Stats 1996 ch 331 § 1 (AB 3355); Stats 2002 ch 311 § 4 (AB 264); Stats 2006 ch 38 § 1 (AB 881), effective January 1, 2007, repealed January 1, 2011; Stats 2010 ch 423 § 1 (AB 2305), effective January 1, 2011, repealed January 1, 2013; Stats 2011 ch 686 § 1 (AB 878), effective January 1, 2012, repealed January 1, 2013; Stats 2012 ch 389 § 1 (AB 2219), effective January 1, 2013; Stat 2022 ch 978 § 1 (SB 216), effective January 1, 2023, repealed effective January 1, 2026; Stat 2022 ch 978 § 2 (SB 216), effective January 1, 2023, operative January 1, 2026; Stat 2024 ch 485 § 13 (SB 1455), effective January 1, 2025, operative January 1, 2028.

§ 7125.1. Time limit for acceptance of certificate

(a) The registrar shall accept a certificate required by Section 7125 as of the effective date shown on the certificate, if the certificate is received by the registrar within 90 days after that date, and shall reinstate the license to which the certificate pertains, if otherwise eligible, retroactive to the effective date of the certificate.

(b) Notwithstanding subdivision (a), the registrar shall accept the certificate as of the effective date shown on the certificate, even if the certificate is not received by the registrar within 90 days after that date, upon a showing by the licensee, on a form acceptable to the registrar, that the failure to have a certificate on file was due to circumstances beyond the control of the licensee. The registrar shall reinstate the license to which the certificate pertains, if otherwise eligible, retroactive to the effective date of the certificate.

Added Stats 1995 ch 467 § 18 (SB 1061).

§ 7125.2. Suspension of license for failure to maintain workers' compensation insurance

The failure of a licensee to obtain or maintain workers' compensation insurance coverage, if required under this chapter, shall result in the automatic suspension of the license by operation of law in accordance with the provisions of this section, but this suspension shall not affect, alter, or limit the status of the licensee as an employer for purposes of Section 3716 of the Labor Code.

(a) The license suspension imposed by this section is effective upon the earlier of either of the following:

(1) On the date that the relevant workers' compensation insurance coverage lapses.

(2) On the date that workers' compensation coverage is required to be obtained.

(b) A licensee who is subject to suspension under paragraph (1) of subdivision (a) shall be provided a notice by the registrar that includes all of the following:

(1) The reason for the license suspension and the effective date.

(2) A statement informing the licensee that a pending suspension will be posted to the license record for not more than 45 days prior to the posting of any license suspension periods required under this article.

(3) The procedures required to reinstate the license.

(c) Reinstatement may be made at any time following the suspension by showing proof of compliance as specified in Sections 7125 and 7125.1.

(d) In addition, with respect to an unlicensed individual acting in the capacity of a contractor who is not otherwise exempted from the provisions of this chapter, a citation may be issued by the registrar under Section 7028.7 for failure to comply with this article and to maintain workers' compensation insurance. An opportunity for a hearing as specified in Section 7028.10 will be granted if requested within 15 working days after service of the citation.

Added Stats 1995 ch 467 § 20 (SB 1061). Amended Stats 2002 ch 311 § 5 (AB 264).

§ 7125.3. Periods of licensure

A contractor shall be considered duly licensed during all periods in which the registrar is required to accept the certificate prescribed by Section 7125, provided the licensee has otherwise complied with the provisions of this chapter.

Added Stats 2002 ch 311 § 6 (AB 264).

§ 7125.4. Causes for disciplinary action; Misdemeanor

(a) The filing of the exemption certificate prescribed by this article that is false, or the employment of a person subject to coverage under the workers' compensation laws after the filing of an exemption certificate without first filing a Certificate of Workers' Compensation Insurance or Certification of Self-Insurance in accordance with the provisions of this article, or the employment of a person subject to coverage under the workers' compensation laws without maintaining coverage for that person, constitutes cause for disciplinary action.

(b) Any qualifier for a license who, under Section 7068.1, is responsible for assuring that a licensee complies with the provisions of this chapter is also guilty of a misdemeanor for committing or failing to prevent the commission of any of the acts that are cause for disciplinary action under this section.

Added Stats 2002 ch 311 § 7 (AB 264). Amended Stats 2005 ch 205 § 2 (SB 488), effective January 1, 2006; Stats 2015 ch 389 § 3 (SB 560), effective January 1, 2016.

§ 7125.5. Renewal of license; Exemption for workers' compensation insurance; Recertification; Retroactive renewal

(a) At the time of renewal, all active licensees with an exemption for workers' compensation insurance on file with the board, submitted pursuant to subdivision (b) of Section 7125, shall either recertify the licensee's exemption by completing a recertification statement on the license renewal form, as provided by the board, or shall provide a current and valid Certificate of Workers' Compensation Insurance or Certificate of Self-Insurance, whichever is applicable.

(b) The license shall not be renewed unless a licensee with an exemption for workers' compensation insurance on file with the board recertifies the exemption status or provides a current and valid Certificate of Workers' Compensation Insurance or Certificate of Self-Insurance in conjunction with the license renewal.

(c) If the documentation required by subdivision (a) is not provided with the license renewal but is received within 30 days after notification by the board of the renewal rejection, the registrar shall grant a retroactive renewal pursuant to Section 7141.5 back to the date of the postmark of the otherwise acceptable renewal. A renewal that is still incomplete for any reason after 30 days after notification of rejection shall not be eligible for retroactive renewal under this subdivision.

Added Stats 2011 ch 546 § 1 (AB 397), effective January 1, 2012.

§ 7125.6. Renewal of license; certification of classification codes

(a) (1) At the time of renewal, all active licensees who have on file a current and valid Certificate of Workers' Compensation Insurance or Certification of Self-Insurance, or who are required to provide those certificates pursuant to subdivision (a) of Section 7125, shall certify on the license renewal form for the three workers' compensation classification codes for which the highest estimated payroll is reported on the policy. If the licensee has fewer than three classification codes reported on the policy, the licensee shall provide every classification code reported on the policy.

(2) The board shall not be required to verify or investigate the accuracy of the licensee's classification code or codes provided by the licensee pursuant to paragraph (1).

(3) The board shall not be held liable for any classification code or codes misreported by a licensee.

(b) (1) Except as provided in paragraph (2), a license shall not be renewed unless the licensee complies with this section.

(2) If the documentation and information required by subdivisions (a) and (b) is not provided with the license renewal form but is received within 30 days after notification by the board of the renewal rejection, the registrar shall grant a retroactive renewal pursuant to Section 7141.5 back to the date of the postmark of the otherwise acceptable renewal. A renewal that is still incomplete for any reason more than 30 days after notification of rejection shall not be eligible for retroactive renewal under this subdivision.

(c) When the board updates the public license detail on its internet website for an active renewal submitted by a licensee pursuant to this section, the update shall include the classification code or codes certified by the licensee pursuant to subdivision (b).

(d) This section shall become operative on July 1, 2024.

Added Stats 2023 ch 323 § 1 (AB 336), effective January 1, 2024, operative July 1, 2024.

§ 7125.7. Exemptions; Verification

By no later than January 1, 2027, the board shall establish a process and procedure, which may include an audit, proof, or other means, to verify that an applicant or licensee without an employee or employees is eligible for exemption from the workers' compensation insurance requirement pursuant to Section 7125.

Added Stats 2024 ch 485 § 14 (SB 1455), effective January 1, 2025.

§ 7126. Misdemeanor violations

(a) Any licensee or agent or officer thereof, who violates, or omits to comply with, any of the provisions of this article is guilty of a misdemeanor.

(b) Any person not licensed in accordance with this chapter who is acting as a contractor and who violates, or omits to comply with, Section 3700 of the Labor Code is guilty of a misdemeanor.

(c) Prosecution of any offense under this section shall be commenced within two years after commission of the offense as provided in Section 802 of the Penal Code.

Added Stats 1943 ch 132 § 1. Amended Stats 2018 ch 323 § 1 (AB 2705), effective January 1, 2019.

—See also Health and Safety Code Section 19825, Declaration of Worker's Compensation Required on Building Permits, in Appendix

§ 7127. Stop order; Failure to observe; Protest

(a)(1) If an employer subject to licensure under this chapter has failed to secure the payment of compensation as required by Section 3700 of the Labor Code, and whether that employer is or is not licensed under this chapter, the registrar may, in addition to any other administrative remedy, issue and serve on that employer a stop order prohibiting the use of employee labor. The stop order shall become effective immediately upon service. An employee affected by the work stoppage shall be paid by the employer for his or her time lost, not exceeding 10 days, pending compliance by the employer.

(2) Failure of any employer, officer, or any person having direction, management, or control of any place of employment or of employees to observe a stop order issued and served upon him or her pursuant to this section is a misdemeanor punishable by imprisonment in the county jail not exceeding 60 days or by a fine not exceeding ten thousand dollars ($10,000), or both.

(b) An employer who is subject to this section may protest the stop order by making and filing with the registrar a written request for a hearing within 20 days after service of the stop order. The hearing shall be held within five days from the date of filing the request. The registrar shall notify the employer of the time and place of the hearing by mail. At the conclusion of the hearing, the stop order shall be immediately affirmed or dismissed, and within 24 hours thereafter the registrar shall issue and serve on all parties to the hearing by registered or certified mail a written notice of findings and findings. A writ of mandate may be taken from the findings to the appropriate superior court. Such writ must be taken within 45 days after the mailing of the notice of findings and findings.

Added Stats 2010 ch 643 § 1 (SB 1254), effective January 1, 2011.

Article 8
Revenue

§ 7135. Disposition of fees and penalties; Appropriation

(a) The fees and civil penalties received under this chapter shall be deposited in the Contractors License Fund. All moneys in the fund are hereby appropriated for the purposes of this chapter.

(b) It is the intent of the Legislature that the board shall use moneys appropriated from the fund to improve its administrative and investigative oversight activities and capacity.

Added Stats 1939 ch 37 § 1. Amended Stats 1979 ch 1013 § 28; Stats 1986 ch 137 § 1; Stats 2020 ch 312 § 64 (SB 1474), effective January 1, 2021.

§ 7135.1. Funds to enforce unlicensed activity provisions

It is the intent of the Legislature that, each fiscal year the board shall designate, if appropriated in the Budget Act and to the extent that it does not conflict with the control language of the Budget Act, no less than 20 percent of the annual amount collected as a result of the fees increased by statutes enacted during the 1993 portion of the 1993–94 Regular Session to be used to enforce the provision of this chapter relative to unlicensed activity.

Added Stats 1993 ch 1188 § 1 (SB 148).

§ 7136. Percentage to be transferred to Consumer Affairs Fund

The director shall designate a sum not to exceed 10 percent of the total income of the Contractors State License Board for each fiscal year to be transferred to the Consumer Affairs Fund as the board's share of the cost of administration of the department.

Added Stats 1939 ch 37 § 1. Amended Stats 1971 ch 716 § 105; Stats 1984 ch 193 § 2; Stats 2020 ch 312 § 65 (SB 1474), effective January 1, 2021.

§ 7137. Fee schedule

(a) The board may set fees by regulation. These fees shall be set according to the following schedule:

(1) Application fees shall be set as follows:

(A) The application fee for an original license in a single classification shall be four hundred fifty dollars ($450) and may be increased to not more than five hundred sixty-three dollars ($563).

(B) The application fee for each additional classification applied for in connection with an original license shall be one hundred fifty dollars ($150) and may be increased to not more than one hundred eighty-eight dollars ($188).

(C) The application fee for each additional classification pursuant to Section 7059 shall be two hundred thirty dollars ($230) and may be increased to not more than two hundred eighty-eight dollars ($288).

(D) The application fee to replace a responsible managing officer, responsible managing manager, responsible managing member, or responsible managing employee pursuant to Section 7068.2 shall be two hundred thirty dollars ($230) and may be increased to not more than two hundred eighty-eight dollars ($288).

(E) The application fee to add personnel, other than a qualifying individual, to an existing license shall be one hundred twenty-five dollars ($125) and may be increased to not more than one hundred fifty-seven dollars ($157).

(F) The application fee for an asbestos certification shall be one hundred twenty-five dollars ($125) and may be increased to not more than one hundred fifty-seven dollars ($157).

(G) The application fee for a hazardous substance removal or remedial action certification shall be one hundred twenty-five dollars ($125) and may be increased to not more than one hundred fifty-seven dollars ($157).

(2) The fee to take an examination conducted or administered by a public or private organization pursuant to Section 7065 shall be no greater than the actual cost of the administration of the examination and shall be paid directly to the organization by the applicant.

(3) Initial license and registration fees shall be set as follows:

(A) The initial license fee for an active or inactive license for an individual owner shall be two hundred dollars ($200) and may be increased to not more than two hundred fifty dollars ($250).

(B) The initial license fee for an active or inactive license for a partnership, corporation, limited liability company, or joint venture shall be three hundred fifty dollars ($350) and may be increased to not more than four hundred thirty-eight dollars ($438).

(C) The registration fee for a home improvement salesperson shall be two hundred dollars ($200) and may be increased to not more than two hundred fifty dollars ($250).

(D) (i) The board shall grant a 50-percent reduction in the fees prescribed by this paragraph to an applicant who is a veteran of the United States Armed Forces, including the National Guard or Reserve components, and was not dishonorably discharged.

(ii) To demonstrate discharge grade at the time of the board's request for the initial license or registration fee, the applicant shall provide the board a copy of a current and valid driver's license or identification card issued by this state or another state with the word "Veteran" printed on its face or a copy of their DD214 long form.

(4) License and registration renewal fees shall be set as follows:

(A) The renewal fee for an active license for an individual owner shall be four hundred fifty dollars ($450) and may be increased to not more than five hundred sixty-three dollars ($563).

(B) The renewal fee for an inactive license for an individual owner shall be three hundred dollars ($300) and may be increased to not more than three hundred seventy-five dollars ($375).

(C) The renewal fee for an active license for a partnership, corporation, limited liability company, or joint venture shall be seven hundred dollars ($700) and may be increased to not more than eight hundred seventy-five dollars ($875).

(D) The renewal fee for an inactive license for a partnership, corporation, limited liability company, or joint venture shall be five hundred dollars ($500) and may be increased to not more than six hundred twenty-five dollars ($625).

(E) The renewal fee for a home improvement salesperson registration shall be two hundred dollars ($200) and may be increased to not more than two hundred fifty dollars ($250).

(5) The delinquency fee is an amount equal to 50 percent of the renewal fee, if the license is renewed after its expiration.

(6) Miscellaneous fees shall be set as follows:

(A) In addition to any other fees charged to C-10 contractors, the board shall charge a fee of twenty dollars ($20), to be assessed with the renewal fee for an active license, which shall be used by the board to enforce provisions of the Labor Code related to electrician certification.

(B) The board shall require a licensee that is subject to a public complaint requiring a professional or expert investigation or inspection and report pursuant to Section 7019 to pay those reasonable fees that are necessary to cover the costs of that investigation or inspection and report, in accordance with the following provisions:

(i) Fees shall be fixed in an amount not more than the board's cost of contracting for the investigation or inspection and report, except that the minimum fee shall be one hundred dollars ($100) for each investigation or inspection and report and may be increased to not more than one thousand dollars ($1,000) for each investigation or inspection and report.

(ii) The fee shall only be assessed for an investigation or inspection and report that resulted in issuance of a letter of admonishment or a citation pursuant to Sections 7099 and 7099.9.

(iii) The full amount of the assessed fee shall be added to the fee for the active or inactive renewal of a licensee who is subject to this subparagraph. A license shall not be renewed without payment of the renewal fee and all fees for the investigation or inspection and report pursuant to this subparagraph.

(C) The service fee to deposit with the registrar lawful money or cashier's check pursuant to paragraph (1) of subdivision (a) of Section 995.710 of the Code of Civil Procedure for purposes of compliance with any provision of Article 5 (commencing with Section 7065) shall be one hundred dollars ($100), which shall be used by the board only to process each deposit filed with the registrar, to cover the reasonable costs to the registrar for holding money or cashier's checks in trust in interest bearing deposit or share accounts, and to offset the costs of processing payment of lawful claims against a deposit in a civil action.

(D) The fee for the processing and issuance of a duplicate copy of any certificate of licensure or other form evidencing licensure or renewal of licensure pursuant to Section 122 shall be twenty-five dollars ($25).

(E) The fee to change the business name of a license as it is recorded under this chapter shall be one hundred dollars ($100) and may be increased to not more than one hundred twenty-five dollars ($125).

(F) The service charge for a dishonored check authorized by Section 6157 of the Government Code shall be twenty-five dollars ($25) for each check.

(b) The board shall, by regulation, establish criteria for the approval of expedited processing of applications. Approved expedited processing of applications for licensure or registration, as required by other provisions of law, shall not be subject to this subdivision.

Added Stats 2016 ch 799 § 37 (SB 1039), effective January 1, 2017, operative July 1, 2017. Amended Stats 2018 ch 925 § 6 (AB 3126), effective January 1, 2019; Stats 2019 ch 378 § 9 (SB 610), effective January 1, 2020; Stats 2020 ch 312 § 66 (SB 1474), effective January 1, 2021; Stats 2021 ch 367 § 22 (SB 607), effective September 28, 2021; Stats 2022 ch 156 § 1 (AB 2105), effective effective January 1, 2023; Stats 2024 ch 485 § 15 (SB 1455), effective effective January 1, 2025.

§ 7137.5. Transfer of funds for use of Uniform Construction Cost Accounting Commission; Recommendation; Reimbursement

The sum of ten thousand dollars ($10,000) shall be transferred from the Contractors License Fund to the Controller for the exclusive use of the California Uniform Construction Cost Accounting Commission.

The commission shall prepare a recommendation to the Legislature for a local public agency source to fund the commission beginning July 1, 1991, which will provide revenue supported by the contract activities represented by the commission's authority.

Upon adoption of this funding program, the commission shall reimburse the Contractors License Fund in the amount of ten thousand dollars ($10,000).

Added Stats 1990 ch 1326 § 8 (AB 3480), effective September 25, 1990. Amended Stats 2020 ch 312 § 67 (SB 1474), effective January 1, 2021.

§ 7138. Earned fee; Nonrefundability when application is filed

Notwithstanding any other provision of law, a fee paid in connection with a service or application covered by Section 7137 shall accrue to the Contractors License Fund as an earned fee and shall not be refunded.

Added Stats 1963 ch 160 § 3. Amended Stats 1966 ch 4 § 6; Stats 1974 ch 423 § 2; Stats 1982 ch 1615 § 3, effective September 30, 1982; Stats 2003 ch 607 § 35 (SB 1077); Stats 2010 ch 698 § 37 (SB 392), effective January 1, 2011; Stats 2020 ch 312 § 68 (SB 1474), effective January 1, 2021.

—See *Unemployment Insurance Code Section 10501, Job Training Program: Waiver of Fees, in Appendix.*

§ 7138.1. Reserve fund level

Notwithstanding Section 7137, the board shall fix fees to be collected pursuant to that section in order to generate revenues sufficient to maintain the board's reserve fund at a level not to exceed approximately six months of annual authorized board expenditures.

Added Stats 1996 ch 528 § 1 (SB 1597). Amended Stats 2002 ch 744 § 9 (SB 1953).

Article 8.5
The Construction Management Education Sponsorship Act of 1991

§ 7139. Title of article

This article shall be known as the Construction Management Education Sponsorship Act of 1991.

Added Stats 1991 ch 1158 § 1 (AB 2158).

§ 7139.1. Legislative findings and declarations

The Legislature hereby finds and declares all of the following:

(a) There is a demand and increasing need for construction management education programs and resources within the postsecondary education system that prepare graduates for the management of construction operations and companies regulated by the Contractors State License Law and enforced by the Contractors State License Board.

(b) Although construction management programs do exist within the state university system, these programs are woefully underfunded and insufficiently funded to provide training on state-of-the-art management information systems for either graduates or extension programs for continuing education of licensed contractors. Construction industry associations have provided some assistance through direct grants and scholarships, but the industrywide service of these programs and the need for additional assistance mandates broad based industrywide support.

(c) It is the intent of the Legislature that by enabling contractors to designate a portion of their licensure fee and providing a format for contractors to contribute funds to construction management education, this article will receive broad based industry support. In addition, this article allows the contractor to demonstrate the importance of construction management education. This assistance will enable greater development of construction management curricula and will improve the overall quality of construction by providing construction management training to California licensed contractors and their current and future management personnel.

Added Stats 1991 ch 1158 § 1 (AB 2158). Amended Stats 2020 ch 312 § 69 (SB 1474), effective January 1, 2021.

§ 7139.2. Creation of account

(a) There is hereby created the Construction Management Education Account (CMEA) as a separate account in the Contractors License Fund for the purposes of construction management education. Funds in the account shall be available for the purposes of this article upon appropriation by the Legislature.

(b) The Contractors State License Board shall allow a contractor to make a contribution to the Construction Management Education Account at the time of the contractor license fee payment. The license fee form shall clearly display this alternative on its face and shall clearly inform the licensee that this provision is a contribution to the Construction Management Education Account and is in addition to the fees.

(c) The board may accept grants from federal, state, or local public agencies, or from private foundations or individuals, in order to assist it in carrying out its duties, functions, and powers under this article. Grant moneys shall be deposited into the Construction Management Education Account.

Added Stats 1991 ch 1158 § 1 (AB 2158). Amended Stats 2003 ch 807 § 15 (SB 1080); Stats 2020 ch 312 § 70 (SB 1474), effective January 1, 2021.

§ 7139.3. Grant awards

(a) The board may award grants to qualified public postsecondary educational institutions for the support of courses of study in construction management.

(b) Any organization of contractors, or organization of contractor organizations, incorporated under Division 2 (commencing with Section 5000) of the Corporations Code may request the board to award grants pursuant to subdivision (a) directly to qualified public postsecondary educational institutions of its choice. However, the total amount of money that may be awarded to one public postsecondary educational institution pursuant to subdivision (a) may not exceed an amount equal to 25 percent of the total funds available under this article.

(c) The board shall establish an advisory committee to recommend grant awards. The advisory committee shall be known as the Construction Management Education Account Advisory Committee and shall consist of 11 members, with at least one representative from each of the following: Associated General Contractors of California, Associated Builders and Contractors, California Building Industry Association, National Electrical Contractors Association, Plumbing-Heating-Cooling Contractor's Association, Southern California Contractor's Association,Associated General Contractors of San Diego, Engineering and Utility Contractors Association, Engineering Contractors Association, California Sheet Metal and Air Conditioning Contractor's Association, and one member representing the California State University and University of California construction management programs accredited by the American Council for Construction Education. Advisory committee member terms shall be for three years and the representatives shall be appointed by each identified group. Members of the advisory committee shall not receive per diem or reimbursement for traveling and other expenses pursuant to Section 103.

(d) The mission of the Construction Management Education Account Advisory Committee is to maintain, and increase the quality and availability of, education programs for the construction industry. The primary focus is to provide financial resources not now available to accredited construction management programs in California colleges and universities to maintain and upgrade facilities and provide greater access by the industry to modern construction standards and management practices. The advisory committee shall do all of the following:

(1) Confirm the qualifications of programs applying for grants.

(2) Award less than full grants when the account has insufficient funds to award full grants to all qualifying programs.

(3) Receive and review year-end reports of use and impact of funds.

(4) Affirm applications for American Council for Construction Education accreditation and, when funds are available, award grants to complete the accreditation process.

(5) Promote close ties between feeder junior colleges and four-year construction management programs.

(6) Support development of new educational programs with specific emphasis on outreach to the construction industry at large.

Section VI

Added Stats 1991 ch 1158 § 1 (AB 2158). Amended Stats 1994 ch 647 § 1 (AB 2934).

§ 7139.4. Postsecondary programs; Qualifications

Qualified public postsecondary educational institutions shall provide postsecondary construction management programs at the baccalaureate or higher level that either award or provide one of the following:

(a) A bachelor of science construction management degree accredited by the American Council for Construction Education.

(b) A degree with an American Council for Construction Education accredited option, including, but not limited to, engineering technology and industrial technology.

(c) A bachelor of science or higher degree program documenting placement of more than 50 percent of their graduates with California licensed contractors. The placement of a person who holds a master or doctorate degree in the faculty of a construction program shall be counted as though placed with a California licensed contractor.

(d) The development of a construction management curriculum to meet the American Council for Construction Education criteria.

Added Stats 1991 ch 1158 § 1 (AB 2158).

§ 7139.5. Amounts of grants

Grants shall be made pursuant to this article to public postsecondary educational institutions that meet the qualifications specified in Section 7139.4 in the following amounts:

(a) Three thousand dollars ($3,000) per graduate during the past academic year for institutions qualifying under subdivision (a) of Section 7139.4.

(b) Three thousand dollars ($3,000) per graduate during the past academic year for institutions qualifying under subdivision (b) of Section 7139.4.

(c) Three thousand dollars ($3,000) per graduate placed with California licensed contractors during the past academic year for institutions qualifying under subdivision (c) of Section 7139.4. These funds shall be used for the purpose of becoming accredited by the American Council for Construction Education and shall be available for up to three years. The board may continue to provide this grant to an institution that in its judgment is meeting the intent of this act and is continuing its development towards accreditation.

(d) Institutions qualifying under subdivision (d) of Section 7139.4 may receive a grant in an amount up to twenty-five thousand dollars ($25,000) per year for up to two years. Thereafter, these institutions may receive grants based upon the criteria described in subdivisions

(a) to (c), inclusive. The board may continue to award a grant to an institution that in its judgment is meeting the intent of this article and is continuing its development towards accreditation.

Added Stats 1991 ch 1158 § 1 (AB 2158).

§ 7139.6. Purposes for which grants may be used

(a) The grants issued pursuant to Sections 7139.3 and 7139.5 may be used for all of the following:

(1) Instructional materials and support, equipment, curriculum development, and delivery.

(2) Support and development of outreach, continuing education, and cooperative education or internship programs.

(3) Administrative and clerical support positions.

(4) Faculty recruitment and development, to include support for postgraduate work leading to advanced degrees, visiting lecturer compensation and expenses, teaching assistant positions, and faculty positions.

(b) Grant moneys may also be used to support general classroom and laboratory operating expenses and related administrative supplies, including, but not limited to, reference materials, testing equipment, and equipment maintenance. The list of support items in this subdivision and subdivision (a) are intended to be descriptive rather than limiting. "Support" does not include faculty salary supplements.

Added Stats 1991 ch 1158 § 1 (AB 2158).

§ 7139.7. [Section repealed 2013.]

Added Stats 1991 ch 1158 § 1 (AB 2158). Repealed Stats 2012 ch 728 § 14 (SB 71), effective January 1, 2013. The repealed section related to an annual report on the condition of the grant program.

§ 7139.8. Report by president of institution receiving grant

The president of each public postsecondary educational institution receiving a grant under this article shall submit, with its respective request for a grant each year following the initial year for which grants are issued, a report to the board delineating the amount of the past grant awarded from the Construction Management Education Account to that institution and the utilization of those funds. The report shall include, but not be limited to, the following:

(a) The number of graduates placed with the California licensed contractors during the previous academic year.

(b) The expected enrollment in construction management courses in the upcoming academic year.

(c) Continuing education and extension courses offered during the previous academic year and their enrollments.

Added Stats 1991 ch 1158 § 1 (AB 2158).

§ 7139.9. Allocation for administration

The board may allocate up to fifteen thousand dollars ($15,000) per year from the Construction Management Education Account for the administration of this article.

Added Stats 1991 ch 1158 § 1 (AB 2158).

§ 7139.10. Intent of Legislature

It is the intent of the Legislature that state funding for the grants authorized to be awarded under this section be provided only from the Contractors' License Fund to the extent that funds are available in that fund and that no other state funding be provided for those grants.

Added Stats 1991 ch 1158 § 1 (AB 2158).

Article 9
Renewal of Licenses

§ 7140. Expiration of licenses; Renewal of unexpired licenses

All licenses issued under the provisions of this chapter shall expire two years from the last day of the month in which the license is issued, or two years from the date on which the renewed license last expired.

To renew a license which has not expired, the licensee shall, before the time at which the license would otherwise expire, apply for renewal on a form prescribed by the registrar and pay the renewal fee prescribed by this chapter. Renewal of an unexpired license shall continue the license in effect for the two-year period following the expiration date of the license, when it shall expire if it is not again renewed.

Added stats 1941 ch 971 § 20; Amended Stats 1961 ch 1636 § 9, operative October 1, 1962; Stats 1978 ch 1161 § 367; Stats 1981 ch 583 § 1; Stats 1991 ch 1160 § 39 (AB 2190).

§ 7141. Time for renewal; Effect; Failure to renew

(a) Except as otherwise provided in this chapter, a license that has expired may be renewed at any time within five years after its expiration by filing an application for renewal on a form prescribed by the registrar and payment of the appropriate renewal fee. Renewal under this section shall be effective on the date an acceptable renewal application is filed with the board. The licensee shall be considered unlicensed and there will be a break in the licensing time between the expiration date and the date the renewal becomes effective. Except as provided in subdivision (b), if the license is renewed after the expiration date, the licensee shall also pay the delinquency fee prescribed by this chapter.

(b) An incomplete renewal application that had originally been submitted on or before the license expiration date shall be returned to the licensee by the registrar with an explanation of the reasons for its rejection. If a corrected and acceptable renewal application is not returned within 30 days after the license expiration date, the delinquency fee shall apply. The 30 day grace period shall apply only to the delinquency fee. The license shall reflect an expired status for any period between the expiration date and the date of submission of a correct and acceptable renewal application.

(c) If so renewed, the license shall continue in effect through the date provided in Section 7140 that next occurs after the effective date of the renewal, when it shall expire if it is not again renewed.

(d) If a license is not renewed within five years, the licensee shall make an application for a license pursuant to Section 7066.

Added Stats 1941 ch 971 § 20. Amended Stats 1961 ch 1636 § 10, operative October 1, 1962; Stats 1970 ch 856 § 1; Stats 1972 ch 1138 § 4.7; Stats 1983 ch 891 § 31; Stats 1999 ch 982 § 3.9 (AB 1678); Stats 2002 ch 1013 § 62 (SB 2026); Stats 2003 ch 607 § 36 (SB 1077); Stats 2013 ch 319 § 9 (SB 822), effective January 1, 2014.

§ 7141.5. Retroactive issuance of license after failure to renew

The registrar shall grant the retroactive renewal of a license if, within 90 days of the expiration of the license, the otherwise eligible licensee submits a completed application for renewal on a form prescribed by the registrar, and pays the appropriate renewal fee and delinquency fee prescribed by this chapter. For the purposes of this section, an application shall be deemed submitted if it is delivered to the board's headquarters or postmarked within 90 days of the expiration of the license.

Added Stats 1972 ch 1138 § 5. Amended Stats 1975 ch 329 § 4; Stats 1983 ch 891 § 32; Stats 1984 ch 1174 § 11; Stats 2020 ch 312 § 71 (SB 1474), effective January 1, 2021.

§ 7143. Renewal of suspended license

A license that is suspended for any reason which constitutes a basis for suspension under this chapter, is subject to expiration and shall be renewed as provided in this chapter, but this renewal does not entitle the licensee, while the license remains suspended, and until it is reinstated, to engage in any activity to which the license relates, or in any other activity or conduct in violation of the order or judgment by which the license was suspended.

Added Stats 1941 ch 971 § 20. Amended Stats 1961 ch 1636 § 12, operative October 1, 1962; Stats 1972 ch 1138 § 7; Stats 1987 ch 930 § 8, effective September 22, 1987; Stats 2003 ch 363 § 8 (AB 1382).

§ 7143.5. Application for new license by person prohibited from renewing

A person who, by reason of the provisions of Section 7141, is not entitled to renew his license, may apply for and obtain a new license only if he pays all of the fees and meets all of the qualifications and requirements set forth in this chapter for obtaining an original license.

Added Stats 1961 ch 1636 § 13, operative October 1, 1962. Amended Stats 1972 ch 1138 § 8.

§ 7144. Reinstatement of revoked license

A revoked license shall be considered as having expired as of the date of revocation and shall not be renewed. To reinstate a revoked license a licensee may apply for reinstatement of the license only if he pays all of the fees and meets all of the qualifications and requirements set forth in this chapter for obtaining an original license.

Added Stats 1941 ch 971 § 20. Amended Stats 1961 ch 1636 § 14, operative October 1, 1962; Stats 1974 ch 433 § 3.

§ 7145. Incompleteness of application as grounds for refusal to renew license; Abandonment of application; Petition

The registrar may refuse to renew a license for the failure or refusal by the licensee to complete the renewal application prescribed by the registrar. If a licensee fails to return an application for renewal which was rejected for insufficiency or incompleteness within 90 days from the original date of rejection, the application and fee shall be deemed abandoned. Any application abandoned may not be reinstated. However, the applicant may file another application accompanied by the required fee.

The registrar may review and accept the petition of a licensee who disputes the invalidation of his or her application for renewal upon a showing of good cause. This petition shall be received within 90 days from the date the renewal application is deemed abandoned.

Added Stats 1941 ch 971 § 20. Amended Stats 1970 ch 524 § 2; Stats 1984 ch 1174 § 12.

§ 7145.5. Failure to resolve outstanding liabilities as grounds for refusal to renew license

(a) The registrar may refuse to issue, reinstate, reactivate, or renew a license or may suspend a license for the failure of a licensee to resolve all outstanding final liabilities, which include taxes, additions to tax, penalties, interest, and any fees that may be assessed by the board, the Department of Industrial Relations, the Employment Development Department, the Franchise Tax Board, or the State Board of Equalization.

(1) Until the debts covered by this section are satisfied, the qualifying person and any other personnel of record named on a license that has been suspended under this section shall be prohibited from serving in any capacity that is subject to licensure under this chapter, but shall be permitted to act in the capacity of a nonsupervising bona fide employee.

(2) The license of any other renewable licensed entity with any of the same personnel of record that have been assessed an outstanding liability covered by this section shall be suspended until the debt has been satisfied or until the same personnel of record disassociate themselves from the renewable licensed entity.

(b) The refusal to issue a license or the suspension of a license as provided by this section shall be applicable only if the registrar has mailed a notice preliminary to the refusal or suspension that indicates that the license will be refused or suspended by a date certain. This preliminary notice shall be mailed to the licensee at least 60 days before the date certain.

(c) In the case of outstanding final liabilities assessed by the Franchise Tax Board, this section shall be operative within 60 days after the Contractors' State License Board has provided the Franchise Tax Board with the information required under Section 30, relating to licensing information that includes the federal employer identification number, individual taxpayer identification number, or social security number.

(d) All versions of the application for contractors' licenses shall include, as part of the application, an authorization by the applicant, in the form and manner mutually agreeable to the Franchise Tax Board and the board, for the Franchise Tax Board to disclose the tax information that is required for the registrar to administer this section. The Franchise Tax Board may from time to time audit these authorizations.

(e) In the case of outstanding final liabilities assessed by the State Board of Equalization, this section shall not apply to any outstanding final liability if the licensee has entered into an installment payment agreement for that liability with the State Board of Equalization and is in compliance with the terms of that agreement.

Added Stats 1990 ch 1386 § 6 (AB 2282). Amended Stats 2006 ch 122 § 1 (AB 2456), effective January 1, 2007; Stats 2007 ch 130 § 29 (AB 299), effective January 1, 2008; Stats 2011 ch 734 § 1 (AB 1307), effective January 1, 2012; Stats 2017 ch 573 § 30 (SB 800), effective January 1, 2018.

Article 10
Home Improvement Business

§ 7150. "Person"

(a) "Person" as used in this article is limited to natural persons, notwithstanding the definition of person in Section 7025.

(b) "Senior citizen" means an individual who is 65 years of age or older.

Added Stats 1961 ch 1021 § 1. Amended Stats 1972 ch 1138 § 9; Stats 2020 ch 158 § 1 (AB 2471), effective January 1, 2021.

§ 7150.1. "Home improvement contractor"

A home improvement contractor, including a swimming pool contractor, is a contractor as defined and licensed under this chapter who is engaged in the business of home improvement either full time or part time. A home improvement contractor shall satisfy all requirements imposed by this article.

Added Stats 1969 ch 1583 § 1 as § 7026.2. Amended and renumbered Stats 1972 ch 1138 § 1.1. Amended Stats 1991 ch 1160 § 40 (AB 2190). Amended Stats 1997 ch 888 § 1 (AB 1213).

§ 7150.2. [Section repealed 2004.]

Added Stats 1997 ch 888 § 2 (AB 1213). Repealed, operative January 1, 2004, by its own terms. The repealed section related to certification for home improvement contractors.

§ 7150.3. [Section repealed 2004.]

Added Stats 1997 ch 888 § 3 (AB 1213). Repealed, operative January 1, 2004, by its own terms. The repealed section related to qualification for home improvement contractor.

§ 7151. "Home improvement"; "Home improvement goods or services"

(a) "Home improvement" means the repairing, remodeling, altering, converting, or modernizing of, or adding to, residential property, as well as the reconstruction, restoration, or rebuilding of a residential property that is damaged or destroyed by a natural disaster for which a state of emergency is proclaimed by the Governor pursuant to Section 8625 of the Government Code, or for which an emergency or major disaster is declared by the President of the United States, and shall include, but not be limited to, the construction, erection, installation, replacement, or improvement of driveways, swimming pools, including spas and hot tubs, terraces, patios, awnings, storm windows, solar energy systems, landscaping, fences, porches, garages, fallout shelters, basements, and other improvements of the structures or land which is adjacent to a dwelling house. "Home improvement" shall also mean the installation of home improvement goods or the furnishing of home improvement services.

(b) For purposes of this chapter, "home improvement goods or services" means goods and services, as defined in Section 1689.5 of the Civil Code, which are bought in connection with the improvement of real property. Such home improvement goods and services include, but are not limited to, carpeting, texture coating, fencing, air conditioning or heating equipment, and termite extermination. Home improvement goods include goods which are to be so affixed to real property as to become a part of real property whether or not severable therefrom.

(c) For purposes of this article, "solar energy system" means a solar energy device to be installed on a residential building or residential property that has the primary purpose of providing for the collection and distribution of solar energy for the generation of electricity, that produces at least one kilowatt, and not more than five megawatts, alternating current rated peak electricity, and that meets or exceeds the eligibility criteria established pursuant to Section 25782 of the Public Resources Code.

Added Stats 1961 ch 1021 § 1. Amended Stats 1969 ch 1583 § 10; Stats 1979 ch 1012 § 2; Stats 1980 ch 138 § 3, effective May 30, 1980; Stats 1981 ch 916 § 2; Stats 1982 ch 1210 § 2; Stats 1991 ch 1160 § 41 (AB 2190); Stats 2020 ch 364 § 4 (SB 1189), effective January 1, 2021; Stats 2021 ch 249 § 1 (SB 757), effective January 1, 2022.

§ 7151.2. "Home improvement contract"

"Home improvement contract" means an agreement, whether oral or written, or contained in one or more documents, between a contractor and an owner or between a contractor and a tenant, regardless of the number of residence or dwelling units contained in the building in which the tenant resides, if the work is to be performed in, to, or upon the residence or dwelling unit of the tenant, for the performance of a home improvement as defined in Section 7151, and includes all labor, services, and materials to be furnished and performed thereunder. "Home improvement contract" also means an agreement, whether oral or written, or contained in one or more documents, between a salesperson, whether or not he or she is a home improvement salesperson, and (a) an owner or (b) a tenant, regardless of the number of residence or dwelling units contained in the building in which the tenant resides, which provides for the sale, installation, or furnishing of home improvement goods or services.

Added Stats 1969 ch 1583 § 11. Amended Stats 1979 ch 1012 § 3; Stats 1991 ch 1160 § 42 (AB 2190).

—See *Civil Code Sections 1689.5, Home Solicitation Contract;1689.6, Cancellation of Home Solicitation Contract;1689.7, Form of Notice of Cancellation; 1689.8 Contract which provides for Lien; 1689.9, Exemptions: 1689.10, After Cancellation, Seller to Return Downpayment; 1689.11, Buyer to Return Goods; 1689.12, Invalidity of Waiver of Statute; 1689.13, Notice Not Required for Emergency Situations; 1689.14, Void Contracts, in Appendix.*

§ 7152. "Home improvement salesperson"

(a) "Home improvement salesperson" is a person who is registered under this chapter and engaged in the business of soliciting, selling, negotiating, or executing contracts for home improvements, for the sale, installation or furnishing of home improvement goods or services, or of swimming pools, spas, or hot tubs on behalf of a home improvement contractor licensed under this chapter.

(b) A home improvement salesperson shall register with the board in order to engage in the business of, or act in the capacity of, a home improvement salesperson.

(c) Subject to the provisions of Section 7154, a home improvement salesperson may be employed by one, or more than one, home improvement contractor. However, prior to engaging in any activity described in subdivision (a) of this section, a home improvement salesperson shall identify to the owner or tenant the business name and license number of the contractor they are representing for the purposes of that transaction. Failure to do so is a cause of disciplinary action within the meaning of Section 7155.

(d) The following shall not be required to be registered as home improvement salespersons:

(1) An officer of record of a corporation licensed pursuant to this chapter, or a manager, member, or officer of record of a limited liability company licensed pursuant to this chapter.

(2) A general partner listed on the license record of a partnership licensed pursuant to this chapter.

(3) A qualifying person, as defined in Section 7025.

(4) A salesperson whose sales are all made pursuant to negotiations between the parties if the negotiations are initiated by the prospective buyer at or with a general merchandise retail establishment that operates from a fixed location where goods or services are offered for sale.

(5) A person who contacts the prospective buyer for the exclusive purpose of scheduling appointments for a registered home improvement salesperson.

(6) A bona fide service repairperson who is in the employ of a licensed contractor and whose repair or service call is limited to the service, repair, or emergency repair initially requested by the buyer of the service.

(e) The exemption to registration provided under paragraphs (1), (2), and (3) of subdivision (c) shall apply only to those individuals who, at the time of the sales transaction, are listed as personnel of record for the licensee responsible for soliciting, negotiating, or contracting for a service or improvement that is subject to regulation under this article.

Added Stats 1972 ch 1138 § 11. Amended Stats 1973 ch 115 § 1, effective June 26, 1973; Stats 1979 ch 1012 § 4; Stats 1980 ch 138 § 4, effective May 30, 1980; Stats 1982 ch 585 § 1; Stats 1985 ch 1281 § 4; Stats 1991 ch 1160 § 43 (AB 2190); Stats 2006 ch 106 § 4 (AB 2457), effective January 1, 2007; Stats 2010 ch 698 § 38 (SB 392), effective January 1, 2011; Stats 2015 ch 281 § 2 (SB 561), effective January 1, 2016; Stats 2021 ch 249 § 2 (SB 757), effective January 1, 2022.

—See Civil Code Sections 1804.3, Security Interest in Goods Paid For Not Sold; Security Interest unreal Property for Sale of Unattached Goods; 1805.6, Undelivered Goods; 1810.10, Finance Charge, in Appendix.

§ 7153. Selling without registration

(a) It is a misdemeanor for any person to engage in the occupation of salesperson for one or more home improvement contractors within this state without having, at the time of the sales transaction, a current and valid home improvement salesperson registration issued by the registrar. If, upon investigation, the registrar has probable cause to believe that a salesperson is in violation of this section, the registrar may issue a citation pursuant to Section 7028.7.

It is a misdemeanor for any person to engage in the occupation of salesperson of home improvement goods or services within this state without having, at the time of the sales transaction, a current and valid home improvement salesperson registration issued by the registrar.

(b) Any security interest taken by a contractor, to secure any payment for the performance of any act or conduct described in Section 7151 that occurs on or after January 1, 1995, is unenforceable if the person soliciting the act or contract was not a duly registered salesperson or was not exempt from registration pursuant to Section 7152 at the time the homeowner signs the home improvement contract solicited by the salesperson.

Added Stats 1972 ch 1138 § 13. Amended Stats 1979 ch 1012 § 5; Stats 1994 ch 888 § 1 (AB 3269); Stats 2001 ch 728 § 63 (SB 724); Stats 2015 ch 281 § 3 (SB 561), effective January 1, 2016.

§ 7153.1. Salesperson's application for registration; Grounds for denial; Fingerprints of applicants; Criminal history and subsequent arrest information

(a) The home improvement salesperson shall submit to the registrar an application in writing containing the statement that he or she desires the issuance of a registration under the terms of this article.

The application shall be made on a form prescribed by the registrar and shall be accompanied by the fee fixed by this chapter.

(b) The registrar may refuse to register the applicant under the grounds specified in Section 480.

(c) As part of an application for a home improvement salesperson, the board shall require an applicant to furnish a full set of fingerprints for purposes of conducting criminal history record checks. Fingerprints furnished pursuant to this subdivision shall be submitted in an electronic format where readily available. Requests for alternative methods of furnishing fingerprints are subject to the approval of the registrar. The board shall use the fingerprints furnished by an applicant to obtain criminal history information on the applicant from the Department of Justice and the United States Federal Bureau of Investigation, including any subsequent arrest information available.

Added Stats 1972 ch 1138 § 14. Amended Stats 1978 ch 1161 § 368; Stats 2002 ch 744 § 10 (SB 1953); Stats 2003 ch 789 § 18 (SB 364); Stats 2004 ch 909 § 27.5 (SB 136), effective September 30, 2004; Stats 2007 ch 240 § 3 (AB 936), effective January 1, 2008.

§ 7153.2. Expiration of registrations

All home improvement salesperson registrations issued under the provisions of this article shall expire two years from the last day of the month in which the registration was issued, or two years from the date on which the renewed registration last expired.

Added Stats 1972 ch 1138 § 15. Amended Stats 1983 ch 891 § 33; Stats 1991 ch 1160 § 44 (AB 2190); Stats 2015 ch 281 § 4 (SB 561), effective January 1, 2016.

§ 7153.3. Renewal of registration; Delinquent renewal penalty; Abandonment of application; Petition

(a) To renew a home improvement salesperson registration, which has not expired, the registrant shall before the time at which the registration would otherwise expire, apply for renewal on a form prescribed by the registrar and pay a renewal fee prescribed by this chapter. Renewal of an unexpired registration shall continue the registration in effect for the two-year period following the expiration date of the registration, when it shall expire if it is not again renewed.

(b) An application for renewal of registration is delinquent if the application is not postmarked or received via electronic transmission as authorized by Section 7156.6 by the date on which the registration would otherwise expire. A registration may, however, still be renewed at any time within three years after its expiration upon the filing of an application for renewal on a form prescribed by the registrar and the payment of the renewal fee prescribed by this chapter and a delinquent renewal penalty equal to 50 percent of the renewal fee. If a registration is not renewed within three years, the person shall make a new application for registration pursuant to Section 7153.1.

(c) (1) The registrar may refuse to renew a registration for failure by the registrant to complete the application for renewal of registration. If a registrant fails to return the application rejected for insufficiency or incompleteness within 90 days from the original date of rejection, the application and fee shall be deemed abandoned. Any application abandoned may not be reinstated. However, the person may file a new application for registration pursuant to Section 7153.1.

(2) The registrar may review and accept the petition of a person who disputes the abandonment of his or her renewal application upon a showing of good cause. This petition shall be received within 90 days of the date the application for renewal is deemed abandoned.

(d) This section shall become operative on July 1, 2017.

Added Stats 2016 ch 799 § 39 (SB 1039), effective January 1, 2017, operative July 1, 2017.

§ 7154. Notification of employment of registered salesperson; Notification when registered salesperson ceases employment; Discipline for failure to report regarding employment of registered salesperson; Discipline for employment of unregistered salesperson

(a) A home improvement contractor licensed under this chapter shall notify the registrar in writing, on a form prescribed by the registrar, about the employment of a registered home improvement salesperson, pursuant to the terms of this article. This notification requirement shall include, but not be limited to, the name and registration number of the home improvement salesperson who is employed by the contractor. The form shall be submitted prior to the home improvement salesperson beginning work for the contractor.

(b) A home improvement contractor shall notify the registrar in writing, on a form prescribed by the registrar, when a registered home improvement salesperson ceases to be employed by the contractor. This notification requirement shall include, but not be limited to, the name and registration number of the home improvement salesperson who had been employed by the contractor. The form shall be submitted within 90 days after the home improvement salesperson ceases to be employed by the contractor.

(c) A home improvement contractor who employs a registered home improvement salesperson to sell home improvement contracts, but who fails to report to the registrar pursuant to subdivision (a) or (b), is subject to disciplinary action by the registrar.

(d) A home improvement contractor who employs a person to sell home improvement contracts while that person is not registered by the registrar as a home improvement salesperson as provided in this article, is subject to disciplinary action by the registrar.

Added Stats 1972 ch 1138 § 18. Amended Stats 2015 ch 281 § 6 (SB 561), effective January 1, 2016.

§ 7155. Discipline of salesman

Violation of any provision of this chapter by a home improvement salesperson constitutes cause for disciplinary action. The registrar may suspend or revoke the registration of the home improvement salesperson if he or she is found to be in violation. The disciplinary proceedings shall be conducted in accordance with Chapter 5 (commencing with Section 11500) of Part 1 of Division 3 of Title 2 of the Government Code.

Added Stats 1972 ch 1138 § 20. Amended Stats 2011 ch 296 § 16 (AB 1023), effective January 1, 2012.

§ 7155.5. Discipline of contractor for salesperson's violations

Violations of any provisions of this chapter by a home improvement salesperson likewise constitute cause for disciplinary action against the contractor, by whom he or she was employed at the time the violation occurred, whether or not the contractor had knowledge of or participated in the act or omission constituting violations of this chapter.

Added Stats 1972 ch 1138 § 21. Amended Stats 1997 ch 812 § 5 (SB 857), ch 813 § 3 (SB 825); Stats 2015 ch 281 § 7 (SB 561), effective January 1, 2016.

§ 7156. Misdemeanors; Grounds for discipline

It shall be a misdemeanor and a cause for disciplinary action to commit any of the following acts:

(a) For any home improvement salesperson to fail to account for or to remit to their employing contractor any payment received in connection with any home improvement transaction or any other transaction involving a work of improvement.

(b) For any person to use a contract form in connection with any home improvement transaction or any other transaction involving a work of improvement if the form fails to disclose the name of the contractor principal by whom the person is employed.

(c) For any home improvement salesperson to assist, recommend, select, or otherwise guide an owner or tenant in the selection of a contractor for the performance or sale of home improvement goods or services if notification of employment by the home improvement contractor, as required by subdivision (a) of Section 7154, has not been received by the Board.

Added Stats 1969 ch 1583 § 2 as § 7026.8. Amended and Renumbered Stats 1972 ch 1138 § 1.2; Stats 1997 ch 812 § 6 (SB 857), ch 813 § 4 (SB 825); Stats 2015 ch 281 § 8 (SB 561), effective January 1, 2016; Stats 2021 ch 249 § 3 (SB 757), effective January 1, 2022.

§ 7156.6. Electronic transmission of applications, renewals, and notices

(a) Notwithstanding any other law, the board may implement a system that provides for the electronic transmission of an initial application or renewal application for the registration required by this article and the electronic transmission of the notices required by Section 7154.

(b) The board by regulation may specify the form and manner of these transmissions, including the adoption of any protocols necessary to ensure the validity and security of any information, data, or document transmitted electronically. Upon the effective date of the regulations, the electronic submission of an initial registration application, a renewal application, or the electronic transmission of a notice required by Section 7154 shall satisfy the requirements of this article.

Added Stats 2015 ch 281 § 9 (SB 561), effective January 1, 2016.

§ 7157. Prohibited inducements

(a) Except as otherwise provided in subdivision (b), as a part of or in connection with the inducement to enter into any home improvement contract or other contract, which may be performed by a contractor, no person may promise or offer to pay, credit, or allow to any owner, compensation or reward for the procurement or placing of home improvement business with others.

(b) A contractor or his or her agent or salesperson may give tangible items to prospective customers for advertising or sales promotion purposes where the gift is not conditioned upon obtaining a contract for home improvement work if the gift does not exceed a value of five dollars ($5) and only one such gift is given in connection with any one transaction.

(c) No salesperson or contractor's agent may accept any compensation of any kind, for or on account of a home improvement transaction, or any other transaction involving a work of improvement, from any person other than the contractor whom he or she represents with respect to the transaction, nor shall the salesperson or agent make any payment to any person other than his or her employer on account of the sales transaction.

(d) No contractor shall pay, credit, or allow any consideration or compensation of any kind to any other contractor or salesperson other than a licensee for or on account of the performance of any work of improvement or services, including, but not limited to, home improvement work or services, except: (1) where the person to or from whom the consideration is to be paid is not subject to or is exempted from the licensing requirements of this chapter, or (2) where the transaction is not subject to the requirements of this chapter.

As used in this section "owners" shall also mean "tenant."

Commission of any act prohibited by this section is a misdemeanor and constitutes a cause for disciplinary action.

Added Stats 1969 ch 1583 § 3, as B & P C § 7026.9. Renumbered by Stats 1972 ch 1138 § 1.3. Amended Stats 1997 ch 812 § 7 (SB 857), ch 813 § 5 (SB 825).

§ 7158. [Section repealed 2021.]

Added Stats 1969 ch 1583 § 5 as § 7028.1. Amended and renumbered Stats 1972 ch 1138 § 1.4; Amended Stats 1994 ch 175 § 2 (SB 634), effective July 9, 1994; Stats 2020 ch 92 § 3 (AB 1869), effective September 18, 2020, repealed July 1, 2021.

—See Penal Code Section 532e, Rebates, in Appendix.

§ 7158. False completion certificates

(a) Any person who shall accept or receive a completion certificate or other evidence that performance of a contract for a work of improvement, including, but not limited to, a home improvement, is complete or satisfactorily concluded, with knowledge that the document is false and that the performance is not substantially completed, and who shall utter, offer, or use the document in connection with the making or accepting of any assignment or negotiation of the right to receive any payment from the owner, under or in connection with a contract, or for the purpose of obtaining or granting any credit or loan on the security of the right to receive any payment shall be guilty of a misdemeanor and subject to a fine of not less than five hundred dollars ($500) nor more than five thousand dollars ($5,000), or to imprisonment in the county jail for a term of not less than one month nor more than one year, or both.

(b) (1) Any person who violates this section as part of a plan or scheme to defraud an owner of a residential or nonresidential structure, including a mobilehome or manufactured home, in connection with the offer or performance of repairs to the structure for damage caused by a natural disaster, shall be ordered by the court to make full restitution to the victim based on the person's ability to pay, defined as the overall capability of the defendant to reimburse the costs, or a portion of the costs, including consideration of, but not limited to, all of the following:

(A) The defendant's present financial position.

(B) The defendant's reasonably discernible future financial position, provided that the court shall not consider a period of more than one year from the date of the hearing for purposes of determining the reasonably discernible future financial position of the defendant.

(C) The likelihood that the defendant will be able to obtain employment within one year from the date of the hearing.

(D) Any other factor that may bear upon the defendant's financial capability to reimburse the county for costs.

(2) In addition to full restitution, and imprisonment authorized by subdivision (a), the court may impose a fine of not less than five hundred dollars ($500) nor more than twenty-five thousand dollars ($25,000), based upon the defendant's ability to pay. This subdivision applies to natural disasters for which a state of emergency is proclaimed by the Governor pursuant to Section 8625 of the Government Code or for which an emergency or major disaster is declared by the President of the United States.

(c) This section shall become operative on July 1, 2021.

Added Stats 2020 ch 92 § 4 (AB 1869), effective September 18, 2020, operative July 1, 2021.

—See Penal Code Section 532e, Rebates, in Appendix.

§ 7159. Requirements for home improvement contracts

(a) (1) This section identifies the projects for which a home improvement contract is required, outlines the contract requirements, and lists the items that shall be included in the contract, or may be provided as an attachment.

(2) This section does not apply to service and repair contracts that are subject to Section 7159.10, if the contract for the applicable services complies with Sections 7159.10 to 7159.14, inclusive.

(3) This section does not apply to the sale, installation, and servicing of a fire alarm sold in conjunction with an alarm system, as defined in Section 7590.1, if all costs attributable to making the fire alarm system operable, including sale and installation costs, do not exceed five hundred dollars ($500), and the licensee complies with the requirements set forth in Section 7159.9.

(4) This section does not apply to any costs associated with monitoring a burglar or fire alarm system.

(5) Failure by the licensee, their agent or salesperson, or by a person subject to be licensed under this chapter, to provide the specified information, notices, and disclosures in the contract, or to otherwise fail to comply with any provision of this section, is cause for discipline.

(b) For purposes of this section, "home improvement contract" means an agreement, whether oral or written, or contained in one or more documents, between a contractor and an owner or between a contractor and a tenant, regardless of the number of residence or dwelling units contained in the building in which the tenant resides, if the work is to be performed in, to, or upon the residence or dwelling unit of the tenant, for the performance of a home improvement, as defined in Section 7151, and includes all labor, services, and materials to be furnished and performed thereunder, if the aggregate contract price specified in one or more improvement contracts, including all labor, services, and materials to be furnished by the contractor, exceeds five hundred dollars ($500). "Home improvement contract" also means an agreement, whether oral or written, or contained in one or more documents, between a salesperson, whether or not they are a home improvement salesperson, and an owner or a tenant, regardless of the number of residence or dwelling units contained in the building in which the tenant resides, which provides for the sale, installation, or furnishing of home improvement goods or services.

(c) In addition to the specific requirements listed under this section, every home improvement contract and any person subject to licensure under this chapter or their agent or salesperson shall comply with all of the following:

(1) The writing shall be legible.

(2) Any printed form shall be readable. Unless a larger typeface is specified in this article, text in any printed form shall be in at least 10-point typeface and the headings shall be in at least 10-point boldface type.

(3) (A) Before any work is started, the contractor shall give the buyer a copy of the contract signed and dated by both the contractor and the buyer. The buyer's receipt of the copy of the contract initiates the buyer's rights to cancel the contract pursuant to Sections 1689.5 to 1689.14, inclusive, of the Civil Code.

(B) The contract shall contain on the first page, in a typeface no smaller than that generally used in the body of the document, both of the following:

(i) The date the buyer signed the contract.

(ii) The name and address of the contractor to which the applicable "Notice of Cancellation" is to be mailed, immediately preceded by a statement advising the buyer that the "Notice of Cancellation" may be sent to the contractor at the address noted on the contract.

(4) The contract shall include a statement that, upon satisfactory payment being made for any portion of the work performed, the contractor, prior to any further payment being made, shall furnish to the person contracting for the home improvement or swimming pool work a full and unconditional release from any potential lien claimant claim or mechanics lien authorized pursuant to Sections 8400 and 8404 of the Civil Code for that portion of the work for which payment has been made.

(5) A change-order form for changes or extra work shall be incorporated into the contract and shall become part of the contract only if it is in writing and signed by the parties prior to the commencement of any work covered by a change order.

(6) The contract shall contain, in close proximity to the signatures of the owner and contractor, a notice stating that the owner or tenant has the right to require the contractor to have a performance and payment bond.

(7) If the contract provides for a contractor to furnish joint control, the contractor shall not have any financial or other interest in the joint control.

(8) The provisions of this section are not exclusive and do not relieve the contractor from compliance with any other applicable provision of law.

(d) A home improvement contract and any changes to the contract shall be in writing and signed by the parties to the contract prior to the commencement of work covered by the contract or an applicable change order and, except as provided in paragraph (8) of subdivision (a) of Section 7159.5, shall include or comply with all of the following:

(1) The name, business address, and license number of the contractor.

(2) If applicable, the name and registration number of the home improvement salesperson that solicited or negotiated the contract.

(3) The following heading on the contract form that identifies the type of contract in at least 10-point boldface type: "Home Improvement."

(4) The following statement in at least 12-point boldface type: "You are entitled to a completely filled in copy of this agreement, signed by both you and the contractor, before any work may be started."

(5) The heading: "Contract Price," followed by the amount of the contract in dollars and cents.

(6) If a finance charge will be charged, the heading: "Finance Charge," followed by the amount in dollars and cents. The finance charge is to be set out separately from the contract amount.

(7) The heading: "Description of the Project and Description of the Significant Materials to be Used and Equipment to be Installed," followed by a description of the project and a description of the significant materials to be used and equipment to be installed. For swimming pools, the project description required under this paragraph also shall include a plan and scale drawing showing the shape, size, dimensions, and the construction and equipment specifications.

(8) If a downpayment will be charged, the details of the downpayment shall be expressed in substantially the following form, and shall include the text of the notice as specified in subparagraph (C):

(A) The heading: "Downpayment."

(B) A space where the actual downpayment appears.

(C) The following statement in at least 12-point boldface type: "THE DOWNPAYMENT MAY NOT EXCEED $1,000 OR 10 PERCENT OF THE CONTRACT PRICE, WHICHEVER IS LESS."

(9) If payments, other than the downpayment, are to be made before the project is completed, the details of these payments, known as progress payments, shall be expressed in substantially the following form, and shall include the text of the statement as specified in subparagraph (C):

(A) A schedule of progress payments shall be preceded by the heading: "Schedule of Progress Payments."

(B) Each progress payment shall be stated in dollars and cents and specifically reference the amount of work or services to be performed and materials and equipment to be supplied.

(C) The section of the contract reserved for the progress payments shall include the following statement in at least 12-point boldface type: "The schedule of progress payments must specifically describe each phase of work, including the type and amount of work or services scheduled to be supplied in each phase, along with the amount of each proposed progress payment. IT IS AGAINST THE LAW FOR A CONTRACTOR TO COLLECT PAYMENT FOR WORK NOT YET COMPLETED, OR FOR MATERIALS NOT YET DELIVERED.

HOWEVER, A CONTRACTOR MAY REQUIRE A DOWNPAY-MENT."

(10) The contract shall address the commencement of work to be performed in substantially the following form:

(A) A statement that describes what constitutes substantial commencement of work under the contract.

(B) The heading: "Approximate Start Date."

(C) The approximate date on which work will be commenced.

(11) The estimated completion date of the work shall be referenced in the contract in substantially the following form:

(A) The heading: "Approximate Completion Date."

(B) The approximate date of completion.

(12) If applicable, the heading: "List of Documents to be Incorporated into the Contract," followed by the list of documents incorporated into the contract.

(13) The heading: "Note About Extra Work and Change Orders," followed by the following statement:

"Extra Work and Change Orders become part of the contract once the order is prepared in writing and signed by the parties prior to the commencement of work covered by the new change order. The order must describe the scope of the extra work or change, the cost to be added or subtracted from the contract, and the effect the order will have on the schedule of progress payments."

(e) Except as provided in paragraph (8) of subdivision (a) of Section 7159.5, all of the following notices shall be provided to the owner as part of the contract form as specified or, if otherwise authorized under this subdivision, may be provided as an attachment to the contract:

(1) A notice concerning commercial general liability insurance. This notice may be provided as an attachment to the contract if the contract includes the following statement: "A notice concerning commercial general liability insurance is attached to this contract." The notice shall include the heading "Commercial General Liability Insurance (CGL)," followed by whichever of the following statements is both relevant and correct:

(A) "(The name on the license or 'This contractor') does not carry commercial general liability insurance."

(B) "(The name on the license or 'This contractor') carries commercial general liability insurance written by (the insurance company). You may call (the insurance company) at _____ to check the contractor's insurance coverage."

(C) "(The name on the license or 'This contractor') is self-insured."

(D) "(The name on the license or 'This contractor') is a limited liability company that carries liability insurance or maintains other security as required by law. You may call (the insurance company or trust

company or bank) at _____
to check on the contractor's insurance coverage or security."

(2) A notice concerning workers' compensation insurance. This notice may be provided as an attachment to the contract if the contract includes the statement: "A notice concerning workers' compensation insurance is attached to this contract." The notice shall include the heading "Workers' Compensation Insurance" followed by whichever of the following statements is correct:

(A) "(The name on the license or 'This contractor') has no employees and is exempt from workers' compensation requirements."

(B) "(The name on the license or 'This contractor') carries workers' compensation insurance for all employees."

(3) A notice that provides the buyer with the following information about the performance of extra or change-order work:

(A) A statement that the buyer may not require a contractor to perform extra or change-order work without providing written authorization prior to the commencement of work covered by the new change order.

(B) A statement informing the buyer that extra work or a change order is not enforceable against a buyer unless the change order also identifies all of the following in writing prior to the commencement of work covered by the new change order:

(i) The scope of work encompassed by the order.

(ii) The amount to be added or subtracted from the contract.

(iii) The effect the order will make in the progress payments or the completion date.

(C) A statement informing the buyer that the contractor's failure to comply with the requirements of this paragraph does not preclude the recovery of compensation for work performed based upon legal or equitable remedies designed to prevent unjust enrichment.

(4) A notice with the heading "Mechanics Lien Warning" written as follows:

MECHANICS LIEN WARNING:

Anyone who helps improve your property, but who is not paid, may record what is called a mechanics lien on your property. A mechanics lien is a claim, like a mortgage or home equity loan, made against your property and recorded with the county recorder.

Even if you pay your contractor in full, unpaid subcontractors, suppliers, and laborers who helped to improve your property may record mechanics liens and sue you in court to foreclose the lien. If a court finds the lien is valid, you could be forced to pay twice or have a court officer sell your home to pay the lien. Liens can also affect your credit.

To preserve their right to record a lien, each subcontractor and material supplier must provide you with a document called a 'Preliminary Notice.' This notice is not a lien. The purpose of the notice is to let you know that the person who sends you the notice has the right to record a lien on your property if they are not paid.

BE CAREFUL. The Preliminary Notice can be sent up to 20 days after the subcontractor starts work or the supplier provides material. This can be a big problem if you pay your contractor before you have received the Preliminary Notices.

You will not get Preliminary Notices from your prime contractor or from laborers who work on your project. The law assumes that you already know they are improving your property.

PROTECT YOURSELF FROM LIENS. You can protect yourself from liens by getting a list from your contractor of all the subcontractors and material suppliers that work on your project. Find out from your contractor when these subcontractors started work and when these suppliers delivered goods or materials. Then wait 20 days, paying attention to the Preliminary Notices you receive.

PAY WITH JOINT CHECKS. One way to protect yourself is to pay with a joint check. When your contractor tells you it is time to pay for the work of a subcontractor or supplier who has provided you with a Preliminary Notice, write a joint check payable to both the contractor and the subcontractor or material supplier.

For other ways to prevent liens, visit CSLB's internet website at www.cslb.ca.gov or call CSLB at 800-321-CSLB (2752).

REMEMBER, IF YOU DO NOTHING, YOU RISK HAVING A LIEN PLACED ON YOUR HOME. This can mean that you may have to pay twice, or face the forced sale of your home to pay what you owe.

(5) The following notice shall be provided in at least 12-point typeface:

Information about the Contractors State License Board (CSLB): CSLB is the state consumer protection agency that licenses and regulates construction contractors.

Contact CSLB for information about the licensed contractor you are considering, including information about disclosable complaints, disciplinary actions, and civil judgments that are reported to CSLB.

Use only licensed contractors. If you file a complaint against a licensed contractor within the legal deadline (usually four years), CSLB has authority to investigate the complaint. If you use an unlicensed contractor, CSLB may not be able to help you resolve your complaint. Your only remedy may be in civil court, and you may be liable for damages arising out of any injuries to the unlicensed contractor or the unlicensed contractor's employees.

For more information:

Visit CSLB's internet website at www.cslb.ca.gov

Call CSLB at 800-321-CSLB (2752)

Write CSLB at P.O. Box 26000, Sacramento, CA 95826.

Section VI

(6) (A) The notice set forth in subparagraph (B) and entitled "Three-Day Right to Cancel," or entitled "Five-Day Right to Cancel" for contracts with a senior citizen, shall be provided to the buyer unless the contract is:

(i) Negotiated at the contractor's place of business.

(ii) Subject to the "Seven-Day Right to Cancel," as set forth in paragraph (7).

(iii) Subject to licensure under the Alarm Company Act (Chapter 11.6 (commencing with Section 7590)), provided the alarm company licensee complies with Sections 1689.5, 1689.6, and 1689.7 of the Civil Code, as applicable.

(B) (i) Three-Day Right to Cancel

You, the buyer, have the right to cancel this contract within three business days. You may cancel by emailing, mailing, faxing, or delivering a written notice to the contractor at the contractor's place of business by midnight of the third business day after you received a signed and dated copy of the contract that includes this notice. Include your name, your address, and the date you received the signed copy of the contract and this notice.

If you cancel, the contractor must return to you anything you paid within 10 days of receiving the notice of cancellation. For your part, you must make available to the contractor at your residence, in substantially as good condition as you received them, goods delivered to you under this contract or sale. Or, you may, if you wish, comply with the contractor's instructions on how to return the goods at the contractor's expense and risk. If you do make the goods available to the contractor and the contractor does not pick them up within 20 days of the date of your notice of cancellation, you may keep them without any further obligation. If you fail to make the goods available to the contractor, or if you agree to return the goods to the contractor and fail to do so, then you remain liable for performance of all obligations under the contract.

(ii) References to "three" and "third" in the notice set forth in clause (i) shall be changed to "five" and "fifth," respectively, for a buyer who is a senior citizen.

(C) The notice required by this paragraph shall comply with all of the following:

(i) The text of the notice is at least 12-point boldface type.

(ii) The notice is in immediate proximity to a space reserved for the owner's signature.

(iii) The owner acknowledges receipt of the notice by signing and dating the notice form in the signature space.

(iv) The notice is written in the same language, e.g., Spanish, as that principally used in any oral sales presentation.

(v) The notice may be attached to the contract if the contract includes, in at least 12-point boldface type, a checkbox with one of the following statements, as applicable:

(I) For a contract with a senior citizen: "The law requires that the contractor give you a notice explaining your right to cancel. Initial the checkbox if the contractor has given you a 'Notice of the Five-Day Right to Cancel.'"

(II) For all other contracts: "The law requires that the contractor give you a notice explaining your right to cancel. Initial the checkbox if the contractor has given you a 'Notice of the Three-Day Right to Cancel.'"

(vi) (I) The notice shall be accompanied by a completed form in duplicate, captioned "Notice of Cancellation," which also shall be attached to the agreement or offer to purchase and be easily detachable, and which shall contain the following statement written in the same language, e.g., Spanish, as used in the contract:

"Notice of Cancellation"

/enter date of transaction/
(Date)

You may cancel this transaction, without any penalty or obligation, within three business days from the above date.

If you cancel, any property traded in, any payments made by you under the contract or sale, and any negotiable instrument executed by you will be returned within 10 days following receipt by the seller of your cancellation notice, and any security interest arising out of the transaction will be canceled.

If you cancel, you must make available to the seller at your residence, in substantially as good condition as when received, any goods delivered to you under this contract or sale, or you may, if you wish, comply with the instructions of the seller regarding the return shipment of the goods at the seller's expense and risk.

If you do make the goods available to the seller and the seller does not pick them up within 20 days of the date of your notice of cancellation, you may retain or dispose of the goods without any further obligation. If you fail to make the goods available to the seller, or if you agree to return the goods to the seller and fail to do so, then you remain liable for performance of all obligations under the contract.

To cancel this transaction, mail or deliver a signed and dated copy of this cancellation notice, or any other written notice, or send a telegram to _____,

/name of seller/

at _____

/address of seller's place of business/

not later than midnight of _____.

(Date)

I hereby cancel this transaction. _____

(Date)

_____

(Buyer's signature)

(II) The reference to "three" in the statement set forth in subclause (I) shall be changed to "five" for a buyer who is a senior citizen.

(7)(A) The following notice entitled "Seven-Day Right to Cancel" shall be provided to the buyer for any contract that is written for the repair or restoration of residential premises damaged by any sudden or catastrophic event for which a state of emergency has been declared by the President of the United States or the Governor, or for which a local emergency has been declared by the executive officer or governing body of any city, county, or city and county:

Seven-Day Right to Cancel

You, the buyer, have the right to cancel this contract within seven business days. You may cancel by emailing, mailing, faxing, or delivering a written notice to the contractor at the contractor's place of business by midnight of the seventh business day after you received a signed and dated copy of the contract that includes this notice. Include your name, your address, and the date you received the signed copy of the contract and this notice.

If you cancel, the contractor must return to you anything you paid within 10 days of receiving the notice of cancellation. For your part, you must make available to the contractor at your residence, in substantially as good condition as you received them, goods delivered to you under this contract or sale. Or, you may, if you wish, comply with the contractor's instructions on how to return the goods at the contractor's expense and risk. If you do make the goods available to the contractor and the contractor does not pick them up within 20 days of the date of your notice of cancellation, you may keep them without any further obligation. If you fail to make the goods available to the contractor, or if you agree to return the goods to the contractor and fail to do so, then you remain liable for performance of all obligations under the contract.

(B) The "Seven-Day Right to Cancel" notice required by this subdivision shall comply with all of the following:

(i) The text of the notice is at least 12-point boldface type.

(ii) The notice is in immediate proximity to a space reserved for the owner's signature.

(iii) The owner acknowledges receipt of the notice by signing and dating the notice form in the signature space.

(iv) The notice is written in the same language, e.g., Spanish, as that principally used in any oral sales presentation.

(v) The notice may be attached to the contract if the contract includes, in at least 12-point boldface type, a checkbox with the following statement: "The law requires that the contractor give you a notice explaining your right to cancel. Initial the checkbox if the contractor has given you a 'Notice of the Seven-Day Right to Cancel.'"

(vi) The notice shall be accompanied by a completed form in duplicate, captioned "Notice of Cancellation," which shall also be attached to the agreement or offer to purchase and be easily detachable, and which shall contain the following statement written in the same language, e.g., Spanish, as used in the contract:

"Notice of Cancellation"

_____

/enter date of transaction/

(Date)

You may cancel this transaction, without any penalty or obligation, within seven business days from the above date.

If you cancel, any property traded in, any payments made by you under the contract or sale, and any negotiable instrument executed by you will be returned within 10 days following receipt by the seller of your cancellation notice, and any security interest arising out of the transaction will be canceled.

If you cancel, you must make available to the seller at your residence, in substantially as good condition as when received, any goods delivered to you under this contract or sale, or you may, if you wish, comply with the instructions of the seller regarding the return shipment of the goods at the seller's expense and risk.

If you do make the goods available to the seller and the seller does not pick them up within 20 days of the date of your notice of cancellation, you may retain or dispose of the goods without any further obligation. If you fail to make the goods available to the seller, or if you agree to return the goods to the seller and fail to do so, then you remain liable for performance of all obligations under the contract.

To cancel this transaction, mail or deliver a signed and dated copy of this cancellation notice, or any other written notice, or send a telegram to _____,

/name of seller/

at _____

/address of seller's place of business/

not later than midnight of _____.

(Date)

I hereby cancel this transaction. _____

(Date)

_____

(Buyer's signature)

(f) The five-day right to cancel added by the act that amended paragraph (6) of subdivision (e) shall apply to contracts entered into on or after January 1, 2021.

Added Stats 2005 ch 48 § 7 (SB 1113), effective July 18, 2005, operative January 1, 2006. Amended Stats 2005 ch 385 § 2 (AB 316), effective January 1, 2006; Stats 2006 ch 114 § 1 (AB 2073), effective January 1, 2007; Stats 2007 ch 130 § 30 (AB 299), effective January 1, 2008, Stats 2007 ch 230 § 1 (AB 244), effective January 1, 2008, (ch 230 prevails); Stats 2008 ch 179 § 18 (SB 1498), effective January 1, 2009; Stats 2009 ch 307 § 74 (SB 821), effective January 1, 2010; Stats 2010 ch 697 § 4 (SB 189), effective January 1, 2011, operative July 1, 2012, ch 698 § 39 (SB 392) (ch 698 prevails), effective January 1, 2011; Stats 2011 ch 44 § 1 (SB 190), effective January 1, 2012, operative July 1, 2012; Stats 2018 ch 406 § 3 (SB 904), effective January 1, 2019; Stats 2020 ch 158 § 2 (AB 2471), effective January 1, 2021; 2020 ch 312 § 73.5 (SB 1474), effective January 1, 2021 (ch 312 prevails).

§ 7159.1. Notice in sale of home improvement goods or services

(a) In any contract for the sale of home improvement goods or services offered by door-to-door sale that contains or is secured by a lien on real property, the contract shall be accompanied by the following notice in 18-point boldfaced type:

"WARNING TO BUYER: IF YOU SIGN THE CONTRACT WHICH ACCOMPANIES THIS NOTICE, YOU WILL BE PUTTING UP YOUR HOME AS SECURITY. THIS MEANS THAT YOUR HOME COULD BE SOLD WITHOUT YOUR PERMISSION AND WITHOUT ANY COURT ACTION IF YOU MISS ANY PAYMENT REQUIRED BY THIS CONTRACT."

This notice shall be written in the same language as the rest of the contract. It shall be on a separate piece of paper from the rest of the contract and shall be signed and dated by the buyer. The home improvement contractor or home improvement salesperson shall deliver to the buyer at the time of the buyer's signing and dating of the notice a legible copy of the signed and dated notice. A security interest created in any contract described in this section that does not provide the notice as required by this section shall be void and unenforceable.

(b) This section shall not apply to any of the following:

(1) Any contract that is subject to Chapter 1 (commencing with Section 1801) of Title 2 of Part 4 of Division 3 of the Civil Code.

(2) A mechanics lien established pursuant to Chapter 4 (commencing with Section 8400) of Title 2 of Part 6 of Division 4 of the Civil Code.

(3) Any contract that is subject to subdivision (a) of Section 7159.2.

Added Stats 1998 ch 571 § 1 (AB 2301). Amended Stats 2010 ch 697 § 5 (SB 189), effective January 1, 2011, operative July 1, 2012.

§ 7159.2. Security interest for home improvement goods or services

(a) No home improvement goods or services contract of a value of five thousand dollars ($5,000) or less shall provide for a security interest in real property, except for a mechanic's lien or other interest in property that arises by operation of law. Any lien in violation of this subdivision is void and unenforceable.

(b) When the proceeds of a loan secured by a mortgage on real property are used to fund goods or services pursuant to a home improvement goods or services contract of more than five thousand dollars ($5,000), the person or entity making the loan shall only pay a contractor under the home improvement goods or services contract from the proceeds of the loan by either of the following methods:

(1) By an instrument payable to the borrower or jointly to the borrower and the contractor.

(2) At the election of the borrower, through a third-party escrow agent pursuant to the terms of a written agreement signed by the borrower, the person or entity making the loan, and the contractor prior to the disbursement.

(c) Any person or entity who violates any provision of this section shall be liable for actual damages suffered by the borrower for damages that proximately result from the violation.

(d) Any person or entity who intentionally or as a pattern or practice violates any provision of this section shall be additionally liable for three times the contract price for the home improvement.

(e) Any person who is a senior citizen or disabled person, as defined in subdivisions (f) and (g) of Section 1761 of the Civil Code, as part of any action for a violation of this section, may seek and be awarded, in addition to the remedies provided in this section, up to five thousand dollars ($5,000) as provided in subdivision (b) of Section 1780 of the Civil Code.

(f) The court shall award court costs and attorney's fees to a prevailing plaintiff in an action brought pursuant to this section. Reasonable attorney's fees may be awarded to a prevailing defendant upon a finding by the court that the plaintiff's prosecution of the action was not in good faith.

Added Stats 1998 ch 571 § 2 (AB 2301). Amended Stats 1999 ch 512 § 1 (SB 187).

§ 7159.5. [Section repealed 2021.]

Added Stats 2004 ch 566 § 8 (SB 30), operative July 1, 2005. Amended Stats 2005 ch 48 § 11 (SB 1113), effective July 18, 2005, operative January 1, 2006; Stats 2005 ch 385 § 5 (AB 316); Stats 2007 ch 230 § 2 (AB 244), effective January 1, 2008; Stats 2009 ch 307 § 75 (SB 821), effective January 1, 2010; Stats 2010 ch 697 § 6 (SB 189), effective January 1, 2011, operative July 1, 2012; Stats 2011 ch 44 § 2 (SB 190), effective January 1, 2012, operative July 1, 2012; Stats 2016 ch 634 § 5 (SB 1479), effective January 1, 2017; Stats 2020 ch 92 § 5 (AB 1869), effective September 18, 2020, repealed July 1, 2021.

§ 7159.5. Contract amount; Finance charges; Downpayment; Violations; Restitution and punishment

This section applies to all home improvement contracts, as defined in Section 7151.2, between an owner or tenant and a contractor, whether a general contractor or a specialty contractor, that is licensed or subject to be licensed pursuant to this chapter with regard to the transaction.

(a) Failure by the licensee or a person subject to be licensed under this chapter, or by their agent or salesperson, to comply with the following provisions is cause for discipline:

(1) The contract shall be in writing and shall include the agreed contract amount in dollars and cents. The contract amount shall include the entire cost of the contract, including profit, labor, and materials, but excluding finance charges.

(2) If there is a separate finance charge between the contractor and the person contracting for home improvement, the finance charge shall be set out separately from the contract amount.

(3) If a downpayment will be charged, the downpayment shall not exceed one thousand dollars ($1,000) or 10 percent of the contract amount, whichever amount is less.

(4) If, in addition to a downpayment, the contract provides for payments to be made prior to completion of the work, the contract shall include a schedule of payments in dollars and cents specifically referencing the amount of work or services to be performed and any materials and equipment to be supplied.

(5) Except for a downpayment, the contractor shall neither request nor accept payment that exceeds the value of the work performed or material delivered. The prohibition prescribed by this paragraph extends to advance payment in whole or in part from any lender or financier for the performance or sale of home improvement goods or services.

(6) Upon any payment by the person contracting for home improvement, and prior to any further payment being made, the contractor shall, if requested, obtain and furnish to the person a full and unconditional release from any potential lien claimant claim

or mechanics lien authorized pursuant to Sections 8400 and 8404 of the Civil Code for any portion of the work for which payment has been made. The person contracting for home improvement may withhold all further payments until these releases are furnished.

(7) If the contract provides for a payment of a salesperson's commission out of the contract price, that payment shall be made on a pro rata basis in proportion to the schedule of payments made to the contractor by the disbursing party in accordance with paragraph (4).

(8) A contractor furnishing a performance and payment bond, lien and completion bond, or a bond equivalent or joint control approved by the registrar covering full performance and payment is exempt from paragraphs (3), (4), and (5), and need not include, as part of the contract, the statement regarding the downpayment specified in subparagraph (C) of paragraph (8) of subdivision (d) of Section 7159, the details and statement regarding progress payments specified in paragraph (9) of subdivision (d) of Section 7159, or the Mechanics Lien Warning specified in paragraph (4) of subdivision (e) of Section 7159. A contractor furnishing these bonds, bond equivalents, or a joint control approved by the registrar may accept payment prior to completion. If the contract provides for a contractor to furnish joint control, the contractor shall not have any financial or other interest in the joint control. Notwithstanding any other law, a licensee shall be licensed in this state in an active status for not less than two years prior to submitting an Application for Approval of Blanket Performance and Payment Bond as provided in Section 858.2 of Title 16 of the California Code of Regulations as it read on January 1, 2016.

(b) (1) A violation of paragraph (1), (3), or (5) of subdivision (a) by a licensee or a person subject to be licensed under this chapter, or by their agent or salesperson, is a misdemeanor punishable by a fine of not less than one hundred dollars ($100) nor more than five thousand dollars ($5,000), or by imprisonment in a county jail not exceeding one year, or by both that fine and imprisonment. If a violation occurs in a location damaged by a natural disaster for which a state of emergency is proclaimed by the Governor pursuant to Section 8625 of the Government Code or for which an emergency or major disaster is declared by the President of the United States, the court shall impose the maximum fine.

(2) (A) An indictment or information against a person who is not licensed but who is required to be licensed under this chapter shall be brought, or a criminal complaint filed, for a violation of this section, in accordance with paragraph (4) of subdivision (d) of Section 802 of the Penal Code, within four years from the date of

the contract or, if the contract is not reduced to writing, from the date the buyer makes the first payment to the contractor.

(B) An indictment or information against a person who is licensed under this chapter shall be brought, or a criminal complaint filed, for a violation of this section, in accordance with paragraph (2) of subdivision (d) of Section 802 of the Penal Code, within two years from the date of the contract or, if the contract is not reduced to writing, from the date the buyer makes the first payment to the contractor.

(C) The limitations on actions in this subdivision shall not apply to any administrative action filed against a licensed contractor.

(c) (1) Any person who violates this section as part of a plan or scheme to defraud an owner or tenant of a residential or nonresidential structure, including a mobilehome or manufactured home, in connection with the offer or performance of repairs to the structure for damage caused by a natural disaster, shall be ordered by the court to make full restitution to the victim based on the person's ability to pay, defined as the overall capability of the defendant to reimburse the costs, or a portion of the costs, including consideration of, but not limited to, all of the following:

(A) The defendant's present financial position.

(B) The defendant's reasonably discernible future financial position, provided that the court shall not consider a period of more than one year from the date of the hearing for purposes of determining the reasonably discernible future financial position of the defendant.

(C) The likelihood that the defendant will be able to obtain employment within one year from the date of the hearing.

(D) Any other factor that may bear upon the defendant's financial capability to reimburse the county for costs.

(2) In addition to full restitution, and imprisonment authorized by this section, the court may impose a fine of not less than five hundred dollars ($500) nor more than twenty-five thousand dollars ($25,000), based upon the defendant's ability to pay. This subdivision applies to natural disasters for which a state of emergency is proclaimed by the Governor pursuant to Section 8625 of the Government Code, or for which an emergency or major disaster is declared by the President of the United States.

(d) This section shall become operative on July 1, 2021.

Added Stats 2020 ch 92 § 6 (AB 1869), effective September 18, 2020, operative July 1, 2021; Amended by Stat 2021 ch 249 § 4 (SB 757), effective January 1, 2022; Stat 2023 ch 403 § 1 (SB 601), effective January 1, 2023.

§ 7159.6. Work or change order

(a) An extra work or change order is not enforceable against a buyer unless the change order sets forth all of the following:

(1) The scope of work encompassed by the order.

(2) The amount to be added or subtracted from the contract.

(3) The effect the order will make in the progress payments or the completion date.

(b) The buyer may not require a contractor to perform extra or change-order work without providing written authorization.

(c) Failure to comply with the requirements of this section does not preclude the recovery of compensation for work performed based upon legal or equitable remedies designed to prevent unjust enrichment.

(d) This section shall become operative on January 1, 2006.

Added Stats 2004 ch 566 § 9 (SB 30), operative July 1, 2005. Amended Stats 2005 ch 48 § 12 (SB 1113), effective July 18, 2005, operative January 1, 2006.

§ 7159.9. Requirements for home improvement contracts, exemption for fire alarm system

(a) Section 7159 does not apply to the sale, installation, and servicing of a fire alarm sold in conjunction with an alarm system, as defined in Section 7590.1 of the Alarm Company Act (Chapter 11.6 (commencing with Section 7590)), provided the licensee does all of the following:

(1) Complies with the contract requirements set forth in Section 7599.54.

(2) Complies with Sections 1689.5, 1689.6, and 1689.7 of the Civil Code, as applicable.

(3) Executes the following certification statement in the contract or in a separate certification document signed by all parties to the contract:

"All costs attributable to making the fire alarm system operable for the residence identified by this document, including sale and installation costs, do not exceed five hundred dollars ($500)."

(4) Certifies to the following if the certification statement described in paragraph (3) is in a separate document:

"I certify that all statements and representations made by me in this document are true and accurate."

(b) The contract or separate certification document shall also include both of the following:

(1) The physical address of the residence for which the certification is applicable.

(2) The name, business address, and license number of the contractor as contained in the official records of the board.

(c) The licensee shall give an exact copy of all documents required pursuant to this section to the party who is contracting to have the alarm system installed.

(d) All documents required pursuant to this section shall be retained by the licensee for a period of five years in accordance with the provisions of Section 7111, and shall be made available to the board within 30 days of a written request.

(e) Failure by the contractor to provide the board with the certification or contract within 30 days of a written request is cause for discipline.

(f) Failure by the licensee to provide the board with the certification or contract within 30 days of a written request creates a presumption that the licensee has violated the provisions of Section 7159, unless evidence to the contrary is presented within the timeframe specified by the board.

Added Stats 2006 ch 114 (AB 2073), effective January 1, 2007. Amended Stats 2007 ch 130 § 31 (AB 299), effective January 1, 2008; Stats 2018 ch 406 § 4 (SB 904), effective January 1, 2019.

§ 7159.10. Service and repair contract defined

(a)(1) "Service and repair contract" means an agreement between a contractor or salesperson for a contractor, whether a general contractor or a specialty contractor, who is licensed or subject to be licensed pursuant to this chapter with regard to the transaction, and a homeowner or a tenant, for the performance of a home improvement as defined in Section 7151, that conforms to the following requirements:

(A) The contract amount is seven hundred fifty dollars ($750) or less.

(B) The prospective buyer initiated contact with the contractor to request the work.

(C) The contractor does not sell the buyer goods or services beyond those reasonably necessary to take care of the particular problem that caused the buyer to contact the contractor.

(D) No payment is due, or accepted by the contractor, until the work is completed.

(2) As used in this subdivision, "the work is completed" means that all of the conditions that caused the buyer to contact the contractor for service and repairs have been fully corrected and, if applicable, the building department has accepted and approved the corrective work.

(b) For any contract written pursuant to subdivision (a) or otherwise presented to the buyer as a service and repair contract, unless all of the conforming requirements for service and repair contracts specified in subdivision (a) are met, the contract requirements for home improvements set forth in subdivisions (c), (d), and (e) of Section 7159 shall be applicable, including any rights to rescind the contract as set forth in Section 1689.6 or 1689.7 of the Civil Code, regardless of the aggregate contract price.

(c) If all of the requirements of subdivision (a) are met, only those notices and other requirements set forth in this section are applicable to the contract.

(d) Every service and repair contract described in subdivision (a) shall include, or otherwise comply with, all of the following:

(1) The contract, any changes to the contract, and any attachments shall be in writing and signed or acknowledged by the parties as set forth in this section, and shall be written in the same language (for example Spanish) as principally used in the oral sales presentation.

(2) The writing shall be legible.

(3) Any printed form shall be readable. Unless a larger typeface is specified in this article, the text shall be in at least 10-point typeface and the headings shall be in at least 10-point boldface type.

(4) Before any work is started, the contractor shall give the buyer a copy of the contract signed and dated by the buyer and by the contractor or the contractor's representative.

(5) The name, business address, and license number of the contractor.

(6) The date the contract was signed.

(7) A notice concerning commercial general liability insurance. This notice may be provided as an attachment to the contract if the contract includes the statement, "A notice concerning commercial general liability insurance is attached to this contract." The notice shall include the heading "Commercial General Liability Insurance (CGL)" followed by whichever of the following statements is both relevant and correct:

(A) "(The name on the license or 'This contractor') does not carry commercial general liability insurance."

(B) "(The name on the license or 'This contractor') carries commercial general liability insurance written by (the insurance company). You may call the (insurance company) at _____ to check the contractor's insurance coverage."

(C) "(The name on the license or 'This contractor') is self-insured."

(D) "(The name on the license or 'This contractor') is a limited liability company that carries liability insurance or maintains other security as required by law. You may call (the insurance company or trust company or bank) at _____ to check on the contractor's insurance coverage or security."

(8) A notice concerning workers' compensation insurance. This notice may be provided as an attachment to the contract if the contract includes the statement "A notice concerning workers' compensation

Section VI

insurance is attached to this contract." The notice shall include the heading "Workers' Compensation Insurance" followed by whichever of the following statements is both relevant and correct:

(A) "(The name on the license or 'This contractor') has no employees and is exempt from workers' compensation requirements."

(B) "(The name on the license or 'This contractor') carries workers' compensation insurance for all employees."

(e) Every service and repair contract described in subdivision (a) shall provide the following information, notices, and disclosures in the contract:

(1) Notice of the type of contract in at least 10-point boldface type: "Service and Repair."

(2) A notice in at least 12-point boldface type, signed and dated by the buyer: Notice to the Buyer: The law requires that service and repair contracts must meet all of the following requirements:

(A) The price must be no more than seven hundred and fifty dollars ($750).

(B) You, the buyer, must have initiated contact with the contractor to request the work.

(C) The contractor must not sell you goods or services beyond those reasonably necessary to take care of the particular problem that caused you to contact the contractor.

(D) No payment is due and the contractor may not accept any payment until the work is completed.

(3) The notice in at least 12-point boldface type: "Notice to the Buyer: You are entitled to a completely filled in and signed copy of this agreement before any work may be started."

(4) If applicable, the heading "List of Documents to be Incorporated into the Contract," followed by the list of documents to be incorporated into the contract.

(5) Where the contract is a fixed contract amount, the heading: "Contract Price" followed by the amount of the contract in dollars and cents.

(6) If a finance charge will be charged, the heading: "Finance Charge" followed by the amount in dollars and cents. The finance charge is to be set out separately from the contract amount.

(7) Where the contract is estimated by a time and materials formula, the heading "Estimated Contract Price" followed by the estimated contract amount in dollars and cents. The contract must disclose the set rate and the estimated cost of materials. The contract must also disclose how time will be computed, for example, in increments of quarter hours, half hours, or hours, and the statement: "The actual contract amount of a time and materials contract may not exceed the estimated contract amount without written authorization from the buyer."

(8) The heading: "Description of the Project and Materials to be Used and Equipment to be Installed" followed by a description of the project and materials to be used and equipment to be installed.

(9) The statement: "The law requires that the contractor offer you any parts that were replaced during the service call. If you do not want the parts, initial the checkbox labeled 'OK for contractor to take replaced parts.'"

(10) A checkbox labeled "OK for contractor to take replaced parts."

(11) If a service charge is charged, the heading "Amount of Service Charge" followed by the service charge, and the statement "You may be charged only one service charge, including any trip charge or inspection fee."

(12) (A) (i) The contract, or an attachment to the contract as specified under subparagraph (C) of this paragraph, must include, in immediate proximity to the space reserved for the buyer's signature, the following statement, in at least 12-point boldface type, which shall be dated and signed by the buyer:

YOUR RIGHTS TO CANCEL BEFORE WORK BEGINS

(A) You, the buyer, have the right to cancel this contract until:

1. You receive a copy of this contract signed and dated by you and the contractor; and

2. The contractor starts work.

(B) However, even if the work has begun you, the buyer, may still cancel the contract for any of the reasons specified in items 1 through 4 of this paragraph. If any of these reasons occur, you may cancel the contract within three business days of signing the contract for normal service and repairs, or within seven business days of signing a contract to repair or correct conditions resulting from any sudden or catastrophic event for which a state of emergency has been declared by the President of the United States or the Governor, or for which a local emergency has been declared by the executive officer or governing body of any city, county, or city and county:

1. You may cancel the contract if the price, including all labor and materials, is more than seven hundred fifty dollars ($750).

2. You may cancel the contract if you did not initiate the contact with the contractor to request the work.

3. You may cancel the contract if the contractor sold you goods or services beyond those reasonably necessary to take care of the particular problem that caused you to contact the contractor.

4. You may cancel the contract if the payment was due or the contractor accepted any money before the work was complete.

(C) If any of these reasons for canceling occurred, you may cancel the contract as specified under paragraph (B) above by e-mailing,

mailing, faxing, or delivering a written notice to the contractor at the contractor's place of business within three business days or, if applicable, seven business days of the date you received a signed and dated copy of this contract. Include your name, your address, and the date you received a signed copy of the contract and this notice.

If you cancel, the contractor must return to you anything you paid within 10 days of receiving the notice of cancellation. For your part, you must make available to the contractor at your residence, in substantially as good condition as you received it, any goods delivered to you under this contract. Or, you may, if you wish, comply with the contractor's instructions on how to return the goods at the contractor's expense and risk. If you make the goods available to the contractor and the contractor does not pick them up within 20 days of the date of your notice of cancellation, you may keep them without any further obligation. If you fail to make the goods available to the contractor, or if you agree to return the goods to the contractor and fail to do so, then you remain liable for performance of all obligations under the contract.

(ii) References to "three" in the statement set forth in clause (i) shall be changed to "five" for a buyer who is a senior citizen.

(iii) The five-day right to cancel added by the act that added clause (ii) to this subparagraph shall apply to contracts entered into on or after January 1, 2021.

(B) This paragraph does not apply to home improvement contracts entered into by a person who holds an alarm company operator's license issued pursuant to Chapter 11.6 (commencing with Section 7590), provided the person complies with Sections 1689.5, 1689.6, and 1689.7 of the Civil Code, as applicable.

(C) The notice required in this paragraph may be incorporated as an attachment to the contract if the contract includes a checkbox and whichever statement is relevant in at least 12-point boldface type:

(i) "The law requires that the contractor give you a notice explaining your right to cancel. Initial the checkbox if the contractor has given you a 'Notice of Your Right to Cancel.'"

(ii) "The law requires that the contractor give you a notice explaining your right to cancel contracts for the repair or restoration of residential premises damaged by a disaster. Initial the checkbox if the contractor has given you a 'Notice of Your Right to Cancel.'"

(f) A bona fide service repairperson employed by a licensed contractor or subcontractor hired by a licensed contractor may enter into a service and repair contract on behalf of that contractor.

(g) The provisions of this section are not exclusive and do not relieve the contractor from compliance with any other applicable provision of law.

Added Stats 2004 ch 566 § 10 (SB 30), operative July 1, 2005. Amended Stats 2005 ch 48 § 13 (SB 1113), effective July 18, 2005, operative January 1, 2006, ch 385 § 6 (AB 316); Stats 2010 ch 698 § 40 (SB 392), effective January 1, 2011; Stats 2020 ch 158 § 3 (AB 2471), effective January 1, 2021.

§ 7159.11. Discipline for violation

A violation of any provision of Section 7159.10 by a licensee, or a person subject to be licensed under this chapter, or by his or her agent or salesperson, is cause for discipline.

Added Stats 2004 ch 566 § 11 (SB 30), operative July 1, 2005. Amended Stats 2005 ch 48 § 14 (SB 1113), effective July 18, 2005, operative January 1, 2006, ch 385 § 7 (AB 316).

§ 7159.14. [Section repealed 2021.]

Added Stats 2004 ch 566 § 14 (SB 30), operative July 1, 2005. Amended Stats 2005 ch 48 § 17 (SB 1113), effective July 18, 2005, operative January 1, 2006; Stats 2007 ch 230 § 3 (AB 244), effective January 1, 2008; Stats 2009 ch 307 § 76 (SB 821), effective January 1, 2010; Stats 2010 ch 697 § 7 (SB 189), effective January 1, 2011, operative July 1, 2012; Stats 2011 ch 44 § 3 (SB 190), effective January 1, 2012, operative July 1, 2012; Stats 2020 ch 92 § 7 (AB 1869), effective September 18, 2020, repealed July 1, 2021.

§ 7159.14. Further requirements; Statement of agreed amount; Payment due; Punishment for violations; Restitution

(a) This section applies to a service and repair contract as defined in Section 7159.10. A violation of this section by a licensee or a person subject to be licensed under this chapter, or by their agent or salesperson, is cause for discipline.

(1) The contract shall not exceed seven hundred fifty dollars ($750).

(2) The contract shall be in writing and shall state the agreed contract amount, which may be stated as either a fixed contract amount in dollars and cents or, if a time and materials formula is used, as an estimated contract amount in dollars and cents.

(3) The contract amount shall include the entire cost of the contract including profit, labor, and materials, but excluding finance charges.

(4) The actual contract amount of a time and materials contract may not exceed the estimated contract amount without written authorization from the buyer.

(5) The prospective buyer shall have initiated contact with the contractor to request work.

(6) The contractor shall not sell the buyer goods or services beyond those reasonably necessary to take care of the particular problem that caused the buyer to contact the contractor.

(7) Payment shall not be due before the project is completed.

(8) A service and repair contractor shall charge only one service charge. For purposes of this chapter, a service charge includes charges such as a service or trip charge, or an inspection fee.

(9) A service and repair contractor charging a service charge shall disclose in all advertisements that there is a service charge and, when the customer initiates the call for service, shall disclose the amount of the service charge.

(10) The service and repair contractor shall offer to the customer any parts that were replaced.

(11) Upon any payment by the buyer, the contractor shall, if requested, obtain and furnish to the buyer a full and unconditional release from any potential lien claimant claim or mechanics lien authorized pursuant to Sections 8400 and 8404 of the Civil Code for any portion of the work for which payment has been made.

(b) A violation of paragraph (1), (2), (3), (4), (5), (6), or (8) of subdivision (a) by a licensee or a person subject to be licensed under this chapter, or by their agent or salesperson, is a misdemeanor punishable by a fine of not less than one hundred dollars ($100) nor more than five thousand dollars ($5,000), or by imprisonment in a county jail not exceeding one year, or by both that fine and imprisonment.

(1) An indictment or information against a person who is not licensed but who is required to be licensed under this chapter shall be brought, or a criminal complaint filed, for a violation of this section, in accordance with paragraph (4) of subdivision (d) of Section 802 of the Penal Code, within four years from the date of the contract or, if the contract is not reduced to writing, from the date the buyer makes the first payment to the contractor.

(2) An indictment or information against a person who is licensed under this chapter shall be brought, or a criminal complaint filed, for a violation of this section, in accordance with paragraph (2) of subdivision (d) of Section 802 of the Penal Code, within two years from the date of the contract or, if the contract is not reduced to writing, from the date the buyer makes the first payment to the contractor.

(3) The limitations on actions in this subdivision do not apply to any administrative action filed against a licensed contractor.

(c) (1) Any person who violates this section as part of a plan or scheme to defraud an owner or tenant of a residential or nonresidential structure, including a mobilehome or manufactured home, in connection with the offer or performance of repairs to the structure for damage caused by a natural disaster, shall be ordered by the court to make full restitution to the victim based on the person's ability to pay, defined as the overall capability of the defendant to reimburse the costs, or a portion of the costs, including consideration of, but not limited to, all of the following:

(A) The defendant's present financial position.

(B) The defendant's reasonably discernible future financial position, provided that the court shall not consider a period of more than one year from the date of the hearing for purposes of determining the reasonably discernible future financial position of the defendant.

(C) The likelihood that the defendant will be able to obtain employment within one year from the date of the hearing.

(D) Any other factor that may bear upon the defendant's financial capability to reimburse the county for costs.

(2) In addition to full restitution, and imprisonment authorized by this section, the court may impose a fine of not less than five hundred dollars ($500) nor more than twenty-five thousand dollars ($25,000), based upon the defendant's ability to pay. This subdivision applies to natural disasters for which a state of emergency is proclaimed by the Governor pursuant to Section 8625 of the Government Code, or for which an emergency or major disaster is declared by the President of the United States.

(d) This section shall become operative July 1, 2021.

Added Stats 2020 ch 92 § 8 (AB 1869), effective September 18, 2020, operative July 1, 2021.

§ 7160. Penalty for fraudulent misrepresentation

Any person who is induced to contract for a work of improvement, including but not limited to a home improvement, in reliance on false or fraudulent representations or false statements knowingly made, may sue and recover from such contractor or solicitor a penalty of five hundred dollars ($500), plus reasonable attorney's fees, in addition to any damages sustained by him by reason of such statements or representations made by the contractor or solicitor.

Added Stats 1969 ch 1583 § 6 as § 7028.2. Renumbered Stats 1972 ch 1138 § 1.5.

§ 7161. [Section repealed 2021.]

Added Stats 1969 ch 1583 § 9 as § 7116.2. Renumbered Stats 1972 ch 1138 § 4. Amended Stats 1994 ch 175 § 4 (SB 634), effective July 9, 1994; Stats 2006 ch 538 § 13 (SB 1852), effective January 1, 2007; Stats 2020 ch 92 § 9 (AB 1869), effective September 18, 2020, repealed July 1, 2021.

§ 7161. Specification of prohibited acts; Misdemeanor

It is a misdemeanor for any person to engage in any of the following acts, the commission of which is cause for disciplinary action against any licensee or applicant:

(a) Using false, misleading, or deceptive advertising as an inducement to enter into any contract for a work of improvement, including, but not limited to, any home improvement contract, whereby any member of the public may be misled or injured.

(b) Making any substantial misrepresentation in the procurement of a contract for a home improvement or other work of improvement or making any false promise of a character likely to influence, persuade, or induce any person to enter into the contract.

(c) Any fraud in the execution of, or in the material alteration of, any contract, trust deed, mortgage, promissory note, or other document incident to a home improvement transaction or other transaction involving a work of improvement.

(d) Preparing or accepting any trust deed, mortgage, promissory note, or other evidence of indebtedness upon the obligations of a home improvement transaction or other transaction for a work of improvement with knowledge that it specifies a greater monetary obligation than the consideration for the improvement work, which consideration may be a time sale price.

(e) Directly or indirectly publishing any advertisement relating to home improvements or other works of improvement that contains an assertion, representation, or statement of fact that is false, deceptive, or misleading, or by any means advertising or purporting to offer to the general public this improvement work with the intent not to accept contracts for the particular work or at the price that is advertised or offered to the public, except that any advertisement that is subject to and complies with the existing rules, regulations, or guides of the Federal Trade Commission shall not be deemed false, deceptive, or misleading.

(f) (1) Any person who violates subdivision (b), (c), (d), or (e) as part of a plan or scheme to defraud an owner of a residential or nonresidential structure, including a mobilehome or manufactured home, in connection with the offer or performance of repairs to the structure for damage caused by a natural disaster, shall be ordered by the court to make full restitution to the victim based on the person's ability to pay, defined as the overall capability of the defendant to reimburse the costs, or a portion of the costs, including consideration of, but not limited to, all of the following:

(A) The defendant's present financial position.

(B) The defendant's reasonably discernible future financial position, provided that the court shall not consider a period of more than one year from the date of the hearing for purposes of determining the reasonably discernible future financial position of the defendant.

(C) The likelihood that the defendant will be able to obtain employment within one year from the date of the hearing.

(D) Any other factor that may bear upon the defendant's financial capability to reimburse the county for costs.

(2) In addition to full restitution and imprisonment as authorized by this section, the court may impose a fine of not less than five hundred dollars ($500) nor more than twenty-five thousand dollars ($25,000), based upon the defendant's ability to pay. This subdivision applies to natural disasters for which a state of emergency is proclaimed by the Governor pursuant to Section 8625 of the Government Code or for which an emergency or major disaster is declared by the President of the United States.

(g) This section shall become operative on July 1, 2021.

Added Stats 2020 ch 92 § 10 (AB 1869), effective September 18, 2020, operative July 1, 2021.

§ 7162. Contents of contract; Representations as to goods and materials

(a) Notwithstanding any other provision of law, any representation by a person licensed pursuant to this chapter with respect to a trademark or brand name, quality, or size of any goods or materials, in reference to bathroom fixtures, a sink, stove, refrigerator, lighting, carpeting and other floor surfaces, burglar and smoke alarms, a solar energy system, paints, textured coatings, siding and other wall surfaces, insulation, roofing, air conditioning and heating systems, and appliances, to be provided by the person pursuant to a home improvement contract, as defined in Section 7151.2, shall set forth, in writing, in the contract or specifications and shall include a description of the goods or materials, including any brand name, model number, or similar designation.

(b) Failure to install the specific goods or materials as represented as required by this section constitutes a cause for disciplinary action under this chapter.

Added Stats 1981 ch 916 § 3; Amended Stats 2021 ch 249 § 5 (SB 757) effective January 1, 2022.

§ 7163. Enforceability of contract prior to buyer obtaining loan

(a) No contract for home improvement shall be enforceable against the buyer if the obtaining of a loan for all or a portion of the contract price is a condition precedent to the contract or if the contractor provides financing, or in any manner assists the buyer to obtain a loan or refers the buyer to any person who may loan or arrange a loan for all or a portion of the contract price unless all of the following requirements are satisfied:

(1) The third party, if any, agrees to make the loan.

(2) The buyer agrees to accept the loan or financing.

(3) The buyer does not rescind the loan or financing transaction, within the period prescribed for rescission, pursuant to the federal Truth in Lending Act (15 U.S.C. Sec. 1601 et seq.) or Regulation Z, if applicable.

(b) Until the requirements of paragraphs (1), (2), and (3) of subdivision (a) are satisfied, it shall be unlawful for the contractor to do any of the following:

(1) Deliver any property or perform any services other than obtaining building permits or other similar services preliminary to the commencement of the home improvement for which no mechanic's lien can be claimed.

(2) Represent in any manner that the contract is enforceable or that the buyer has any obligation thereunder.

Any violation of this subdivision shall render the contract unenforceable.

(c) If the contract is unenforceable pursuant to subdivision (a) or subdivision (b), the contractor shall immediately and without condition return all money, property, and other consideration given by the buyer. If the buyer gave any property as consideration and the contractor does not or cannot return it for whatever reason, the contractor shall immediately return the fair market value of the property or its value as designated in the contract, whichever is greater. Nothing herein shall prohibit a contractor from receiving a downpayment otherwise permitted by law provided the contractor returns the downpayment as herein required if the contract is unenforceable pursuant to subdivision (a) or (b).

(d)(1) Except as provided in paragraph (2), the buyer may retain without obligation in law or equity any services or property provided pursuant to a contract that is unenforceable pursuant to subdivision (a) or subdivision (b).

(2) If the contractor has delivered any property to the buyer pursuant to a contract which is unenforceable pursuant to subdivision (a) or subdivision (b), the buyer shall make the property available to the contractor for return provided that all of the following requirements are satisfied:

(A) The property can be practically returned to the contractor without causing any damage to the buyer.

(B) The contractor, at the contractor's expense, first returns to the buyer any money, property, and other consideration taken by the contractor provided that the property is returned in the condition that it was in immediately prior to its taking. If applicable, the contractor shall also, at its expense, reinstall any property taken in the manner in which the property had been installed prior to its taking.

(C) The contractor, at the contractor's expense, picks up the property within 60 days of the execution of the contract.

(e) For the purpose of this section, "home improvement" means "home improvement" as defined in Section 7151. Goods are included within the definition notwithstanding whether they are to be attached to real property or to be so affixed to real property as to become a part thereof whether or not severable therefrom.

(f) The rights and remedies provided the buyer under this section are nonexclusive and cumulative to all other rights and remedies under other laws.

(g) Any waiver of this section shall be deemed contrary to public policy and shall be void and unenforceable. However, the buyer may waive subdivisions (a) and (b) to the extent that the contract is executed in connection with the making of emergency repairs or services that are necessary for the immediate protection of persons or real or personal property. The buyer's waiver for emergency repairs or services shall be in a dated written statement that describes the emergency, states that the contractor has informed the buyer of subdivisions (a) and (b) and that the buyer waives those provisions, and is signed by each owner of the property. Waivers made on printed forms are void and unenforceable.

Added Stats 1985 ch 989 § 1. Amended Stats 1986 ch 1404 § 1, effective September 30, 1986; Stats 1991 ch 1160 § 46 (AB 2190); Stats 1993 ch 589 § 13 (AB 2211).

§ 7164. Contract and changes to be in writing; Requirements

(a) Notwithstanding Section 7044, every contract and any changes in a contract, between an owner and a contractor, for the construction of a single-family dwelling to be retained by the owner for at least one year shall be evidenced in writing signed by both parties.

(b) The writing shall contain the following:

(1) The name, address, and license number of the contractor.

(2) The approximate dates when the work will begin and be substantially completed.

(3) A legal description of the location where the work will be done.

(4) A statement with the heading "Mechanics Lien Warning" as follows:

"MECHANICS LIEN WARNING:

Anyone who helps improve your property, but who is not paid, may record what is called a mechanics lien on your property. A mechanics lien is a claim, like a mortgage or home equity loan, made against your property and recorded with the county recorder.

Even if you pay your contractor in full, unpaid subcontractors, suppliers, and laborers who helped to improve your property may record mechanics liens and sue you in court to foreclose the lien. If a court finds the lien is valid, you could be forced to pay twice or have a court officer sell your home to pay the lien. Liens can also affect your credit.

Section VI

To preserve their right to record a lien, each subcontractor and material supplier must provide you with a document called a 'Preliminary Notice.' This notice is not a lien. The purpose of the notice is to let you know that the person who sends you the notice has the right to record a lien on your property if he or she is not paid.

BE CAREFUL. The Preliminary Notice can be sent up to 20 days after the subcontractor starts work or the supplier provides material. This can be a big problem if you pay your contractor before you have received the Preliminary Notices.

You will not get Preliminary Notices from your prime contractor or other persons you contract with directly or from laborers who work on your project. The law assumes that you already know they are improving your property.

PROTECT YOURSELF FROM LIENS. You can protect yourself from liens by getting a list from your contractor of all the subcontractors and material suppliers that work on your project. Find out from your contractor when these subcontractors started work and when these suppliers delivered goods or materials. Then wait 20 days, paying attention to the Preliminary Notices you receive.

PAY WITH JOINT CHECKS. One way to protect yourself is to pay with a joint check. When your contractor tells you it is time to pay for the work of a subcontractor or supplier who has provided you with a Preliminary Notice, write a joint check payable to both the contractor and the subcontractor or material supplier.

For other ways to prevent liens, visit CSLB's Web site at www.cslb.ca.gov or call CSLB at 800-321-CSLB (2752).

REMEMBER, IF YOU DO NOTHING, YOU RISK HAVING A LIEN PLACED ON YOUR HOME. This can mean that you may have to pay twice, or face the forced sale of your home to pay what you owe."

(5)(A) A statement prepared by the board through regulation that emphasizes the value of commercial general liability insurance and encourages the owner to verify the contractor's insurance coverage and status.

(B) A check box indicating whether or not the contractor carries commercial general liability insurance, and if that is the case, the name and the telephone number of the insurer.

(c) The writing may also contain other matters agreed to by the parties to the contract. The writing shall be legible and shall clearly describe any other document which is to be incorporated into the contract. Prior to commencement of any work, the owner shall be furnished a copy of the written agreement, signed by the contractor. The provisions of this section are not exclusive and do not relieve the contractor from compliance with all other applicable provisions of law.

(d) Every contract subject to the provisions of this section shall contain, in close proximity to the signatures of the owner and contractor, a notice in at least 10-point boldface type or in all capital letters, stating that the owner has the right to require the contractor to have a performance and payment bond and that the expense of the bond may be borne by the owner.

(e) The requirements in paragraph (5) of subdivision (b) shall become operative three months after the board adopts the regulations referenced in subparagraph (A) of paragraph (5) of subdivision (b).

(f) This section shall become operative on January 1, 2006.

Added Stats 2005 ch 48 § 19 (SB 1113), effective July 18, 2005, operative January 1, 2006. Amended Stats 2010 ch 697 § 8 (SB 189), effective January 1, 2011, operative July 1, 2012.

§ 7165. Conditions under which swimming pool contract financed by third-party lender is enforceable

The requirements of this section may be substituted for the requirements of paragraphs (1), (2), and (3) of subdivision (a) of Section 7163 if a swimming pool contract is to be financed by a third-party lender and if all the following conditions are met:

(a) The lender has agreed, in writing, to provide financing to the buyer for the maximum estimated construction cost of the swimming pool.

(b) The lender has provided the buyer a written copy of the terms and conditions of the loan for the maximum estimated construction cost of the swimming pool, including the following terms disclosed in the manner required by the federal Truth in Lending Act and Regulation Z: the annual percentage rate, the finance charge, the amount financed, the total number of payments, the payment schedule, and a description of the security interest to be taken by the lender.

(c) The lender has agreed in writing to the following:

(1) To offer to loan the maximum estimated construction cost on the terms and conditions disclosed pursuant to subdivision (b).

(2) If the construction cost of the swimming pool is determined after the completion of excavation to be less than the maximum estimated construction cost, to offer to loan the lesser amount needed to complete the construction of the swimming pool on the same security as, and at an annual percentage rate and monthly payment amount not to exceed, that disclosed in subdivision (b).

The lender's written agreement shall state the duration of the offer, which shall not be less than 15 days following the completion of the excavation of the swimming pool.

(d) The buyer acknowledges receipt of the writings required by subdivisions (a), (b), and (c) and, no sooner than three business days after

Section VI

receiving all of these writings, requests on the form prescribed in subdivision (e) that the contractor begin performance of the swimming pool contract prior to the expiration of any rescission period applicable to the loan.

(e) The request of a buyer, described in subdivision (d), shall be set forth on a document separate and apart from the swimming pool contract and shall contain the following notice in at least 10-point type unless otherwise stated:

"NOTICE

Under the law, this contract is not enforceable until:

(1) A third party agrees to make a loan to finance the construction cost of the swimming pool;

(2) You agree to accept the loan; and

(3) You do not cancel the loan within the period prescribed for cancellation under the federal Truth in Lending Act or Regulation Z (usually three business days after the loan is consummated).

Until the cancellation period is over, the contractor cannot deliver any materials or perform any services except preliminary services for which no mechanic's lien can be claimed.

However, as an alternative to the above, you can ask the contractor to start work and deliver materials before the cancellation period on the loan is over if all of the following have occurred:

(1) The lender has agreed, in writing, to provide you with financing for up to the maximum estimated construction cost of the swimming pool.

(2) The lender has provided you with a written copy of the terms and conditions of a loan for the maximum estimated cost, including the annual percentage rate, the finance charge, the amount financed, the total of payments, the payment schedule, and a description of the security interest to be taken by the lender.

(3) The lender has agreed in writing to offer these terms and conditions for a period not less than 15 days following completion of the excavation of the swimming pool.

(4) Three business days have passed since you received the writing mentioned in paragraphs (1), (2), and (3), and you then sign a copy of this form to request that the contractor begin construction of the swimming pool before the cancellation period on your loan is over.

The first day you can sign the request for the contractor to begin construction of the swimming pool is

---

(contractor to insert third business day after buyer receives
writings described in subdivisions (a), (b), and (c))

If you sign this request, the contractor will be permitted to immedi-ately begin performance of the contract, and if the contractor is not paid in accordance with the terms of the contract, he or she may file a lien against your property for the value of the labor and materials provided. [This paragraph shall be printed in 12-point type.]

REQUEST

I/we request that the contractor immediately start
construction of the swimming pool.

_____
Date

Buyer(s)"

(f) The contractor shall provide the buyer a copy of the buyer's signed request at the time of signature.

(g) This section applies to each buyer who signs the swimming pool contract or the promissory note, other evidence of indebtedness, or security instrument incident to the loan for swimming pool construc-tion.

(h) For the purpose of this section, "business day" has the meaning provided in Section 9 of the Civil Code.

Added Stats 1986 ch 1404 § 2, effective September 30, 1986, as § 7167.5. Renumbered by Stats 1991 ch 1160 § 51 (AB 2190).

—*See Health and Safety Code Section 115920, Citations; 115921, Definitions; 115922, Safety Features; 115923, Enclosure; 115924, Consumer Notice; 15925, Inapplicability, in Appendix.*

§ 7166. Application of article to contracts for construction of specified swimming pools

The provisions of Article 10 shall not apply to contracts for the con-struction of swimming pools to be built for the use and enjoyment of other than a single-family unit upon or contiguous to premises occu-pied only by a single-family unit, nor shall they apply to the construc-tion of swimming pools built as part of an original building plan by the same contractor who builds a single-family dwelling unit on the premises.

Added Stats 1979 ch 747 § 2 as § 7170. Amended Stats 1980 ch 138 § 8, effective May 30, 1980. Amended and renumbered Stats 1991 ch 1160 § 54 (AB 2190).

§ 7167. Certain contracts for construction of swimming pool void; Recovery for work performed

(a) Any contract, the primary purpose of which is the construction of a swimming pool, that does not substantially comply with paragraph (4) or (5) of subdivision (c) or paragraph (7), (8), or (9) of subdivision (d) of Section 7159, shall be void and unenforceable by the contractor as contrary to public policy.

(b) Failure by the contractor to comply with paragraph (5) of subdivision (c) of Section 7159 as set forth in subdivision (a) of this section does not preclude the recovery of compensation for work performed based on quasi-contract, quantum meruit, restitution, or other similar legal or equitable remedies designed to prevent unjust enrichment.

Added Stats 2005 ch 48 § 21 (SB 1113), effective July 18, 2005, operative January 1, 2006. Amended Stats 2005 ch 385 § 10 (AB 316), effective January 1, 2006.

§ 7168. Reasonable attorney's fees

In any action between a person contracting for construction of a swimming pool and a swimming pool contractor arising out of a contract for swimming pool construction, the court shall award reasonable attorney's fees to the prevailing party.

Added Stats 1979 ch 747 § 2 as § 7169. Amended and renumbered Stats 1991 ch 1160 § 53 (AB 2190).

§ 7169. Development and availability of "solar energy system disclosure document"

(a) The board, in collaboration with the Public Utilities Commission, shall develop and make available a "solar energy system disclosure document" or documents that provide a consumer, at a minimum, accurate, clear, and concise information regarding the installation of a solar energy system, total costs of installation, anticipated savings, the assumptions and inputs used to estimate the savings, and the implications of various financing options.

(b) On or before July 1, 2018, the board, in collaboration with the Public Utilities Commission, shall develop, and make available on its internet website the disclosure document described in subdivision (a) that a solar energy system company shall provide to a consumer prior to completion of a sale, financing, or lease of a solar energy system. The "solar energy system disclosure document" shall be printed on the front page or cover page of every solar energy contract. The "solar energy system disclosure document" shall be printed in boldface 16-point type and include the following types of primary information:

(1) The total cost and payments for the system, including financing costs.

(2) Information on how and to whom customers may provide complaints.

(3) The consumer's right to the applicable cancellation period pursuant to Section 7159 of the Business and Professions Code.

(c) At the board's discretion, other types of supporting information the board and the commission deem appropriate or useful in furthering the directive described in subdivision (a) may be included in the solar energy disclosure document following the front page or cover page, including, but not limited to:

(1) The amounts and sources of financing obtained.

(2) The calculations used by the home improvement salesperson to determine how many panels the homeowner needs to install.

(3) The calculations used by the home improvement salesperson to determine how much energy the panels will generate.

(4) Any additional monthly fees the homeowner's electric company may bill, any turn-on charges, and any fees added for the use of an internet monitoring system of the panels or inverters.

(5) The terms and conditions of any guaranteed rebate.

(6) The final contract price, without the inclusion of possible rebates.

(7) The solar energy system company's contractor's license number.

(8) The impacts of solar energy system installations not performed to code.

(9) Types of solar energy system malfunctions.

(10) Information about the difference between a solar energy system lease and a solar energy system purchase.

(11) The impacts that the financing options, lease agreement terms, or contract terms will have on the sale of the consumer's home, including any balloon payments or solar energy system relocation that may be required if the contract is not assigned to the new owner of the home.

(12) A calculator that calculates performance of solar projects to provide solar customers the solar power system's projected output, which may include an expected performance-based buy-down calculator.

(d) A contract for sale, financing, or lease of a solar energy system and the solar energy system disclosure document shall be written in the same language as was principally used in the oral sales presentation made to the consumer or the print or digital marketing material given to the consumer.

(e) For solar energy systems utilizing Property Assessed Clean Energy (PACE) financing, the Financing Estimate and Disclosure form required by subdivision (b) of Section 5898.17 of the Streets and Highways Code shall satisfy the requirements of this section with respect to the financing contract only, but not, however, with respect to the underlying contract for installation of the solar energy system.

(f) The board shall post the PACE Financing Estimate and Disclosure form required by subdivision (b) of Section 5898.17 of the Streets and Highways Code on its internet website.

(g) For purposes of this section, "solar energy system" means a solar energy device to be installed on a residential building that has the primary purpose of providing for the collection and distribution of solar energy for the generation of electricity, that produces at least one kW, and not more than five MW, alternating current rated peak electricity, and that meets or exceeds the eligibility criteria established pursuant to Section 25782 of the Public Resources Code.

(h) This section does not apply to a solar energy system that is installed as a standard feature on new construction.

Added Stats 2017 ch 662 § 1 (AB 1070), effective January 1, 2018. Amended Stats 2019 ch 378 § 10 (SB 610), effective January 1, 2020; Stats 2021 ch 188 § 11 (SB 826), effective January 1, 2022.

§ 7170. Complaints regarding solar energy systems companies and solar contractors

(a) The Contractors State License Board shall receive and review complaints and consumer questions regarding solar energy systems companies and solar contractors. The board shall also receive complaints received from state agencies regarding solar energy systems companies and solar contractors.

(b) Beginning on July 1, 2019, the board annually shall compile a report documenting consumer complaints relating to solar contractors. The report shall be made available publicly on the board's and the Public Utilities Commission's internet websites. The report shall contain all of the following:

(1) The number and types of complaints.

(2) The ZIP Code where the consumer complaint originated.

(3) The disposition of all complaints received against a solar contractor.

Added Stats 2017 ch 662 § 2 (AB 1070), effective January 1, 2018. Amended Stats 2020 ch 312 § 74 (SB 1474), effective January 1, 2021; Amended Stats 2021 ch 249 § 6 (SB 757) effective September 23, 2021.

Article 11
Asbestos Consultants

§ 7180. Requirement of certification

(a) No person shall, on or after July 1, 1992, engage in the practice of an asbestos consultant as defined in Section 7181, or as a site surveillance technician as defined in Section 7182, unless he or she is certified by the Division of Occupational Safety and Health pursuant to regulations required by subdivision (b) of Section 9021.5 of the Labor Code.

(b) Certification as an asbestos consultant or site surveillance technician shall not be required when a licensed contractor or registered asbestos abatement contractor takes no more than 12 bulk samples of suspected asbestos-containing material that is required to be removed, repaired, or disturbed as part of a construction project in a residential dwelling solely for any of the following purposes: (1) bid preparation for asbestos abatement; (2) evaluating exposure to its own employees during construction or asbestos abatement; or (3) determining for its own purposes or for the purpose of communicating whether or not a contract for asbestos abatement has been satisfactorily completed. Persons taking samples for the purposes described in this section shall be certified building inspectors under the Asbestos Hazard Emergency Response Act, as specified in Section 763 of Title 40 of the Code of Federal Regulations, appendix (c) to subpart (e). No licensed contractor or asbestos abatement contractor may provide professional health and safety services or perform any asbestos risk assessment. A bid for asbestos abatement may communicate the results and location of sampling for the presence of asbestos and how the asbestos will be abated. This section does not affect the requirement that asbestos abatement contractors be registered under Section 6501.5 of the Labor Code, nor does it permit a licensed contractor or asbestos abatement contractor to perform clearance air monitoring following asbestos abatement, unless otherwise permitted by law.

Added Stats 1990 ch 1255 § 1 (SB 732). Amended Stats 1996 ch 526 § 1 (SB 1486).

§ 7180.5. Requirement of certification for building owner or operator contracts

When a building owner or operator engages the services of a person to perform asbestos consulting or site surveillance technician activities as defined in Sections 7181 and 7182 after July 1, 1992, the building owner or operator shall contract with a person who is certified by the Division of Occupational Safety and Health pursuant to the regulations required by subdivision (b) of Section 9021.5 of the Labor Code.

Added Stats 1990 ch 1255 § 1 (SB 732).

§ 7181. "Asbestos consultant"

An "asbestos consultant," as used in this chapter, means any person who contracts to provide professional health and safety services relating to asbestos-containing material, as defined in subdivision (b) of Section 6501.8 of the Labor Code, including building inspections, abatement project design, contract administration, supervision of site surveillance technicians as defined in Section 7182, sample collections, preparation of asbestos management plans, and clearance air monitoring.

Added Stats 1990 ch 1255 § 1 (SB 732).

§ 7182. "Site surveillance technician"

A "site surveillance technician" means any person who acts as an independent onsite representative of an asbestos consultant who monitors the asbestos abatement activities of others, provides asbestos air monitoring services for area and personnel samples, and performs building surveys and contract administration at the direction of an asbestos consultant.

Added Stats 1990 ch 1255 § 1 (SB 732).

§ 7183. Notice of complete application; Issuance of certificate; Provisional certification card

(a) Within 15 days of receipt of an application for certification pursuant to this article, the division shall inform the applicant in writing either (1) that the application is complete and accepted, or (2) that it is deficient and that additional information, documentation, or examination, specified in the notification, is required to complete the application. Within 45 days of the date of filing of a completed application, the division shall issue to each person who qualifies for certification pursuant to this article, a certification card which shall identify the holder thereof and the type of certification for which he or she has qualified. If the division cannot comply with the notification deadlines specified in this section, the division shall issue a provisional certification card until all procedures specified in this section are completed.

(b) The certification required by this article shall satisfy all certification requirements of the division for asbestos consultants and site surveillance technicians.

Added Stats 1990 ch 1255 § 1 (SB 732).

§ 7183.5. Enforcement by division

The division shall enforce this article. In the event the division determines that a certified asbestos consultant or site surveillance technician obtained certification under false pretenses, or that a certified asbestos consultant or site surveillance technician acted in a grossly negligent or fraudulent manner, or engaged in repeated acts of negligence, the division shall revoke that person's certification. The division shall only revoke a certification after complying with all of the procedural requirements of Chapter 5 (commencing with Section 11500) of Division 3 of Part 1 of Title 2 of the Government Code.

Added Stats 1990 ch 1255 § 1 (SB 732).

§ 7184. Requirements for qualification as certified asbestos consultant

A person shall qualify as a certified asbestos consultant by meeting all of the following requirements:

(a) Having any one of the following:

(1) One year of asbestos-related experience, and a bachelor of science degree in engineering, architecture, industrial hygiene, construction management, or a related biological or physical science.

(2) Two years of asbestos-related experience, and a bachelor's degree.

(3) Three years of asbestos-related experience, and an associate of arts degree in engineering, architecture, industrial hygiene, construction management, or a related biological or physical science.

(4) Four years of asbestos-related experience and a high school diploma or its equivalent.

(b) Possession of a valid federal Asbestos Hazard Emergency Response Act (Subchapter II (commencing with Section 2641) of Chapter 53 of Title 15 of the United States Code) certificate for the type of work being performed, or its equivalent, as determined by the division.

(c) Demonstration of proficiency by achieving a passing score as determined by the division on an examination approved or administered by the division including, but not limited to, the following subjects:

(1) Physical characteristics of asbestos.

(2) Health effects of asbestos.

(3) Federal Occupational Safety and Health Administration, Division of Occupational Safety and Health, Environmental Protection Agency, air quality management districts, and State Department of Health Services regulatory requirements, including protective clothing, respiratory protection, exposure limits, personal hygiene, medical monitoring, disposal, and general industry safety hazards.

(4) State-of-the-art asbestos abatement and control work procedures. The division shall define and incorporate into the certification standards the term "state-of-the-art" for purposes of this article, in the regulations required by subdivision (b) of Section 9021.5 of the Labor Code.

(5) Federal Asbestos Hazard Emergency Response Act training information and procedures for inspectors, management planners, and supervisors, as provided for under Subchapter II (commencing with

Section 2641) of Chapter 53 of Title 15 of the United States Code, or the equivalent, as determined by the division.

(6) Information concerning industrial hygiene sampling methodology, including asbestos sampling and analysis techniques and record-keeping.

Added Stats 1990 ch 1255 § 1 (SB 732).

§ 7185. Requirements for qualification as certified site surveillance technician

A person shall qualify as a certified site surveillance technician by meeting all of the following requirements:

(a) Having six months of asbestos-related experience under the supervision of an asbestos consultant.

(b) Possession of a high school diploma or equivalent.

(c) Possession of a valid federal Asbestos Hazard Emergency Response Act (Subchapter II (commencing with Section 2641) of Chapter 53 of Title 15 of the United States Code) certificate for the type of work being performed, or its equivalent, as determined by the division.

(d) Demonstration of proficiency by achieving a passing score, as determined by the division, on an examination approved or administered by the division covering the following subjects:

(1) Physical characteristics of asbestos.

(2) Health effects of asbestos.

(3) Federal Occupational Safety and Health Administration, Division of Occupational Safety and Health, Environmental Protection Agency, air quality management districts, and State Department of Health Services regulatory requirements, including protective clothing, respiratory protection, exposure limits, personal hygiene, medical monitoring, and general industry safety hazards.

(4) State-of-the-art asbestos abatement and control work procedures.

(5) Industrial hygiene sampling methodology, including sampling techniques and recordkeeping.

Added Stats 1990 ch 1255 § 1 (SB 732).

§ 7187. Financial conflict of interest; Legislative intent

When a building owner or operator contracts with an asbestos consultant or site surveillance technician for performance of the activities described in Sections 7181 and 7182, that asbestos consultant or site surveillance technician shall not have any financial or proprietary interest in an asbestos abatement contractor hired for the same project. However, this section shall not preclude the hiring of a consultant by a contractor for the purpose of providing health and safety services for the personnel of the contractor. This section shall not apply when a licensed contractor or registered asbestos abatement contractor takes no more than 12 bulk samples of suspected asbestos-containing material that is required to be removed, repaired, or disturbed as part of a construction project in a residential dwelling solely for any of the following purposes: (1) bid preparation for asbestos abatement; (2) evaluating exposure to its own employees during construction or asbestos abatement; or (3) determining for its own purposes or for the purpose of communicating whether or not a contract for asbestos abatement has been satisfactorily completed. Persons taking samples for the purposes described in this section shall be certified building inspectors under the Asbestos Hazard Emergency Response Act, as specified in Section 763 of Title 40 of the Code of Federal Regulations, appendix (c) to subpart (e). No licensed contractor or asbestos abatement contractor may provide professional health and safety services or perform any asbestos risk assessment. A licensed contractor or asbestos abatement contractor may seek compensation for bid preparation, including the cost of laboratory analysis of asbestos-containing material.

It is the intent of the Legislature in enacting this section to make certain that the asbestos-related work performed by a consultant, including, but not limited to, clearance air monitoring, project design, and contract administration, is performed in a manner which provides for independent professional judgment undertaken without consideration of the financial or beneficial interest of the contractor.

Added Stats 1990 ch 1255 § 1 (SB 732). Amended Stats 1996 ch 526 § 2 (SB 1486).

§ 7189. Penalties for violation

Any person who engages in the practices of an asbestos consultant or a site surveillance technician, who is not certified pursuant to this article, or who violates Section 7187, is subject to one of the following penalties:

(a) Conviction of a first offense is an infraction punishable by a fine of not less than one thousand dollars ($1,000) or more than three thousand dollars ($3,000).

(b) Conviction of a subsequent offense is a misdemeanor requiring revocation or suspension of any asbestos consultant's or site surveillance technician's certification, and a fine not not less than three thousand dollars ($3,000) or more than five thousand dollars ($5,000), or imprisonment in the county jail not exceeding one year, or both the fine and imprisonment.

The division shall only impose these penalties after complying with all of the procedural requirements of Chapter 5 (commencing with

Section VI

Section 11500) of Division 3 of Part 1 of Title 2 of the Government Code.

Added Stats 1990 ch 1255 § 1 (SB 732).

§ 7189.5. Application of article

This article shall apply to asbestos abatement projects within the meaning of asbestos-related work as defined in Section 6501.8 of the Labor Code, and which involves 100 square feet or more of surface area of asbestos containing material.

Added Stats 1990 ch 1255 § 1 (SB 732).

§ 7189.7. Construction of article

(a) Nothing in this article shall be construed to require agencies of the state to contract with asbestos consultants or site surveillance technicians who are not employees of the state as long as employees of the state who are assigned to perform the activities described in Sections 7181 and 7182 have been certified by the division pursuant to the regulations required by subdivision (b) of Section 9021.5 of the Labor Code. Where feasible, the state shall assign a state civil service classification of associate industrial hygienist or senior industrial hygienist to carry out asbestos consultation activities as described in Section 7181 for state-owned and leased buildings. The individuals in the classification assigned shall be certified as required in this article before performing these activities.

(b) Nothing in this article shall be construed to require attorneys who provide legal advice on asbestos-related matters to building owners or operators to be certified by the division pursuant to the regulations required by subdivision (b) of Section 9021.5 of the Labor Code.

Added Stats 1990 ch 1255 § 1 (SB 732).

Article 12
Prohibitions

§ 7190. Use of name or position of public official in advertisement or promotional material; Disclaimer

(a) The name or position of a public official may not be used in an advertisement or any promotional material by a person licensed under this chapter, without the written authorization of the public official. A printed advertisement or promotional material that uses the name or position of a public official with that public official's written authorization, shall also include a disclaimer in at least 10-point roman boldface type, that shall be in a color or print which contrasts with the background so as to be easily legible, and set apart from any other printed matter. The disclaimer shall consist of a statement that reads "The name of (specify name of public official) does not imply that (specify name of public official) endorses this product or service in (his or her) official capacity and does not imply an endorsement by any governmental entity." If the advertisement is broadcast, this statement shall be read in a clearly audible tone of voice.

(b) For purposes of this section, "public official" means a member, officer, employee, or consultant of a local government agency, as defined in Section 82041 of the Government Code, or state agency, as defined in Section 82049 of the Government Code.

Added Stats 1994 ch 1135 § 5 (AB 3302).

—*See Civil Code Section 1770, Unfair Practices, in Appendix.*

§ 7191. Title of provision for arbitration of disputes in contract for work on specified residential property

(a) If a contract for work on residential property with four or fewer units contains a provision for arbitration of a dispute between the principals in the transaction, the provision shall be clearly titled "ARBITRATION OF DISPUTES."

If a provision for arbitration is included in a printed contract, it shall be set out in at least 10-point roman boldface type or in contrasting red print in at least 8-point roman boldface type, and if the provision is included in a typed contract, it shall be set out in capital letters.

(b) Immediately before the line or space provided for the parties to indicate their assent or nonassent to the arbitration provision described in subdivision (a), and immediately following that arbitration provision, the following shall appear:

"NOTICE: BY INITIALING IN THE SPACE BELOW YOU ARE AGREEING TO HAVE ANY DISPUTE ARISING OUT OF THE MATTERS INCLUDED IN THE 'ARBITRATION OF DISPUTES' PROVISION DECIDED BY NEUTRAL ARBITRATION AS PROVIDED BY CALIFORNIA LAW AND YOU ARE GIVING UP ANY RIGHTS YOU MIGHT POSSESS TO HAVE THE DISPUTE LITIGATED IN A COURT OR JURY TRIAL. BY INITIALING IN THE SPACE BELOW YOU ARE GIVING UP YOUR JUDICIAL RIGHTS TO DISCOVERY AND APPEAL, UNLESS THOSE RIGHTS ARE SPECIFICALLY INCLUDED IN THE 'ARBITRATION OF DISPUTES' PROVISION. IF YOU REFUSE TO SUBMIT TO ARBITRATION AFTER AGREEING TO THIS PROVISION, YOU MAY BE COMPELLED TO ARBITRATE UNDER THE AUTHORITY OF THE BUSINESS AND PROFESSIONS CODE OR OTHER APPLICABLE LAWS. YOUR AGREEMENT TO THIS ARBITRATION PROVISION

Section VI

IS VOLUNTARY." "WE HAVE READ AND UNDERSTAND THE FOREGOING AND AGREE TO SUBMIT DISPUTES ARISING OUT OF THE MATTERS INCLUDED IN THE 'ARBITRATION OF DISPUTES' PROVISION TO NEUTRAL ARBITRATION."

If the above provision is included in a printed contract, it shall be set out either in at least 10-point roman boldface type or in contrasting red print in at least 8-point roman boldface type, and if the provision is included in a typed contract, it shall be set out in capital letters.

(c) A provision for arbitration of a dispute between a principal in a contract for work on a residential property with four or fewer units that does not comply with this section may not be enforceable against any person other than the licensee.

(d) This section does not limit the board's authority to investigate complaints or to discipline a licensee for violations of this code.

Added Stats 1994 ch 1135 § 5 (AB 3302).

Chapter 9.3

Home Inspectors

§ 7195. Definitions

For purposes of this chapter, the following definitions apply:

(a) (1) "Home inspection" is a noninvasive, physical examination, performed for a fee in connection with a transfer, as defined in subdivision (e), of real property, of the mechanical, electrical, or plumbing systems or the structural and essential components of a residential dwelling of one to four units designed to identify material defects in those systems, structures, and components. "Home inspection" includes any consultation regarding the property that is represented to be a home inspection or any confusingly similar term.

(2) In connection with a transfer, as defined in subdivision (e), of real property with a swimming pool or spa, a "home inspection" shall include a noninvasive physical examination of the pool or spa and dwelling for the purpose of identifying which, if any, of the seven drowning prevention safety features listed in subdivision (a) of Section 115922 of the Health and Safety Code the pool or spa is equipped.

(3) "Home inspection," if requested by the client, may include an inspection of energy efficiency. Energy efficiency items to be inspected may include the following:

(A) A noninvasive inspection of insulation R-values in attics, roofs, walls, floors, and ducts.

(B) The number of window glass panes and frame types.

(C) The heating and cooling equipment and water heating systems.

(D) The age and fuel type of major appliances.

(E) The exhaust and cooling fans.

(F) The type of thermostat and other systems.

(G) The general integrity and potential leakage areas of walls, window areas, doors, and duct systems.

(H) The solar control efficiency of existing windows.

(b) A "material defect" is a condition that significantly affects the value, desirability, habitability, or safety of the dwelling. Style or aesthetics shall not be considered in determining whether a system, structure, or component is defective.

(c) A "home inspection report" is a written report prepared for a fee and issued after a home inspection. The report clearly describes and identifies the inspected systems, structures, or components of the dwelling, any material defects identified, and any recommendations regarding the conditions observed or recommendations for evaluation by appropriate persons. In a dwelling with a pool or spa, the "home inspection report" shall identify which, if any, of the seven drowning prevention safety features listed in subdivision (a) of Section 115922 of the Health and Safety Code the pool or spa is equipped with and shall specifically state if the pool or spa has fewer than two of the listed drowning prevention safety features.

(d) A "home inspector" is any individual who performs a home inspection.

(e) "Transfer" is a transfer by sale, exchange, installment land sales contract, as defined in Section 2985 of the Civil Code, lease with an option to purchase, any other option to purchase, or ground lease coupled with improvements, of real property or residential stock cooperative, improved with or consisting of not less than one nor more than four dwelling units.

Added Stats 1996 ch 338 § 2 (SB 258). Amended Stats 2001 ch 773 § 2 (AB 1574); Stats 2017 ch 670 § 3 (SB 442), effective January 1, 2018.

§ 7195.5. Home inspection report for dwelling unit with in-ground landscape irrigation system

(a) For purposes of improving landscape water use and irrigation efficiency, a home inspection report on a dwelling unit prepared pursuant to this chapter on a parcel containing an in-ground landscape irrigation system, the operation of which is under the exclusive control of the owner or occupant of the dwelling, may include an irrigation system inspection report, prepared by either a home inspector or certified landscape irrigation auditor, that contains all of the following:

(1) Examination of the irrigation system controller, if present, noting observable defects in installation or operation, or both.

(2) Activation of each zone or circuit providing irrigation water to turf grass, noting malfunctions observed in the operation of each of the following:

(A) The irrigation valve.

(B) Visible irrigation supply piping.

(C) Sprinkler heads and stems.

(3) During activation of the system pursuant to paragraph (2), observation of any of the following during the period of operation, in minutes, specified in the report:

(A) Irrigation spray being directed to hardscape.

(B) Irrigation water leaving the irrigated area as surface runoff.

(C) Ponding of irrigation water on the surface of the irrigated area.

(4) Notation whether inspection is limited due to snow, ice, or other site conditions that impede an inspection.

(b) Notwithstanding any other law, a sanction or penalty regarding prohibited hours, days, or effects of operation of a landscape irrigation system shall not be levied upon either the home inspector, the landscape irrigation auditor, the occupant, or the owner of a property by any state or local agency or water purveyor as a consequence of the operation of a landscape irrigation system for the purpose of an irrigation system inspection carried out under this section.

(c) A home inspector is encouraged to provide information or access to information regarding water-efficient landscape irrigation systems within the home inspection report.

(d) To the extent funds are available, the Department of Water Resources, in consultation with the California Real Estate Inspection Association and the Department of Housing and Community Development, shall compile an estimate of the number of properties for which an irrigation system inspection report has been prepared each year, beginning with 2018, for inclusion in an update to the California Water Plan.

Added Stats 2018 ch 867 § 3 (AB 2371), effective January 1, 2019.

§ 7195.7. Opinion of valuation on property

A home inspector shall not give an opinion of valuation on a property.

Added Stats 2019 ch 267 § 1 (AB 1018), effective January 1, 2020.

§ 7196. Duties

It is the duty of a home inspector who is not licensed as a general contractor, structural pest control operator, or architect, or registered as a professional engineer to conduct a home inspection with the degree of care that a reasonably prudent home inspector would exercise.

Added Stats 1996 ch 338 § 2 (SB 258).

§ 7196.1. Application

(a) Nothing in this chapter shall be construed to allow home inspectors who are not registered engineers to perform any analysis of the systems, components, or structural integrity of a dwelling that would constitute the practice of civil, electrical, or mechanical engineering, or to exempt a home inspector from Chapter 3 (commencing with Section 5500), Chapter 7 (commencing with Section 6700), Chapter 9 (commencing with Section 7000), Chapter 14 (commencing with Section 8500) of Division 3, or Part 3 (commencing with Section 11300) of Division 4.

(b) This chapter does not apply to a registered engineer, licensed land surveyor, or licensed architect acting pursuant to their professional registration or license, nor does it affect the obligations of a real estate licensee or transferor under Article 1.5 (commencing with Section 1102) of Chapter 2 of Title 4 of Part 3 of Division 2 of, or Article 2 (commencing with Section 2079) of Chapter 3 of Title 6 of Part 4 of Division 3 of, the Civil Code.

(c) Except as required to comply with standards set forth in law or regulation, a real estate appraiser licensed under Part 3 (commencing with Section 11300) of Division 4, performing a real estate appraisal, shall not engage in the activity of a home inspector performing a home inspection.

Added Stats 1996 ch 338 § 2 (SB 258). Amended Stats 2019 ch 267 § 2 (AB 1018), effective January 1, 2020.

§ 7196.2. Yellow corrugated stainless steel; Home inspection report

(a) If a home inspector observes any shade of yellow corrugated stainless steel tubing during a home inspection, the home inspector shall include that observation, and the following notification, in the home inspection report:

"Manufacturers of yellow corrugated stainless steel tubing believe that yellow corrugated stainless steel tubing is safer if properly bonded and grounded as required by the manufacturer's installation instructions. Proper bonding and grounding of this product can only be determined by a licensed electrical contractor."

(b) For purposes of this section, "corrugated stainless steel tubing" means a flexible, stainless steel pipe used to supply natural gas and propane in residential, commercial, and industrial structures.

Section VI

(c) The degree of care specified in Section 7196 shall be used in determining whether a home inspector has complied with the requirements of subdivision (a).

Added Stats 2018 ch 225 § 2 (SB 988), effective January 1, 2019.

§ 7197. Unfair practices

(a) It is an unfair business practice for a home inspector, a company that employs the inspector, or a company that is controlled by a company that also has a financial interest in a company employing a home inspector, to do any of the following:

(1) To perform or offer to perform, for an additional fee, any repairs to a structure on which the inspector, or the inspector's company, has prepared a home inspection report in the past 12 months.

(2) Inspect for a fee any property in which the inspector, or the inspector's company, has any financial interest or any interest in the transfer of the property.

(3) To offer or deliver any compensation, inducement, or reward to the owner of the inspected property, the broker, or agent, for the referral of any business to the inspector or the inspection company.

(4) Accept an engagement to make an inspection or to prepare a report in which the employment itself or the fee payable for the inspection is contingent upon the conclusions in the report, preestablished findings, or the close of escrow.

(b) A home protection company that is affiliated with or that retains the home inspector does not violate this section if it performs repairs pursuant to claims made under the home protection contract.

(c) This section shall not affect the ability of a structural pest control operator to perform repairs pursuant to Section 8505 as a result of a structural pest control inspection.

(d) Paragraph (1) of subdivision (a) shall not affect the ability of a roofing contractor who holds a C-39 license, as defined in Section 832.39 of Title 16 of the California Code of Regulations, to perform repairs pursuant to the contractor's inspection of a roof for the specific purpose of providing a roof certification if all of the following conditions are met:

(1) Different employees perform the home inspection and the roof inspection.

(2) The roof inspection is ordered prior to, or at the same time as, the home inspection, or the roof inspection is completed before the commencement of the home inspection.

(3) The consumer is provided a consumer disclosure before the consumer authorizes the home inspection that includes all of the following:

(A) The same company that performs the roof inspection and roof repairs will perform the home inspection on the same property.

(B) Any repairs that are authorized by the consumer are for the repairs identified in the roofing contractor's roof inspection report and no repairs identified in the home inspection are authorized or allowed as specified in the roof inspection.

(C) The consumer has the right to seek a second opinion.

(4) For purposes of this subdivision, "roof certification" means a written statement by a licensed C-39 Roofing Contractor who has performed a roof inspection, made any necessary repairs, and warrants that the roof is free of leaks at the time that the certification is issued and should perform as designed for the specified term of the certification.

(e) Paragraph (1) of subdivision (a) shall not affect the ability of a plumbing contractor who holds a C-36 license, as defined in Section 832.36 of Title 16 of the California Code of Regulations, to perform repairs pursuant to the inspection of a sewer lateral pipe connecting a residence or business to a sewer system if the consumer is provided a consumer disclosure before the consumer authorizes the home inspection that includes all of the following notifications:

(1) The same company that performs the sewer lateral inspection and the sewer lateral repairs will perform the home inspection on the same property.

(2) Any repairs that are authorized by the consumer are for the repairs identified in the sewer lateral inspection report and no repairs identified in the home inspection report are authorized or allowed except as specified in the sewer lateral inspection report.

(3) The consumer has the right to seek a second opinion on the sewer lateral inspection.

Added Stats 1996 ch 338 § 2 (SB 258). Amended Stats 2004 ch 443 § 1 (AB 1725); Stats 2017 ch 508 § 1 (AB 1357), effective January 1, 2018; Stats 2021 ch 545 § 1 (SB 484), effective January 1, 2022.

§ 7198. Public policy

Contractual provisions that purport to waive the duty owed pursuant to Section 7196, or limit the liability of the home inspector to the cost of the home inspection report, are contrary to public policy and invalid.

Added Stats 1996 ch 338 § 2 (SB 258).

Section VI

§ 7199. Statute of limitation

The time for commencement of a legal action for breach of duty arising from a home inspection report shall not exceed four years from the date of the inspection.

Added Stats 1996 ch 338 § 2 (SB 258).

Chapter 9.4

Home Energy Rating System (HERS) Home Inspections

§ 7199.5. HERS California home energy audit

(a) All home inspections, including those defined in paragraph (1) of subdivision (a) of Section 7195, may, if requested by the client, be accompanied by a Home Energy Rating System (HERS) California home energy audit pursuant to regulations adopted by the Energy Commission in compliance with Section 25942 of the Public Resources Code.

(b) If the client requests a HERS California home energy audit, the HERS California home inspection report accompanying any home inspection report defined in subdivision (c) of Section 7195 shall comply with the standards and requirements established by the Energy Commission for HERS California home energy audits as specified in Article 8 (commencing with Section 1670) of Chapter 4 of Division 2 of Title 20 of the California Code of Regulations, implementing the California Home Energy Rating System Program.

Added Stats 2010 ch 453 § 1 (AB 1809), effective January 1, 2011.

§ 7199.7. Legislative intent

It is the intent of the Legislature that a Home Energy Rating System (HERS) California home energy audit may, at the request of the client, be performed by a home inspector who meets the requirements of Article 8 (commencing with Section 1670) of Chapter 4 of Division 2 of Title 20 of the California Code of Regulations.

Added Stats 2010 ch 453 § 1 (AB 1809), effective January 1, 2011.

Chapter 9.

Contractors State License Board
Rules and Regulations

Rules and regulations serve to interpret or make laws specific. The laws provide the authority for rules and regulations. Laws take precedence and are in effect, even if the affected rules and regulations have not been corrected to reflect any changes in the law.

If you have questions concerning a particular regulation, refer to the sections of the Business and Professions Code cited in the note after the particular regulation.

What follows is the statute text, history notes for current rules and regulations, and history notes for repealed rules and regulations. You can follow the progress of proposed regulatory actions on CSLB's website at *http://www.cslb.ca.gov/About_Us/Library/Laws/*.

LIST OF CURRENT BOARD RULES AND REGULATIONS

CALIFORNIA CODE OF REGULATIONS

TITLE 16. DIVISION 8. CONTRACTORS STATE LICENSE BOARD

ARTICLE 1. DEFINITIONS

810. Definitions*

(a) For purposes of this division, "battery energy storage system" means one or more devices, assembled together, capable of storing energy in order to supply electrical energy at a future time.

(b) For the purposes of this division, "Board" means the Contractors State License Board and "Code," unless otherwise defined, means the Business and Professions Code.

Effective date temporarily stayed at time of printing

(Authority cited: Section 7008, Business and Professions Code. Reference: Section 7008, Business and Professions Code.)

ARTICLE 1.5. REVENUE

811. Fees

(a) The fees for applications are as follows:

(1) An application for an original license in a single classification is $450.

(2) An application for each additional classification applied for in connection with an original license is $150.

(3) An application for each additional classification pursuant to Business and Professions Code Section 7059 is $230.

(4) An application to replace a responsible managing officer, responsible managing manager, responsible managing member, or responsible managing employee pursuant to Business and Professions Code Section 7068.2 is $230.

(5) An application to add personnel, other than a qualifying individual, to an existing license is $125.

(6) An application for an asbestos certification examination is $125.

(7) An application for a hazardous substance removal or remedial action certification examination is $125.

(b) The fees for scheduling examinations are as follows:

(1) Rescheduling an examination for an applicant who has applied for an original license, additional classification, a change of responsible managing officer, responsible managing manager, responsible managing member, or responsible managing employee, or for an asbestos certification or hazardous substance removal certification is $100.

(2) Scheduling or rescheduling an examination for a licensee who is required to take the examination as a condition of probation is $100.

(c) The fees for initial license and registration fees are as follows:

(1) The initial license fee for an active or inactive license for an individual owner is $200.

(2) The initial license fee for an active or inactive license for a partnership, corporation, limited liability company, or joint venture is $350.

(3) The registration fee for a home improvement salesperson is $200.

(d) The fees for license and registration renewals are as follows:

(1) The renewal fee for an active license for an individual owner is $450.

(2) The renewal fee for an inactive license for an individual owner is $300.

(3) The renewal fee for an active license for a partnership, corporation, limited liability company, or joint venture is $700.

(4) The renewal fee for an inactive license for a partnership, corporation, limited liability company, or joint venture is $500.

(5) The renewal fee for a home improvement salesperson registration is $200.

(e) Miscellaneous fees are as follows:

(1) The fee to change the business name of a license as it is recorded under Chapter 9 of Division 3 of the Business and Professions Code is $100.

(Authority cited: Section 7008, Business and Professions Code. Reference: Sections 7076.5 and 7137, Business and Professions Code.)

812. Dishonored Check Service Charge [Repealed]

(Authority cited: Section 7008, Business and Professions Code. Reference: Section 7008, Business and Professions Code; and Section 6157, Government Code.)

813. Abandonment of Application

(a) An application, other than a renewal application, shall be deemed abandoned whenever an applicant fails to return an application rejected for insufficiency or incompleteness within 90 days from date of original notice of rejection. This 90-day period may be extended by the Registrar for good cause.

(b) Any application so abandoned may not be reinstated; however, the applicant may file a new application accompanied by the required fee.

(Authority cited: Section 7008, Business and Professions Code. Reference: Section 7067, Business and Professions Code.)

ARTICLE 2. APPLICATION FOR LICENSE

816. Application Form for Original License

(a) The license application form prescribed by the Registrar shall seek from each member of the personnel of the applicant the following information:

(1) A record of the previous experience in the field of construction of the member of applicant's personnel who will qualify for the classification requested.

(2) Whether the applicant or a member of applicant's personnel or whether to his or her knowledge anyone with whom he/she has been associated in the contracting field has ever been licensed or had a professional or vocational license refused or revoked.

(b) The application shall be signed, under penalty of perjury, by each member of the personnel of the applicant.

(c) Nothing in this Rule shall be interpreted to limit the Registrar's authority to require an applicant to provide any other information necessary to determine the applicant's qualifications, or to exempt the applicant therefrom, or to enforce the provisions of the Contractors License Law, except as otherwise required by law. The Registrar may exempt applicants who are eligible for waiver of examination, pursuant to Section 7065.1 of the Code, or who are not required to take the examination, pursuant to Section 7065 of the Code, from the requirement to submit information described in subsection (a)(1).

(Authority cited: Section 7008, Business and Professions Code. Reference: Sections 7066, 7067.6 and 7070, Business and Professions Code.)

819. Requirement of Corporations

A foreign or domestic corporation, applying for a license, shall complete a certification as prescribed by the Registrar, showing that it has fulfilled the filing requirements of the California Secretary of State as set out in Sections 200 and 2105 of the Corporations Code.

(Authority cited: Section 7008, Business and Professions Code. Reference: Section 7067, Business and Professions Code.)

824. Application Investigation Required

In addition to a review and verification of all applications for licensure, the Registrar shall conduct a comprehensive field investigation of a minimum of 3% of all such applications. Such investigation shall include those areas of experience claimed and such other areas as the Registrar deems appropriate for the protection of the public.

All claimed experience shall be supportable by documentation satisfactory to the Board. The Registrar shall provide to the Board, for its approval, acceptable forms of such documentation and shall inform the applicant in the application form that such documentation may be requested by the Board.

(Authority cited: Section 7008, Business and Professions Code. Reference: Section 7068, Business and Professions Code.)

825. Experience Requirement of Applicant

(a) Every applicant for a contractor's license must have had, within the last 10 years immediately preceding the filing of the application, not less than four years experience as a journeyman, foreman, supervising employee or contractor in the particular class within which the applicant intends to engage as a contractor. For purposes of this section, "journeyman" means an experienced worker in the trade who is fully qualified, as opposed to a trainee, and is able to perform the trade without supervision; or one who has completed an apprenticeship program.

(b) An applicant who was formerly a qualifier on a license in the same classification applied for may compute experience without regard to the ten-year limitation.

(c) An applicant shall not be jeopardized in computing time for service in the armed forces of the United States during a National Emergency and the length of service may be added to the 10 years mentioned above.

(d) Acceptable training in an accredited school or completion of an approved apprenticeship program in accordance with the California Labor Code (commencing with Section 3070 of the Labor Code, Chapter 4, of Division 3) or its equivalent, as approved by the Registrar, in the construction trade for which application is made will be counted as experience. In no case, however, will such training or completion of an approved apprenticeship program count for more than 3 years of the experience.

(e) The required experience shall be possessed by one member of the applicant entity or by a responsible managing employee therefore, and the member or responsible managing employee shall be required to take the examination.

(Authority cited: Section 7008, Business and Professions Code. Reference: Section 7068, Business and Professions Code.)

825.5. General Manufactured Housing Contractor Initial Installer Training Requirement

(a) Effective September 30, 2021, in addition to the experience requirements in California Code of Regulations, title 16, section 825 and other requirements for licensure in the Business and Professions Code, an applicant for a C–47 – general manufactured housing contractor license shall complete the initial installer training that is compliant with the training curriculum contained in section 3286.308(a) of the Code of Federal Regulations, title 24, subtitle B, chapter XX, subpart D.

(b) Applicants shall submit proof of compliance with subdivision (a) to the Board with their application for licensure. Proof of compliance shall be shown by the Certificate of Completion of Training identified in section 3286.303(c) of the Code of Federal Regulations, title 24, subtitle B, chapter XX, subpart D. An application submitted without the certificate prescribed by this subdivision is not complete within the meaning of section 7072 of the Business and Professions Code.

(c) The initial installer training shall be obtained through one or more qualified trainers, as confirmed by the United States Department of Housing and Urban Development under part 3286 of the Code of Federal Regulations, title 24, subtitle B, chapter XX, subpart D, commencing with section 3286.301

(Authority cited: Sections 7008 and 7059, Business and Professions Code. Reference: Sections 7026.11, 7058, 7059, 7065 and 7068, Business and Professions Code; and part 3286 of the Code of Federal Regulations, title 24, subtitle B, chapter XX, subpart D, section 3286.301 et seq.)

826. Registrar to Pass on Experience

The Registrar may determine that an applicant who does not have the specific experience required in Section 825 has some comparable knowledge, training, and/or experience which is equivalent to the required experience.

827. Review of Application for Original License, Additional Classification, or Replacement of Qualifying Person

(a) Application Requiring Examination:

(1) The Board shall inform an applicant in writing within 60 days of receipt whether the application is complete and has been referred for examination or is deficient and what specific information is required. An application is "complete" when an acceptable application and fee have been filed by the applicant.

(2) When an application is returned which was previously rejected for deficiencies, the Board shall decide within 5 days of receipt whether the application is complete and accepted for filing.

(3) The Board shall decide within 115 days after a complete application has been referred for examination whether an applicant meets the requirements for licensure, provided that the examination has been successfully completed and the applicant has filed the bond(s), fee and other documents required by Division 3 of the Business and Professions Code.

(4) If an applicant has not successfully completed the examination as scheduled in subsection (3), or met the other requirements of that subsection (subject to the limitations of Business and Professions Code Section 7074), the Board shall decide within 45 days of the successful completion of a subsequently scheduled examination and the filing of acceptable bond(s), fee and other documents required by Division 3 of the Business and Professions Code, whether the applicant meets the requirements for licensure.

(5) The periods specified in subsection (3) and (4) shall be extended by a period of 60 days, if the application must be investigated.

(6) The minimum, median and maximum times for an application requiring examination for licensure as a contractor, for an additional classification, or for replacement of the qualifying person from the time of receipt of the application until the Board decided to issue the license, grant the additional classification or the replacement of the qualifying person, based on the Board's past two years performance, were:

(A) Application for Original License, with Examination:

Minimum.......... 11 days

Median............ 253 days

Maximum .... 726 days

(B) Application for Additional Classification, with Examination:

Minimum.......... 20 days

Median............. 96 days

Maximum ...... 617 days

(C) Application for Replacement of the Qualifying Person, with Examination:

Minimum.......... 20 days

Median............. 78 days

Maximum ...... 428 days

These periods include not only the Board's processing time, but also the time for which the applicant is responsible: e.g., the return of a rejected application, failure of and/or failure to appear at examinations, filing of the required bond(s) and fee.

(b) Applications Not Requiring Examination:

(1) The Board shall inform an applicant for licensure, without examination, as a contractor, for an additional classification, or for replacement of the qualifying person pursuant to Sections 7065 or 7065.1 of the Business and Professions Code within 50 days of receipt whether the application is complete and what the issuance or granting requirements are or that the application is deficient and what specific information is required.

(2) When an application is returned which was previously rejected for deficiencies, the Board shall decide within 5 days of receipt if the application is now complete and accepted for filing.

(3) Once the applicant has filed acceptable bond(s) and other documents required by Division 3 of the Business and Professions Code, the Board shall decide within 15 days whether the applicant meets the requirements for licensure.

(4) The period outlined in subsection (1) may be extended by 60 days if the application must be investigated.

(5) The minimum, median and maximum times for an application for licensure, without examination, as a contractor, for an additional classification, or for replacement of the qualifying person from the time of receipt of the application until the Board decided to issue the license, grant the additional classification or the replacement of the qualifying person, based on the Board's past two years performance were:

(A) Application for Original License, without Examination:

Minimum............. 1 day

Median............. 48 days

Maximum .... 349 days

(B) Application for Additional Classification, without Examination:

Minimum .... 24 days

Median .... 58.5 days

Maximum .... 358 days

(C) Application for Replacement of the Qualifying Person, without Examination:

Minimum .... 1 day

Median .... 29 days

Maximum .... 253 days

These periods include not only the Board's processing time, but also the time for which the applicant is responsible: e.g., return of a rejected application and filing of the required bond(s) and fee.

(Authority cited: Section 7008, Business and Professions Code; and Section 15376, Government Code. Reference: Section 15376, Government Code; and Sections 7065, 7065.1 and 7074, Business and Professions Code.)

828. Review of Application for Home Improvement Salesman Registration

(a) The Board shall inform, in writing, an applicant for registration as home improvement salesman within 30 days of receipt whether the application is deficient and what specific information is required or whether the registration has been issued.

(b) When an application is returned which was previously rejected for deficiencies, the Board shall decide whether the applicant meets the requirements for registration within 5 days after return of the completed application. A "completed application" means that an acceptable application form together with all required information, documentation and fee has been filed by the applicant.

(c) The time periods outlined in (a) and (b) may be extended by 5 weeks if the fee is in the form of a personal or company check, or by 60 days if an application requires investigation to determine if a statement of issues must be filed.

(d) The minimum, median and maximum processing times for an application for registration as a home improvement salesman from the time of receipt of the initial application until the Board makes a final decision on the application, based on the Board's past two years performance, are:

Minimum:.............1 day

Median:..............8 days

Maximum:.......53 days

(Authority cited: Section 7008, Business and Professions Code. Reference: Section 15376, Government Code; and Section 7153.1, Business and Professions Code.)

ARTICLE 3. CLASSIFICATION

830. Classification Policy

(a) All contractors to whom licenses are issued shall be classified by the Registrar as a specialty contractor, as defined in this article; a general engineering contractor (Class A), as defined in Section 7056 of the Code; or a general building contractor (Class B), as defined in Section 7057 of the Code.

(b) Contractors licensed in one classification shall be prohibited from contracting in the field of any other classification unless they are also licensed in that classification or are permitted to do so by Section 831.

(Authority cited: Section 7008, Business and Professions Code. Reference: Section 7059, Business and Professions Code.)

831. Incidental and Supplemental Defined

For purposes of Section 7059, work in other classifications is "incidental and supplemental" to the work for which a specialty contractor is licensed if that work is essential to accomplish the work in which the contractor is classified. A specialty contractor may use subcontractors to complete the incidental and supplemental work, or he may use his own employees to do so.

(Authority cited: Sections 7008 and 7059, Business and Professions Code. Reference: Section 7059, Business and Professions Code.)

832. Specialty Contractors Classified

Specialty contractors shall perform their trade using the art, experience, science and skill necessary to satisfactorily organize, administer, construct and complete projects under their classification, in accordance with the standards of their trade.

They are classified into the following subclassifications:

Asbestos Abatement.. C-22

Boiler, Hot Water Heating and Steam Fitting........................ C-4

Section VI

(Authority cited: Sections 7008 and 7059, Business and Professions Code. Reference: Sections 7058 and 7059, Business and Professions Code.)

832.02. Class C-2—Insulation and Acoustical Contractor

An insulation and acoustical contractor installs any insulating media and preformed architectural acoustical materials for the purpose of temperature and/or sound control.

(Authority cited: Sections 7008 and 7059, Business and Professions Code. Reference: Sections 7058 and 7059, Business and Professions Code.)

832.04. Class C-4—Boiler, Hot-Water Heating and Steam Fitting Contractor

A boiler, hot-water heating and steam fitting contractor installs, services and repairs power boiler installations, hot-water heating systems and steam fitting, including fire-tube and water-tube steel power boilers and hot-water heating low pressure boilers, steam fitting and piping, fittings, valves, gauges, pumps, radiators, convectors, fuel oil tanks, fuel oil lines, chimneys, flues, heat insulation and all other equipment, including solar heating equipment, associated with these systems.

(Authority cited: Sections 7008 and 7059, Business and Professions Code. Reference: Sections 7058 and 7059, Business and Professions Code.)

832.05. Class C-5—Framing and Rough Carpentry Contractor

A framing and rough carpentry contractor performs any form work, framing or rough carpentry necessary to construct framed structures; installs or repairs individual components of framing systems and performs any rough carpentry or associated work, including but not limited to the construction or installation of: sub-flooring, siding, exterior staircases and railings, overhead doors, roof decking, truss members, and sheathing.

(Authority cited: Sections 7008 and 7059, Business and Professions Code. Reference: Sections 7058 and 7059, Business and Professions Code.)

832.06. Class C-6—Cabinet, Millwork and Finish Carpentry Contractor

A cabinet, millwork and finish carpentry contractor makes cabinets, cases, sashes, doors, trims, nonbearing partitions and other items of "finish carpentry" by cutting, surfacing, joining, gluing and fabricating wood or other products to provide a functional surface. This contractor also places, erects, and finishes such cabinets and millwork in structures.

(Authority cited: Sections 7008 and 7059, Business and Professions Code. Reference: Sections 7058 and 7059, Business and Professions Code.)

832.07. Class C-7—Low Voltage Systems Contractor

A communication and low voltage contractor installs, services and maintains all types of communication and low voltage systems which are energy limited and do not exceed 91 volts. These systems include, but are not limited to telephone systems, sound systems, cable television systems, closed-circuit video systems, satellite dish antennas, instrumentation and temperature controls, and low voltage landscape lighting. Low voltage fire alarm systems are specifically not included in this section.

(Authority cited: Sections 7008 and 7059, Business and Professions Code. Reference: Sections 7058 and 7059, Business and Professions Code.)

832.08. Class C-8—Concrete Contractor

A concrete contractor forms, pours, places, finishes and installs specified mass, pavement, flat and other concrete work; and places and sets screeds for pavements or flatwork. This class shall not include contractors whose sole contracting business is the application of plaster coatings or the placing and erecting of steel or bars for the reinforcing of mass, pavement, flat and other concrete work.

(Authority cited: Sections 7008 and 7059, Business and Professions Code. Reference: Sections 7058 and 7059, Business and Professions Code.)

832.09. Class C-9—Drywall Contractor

A drywall contractor lays out and installs gypsum wall board and gypsum wallboard assemblies including nonstructural metal framing members, and performs the taping and texturing operations including the applications of compounds that adhere to wall board to produce a continuous smooth or textured surface.

(Authority cited: Sections 7008 and 7059, Business and Professions Code. Reference: Sections 7058 and 7059, Business and Professions Code.)

832.10. Class C-10—Electrical Contractor*

An electrical contractor places, installs, erects or connects any electrical wires, fixtures, appliances, apparatus, raceways, conduits, battery energy storage systems, photovoltaic solar energy systems or any part thereof, which generate, transmit, transform or utilize electrical energy in any form or for any purpose.

Effective date temporarily stayed at time of printing

(Authority cited: Sections 7008 and 7059, Business and Professions Code. Reference: Sections 7058 and 7059, Business and Professions Code.)

832.11. Class C-11—Elevator Contractor

An elevator contractor fabricates, erects, installs and repairs elevators, including sheave beams, motors, sheaves, cable and wire rope, guides, cab, counterweights, doors (including sidewalk elevator doors), automatic and manual controls, signal systems, and all other devices and equipment associated with the safe and efficient installation and operation of electrical, hydraulic and manually operated elevators.

(Authority cited: Sections 7008 and 7059, Business and Professions Code. Reference: Sections 7058 and 7059, Business and Professions Code.)

832.12. Class C-12—Earthwork and Paving Contractors

An earthwork and paving contractor digs, moves, and places material forming the surface of the earth, other than water, in such a manner that a cut, fill, excavation, grade, trench, backfill, or tunnel (if incidental thereto) can be executed, including the use of explosives for these purposes. This classification includes the mixing, fabricating and placing of paving and any other surfacing materials.

(Authority cited: Sections 7008 and 7059, Business and Professions Code. Reference: Sections 7058 and 7059, Business and Professions Code.)

832.13. Class C-13—Fencing Contractor

A fencing contractor constructs, erects, alters, or repairs all types of fences, corrals, runs, railings, cribs, game court enclosures, guard rails and barriers, playground game equipment, backstops, posts, flagpoles, and gates, excluding masonry walls.

(Authority cited: Sections 7008 and 7059, Business and Professions Code. Reference: Sections 7058 and 7059, Business and Professions Code.)

832.15. Class C-15—Flooring and Floor Covering Contractors

A flooring and floor covering contractor prepares any surface for the installation of flooring and floor coverings, and installs carpet, resilient sheet goods, resilient tile, wood floors and flooring (including the finishing and repairing thereof), and any other materials established as flooring and floor covering material, except ceramic tile.

(Authority cited: Sections 7008 and 7059, Business and Professions Code. Reference: Sections 7058 and 7059, Business and Professions Code.)

832.16. Class C-16—Fire Protection Contractor

A fire protection contractor lays out, fabricates and installs all types of fire protection systems; including all the equipment associated with these systems, excluding electrical alarm systems.

(Authority cited: Section 7008 and 7059 of the Business and Professions Code. Reference: Sections 7058 and 7059, Business and Professions Code.)

832.17. Class C-17—Glazing Contractor

A glazing contractor selects, cuts, assembles and/or installs all makes and kinds of glass, glass work, mirrored glass, and glass substitute materials for glazing; executes the fabrication and glazing of frames, panels, sashes and doors; and/or installs these items in any structure.

(Authority cited: Sections 7008 and 7059, Business and Professions Code. Reference: Sections 7058 and 7059, Business and Professions Code.)

832.20. Class C-20—Warm-Air Heating, Ventilating and Air-Conditioning Contractor

A warm-air heating, ventilating and air-conditioning contractor fabricates, installs, maintains, services and repairs warm-air heating systems and water heating heat pumps, complete with warm-air appliances; ventilating systems complete with blowers and plenum chambers; air-conditioning systems complete with air-conditioning unit; and the ducts, registers, flues, humidity and thermostatic controls and air filters in connection with any of these systems. This classification shall include warm-air heating, ventilating and air-conditioning systems which utilize solar energy.

(Authority cited: Sections 7008 and 7059, Business and Professions Code. Reference: Sections 7026.1, 7058 and 7059, Business and Professions Code.)

832.21. Class C–21—Building Moving/Demolition Contractor

A building moving/demolition contractor raises, lowers, cribs, underpins, demolishes and moves or removes structures, including their foundations. This classification does not include the alterations, additions, repairs or rehabilitation of the permanently retained portions of such structures.

(Authority cited: Sections 7008 and 7059, Business and Professions Code. Reference: Sections 7058 and 7059, Business and Professions Code.)

832.22. Class C–22—Asbestos Abatement Contractor

(a) An asbestos abatement contractor performs abatement, including containment, encapsulation, or removal, and disposal of asbestos containing construction materials, as defined in Section 6501.8 of the Labor Code, in and on buildings and structures. All work performed and all documentation prepared by an asbestos abatement contractor shall be done in accordance with regulations and requirements of the Division of Occupational Safety and Health (DOSH) of the Department of Industrial Relations.

(b) The Board shall not issue an asbestos abatement contractor license unless the applicant or contractor is duly registered with DOSH pursuant to Section 6501.5 of the Labor Code or has an active application for registration in process with DOSH. All holders of the C-22—asbestos abatement contractor classification shall have completed DOSH registration training requirements, as contained in Title 8, California Code of Regulations, Section 1529.

(c) Within 90 days after the asbestos abatement contractor license is issued, the contractor shall submit to the Board proof that he or she is duly registered with DOSH pursuant to Section 6501.5 of the Labor Code.

No asbestos abatement work shall be performed nor documentation prepared until the contractor has submitted proof of his or her DOSH registration to the Board.

Failure of a licensee to provide proof of current registration with DOSH within 90 days after issuance shall result in the automatic suspension of the license or removal of the C-22—asbestos abatement contractor classification at the end of the 90 days.

(d) Every applicant for the C-22—asbestos abatement contractor classification must have had, within the last 10 years immediately preceding the filing of the application, not less than four years of experience performing asbestos abatement duties as a journeyman, foreman, supervising employee, or contractor working for or as any of the following:

(1) A licensed contractor who holds the C-22—asbestos abatement contractor classification or the asbestos certification, as defined in Section 7058.5 of the Code, and DOSH registration;

(2) A contractor who provides asbestos abatement services and is licensed in another state or federal jurisdiction;

(3) A utility company operating under the laws of a state or federal regulatory agency;

(4) A division of a state or the federal government; or

(5) The armed forces of the United States.

(e) The Board shall require as a condition precedent to the renewal of an asbestos abatement contractor license that the licensee have on file proof of current registration with DOSH pursuant to Section 6501.5 of the Labor Code.

(f) This classification does not include any addition to or alteration, repair, or rehabilitation of the permanently retained portions of such buildings and structures. Hazardous substance removal and remediation, as defined in Section 7058.7 of the Code, are specifically not included in this classification.

(Authority cited: Sections 7008 and 7059, Business and Professions Code. Reference: Sections 7058, 7058.5, 7058.7 and 7059, Business and Professions Code; and Sections 6501.5 and 6501.8, Labor Code.)

832.23. Class C-23—Ornamental Metal Contractor

An ornamental metals contractor assembles, casts, cuts, shapes, stamps, forges, welds, fabricates and installs, sheet, rolled and cast, brass, bronze, copper, cast iron, wrought iron, monel metal, stainless steel, steel, and/or any other metal for the architectural treatment and ornamental decoration of structures. This classification does not include the work of a sheet metal contractor.

(Authority cited: Sections 7008 and 7059, Business and Professions Code. Reference: Sections 7058 and 7059, Business and Professions Code.)

832.27. Class C-27—Landscaping Contractor

A landscape contractor constructs, maintains, repairs, installs, or subcontracts the development of landscape systems and facilities for public and private gardens and other areas which are designed to aesthetically, architecturally, horticulturally, or functionally improve the grounds within or surrounding a structure or a tract or plot of land. In connection therewith, a landscape contractor prepares and grades plots and areas of land for the installation of any architectural, horticultural and decorative treatment or arrangement.

(Authority cited: Sections 7008 and 7059, Business and Professions Code. Reference: Sections 7058 and 7059, Business and Professions Code.)

832.28. Class C-28—Lock and Security Equipment Contractor

A lock and security equipment contractor evaluates, sets up, installs, maintains and repairs all doors and door assemblies, gates, locks and locking devices, panic and fire rated exit devices, manual and automatic operated gate and door closures and releases, jail and prison locking devices and permanently installed or built in safes and vaults. This classification includes but is not limited to master key systems, metal window guards, security doors, card activated and electronic access control systems for control equipment, motion and other types of detectors and computer systems for control and audit of control systems and other associated equipment. Fire alarm systems are specifically not included in this section.

(Authority Cited: Sections 7008 and 7059, Business and Professions Code. Reference: Sections 7058 and 7059, Business and Professions Code.)

832.29. Class C-29—Masonry Contractor

A masonry contractor installs concrete units and baked clay products; concrete, glass and clay block; natural and manufactured stone; terra cotta; and fire brick or other material for refractory work. This classification includes the fabrication and installation of masonry component units for structural load bearing and non-load bearing walls for structures and fences installed with or without mortar; ceramic veneer (not tile) and thin brick that resembles full brick for facing; paving; and clear waterproofing, cleaning and caulking incidental to masonry construction.

(Authority cited: Sections 7008 and 7059, Business and Professions Code. Reference: Sections 7058 and 7059, Business and Professions Code.)

832.31. Class C-31—Construction Zone Traffic Control Contractor

A construction zone traffic control contractor prepares or removes lane closures, flagging or traffic diversions, utilizing portable devices, such as cones, delineators, barricades, sign stands, flashing beacons, flashing arrow trailers, and changeable message signs, on roadways, including, but not limited to, public streets, highways, or any public conveyance.

(Authority cited: Sections 7008 and 7059, Business and Professions Code. Reference: Sections 7058 and 7059, Business and Professions Code.)

832.32. Class C-32—Parking and Highway Improvement Contractor

A parking and highway improvement contractor applies and installs protective coatings, vehicle stops, guard rails and mechanical devices, directional lines, buttons, markers, signs and arrows on the horizontal surface of any game court, parking facility, airport, highway or roadway constructed of concrete, asphalt or similar material. This classification includes the surface preparatory work necessary for the application of protective coatings but does not include the re-paving of these surfaces.

(Authority cited: Sections 7008 and 7059, Business and Professions Code. Reference: Sections 7058 and 7059, Business and Professions Code.)

832.33. Class C-33—Painting and Decorating Contractors

A painting and decorating contractor prepares by scraping, sandblasting or other means and applies any of the following: paints, papers, textures, fabrics, pigments, oils, turpentines, japans, driers, thinners, varnishes, shellacs, stains, fillers, waxes, adhesives, water and any other vehicles, mediums and materials which adhere by evaporation and may be mixed, used and applied to the surfaces of structures and the appurtenances thereto for purposes of decorating, protecting, fireproofing and waterproofing.

(Authority cited: Sections 7008 and 7059, Business and Professions Code. Reference: Sections 7058 and 7059, Business and Professions Code.)

832.34. Class C-34—Pipeline Contractor

A pipeline contractor fabricates and installs pipelines for the conveyance of fluids, such as water, gas, or petroleum, or for the containment or protection of any other material, including the application of protective coatings or systems and the trenching, boring, shoring, backfilling, compacting, paving and surfacing necessary to complete the installation of such pipelines.

(Authority cited: Sections 7008 and 7059, Business and Professions Code. Reference: Sections 7058 and 7059, Business and Professions Code.)

832.35. Class C-35—Lathing and Plastering Contractor

(a) A lathing and plastering contractor coats surfaces with a mixture of sand, gypsum plaster, quick-lime or hydrated lime and water, or sand and cement and water, or a combination of such other materials that create a permanent surface coating, including coatings for the purpose of soundproofing and fireproofing. These coatings are applied with a plasterer's trowel or sprayed over any surface which offers a mechanical means for the support of such coating, and will adhere by suction. This contractor also installs lath (including metal studs) or any

Section VI

other material prepared or manufactured to provide a base or bond for such coating.

(b) A lathing and plastering contractor also applies and affixes wood and metal lath, or any other material prepared or manufactured to provide key or suction bases for the support of plaster coatings. This classification includes the channel work and metal studs for the support of metal or any other lathing material and for solid plaster partitions.

(Authority cited: Sections 7008 and 7059, Business and Professions Code. Reference: Sections 7058 and 7059, Business and Professions Code.)

832.36. Class C-36—Plumbing Contractor

A plumbing contractor provides a means for a supply of safe water, ample in volume and of suitable temperature for the purpose intended and the proper disposal of fluid waste from the premises in all structures and fixed works. This classification includes but is not limited to:

(a) Complete removal of waste from the premises or the construction and connection of on-site waste disposal systems;

(b) Piping, storage tanks and venting for a safe and adequate supply of gases and liquids for any purpose, including vacuum, compressed air and gases for medical, dental, commercial and industrial uses;

(c) All gas appliances, flues and gas connections for all systems including suspended space heating units. This does not include forced warm air units;

(d) Water and gas piping from the property owner's side of the utility meter to the structure or fixed works;

(e) Installation of any type of equipment to heat water, or fluids, to a temperature suitable for the purposes listed in this section, including the installation of solar equipment for this purpose; and

(f) The maintenance and replacement of all items described above and all health and safety devices such as, but not limited to, gas earthquake valves, gas control valves, back flow preventors, water conditioning equipment and regulating valves.

(Authority Cited: Sections 7008 and 7059, Business and Professions Code. Reference: Sections 7058 and 7059, Business and Professions Code.)

832.38. Class C-38—Refrigeration Contractor

A refrigeration contractor constructs, fabricates, erects, installs, maintains, services and repairs refrigerators, refrigerated rooms, and insulated refrigerated spaces, temperature insulation, air-conditioning units, ducts, blowers, registers, humidity and thermostatic controls for the control of air, liquid, and/or gas temperatures below fifty degrees Fahrenheit (50°), or ten degrees Celsius (10°).

(Authority cited: Sections 7008 and 7059, Business and Professions Code. Reference: Sections 7026.1, 7058 and 7059, Business and Professions Code.)

832.39. Class C-39—Roofing Contractor

A roofing contractor installs products and repairs surfaces that seal, waterproof and weatherproof structures. This work is performed to prevent water or its derivatives, compounds or solids from penetrating such protection and gaining access to material or space beyond. In the course of this work, the contractor examines and/or prepares surfaces and uses the following material: asphaltum, pitch, tar, felt, glass fabric, urethane foam, metal roofing systems, flax, shakes, shingles, roof tile, slate or any other roofing, waterproofing, weatherproofing or membrane material(s) or a combination thereof.

(Authority cited: Sections 7008 and 7059, Business and Professions Code. Reference: Sections 7058 and 7059, Business and Professions Code.)

832.42. Class C-42—Sanitation System Contractor

A sanitation system contractor fabricates and installs cesspools, septic tanks, storm drains, and other sewage disposal and drain structures. This classification includes the laying of cast-iron, steel, concrete, vitreous and non-vitreous pipe and any other hardware associated with these systems.

(Authority cited: Sections 7008 and 7059, Business and Professions Code. Reference: Sections 7058 and 7059, Business and Professions Code.)

832.43. Class C-43—Sheet Metal Contractor

A sheet metal contractor selects, cuts, shapes, fabricates and installs sheet metal such as cornices, flashings, gutters, leaders, pans, kitchen equipment, duct work (including insulation, patented chimneys, metal flues, metal roofing systems and any other installations requiring sheet metal).

(Authority cited: Sections 7008 and 7059, Business and Professions Code. Reference: Sections 7058 and 7059, Business and Professions Code.)

832.45. Class C-45—Sign Contractor

A sign contractor fabricates, installs, and erects electrical signs, including the wiring of such electrical signs, and non-electrical signs, including but not limited to: post or pole supported signs, signs attached to structures, painted wall signs, and modifications to existing signs.

(Authority cited: Sections 7008 and 7059, Business and Professions Code. Reference: Sections 7058 and 7059, Business and Professions Code.)

832.46. Class C-46—Solar Contractor*

(a) A solar contractor installs, modifies, maintains, and repairs thermal and photovoltaic solar energy systems. A licensee classified in this section shall not undertake or perform building or construction trades, crafts, or skills, except when required to install a thermal or photovoltaic solar energy system.

(b) For the purposes of this section, a battery energy storage system, as defined in section 810, shall not be considered part of a photovoltaic solar energy system or required to install a photovoltaic solar energy system. Except as provided in subdivision (c), a licensee classified in this section shall not install, connect, modify, maintain, or repair a battery energy storage system.

(c) For purposes of Section 7059 of the Code and this division, a licensee classified in this section may install a battery energy storage system as "incidental and supplemental" to the installation of a photovoltaic solar energy system if the battery energy storage system does not exceed a rating of 80 kilowatt-hours (kWh).

Effective date temporarily stayed at time of printing

(Authority cited: Sections 7008 and 7059, Business and Professions Code. Reference: Sections 7058 and 7059, Business and Professions Code.)

832.47. Class C-47—General Manufactured Housing Contractor

(a) A general manufactured housing contractor installs, alters, repairs, or prepares for moving any type of manufactured home as defined in Section 18007 of the Health and Safety Code, any; type of mobilehome as defined in Section 18008 of the Health and Safety Code, and any type of multifamily manufactured home as defined in Section 18008.7 of the Health and Safety Code, including the accessory buildings or structures, and the foundations. A manufactured home does not include any recreational vehicle, commercial coach, or factory-built housing as defined in Section 19971 of the Health and Safety Code.

(b) A general manufactured housing contractor may provide utility services on a single-family individual site placement. Utility services mean the connection of gas, water, sewer, and electrical utilities to the home.

(Authority cited: Sections 7008 and 7059, Business and Professions Code. Reference: Sections 7026.11, 7058 and 7059, Business and Professions Code.)

832.49. Class C-49—Tree and Palm Contractor

(a) A tree and palm contractor plants, maintains, and removes trees and palms. The duties include pruning, stump grinding, and tree, palm, or limb guying.

(b) Effective January 1, 2024, this regulation shall become operative.

(c) This regulation does not apply to, and a license shall not be required for, incidental pruning of trees or guying of planted trees and their limbs by a nurseryperson or incidental pruning of trees by a gardener as described in Section 7026.1 of the Code.

(Authority cited: Sections 7008 and 7059, Business and Professions Code. Reference: Sections 7026.1, 7058 and 7059, Business and Professions Code.)

832.50. Class C-50—Reinforcing Steel Contractor

A reinforcing steel contractor fabricates, places and ties steel mesh or steel reinforcing bars (rods), of any profile, perimeter, or cross-section, that are or may be used to reinforce concrete structures.

(Authority cited: Sections 7008 and 7059, Business and Professions Code. Reference: Sections 7058 and 7059, Business and Professions Code.)

832.51. Class C-51—Structural Steel Contractor

A structural steel contractor fabricates and erects structural steel shapes and plates, of any profile, perimeter or cross-section, that are or may be used as structural members for buildings and structures, including the riveting, welding, rigging, and metal roofing systems necessary to perform this work.

(Authority cited: Sections 7008 and 7059, Business and Professions Code. Reference: Sections 7058 and 7059, Business and Professions Code.)

832.53. Class C-53—Swimming Pool Contractor

A swimming pool contractor constructs swimming pools, spas or hot tubs, including installation of solar heating equipment using those trades or skills necessary for such construction.

(Authority cited: Sections 7008 and 7059, Business and Professions Code. Reference: Sections 7058 and 7059, Business and Professions Code.)

832.54. Class C-54—Tile Contractors (Ceramic and Mosaic)

A ceramic and mosaic tile contractor prepares surfaces as necessary and installs glazed wall, ceramic, mosaic, quarry, paver, faience, glass mosaic and stone tiles; thin tile that resembles full brick, natural or simulated stone slabs for bathtubs, showers and horizontal surfaces inside of buildings, or any tile units set in the traditional or innovative tile methods, excluding hollow or structural partition tile.

(Authority cited: Sections 7008 and 7059, Business and Professions Code. Reference: Sections 7058 and 7059, Business and Professions Code.)

832.55. Class C-55—Water Conditioning Contractor

A water conditioning contractor installs water conditioning equipment with the use of only such pipe and fittings as are necessary to connect the water conditioning equipment to the water supply system and to by-pass all those parts of the water supply system within the premises from which conditioned water is to be excluded.

(Authority cited: Sections 7008 and 7059, Business and Professions Code. Reference: Sections 7058 and 7059, Business and Professions Code.)

832.57. Class C-57—Well Drilling Contractor

A well drilling contractor installs and repairs water wells and pumps by boring, drilling, excavating, casing, cementing and cleaning to provide a supply of uncontaminated water.

(Authority cited: Sections 7008 and 7059, Business and Professions Code. Reference: Sections 7026.3, 7058 and 7059, Business and Professions Code.)

832.60. Class C-60—Welding Contractor

A welding contractor causes metals to become permanently attached, joined and fabricated by the use of gases and electrical energy, which creates temperatures of sufficient heat to perform this work.

(Authority cited: Sections 7008 and 7059, Business and Professions Code. Reference: Sections 7058 and 7059, Business and Professions Code.)

832.61. Classification C-61—Limited Specialty

(a) Limited specialty is a specialty contractor classification limited to a field and scope of operations of specialty contracting for which an applicant is qualified other than any of the specialty contractor classifications listed and defined in this article.

(b) An applicant classified and licensed in the classification Limited Specialty shall confine activities as a contractor to that field or fields and scope of operations set forth in the application and accepted by the Registrar or to that permitted by Section 831.

(c) Upon issuance of a C-61 license, the Registrar shall endorse upon the face of the original license certificate the field and scope of operations in which the licensee has demonstrated qualifications.

(d) A specialty contractor, other than a C-61 contractor, may perform work within the field and scope of the operations of Classification C-61, provided the work is consistent with established usage and procedure in the construction industry and is related to the specialty contractor's classification.

(Authority cited: Sections 7008 and 7059, Business and Professions Code. Reference: Sections 7058 and 7059, Business and Professions Code.)

832.62. Solar System Work Within Scope of Class A, Class B, and Class C-61 (Swimming Pool Maintenance)

(a) The phrase "in connection with fixed works requiring specialized engineering knowledge and skill" in Section 7056 of the Business and Professions Code shall include but not be limited to an active solar energy system.

(b) An active solar energy system constitutes use of more than two unrelated building trades or crafts within the meaning of Section 7057 of the Business and Professions Code.

(c) C-61 (Swimming Pool Maintenance Contractors) currently holding the SC-44 supplemental solar classification may continue to perform solar work authorized by Class SC-44 until one year after the implementation of the C-46 Solar Classification. Thereafter, classification C-61 (Swimming Pool Maintenance) is authorized to repair active solar heating systems for swimming pools.

(Authority cited: Sections 7008 and 7059, Business and Professions Code. Reference: Sections 7056, 7057 and 7058, Business and Professions Code.)

833. Asbestos Classification and Certification Limitations and Examination Requirement

(a) The C-22—asbestos abatement contractor classification shall operate as a stand-alone specialty contractor classification for asbestos abatement work, notwithstanding any other classification held by the licensed contractor.

(b) No general building contractor, as defined in Section 7057 of the Code, shall contract for any project that includes asbestos abatement work unless the general building contractor holds the C-22—asbestos abatement contractor classification or the asbestos certification, as defined in Section 7058.5 of the Code, and DOSH registration or unless the general building contractor subcontracts with an appropriately licensed contractor.

(c) The asbestos certification, as defined in Section 7058.5 of the Code, shall operate in conjunction with other classification(s) held by the licensed contractor. No licensed contractor who holds the asbestos certification shall contract for any project that includes asbestos abatement work in a trade for which the contractor is not licensed, unless the licensee also holds the C-22—asbestos abatement contractor classification.

(d) The Registrar may waive the trade examination, pursuant to Section 7065.3 of the Code, for the C-22—asbestos abatement contractor classification for a licensed contractor who holds the asbestos certification, as defined in Section 7058.5 of the Code, upon application and conclusive showing by the licensee that he or she possesses not less than four years journey-level experience in the C-22—asbestos abatement contractor classification within the last 10 years immediately preceding the filing of the application. The licensee shall have obtained the asbestos certification after having passed the written asbestos certification examination and shall have held the asbestos certification in active and good standing throughout the four-year experience period at a minimum.

(Authority cited: Sections 7008 and 7059, Business and Professions Code. Reference: Sections 7057, 7058, 7058.5, 7059 and 7065.3, Business and Professions Code.)

834. Limitation of Classification

(a) A licensee classified as a general engineering contractor shall operate only within those areas defined in Section 7056 of the Code.

(b) A licensee classified as a general building contractor, as defined in Section 7057 of the Code, shall take a prime contract or subcontract only as authorized by Section 7057.

(c) A licensee classified as a specialty contractor, as defined in Section 7058 of the Code, shall not act in the capacity of a contractor in any classification other than one in which he/she is classified except on work incidental or supplemental to the performance of a contract in a classification in which any contractor is licensed by the Board.

(Authority cited: Sections 7008 and 7059, Business and Professions Code. Reference: Sections 7056, 7057, 7058 and 7059, Business and Professions Code.)

ARTICLE 4. EXAMINATIONS

840. Written Examinations Required of All Applicants

Except as provided in Section 7065.1 of the Code, an applicant, including an applicant for an additional classification or classifications, must pass the written examination prescribed by the Registrar. No oral examination shall be given to any applicant. The reading of the examination instructions or questions or the explanation of the wording or intent of any of the questions to an examinee by any Board personnel authorized to conduct examinations, or by any duly sworn translators, shall not be considered an oral examination.

(Authority cited: Section 7008, Business and Professions Code. Reference: Sections 7065 and 7068, Business and Professions Code.)

841. Elimination and Revision of Examination Questions

The Registrar shall, under the Board's direction, prepare and revise the written examinations for contractors' licenses.

The Registrar shall replace, eliminate or change any examination question or answer thereto brought to his/her attention if, in the Registrar's opinion, the question is misleading or unfair, or the approved answer is incorrect.

(Authority cited: Section 7008, Business and Professions Code. Reference: Sections 7011, 7065, 7065.05 and 7068, Business and Professions Code.)

ARTICLE 5. RENEWAL OF LICENSE

853. Renewal Application Form

(a) The Registrar shall mail to each licensee, prior to the expiration of the license, a renewal form with complete instructions for renewal of the license.

(b) A renewal application and fee must be postmarked or hand delivered to the Board's headquarters office on or before the expiration date of the license. Failure to comply with the requirements of this subsection shall result in the renewal application being deemed delinquent.

(c) An incomplete renewal application shall be returned to the licensee by the Registrar with an explanation of the reasons for its rejection. The licensee shall resubmit the completed renewal application to the Board, postmarked or hand delivered to the Board's headquarters office on or before the expiration date of the license. Failure to comply with this subsection shall result in the expiration of the license as provided in Section 7140 of the Code.

(d) An expired license shall not be renewed until any accrued delinquency fee has been paid.

(Authority cited: Section 7008, Business and Professions Code. Reference: Sections 7137, 7140 and 7141, Business and Professions Code.)

ARTICLE 6. BONDS

856. Security in Lieu of Bond

(a) A certificate of deposit, submitted pursuant to Section 7071.12(a) of the code, shall:

(1) When filed in lieu of a contractor's bond

(A) by an applicant, show the name style as set out on page one of the application.

(B) by a licensee, show the name style as currently recorded in the official files of the Board.

(2) When filed in lieu of a bond of qualifying individual, show the name style as in (1) above and the name of the responsible managing individual.

(3) Be made payable to the Contractors State License Board. The word "trustee" shall not be included.

(4) Be issued for a period of not less than one year.

(5) Be automatically renewable at each maturity date.

(6) Provide that any interest earned shall be paid to the depositor.

(b) Assignment of a savings and loan association investment certificate or share account, or of a credit union certificate for funds or share account shall be upon a form prescribed and approved by the Registrar.

(1) The form shall show:

(A) The assignment of the account to the board.

(B) The name style as prescribed in subsection (a) above.

(C) The current address of the applicant or licensee.

(D) The name and address of the savings and loan association or credit union having custody of such funds.

(E) A declaration signed by an officer of the savings and loan association or the credit union that it received written notice of the assignment. This declaration shall include the title of the officer signing it.

(F) A receipt for the assignment from the Board with direction to the savings and loan association or the credit union that the earnings on the assigned account or certificate shall be paid to the assignor.

(2) The assignment form shall be accompanied by the savings and loan association pass book or investment certificate, the credit union certificate for funds or share account pass book of the assignor which shall show the name of the depositor-investor, that of the licensee or applicant, and the responsible managing individual, if applicable, and the amount of the assignment required by law.

(c) Eligible bearer bonds submitted pursuant to Section 7071.12(c) of the code shall be delivered to a bank in Sacramento, California, which shall act as agent for the applicant, licensee or responsible managing employee. The bank shall deliver the bonds to the Treasurer of the State of California only on order of the Registrar or an employee designated by the Registrar.

(1) The Registrar shall prescribe and approve the forms for the deposit or withdrawal of bearer bonds.

(2) Interest coupons shall remain attached to bearer bonds deposited with the Treasurer until such bonds are permanently withdrawn from the depository, not be resubmitted for deposit.

(3) In order to insure that sufficient security is on deposit, the bid price of bearer bonds, as recorded in the bond securities listed on the Pacific Coast Stock Exchange or some other authoritative source on the first day of the month in which such bonds are submitted for deposit, shall be at least 25% in excess of the amount of the surety bond or cash deposit required to be submitted.

The Registrar shall prescribe such procedures and forms, and issue such orders as necessary to accept and process any cash deposit submitted pursuant to Section 7071.12(d) of the code. Personal checks shall not be accepted as cash.

(Authority cited: Section 7008, Business and Professions Code. Reference: Sections 7071.5, 7071.6, 7071.8, 7071.9, 7071.10 and 7071.12, Business and Professions Code.)

858. Blanket Performance and Payment Bond Defined

(a) The purpose of these sections is to establish requirements for contractors seeking to obtain approval from the Registrar for a blanket performance and payment bond (hereafter referred to as "blanket bond") as specified under the provisions of paragraph (a)(8) of Section 7159.5 of the Code.

(b) For the purposes of this Article, the term "blanket bond" means a single surety instrument, executed by an admitted surety that is conditioned for the payment in full of all claims that arise from the obligations created by a licensee under any contract that is subject to the provisions of Section 7159 of the Code (hereafter referred to as "home improvement contract") and as set forth in Section 858.1 of this Article.

(c) For the purposes of this Article, the term "obligation" has the same meaning as set forth under Section 1427 of the Civil Code: "An obligation is a legal duty, by which a person is bound to do or not to do a certain thing."

(Authority cited: Section 7008, Business and Professions Code. Reference: Sections 7151, 7159 and 7159.5, Business and Professions Code.)

858.1. Blanket Performance and Payment Bond Requirements

(a) A blanket bond that is filed on behalf of a licensee to satisfy the provisions of Section 858 shall be underwritten for a dollar amount that is sufficient to cover one-hundred percent (100%) of the home improvement contracts for which the licensee has an obligation.

(b) Upon written request by a licensee, the Registrar is authorized to approve a blanket bond that is capped according to the schedule listed under subsection (c) provided the following conditions are met:

(1) The licensee, or the parent company of the licensee, is required to submit annual reports (Form 10-K) to the United States Securities and Exchange Commission (U.S. SEC).

(2) Upon the filing of a request that the blanket bond be capped, a copy of the most recently filed Form 10-K shall be submitted to the Registrar. Thereafter, a copy of any Form 10-K report shall be submitted to the Registrar within 10 days of filing with the U.S. SEC.

(3) The net worth of the applicable firm shall, initially and annually thereafter, be not less than 10 times the sum of the blanket bond as determined by the Registrar. Each net worth calculation shall be applicable to the period for which the most recent Form 10-K report was submitted to the U.S. SEC.

(c) The blanket bonds for which a request has been submitted under subsection (b) shall comply with the following schedule:

(1) If a licensee, or the parent company of a licensee, is classified as a "large accelerated filer" by the U.S. SEC, the amount of the blanket bond shall be $10 million.

(2) If a licensee, or the parent company of a licensee, is classified as an "accelerated filer" by the U.S. SEC, the amount of the blanket bond shall be $5 million.

(3) If a licensee, or the parent company of a licensee, is classified as a "non-accelerated filer" by the U.S. SEC, the amount of the blanket bond shall be $1 million.

(d) A licensee who is granted approval of a blanket bond pursuant to subsections (b) and (c) is not subject to the biennial financial reporting requirement specified under Section 858.4(a)(2). However, the qualifier's certification statement must be submitted biennially as specified under that section.

(e) For the purpose of executing the qualifier's certification statement required under Section 858.2(a)(4), the provisions of subsections (a), (b), and (c) of Section 858.1 shall be referenced collectively as "the 100% rule."

On the date that this section becomes effective, any licensee that has a blanket bond on file with the Board that fails to comply with the 100% rule shall achieve compliance not later than 90 days after the effective date of the section. The Registrar is authorized to rescind the approval of the blanket bond in accordance with the provisions of

Section 858.8 of this Article if the licensee fails to comply with any provision of this section.

(f) The form of the blanket bond specified under this section is subject to the approval of the Registrar and shall conform to the following with regard to content:

This bond shall be filed with the Registrar of Contractors
State of California
Contractors State License Board

Surety Code: _____
Bond No.: _____
License No.: _____

BLANKET PERFORMANCE AND PAYMENT BOND
(Business and Professions Code Section 7159.5)

The term of this bond is _____ to _____.

KNOW ALL BY THESE PRESENTS: That _____
(Business Name as Shown on the License)

whose address for service is

_____

(Street Address)	(City)	(State)	(Zip Code)

as Principal, and _____
(Name of Surety)

a corporation organized under the laws of the State of _____ and authorized to transact a general surety business in the State of California, as Surety, are held and firmly bound unto each owner or tenant of a residence or dwelling unit as the beneficiaries with whom the Principal, as of the date of this bond and thereafter, enters into a home improvement contract as defined in Section 7151.2 of the Business and Professions Code for repairing, remodeling, altering, converting, or modernizing such building or structure; and the aggregate contract price specified in one or more improvement contracts including all labor services and materials to be furnished by the Principal as the contractor exceeds the dollar amount prescribed in subdivision (b) of Section 7759. of the Business and Professions Code in the just and full sum of the amount of each individual contract for which sum, well and truly to be paid, we bind ourselves, our heirs, executors, successors, and assigns, jointly and severally, firmly by these presents. blanket performance and payment bond is issued in the amount of

_____($_____).

THE CONDITION OF THE OBLIGATION IS SUCH, That, WHEREAS, Sections 7159 and 7159.5 of the Business and Professions Code provide for bonding requirements for contractors entering into contracts covered by these provisions of law, AND, WHEREAS, the Principal desires to file a blanket guarantee to operate as security in accordance with Section 995.020 of the Code of Civil Procedure, to cover the performance and payment of all obligations resultant from such contracts in order to conduct business under the exemptions specified under paragraph (8) of subdivision (a) of Section 7159.5 of the Business and Professions Code.

NOW THEREFORE, if the Principal shall well and truly perform and fulfill all the understandings, covenants, terms, conditions, and agreements of said contracts, and shall also well and truly perform and fulfill all the undertakings, covenants, terms, conditions, and agreements of any and all duly authorized modifications of said contracts; and if the Principal shall promptly make payments to all persons, whether or not in direct contractual relationship with Principal, supplying labor or material or both for the prosecution of the work provided in said contracts, then this obligation is to be void; otherwise, it is to remain in full force and effect as though separate bonds in the full amount of the contract price had been written on the individual contracts.

PROVIDED, HOWEVER, this bond is issued subject to the following express conditions:

1. This bond may be cancelled by the Surety in accordance with the provisions of Sections 996.310 et seq. of the Code of Civil Procedure.

2. This bond shall be deemed continuous in form and shall remain in full force and effect and shall run concurrently with the license period for which the license is granted and shall continue beyond that period and every succeeding license period or periods for which said Principal may hold this license or until the effective date of rescission of the Registrar's approval of the bond, after which liability hereunder shall cease in accordance with provisions of Section 996.360 of the Code of Civil Procedure.

3. This bond to become effective _____

(Date)

4. Even though this bond may be in effect for more than one year, the Surety's aggregate liability for all contracts covered hereunder shall in no event exceed the amount set forth above.

5. The Surety signing this bond is jointly and severally liable on the obligations of the bond, the obligations of the statutes providing for this bond, and the applicable provisions of the Code of Civil Procedure regarding bonds.

_____
(Name of Surety)   (Address for Service)

I declare under penalty of perjury under the laws of the State of California that I have executed the foregoing bond under an unrevoked power of attorney. I further declare that I have relied upon the "Qualifier's Certification Statement" to determine that, as of the date of execution, the penal sum of this bond is a good faith valuation of the funds required to safeguard the financial interests of the beneficiaries relative to the obligations for which this bond is posted.

Executed in _____, _____ on _____,
                    (City and State)   (Date)

under the laws of the State of California.
Certificate of Authority # _____
Signature of Attorney-in-Fact _____
Printed or Typed Name of Attorney-in-Fact _____
Address of Attorney-in-Fact _____
Telephone Number of Attorney-in-Fact (___) _____
Signature of Principal (Qualifier for the License) _____
13B-39 rev. 07/2021

(Authority cited: Section 7008, Business and Professions Code. Reference: Sections 7151.2, 7159 and 7159.5, Business and Professions Code.)

858.2. Application for Approval of Blanket Performance and Payment Bond

(a) A licensee seeking approval of a blanket bond shall meet the applicable conditions specified under this Article and submit to the Board an Application for Approval of Blanket Performance and Payment Bond, form 13B-35 (rev. 9/2022), that includes the following information:

(1) The name and address of the licensee as listed on the license record and the license number.

(2) The name of every person listed on the license record of the applicant who, as specified under Section 7068 of the Code, is acting as a qualifier for the license.

(3) The reviewed year-end financial statements and a report prepared by a certified public accountant (CPA) duly licensed by the California Board of Accountancy or licensed by another state board of accountancy. The reviewed financial statements shall include

supplemental information related to the liquidity ratios of the licensee's business and shall particularly include the current ratio and the quick ratio, the calculations for which are specified under subparagraphs (A) and (B) below. The review report, or a separate supplementary report, shall include an explanation that the information has been subject to the review of the CPA. The review report shall cover the two fiscal years immediately preceding application for approval of the blanket bond and should be prepared in accordance with the current Statements of Standards for Accounting and Review Services issued by the American Institute of Certified Public Accounts.

(A) Current ratio calculation: current assets; divided by current liabilities.

(B) Quick ratio calculation: current assets minus inventory; divided by current liabilities.

(4) A certification statement, signed under penalty of perjury by the qualifier for the license, that shall conform to the following language:

QUALIFIER'S CERTIFICATION STATEMENT

(Unless otherwise noted, all section references are to the California Business and Professions Code.)

The undersigned declares that, in accordance with Sections 7068 and 7068.1 of the Code, they are a qualifier for the licensee identified below (hereafter referred to as "licensee") and are responsible for exercising the direct supervision and control of the licensee's operations as is necessary to secure full compliance with the laws and regulations that are under the jurisdiction of the Contractors State License Board. As a qualifier of the licensee, the undersigned has reviewed sufficient financial information to execute this certification as it pertains to the licensee's home improvement sales and services that are subject to the home improvement contract requirements specified under Section 7159 of the Code. As of close of business on (Date) _____, the blanket performance and payment bond (bond) number (Bond Number) _____ issued by (Name of Surety Company) _____ as Surety is, according to the qualifier's comprehension of the data derived from the licensee, in an aggregate amount that is sufficient to comply with the "100% rule" as specified in the provisions of Section 858.1 of Title 16, Division 8 of the California Code of Regulations.

The undersigned also certifies that they will monitor the relevant business activity of the licensee, exercise due diligence to secure ongoing compliance with the 100% rule, and notify the Registrar within 30 days of the licensee's refusal, failure, or inability to comply with the 100% rule.

The undersigned also certifies that, upon approval of the blanket bond by the Registrar, the contract forms that will be used by the licensee for all transactions that are subject to Section 7159 of the Code will contain a notice that informs the property owner that a blanket performance and payment bond is on file with the Registrar of Contractors, or in lieu thereof, a notice that clearly identifies the name and address of the Surety that has issued the blanket performance and payment bond.

As a qualifying individual for the licensee, the undersigned declares under penalty of perjury under the laws of the State of California that the foregoing is true and correct and that this declaration was executed on (Date) _____ at (City and State) _____, _____.

_____   _____
(Name of Licensee as it Appears on the License)   (License Number)

_____   _____
(Printed Name of Qualifier)   (Signature of Qualifier)

(b) A licensee shall be licensed in this state in an active status for not less than two years prior to submitting the application provided for by this section.

(c) Except as otherwise provided under this subsection, an application for approval of a blanket bond shall not be accepted for consideration if any member of the personnel of record of the licensee, or any home improvement salespersons registered to the licensee, was found to have been responsible for, participated in, or otherwise culpable relative to any legal action that is subject to disclosure under Section 7124.6(e)(2) or 7124.6(e)(3) of the Code, or is named on a license that is suspended pursuant to Section 7071.17 of the Code.

(1) Any person who, after the effective date of the most recent disciplinary order applicable to that individual, is listed on an active license for three consecutive years with no violations resulting in disciplinary action may make application as provided under this Article.

(d) The application shall be signed by the person qualifying on behalf of the licensee who has executed the qualifier's certification statement required under this section. In the case of a responsible managing employee qualifier, the application shall also be signed by the owner, partner, or current corporate officer.

(e) The application shall be accompanied by a blanket bond that complies with the provisions of Section 858.1 of this Article and is underwritten by a surety that has been admitted in the State of California.

(Authority cited: Section 7008, Business and Professions Code. Reference: Sections 7068, 7068.1, 7071.17, 7124.6, 7159 and 7159.5, Business and Professions Code.)

858.3. Minimum Standards for Blanket Performance and Payment Bond Approval—Cause for Denial

(a) For each of the year-end financial statements for which a report is required under Section 858.2, the following standards must be met in order to qualify for blanket bond approval:

(1) The quick ratio shall not be less than 1:1, or, in lieu thereof, the current ratio shall not be less than 2:1.

(b) In addition to any other cause for denial, the Registrar may deny or rescind approval of the blanket bond based on information in the reviewed report or the information contained in the supplemental information required under subparagraph (a)(3) of Section 858.2 if the information demonstrates the licensee will be unable to meet current liabilities.

(Authority cited: Section 7008, Business and Professions Code. Reference: Section 7159.5, Business and Professions Code.)

858.4. Blanket Performance and Payment Bond Biennial Certification and Financial Reporting Requirements

(a) Except as otherwise provided under this Article, a licensee that maintains a blanket bond under this Article shall comply with the following:

(1) A certification statement as specified in Section 858.2 of this Article, signed under penalty of perjury by the member of the personnel of record who is listed as the qualifier for the license in accordance with Section 7068 of the Code, shall be submitted biennially to the Registrar as specified under subsection (b).

(2) With each application to renew the license for which the blanket bond has been posted, reviewed year-end financial statements and a report prepared in accordance with the provisions of Section 858.2(a)(3) shall be submitted to the Registrar as follows:

(A) If it has been one calendar year or more since the Registrar's approval of the blanket bond, the licensee shall submit a copy of a review report and the accompanying financial statements covering the entire period that is subsequent to the approval, but not more than the two fiscal years immediately preceding the license renewal date.

(B) If it has been less than one calendar year since the Registrar's initial approval of the blanket bond, the reviewed report required by this subsection shall be submitted at next renewal period that is more than one calendar year subsequent to the initial approval of the blanket bond.

(b) The due date for the qualifier's certification statement and any reports required under this section shall coincide with the license renewal period of the license for which blanket bond approval has been granted. For each subsequent renewal cycle, the certification statement and reports of financial statements shall be submitted to the Registrar no later than the date the license is due to expire.

(c) The Registrar may rescind approval of the blanket bond based on information in the reviewed report or in the supplemental information that demonstrates the licensee's business may not be able to meet its current liabilities.

(d) If a licensee fails to submit the certification statement or comply with the financial reporting requirements as specified by this section, the Registrar may rescind approval of the blanket bond in accordance with the provisions of Section 858.8 of this Article.

(Authority cited: Section 7008, Business and Professions Code. Reference: Sections 7068, 7068.1 and 7159.5, Business and Professions Code.)

858.5. Blanket Performance and Payment Bond Audit Authorization and Procedures

(a) The Registrar may order an audit of a licensee that has an approved blanket bond on file if he or she deems an audit is necessary to ensure that the sum for which the blanket bond has been filed is sufficient to protect the public.

(1) The Registrar shall provide a licensee with not less than 30 days written notification that an audit is to be conducted pursuant to this section. The notice shall specify the period to be covered by the audit and set a date for the audit to begin. The audit period shall not exceed the period that is specified for the retention of licensee records under Section 7111 of the Code. Delivery of the notice shall be by certified mail to the current business address of record listed on the license record. Upon written request, the Registrar may grant the licensee an additional 30 days to prepare for the audit.

(2) For any audit conducted pursuant to this section, the licensee shall, pursuant to the receipt of the audit notice, provide access to the licensee's books, business records, and documents in accordance with the provisions of Section 7111 of the Code.

(b) Upon completion and review of the audit and all relevant information, the Registrar shall determine if the licensee is in compliance with the 100% rule specified under Section 858.1.

(Authority cited: Section 7008, Business and Professions Code. Reference: Sections 7111 and 7159.5, Business and Professions Code.)

858.6. Authorization and Procedures for Ordering the Amount of Blanket Performance and Payment Bond to Be Increased

(a) Pursuant to an audit conducted in accordance with Section 858.5 of this Article, the Registrar is authorized to order an increase in the dollar amount of the blanket bond to an amount that meets the requirements specified in Section 858.1 of this Article. The adjustment determination shall be based on the information contained in records of the licensee that are required to be made available for an audit as specified under this Article.

(b) An order to increase the sum of the blanket bond pursuant to this section shall be sent by certified and regular mail to the licensee's address of record. The order shall include a notice that failure to increase the dollar amount of the blanket bond within 30 days of the date of the order is cause for rescission of approval of the blanket bond.

(c) If a licensee fails to comply within 30 days of the date of an order that is issued pursuant to this section, the Registrar shall rescind approval of the blanket bond in accordance with the provisions of Section 858.8 of this Article.

(Authority cited: Section 7008, Business and Professions Code. Reference: Section 7159.5, Business and Professions Code.)

858.7. Maintenance of the Blanket Performance and Payment Bond

(a) In order for any licensee to maintain the Registrar's approval of a blanket bond in accordance with this Article, all provisions of this section are applicable:

(1) No member of the personnel of record of the licensee, nor home improvement salesperson registered to the licensee, shall have been found to have been responsible for, participated in, or otherwise culpable relative to any acts or omissions that resulted in any discipline that is subject to disclosure under Section 7124.6(e)(2) or 7124.6(e)(3) of the Code. The approval of the blanket bond posted by a licensee found to be in violation of this section is subject to rescission in accordance with the provisions of Section 858.8 of this Article. In determining whether or not to rescind approval of the blanket bond for violations of this section, the Registrar shall give due

consideration to protection of the public as set forth in Section 7000.6 of the Code.

(2) No member of the personnel of record of the licensee, nor home improvement salespersons registered to the licensee, shall be named on a license that is suspended pursuant to Section 7071.17 of the Code. The approval of the blanket bond posted by a licensee found to be in violation of this section is subject to rescission in accordance with the provisions of Section 858.8 of this Article. In determining whether or not to rescind approval of the blanket bond for violations of this section, the Registrar shall give due consideration to protection of the public as set forth in Section 7000.6 of the Code.

(3) Whenever any qualifier who has executed and filed the qualifier's certification statement required under this Article disassociates from the licensee, a subsequent qualifier for the licensee shall complete, execute, and file the qualifier's certification statement contained in the application form specified under Section 858.2 of this Article. The qualifier's certification statement required by this paragraph must be filed within 90 days of the date that the former qualifier who executed the qualifier's certification statement disassociated from the license, as noted on the official license record of the Board.

(4) The failure to file an acceptable qualifier's certification statement within 90 days as specified under subdivision (3) of this subsection is cause for rescission of approval of the bond in accordance with the provisions of Section 858.8 of this Article. If a licensee files a written request prior to the date the qualifier's certification statement is due, the Registrar may grant an additional 30 days within which to file the certification statement. The licensee's request shall clearly state the reason(s) why additional time is needed to file the qualifier's certification statement.

(Authority cited: Section 7008, Business and Professions Code. Reference: Sections 7000.6, 7071.17, 7124.6 and 7159.5, Business and Professions Code.)

858.8. Rescission of Blanket Performance and Payment Bond Approval

(a) The Registrar may rescind the approval of any blanket bond (also referenced as "approval rescission" under this section) if any provision or condition specified under this Article is not satisfied.

(b) To rescind the approval of a blanket bond, the Registrar shall send written notice by certified and regular mail to the licensee's address of record that specifies the date of and the reasons for the Registrar's decision to rescind approval of the blanket bond. When appropriate, the notice shall also contain the conditions that must be met to prevent the rescission.

(c) The rescission shall, as of the date specified, extinguish the licensee's authorization to use the blanket bond in satisfaction of the provisions under subsection (a)(8) of Section 7159.5 of the Code.

(d) The licensee shall be given not less than 30 days notice prior to the effective date of the rescission of the blanket bond. Prior to the effective date of the rescission, the licensee may file a written appeal of the rescission of the blanket bond with the Registrar. A written appeal is considered timely if it is postmarked prior to the date the rescission would otherwise become effective. Where a rescission is not appealed timely, the blanket bond shall be rescinded on the effective date specified by the Registrar. If the rescission is appealed timely, the effective date of the rescission shall be delayed until a decision on the appeal is issued, and a notice regarding the appeal and the pending decision of the Registrar shall be posted as specified under subsection (b) of Section 858.9.

(e) Upon cancellation of the blanket bond, the Registrar's approval shall be automatically rescinded effective on the date of the cancellation.

(f) Upon the effective date of the Registrar's approval rescission, the licensee shall be subject to and comply with the provisions of subsections (a)(3), (4), and (5) of Section 7159.5 of the Code and shall, in addition to complying with all other requirements specified under Section 7159 of the Code, include the Mechanics' Lien Warning disclosure as part of all home improvement contracts that are subject to that section.

(Authority cited: Section 7008, Business and Professions Code. Reference: Sections 7159 and 7159.5, Business and Professions Code.)

858.9. Posting of Blanket Performance and Payment Bond Information to License Records

(a) Upon approval of a blanket bond by the Registrar, regardless of the effective date of the blanket bond, the following information shall be posted to the public license record of the licensee named as principal on the blanket bond:

(1) A statement indicating that the licensee has an approved blanket performance and payment bond on file with the Board.

(2) The date that the blanket bond was approved.

(3) The number of the blanket bond.

(4) The dollar amount for which the blanket bond has been filed.

(5) The name and address of the surety company on the blanket bond.

(b) Whenever a licensee is notified of a decision to rescind the approval of the licensee's blanket bond, the Registrar shall post a notice on the public license record indicating that the rescission is pending. The notice shall be posted to the license record no earlier than 5 calendar days and no later than 10 calendar days after the date that written notification of the rescission is sent to the licensee. If the rescission is appealed timely by the licensee, the Registrar shall also post a notice that an appeal has been filed and indicate that the decision to rescind the approval of the blanket bond is delayed pending the outcome of the licensee's appeal.

(c) Upon rescission of approval of a blanket bond or its cancellation, the statement specified in paragraph (1) of subsection (a) shall be changed to indicate the disposition of the blanket bond and the effective date thereof. The information in paragraphs (2), (3), (4), and (5) of subsection (a) shall remain on the license record for not less than five years after the date the blanket bond was rescinded or cancelled.

(Authority cited: Section 7008, Business and Professions Code. Reference: Section 7159.5, Business and Professions Code.)

ARTICLE 7. SPECIAL PROVISIONS

860. Penalty for Failure to Comply with Rules

Licensees and applicants for licenses shall comply with all rules and regulations of the Board and regulations issued by the Registrar. Violation of such rules and regulations shall constitute grounds for disciplinary action, or for the denial of a license.

(Authority cited: Section 7008, Business and Professions Code. Reference: Section 7008, Business and Professions Code.)

861. "Advertising" Defined

As used in Section 7030.5 of the Code, the term "advertising" includes but is not limited to the following: any card, contract proposal, sign, billboard, lettering on vehicles registered in this or any other state, brochure, pamphlet, circular, newspaper, magazine, airwave or any electronic transmission, and any form of directory under any listing denoting "Contractor" or any word or words of a similar import or meaning requesting any work for which a license is required by the Contractors License Law.

(Authority cited: Section 7008, Business and Professions Code. Reference: Section 7030.5, Business and Professions Code.)

Section VI

861.5. Definition of "Structural Defect"

For the purpose of subdivision (b) of Section 7091 of the Code, "structural defect" is defined as meaning:

(1) A failure or condition that would probably result in a failure in the load bearing portions of a structure,

(2) which portions of the structure are not constructed in compliance with the codes in effect at the time for the location of the structure, provided that,

(3) such failure or condition results in the inability to reasonably use the affected portion of the structure for the purpose for which it was intended.

(Authority cited: Sections 7008, 7091, Business and Professions Code. Reference: Section 7091, Business and Professions Code.)

863. Public Access to Information

The Registrar shall establish a system whereby members of the public may obtain from board records information regarding complaints made against licensed contractors, their history of legal actions taken by the board, and license status, as hereafter specified. For purposes of this section, "complaint" means a written allegation which has been investigated and has been referred for legal action against the licensee. For purposes of this section, "legal action" means referral of the complaint for the issuance of a citation, accusation, statement of issues, or for the initiation of criminal action or injunctive proceedings.

(a) The Registrar shall maintain records showing the complaints received against licensees and, with respect to such complaints, shall make available to members of the public, upon request, the following information:

(1) The nature of all complaints on file against a licensee which have been investigated by a Deputy Registrar and referred for legal action against the licensee by the District Office. Information regarding complaints which are in the process of being screened, mediated, arbitrated or investigated shall not be disclosed.

(2) Such general cautionary statements as may be considered appropriate regarding the usefulness of complaint information to individual consumers in their selection of a contractor.

(3) Whenever complaint information is requested, the information disclosable under subsections (c) and (d) below shall also be released.

(b) If a complaint results in a legal action and is subsequently determined by the registrar, the Office of the Attorney General or a court of competent jurisdiction not to have merit, it shall be deleted from the complaint disclosure system.

(c) The Registrar shall maintain records showing a history of any legal actions taken by the board against all current license holders and shall make available to members of the public, upon request, all the following information:

(1) Whether any current license holder has ever been disciplined by the registrar and, if so, when and for what offense; and

(2) Whether any current licensee has ever been cited, and, if so, when and for what offense, and, whether such citation is on appeal or has been complied with;

(3) Whether any current license holder is named as a respondent in any currently pending disciplinary or legal action.

(d) The Registrar shall maintain records showing certain licensing and bonding information for all current license holders and shall make available to members of the public, upon request, all the following information regarding current license holders:

(1) The name of the licensee as it appears in the board's records; and

(2) The license number; and

(3) The classification(s) held; and

(4) The address of record; and

(5) The personnel of the licensee; and

(6) The date of original licensure; and

(7) Whether a bond or cash deposit is maintained and, if so, its amount; and

(8) If the licensee maintains a bond, the name and address of the bonding company and the bond's identification number, if any.

(e) Limitation of access to information. Further, the Registrar may set reasonable limits upon the number of requests for information responded per month from any one requestor.

(Authority cited: Section 7008, Business and Professions Code. Reference: Sections 7124.5 and 7124.6, Business and Professions Code.)

864. Continuance of License Under Section 7068.2

When a notice of disassociation of the responsible managing officer, responsible managing employee, responsible managing member, or responsible managing manager is given within the time and in the manner prescribed by Section 7068.2 of the code, the license shall remain in force for a period of 90 days from the date of such disassociation.

(Authority cited: Section 7008, Business and Professions Code. Reference: Section 7068.2, Business and Professions Code.)

865. Continuance of License Under Section 7076

(a) An application for the continuation of a business under an existing license may be submitted to the Registrar within 90 days of:

(1) the death of a person licensed as an individual,

(2) the death or the disassociation of a partner of a licensed partnership, or

(3) the death of an individual member or the disassociation of any entity of a licensed joint venture.

If the application is approved by the Registrar, the license shall remain in force for a period of up to one year from the date of death or disassociation.

(b) The Registrar may approve an extension to the one-year provision outlined in subsection (a) if additional time is necessary to complete projects contracted for or commenced before the disassociation or death.

(c) A license so extended is subject to all the provisions of the Contractors License Law including those relating to renewal and bond requirements.

(Authority cited: Section 7008, Business and Professions Code. Reference: Section 7076, Business and Professions Code.)

867. Procedure to Reactivate an Inactive License

(a) A reactivation of an inactive license shall be effective on the date on which an acceptable form is received by the Registrar, on the date on which the full renewal fee for an active license provided for in Section 7137 of the Code is paid, or on the date, if any, requested by the licensee, whichever last occurs.

(b) When an inactive license is reactivated, the Registrar shall issue to the licensee an active pocket license.

(c) The name, address, license number and classification of the reactivated licensee shall be posted publicly as prescribed by the Registrar.

(Authority cited: Section 7008, Business and Professions Code. Reference: Section 7076.5, Business and Professions Code.)

868. Criteria to Aid in Determining if Crimes, Professional Misconduct, or Acts Are Substantially Related to Qualifications, Functions, or Duties of a Licensee or Registrant.

(a) For the purposes of denial, suspension, or revocation of a license or registration pursuant to Section 141, Division 1.5 (commencing with Section 475), or Sections 7073 or 7123 of the Code, a crime, professional misconduct, or act shall be considered to be substantially related to the qualifications, functions, or duties of a licensee or registrant (under Division 3, Chapter 9 of the Code) if it evidences present or potential unfitness of an applicant, licensee, or registrant to perform the functions authorized by the license or registration in a manner consistent with the public health, safety, and welfare.

(b) In making the substantial relationship determination required under subdivision (a) for a crime, the Board or Registrar shall consider the following criteria:

(1) The nature and gravity of the offense,

(2) The number of years elapsed since the date of the offense, and

(3) The nature and duties of a contractor or home improvement salesperson.

(c) For purposes of subdivision (a), substantially-related crimes, professional misconduct, or acts shall include, but are not limited to, the following:

(1) Any violation of the provisions of Chapter 9 of Division 3 of the Code or other state or federal laws governing contractors or home improvement salespersons.

(2) Failure to comply with the provisions of the California Code of Regulations, Title 16, Division 8.

(3) Crimes, professional misconduct, or acts involving dishonesty, fraud, deceit, or theft with the intent to substantially benefit oneself or another or to substantially harm another.

(4) Crimes, professional misconduct, or acts involving physical violence against persons.

(5) Crimes, professional misconduct, or acts that indicate a substantial or repeated disregard for the health, safety, or welfare of the public.

(Authority cited: Section 7008, Business and Professions Code. Reference: Sections 141, 480, 481, 490, 493, 7066, 7069, 7073, 7090, 7123 and 7124, Business and Professions Code.)

Section VI

868.1. Criteria to Aid in Determining if Financial Crimes Are Directly and Adversely Related to Fiduciary Qualifications, Functions, or Duties of a Licensee or Registrant for the Purpose of Considering Denials of Applications.

For the purpose of determining whether there are grounds to deny a license or registration to an applicant who has been convicted of a financial crime currently classified as a felony pursuant to Section 480 of the Code, the crime shall be considered to be directly and adversely related to the fiduciary qualifications, functions, or duties of a licensee or registrant if it involves dishonesty, fraud, deceit, or theft that resulted in: (i) direct financial benefit to the applicant or another person or entity, (ii) direct financial harm to another person or entity, or (iii) an attempt to obtain direct financial benefit or cause direct financial harm to another person or entity. The felony financial crimes shall include, but not be limited to, the following:

(a) Crimes involving the acquisition or provision of false, altered, forged, counterfeit, or fraudulent document(s), or the acquisition or provision of false or fraudulent statement(s).

(b) Crimes involving the use of personal identifying information for an unlawful purpose, including for the purpose of illegally obtaining money, credit, goods, services, real property, or medical information of another person (also known as identify theft).

(c) Crimes involving stolen property, embezzlement, grand theft, larceny, burglary, monetary transactions in property derived from a specified unlawful activity (also known as money laundering), or crimes related to obtaining money, labor, or property under false or fraudulent pretenses.

(d) Crimes involving an attempt or conspiracy to commit such crimes listed in subsections (a), (b), or (c).

(e) For the purposes of this section, "personal identifying information" has the meaning set forth in Penal Code section 530.55.

(Authority cited: Section 7008, Business and Professions Code. Reference: Sections 7.5, 480, 7069, 7073, 7090 and 7124, Business and Professions Code.)

869. Criteria for Rehabilitation

(a) When considering the denial, suspension, or revocation of a license or registration pursuant to Division 1.5 (commencing with Section 475) of the Code on the ground that the individual has been convicted of a crime, the Board or Registrar shall consider whether the applicant, licensee, or registrant made a showing of rehabilitation if the applicant, licensee, or registrant completed the criminal sentence at issue without a violation of parole or probation. In making this determination, the Board or Registrar shall consider the following criteria:

(1) The nature and gravity of the crime(s);

(2) The length(s) of the applicable parole or probation period(s);

(3) The extent to which the applicable parole or probation period was shortened or lengthened, and the reason(s) the period was modified;

(4) The terms or conditions of parole or probation, and the extent to which they bear on the applicant's rehabilitation; and

(5) The extent to which the terms or conditions of parole or probation were modified, and the reason(s) for modification.

(b) If subsection (a) is inapplicable, or the Board or Registrar determines that an applicant, licensee, or registrant did not make a showing of rehabilitation based on the criteria in subsection (a), the Board or Registrar shall apply the following criteria in evaluating an applicant's, licensee's, or registrant's rehabilitation:

(1) The Board or Registrar shall find that an applicant, licensee, or registrant made a showing of rehabilitation if, after considering the following criteria and the provisions of subsection (b)(2), the Board or Registrar finds that the individual is rehabilitated:

(A) Denial Based on Felony Convictions Within Seven Years of Application When considering the denial of a license or registration, the Board or Registrar may consider the applicant rehabilitated if the applicant was convicted of a felony within the preceding seven (7) years from the date of application that is substantially related to the qualifications, functions, or duties of a licensee or registration as defined in Section 868, and five (5) years have passed from the time of the applicant's release from incarceration or completion of probation if no incarceration was imposed, without the occurrence of additional substantially-related criminal activity, professional misconduct, acts, or omissions that also could be grounds for denial. This subsection does not apply to any crimes listed in subsection (b)(1)(B).

(B) Denial Based on Serious Felonies, Felonies Requiring Sex Offender Registration, or Felony Financial Crimes Directly and Adversely Related to the Qualifications, Functions, or Duties of a Licensee or Registrant When considering the denial of a license or registration on the ground that the applicant was convicted of a crime identified in Section 480(a)(1)(A) of the Code or a felony financial crime as defined in Section 868.1, the Board or Registrar may consider an applicant rehabilitated if seven (7) years have passed from the time of the applicant's release from incarceration or completion of probation if no incarceration was imposed, and the applicant committed no additional substantially-related criminal activity, professional misconduct, acts, or omissions that also could be grounds for denial.

(C) Discipline Based on Felony Convictions When considering the suspension or revocation of a license or registration, the Board or Registrar may consider a licensee or registrant rehabilitated if the licensee or registrant was convicted of a felony that is substantially related to the qualifications, functions, or duties of a licensee or registrant as defined in Section 868, and seven (7) years have passed from the time of release from incarceration or completion of probation if no incarceration was imposed, without the occurrence of additional substantially-related criminal activity, acts, or omissions that also could be grounds for suspension or revocation.

(D) Denial or Discipline Based on Misdemeanor Convictions When considering the denial, suspension, or revocation of a license or registration, the Board or Registrar may consider an applicant, licensee, or registrant rehabilitated if the applicant, licensee, or registrant was convicted of a misdemeanor that is substantially related to the qualifications, functions, or duties of a licensee or registrant as defined in Section 868, and three (3) years have passed from the time of release from incarceration or completion of probation if no incarceration was imposed, without the occurrence of additional substantially-related criminal activity, act(s), or omission(s) that also could be grounds for denial, suspension, or revocation.

(E) Denial or Discipline Based on Professional Misconduct, Acts, or Omissions For professional misconduct or acts that are substantially related to the qualifications, functions, or duties of a licensee or registrant as defined in Section 868, or for other acts or omissions that are grounds for denial, suspension, or revocation, the Board or Registrar may consider the applicant, licensee, or registrant rehabilitated if three (3) years have passed from the time of commission of the professional misconduct, act(s), or omission(s) without the occurrence of additional substantially-related criminal activity, professional misconduct, act(s), or omission(s) that also could be grounds for denial, suspension, or revocation.

(2) The amount of time needed to demonstrate rehabilitation under subsection (b)(1) may be increased or decreased by taking into account the following:

(A) The nature and gravity of the crime(s), professional misconduct, act(s), or omission(s) that are under consideration as, or that were, the grounds for denial, suspension, or revocation.

(B) Evidence of any crime(s), professional misconduct, act(s), or omission(s) committed subsequent to the crime(s), professional misconduct, act(s), or omission(s) that are under consideration as, or that were, the grounds for denial, suspension, or revocation, which also could be considered as grounds for denial, suspension, or revocation.

(C) The time that has elapsed since commission of the crime(s), professional misconduct, act(s), or omission(s) that are under consideration as, or that were, the grounds for denial, suspension, or revocation.

(D) The extent to which the applicant, licensee, or registrant has complied with any terms of parole, probation, restitution, or any other sanctions lawfully imposed against the applicant, licensee, or registrant.

(E) Consistent work history subsequent to the release from incarceration, or the completion of probation if no incarceration was imposed, or subsequent to the time of commission of the professional misconduct, act(s), or omission(s).

(F) Documents or testimony from credible individuals who have personal knowledge of the applicant's, licensee's, or registrant's life and activities subsequent to the time of commission of the crime(s), professional misconduct, act(s), or omission(s) who can attest to the applicant's, licensee's, or registrant's present fitness for licensure or registration.

(G) The acts underlying the conviction have been dismissed pursuant to Section 1203.4, 1203.4a, 1203.41, 1203.42, or 1203.425 of the Penal Code, or a comparable dismissal or expungement. An applicant who has a conviction that has been dismissed pursuant to Section 1203.4, 1203.4a, 1203.41, or 1203.42 of the Penal Code shall provide proof of the dismissal if it is not reflected on the report furnished by the Department of Justice.

(H) Other relevant evidence, if any, of rehabilitation submitted by the applicant, licensee, or registrant. For example, relevant evidence may include evidence of recovery from drug and/or alcohol addiction or abuse or completion of a drug and/or alcohol aversion or diversion program if the crime(s), professional misconduct, act(s), or omission(s) related to or involved drug and/or alcohol use; or evidence of completion of an anger management program if the crime(s), professional misconduct, act(s), or omission(s) demonstrated the applicant's, licensee's, or registrant's inability to control one's temper.

(c) When considering a petition for reinstatement of the license of a contractor or the registration of a home improvement salesperson, the

Board shall evaluate evidence of rehabilitation submitted by the petitioner, considering those criteria specified in subsections (a) and (b) relating to licensees or registrants.

(Authority cited: Sections 481, 482 and 7008, Business and Professions Code. Reference: Sections 7.5, 141, 480, 481, 482, 488, 490, 493, 496, 7066, 7069, 7073, 7090, 7102, 7123 and 7124, Business and Professions Code.)

869.1. Applicant Defined

(a) All applicants for licensure shall furnish a full set of fingerprints for purposes of the board conducting a criminal history record check. The fingerprints will be used to allow the California Department of Justice and the Federal Bureau of Investigation to provide criminal history to the Board.

(b) For purposes of fingerprinting, "applicant" means any individual applying to be a member of the personnel of record.

(c) For purposes of fingerprinting, "applicant" means an individual applying for a home improvement salesperson registration.

(Authority cited: Section 7008, Business and Professions Code. Reference: Sections 7069 and 7153.1, Business and Professions Code.)

869.2. Exemptions

(a) Applicants for a joint venture license who hold a current active license in good standing are not subject to fingerprinting.

(b) Individuals already fingerprinted as required by Section 869.1 and for whom subsequent arrest information remains available at the Board need not submit fingerprints when submitting a subsequent application.

(Authority cited: Section 7008, Business and Professions Code. Reference: Sections 7069 and 7153.1, Business and Professions Code.)

869.3. Methods for Submitting Fingerprints

(a) Applicants residing inside the State of California shall submit their fingerprints through the electronic format certified by the California Department of Justice but, with approval of the Registrar, may submit their fingerprints on hard copy forms provided by the Registrar.

(b) Applicants residing outside the State of California may submit their fingerprints using the electronic format certified by the California Department of Justice but also may submit their fingerprints on hard copy forms provided by the Registrar.

(Authority cited: Section 7008, Business and Professions Code. Reference: Sections 7069 and 7153.1, Business and Professions Code.)

869.4. Subsequent Arrest History

(a) Once an applicant has been fingerprinted, the Board will maintain access to the applicant's subsequent arrest history until such time as the individual's license is cancelled, revoked or no longer renewable.

(b) Once the Board no longer receives subsequent arrest information, an individual seeking to apply for a license must be fingerprinted as required in Section 869.1.

(Authority cited: Section 7008, Business and Professions Code. Reference: Sections 7069 and 7153.1, Business and Professions Code.)

869.9. Criteria to Aid in Determining Earliest Date a Denied Applicant May Reapply for Licensure or Registration.

(a) For an applicant who is denied licensure or registration pursuant to subsection (a) of Section 480 of the Business and Professions Code, the date of reapplication shall be set by the Registrar at not less than one (1) year nor more than five (5) years after the denial. When computing the date for reapplication, the time shall commence from the effective date of the decision if an appeal is made or from the service of the notice of denial under Section 485(b) if a request for hearing is not made. The Registrar will consider the following criteria when setting the reapplication date of an individual who was denied a license or registration:

(1) For felony convictions listed in Section 869(b)(1)(B) that are substantially related to the qualifications, functions, or duties of a licensee as defined in Section 868, seven (7) years have passed from the time of release from incarceration or completion of probation if no incarceration was imposed, without the occurrence of additional substantially-related criminal activity, professional misconduct, act(s), or omission(s) that also could be grounds for denial.

(2) For felony convictions not listed in Section 869(b)(1)(B) that are substantially related to the qualifications, functions, or duties of a licensee as defined in Section 868, five (5) years have passed from the time of the applicant's release from incarceration or completion of probation if no incarceration was imposed, without the occurrence of additional substantially-related criminal activity, professional misconduct, act(s), or omission(s) that also could be grounds for denial.

(3) For misdemeanor convictions that are substantially related to the qualifications, functions, or duties of a licensee or registrant as defined in Section 868, three (3) years have passed from the time of release from incarceration or completion of probation if no incarceration was imposed, without the occurrence of additional

substantially-related criminal activity, professional misconduct, act(s), or omission(s) that also could be grounds for denial.

(4) For professional misconduct that is substantially related to the qualifications, functions, or duties of a licensee or registrant as defined in Section 868, or for other acts or omissions that are grounds for denial, three (3) years have passed from the time of commission of the professional misconduct, act(s), or omission(s), without the occurrence of substantially-related criminal activity, professional misconduct, act(s), or omission(s) that also could be grounds for denial.

(5) The nature and gravity of the crime(s), professional misconduct, act(s), or omission(s) that were the grounds for denial.

(6) Evidence of any crime(s), professional misconduct, act(s), or omission(s) committed subsequent to the crime(s), professional misconduct, act(s), or omission(s) that were the grounds for denial, which also could be considered as grounds for denial.

(7) The time that has elapsed since commission of the crime(s), professional misconduct, act(s), or omission(s) that were the grounds for denial.

(8) The extent to which the applicant has complied with any terms of parole, probation, restitution, or any other sanctions lawfully imposed against the applicant in connection with the crime(s), professional misconduct, act(s), or omission(s) that were the grounds for denial.

(9) Consistent work history subsequent to the release from incarceration, or the completion of probation if no incarceration was imposed, or subsequent to the date of commission of the crime(s), professional misconduct, act(s), or omission(s) that were the grounds for denial.

(10) Documents or testimony from credible individuals who have personal knowledge of the applicant's life and activities subsequent to the date of commission of the crime(s), professional misconduct, act(s), or omission(s) that were the grounds for denial and who can attest to the applicant's present fitness for licensure or registration.

(11) Other relevant evidence, if any, of eligibility for reapplication submitted by the applicant. For example, relevant evidence may include evidence of recovery from drug and/or alcohol addiction or abuse or completion of a drug and/or alcohol aversion or diversion program if the crime(s), professional misconduct, act(s), or omission(s) that were the grounds for denial related to or involved drug and/or alcohol use; or evidence of completion of an anger management

program if the crime(s), professional misconduct, act(s), or omission(s) demonstrated the applicant's inability to control one's temper.

(b) Nothing in this section shall preclude the Registrar from denying the license or registration of an applicant who was previously denied a license or registration and who is eligible for reapplication in accordance with this section.

(Authority cited: Sections 481, 482 and 7008, Business and Professions Code. Reference: Sections 480, 482, 485, 486, 496, 7066, 7069, 7073 and 7124, Business and Professions Code.)

870. Factors to Apply in Determining Earliest Date a Revoked Licensee May Apply for Licensure

(1) The Registar shall have exclusive authority in setting the earliest date a revoked licensee may reapply for reissuance or reinstatement of a license.

(2) When extending the minimum one year period, the Registrar shall give due consideration to the gravity of the violation, the history of previous violations and criminal convictions and evaluate the application based on the following criteria:

Reapplication Dates:

5 years License has been revoked:

(1) one or more times or

(2) for committing fraudulent acts or

(3) committing acts which have seriously endangered the public welfare and safety or

(4) for being convicted of a construction-related crime. (For the purposes of determining if a crime is construction-related, CCR Title 16, Chapter 8, Section 868 shall apply.)

4 years License has been revoked:

(1) for committing violations on multiple construction projects; or

(2) for committing multiple violations of law for reasons other than fraud, danger to the public welfare and safety and for conviction of a construction-related crime.

3 years License has been revoked and revoked licensee:

Section VI

(1) has been issued more than one citation which has become final within one year immediately preceding the date of revocation or

(2) has been previously suspended by the Register as the result of a disciplinary action.

2 years   License has been revoked and revoked licensee has been issued a citation, which has become final within one year immediately preceding the date of revocation.

1 year   Licensee has been revoked for the first time and revoked licensee has no previous legal action history with the Board.

(Authority cited: Sections 7008 and 7059, Business and Professions Code. Reference: Sections 7058 and 7059, Business and Professions Code.)

871. Disciplinary Guidelines

In reaching a decision on a disciplinary action under the Administrative Procedure Act (Government Code Section 11400 et seq.), the board shall consider the disciplinary guidelines entitled "Disciplinary Guidelines" (rev. 12/11/96) which are hereby incorporated by reference. Deviation from these guidelines and orders, including the standard terms of probation, is appropriate where the board in its sole discretion determines that the facts of the particular case warrant such a deviation—for example, the presence of mitigating factors such as the age of the case; evidentiary problems.

(Authority cited: Section 7008, Business and Professions Code; and Sections 11400.20 and 11400.21, Government Code. Reference: Sections 7090 and 7095, Business and Professions Code; and Section 11425.50(e), Government Code.)

DISCIPLINARY GUIDELINES
(Rev. 12/11/96)

In assessing a disciplinary penalty against a person who has not had a previous citation, revocation, suspension nor denial of application, as the result of the filing of an accusation or a statement of issues, the Registrar shall give due consideration to the following guidelines. In addition to any penalties imposed, all persons that have had a license disciplined, whether or not the disciplinary action has been stayed, will be required to post a disciplinary bond pursuant to Section 7071.8. Unless otherwise specified, all references are to the Business and Professions Code.

Factors To Be Considered

In determining whether revocation, suspension or probation is to be imposed in a given case, factors such as the following should be considered:

1. Nature and severity of the act(s), offenses, or crime(s) under consideration.

2. Actual or potential harm to the public.

3. Performed work that was potentially hazardous to the health, safety, or general welfare of the public.

4. Prior disciplinary record.

5. Number and/or variety of current violations.

6. Mitigation evidence.

7. Rehabilitation evidence.

8. In case of a criminal conviction, compliance with terms of sentence and/or court-ordered probation.

Sections and Disciplinary Guidelines

125. Conspiracy with an Unlicensed Person

Minimum Penalty: Revocation, stayed, 3 years probation

Maximum Penalty: Revocation

If warranted:

1. Actual suspension of 5 days or more.

2. Standard terms and conditions in cases of probation. *(See page 566.)*

3. Submit copies of construction contracts to the Registrar upon demand during the probation period.

4. If not taken within the past 5 years, take and pass the CSLB law and business examination.

5. Take and pass a course in Contractors License Law or a course related to construction law at an accredited community college. All courses must be approved in advance by the Registrar.

6. Community Service time as determined by the Registrar; 5-21 days.

7. Pay CSLB investigation and enforcement costs.

141. Disciplinary Action by Foreign Jurisdiction

Minimum Penalty: Revocation, stayed, 3 years probation

Maximum Penalty: Revocation

If warranted:

1. Actual suspension of 5 days or more.

2. Standard terms and conditions in cases of probation. *(See page 566.)*

3. Pay CSLB investigation and enforcement costs.

4. Community Service as determined by the Registrar; 5-21 days.

490. Conviction of a Crime—Substantial Relationship Required

Minimum Penalty: Revocation, stayed, 3 years probation

Maximum Penalty: Revocation

If warranted:

1. Absent compelling mitigating circumstances, conviction of a crime related to the functions of a contractor is a serious offense that warrants an outright revocation.

2. Actual suspension of at least 30 days.

3. Standard terms and conditions in cases of probation. *(See page 566.)*

4. Make restitution.

5. If not taken within the past 5 years, take and pass the CSLB law and business examination.

6. Prohibit receipt of down payments.

7. Community Service as determined by the Registrar; 5-21 days.

8. Pay CSLB investigation and enforcement costs.

496. Violation of Section 123—Subversion of Licensee Examinations

Minimum Penalty: Revocation

Maximum Penalty: Revocation

If warranted:

1. Pay CSLB investigation and enforcement costs.

498. Securing a License through Fraud, Deceit or Knowing Misrepresentation

Minimum Penalty: Revocation

Maximum Penalty: Revocation

If warranted:

1. Pay CSLB investigation and enforcement costs.

499. False Statement in Support of Application

Minimum Penalty: Revocation, stayed, 3 years probation

If warranted:

1. Absent compelling mitigating circumstances, making a false statement in support of an application of another person, is a serious offense that warrants an outright revocation.

2. Actual suspension of at least 30 days.

3. Standard terms and conditions in cases of probation. *(See page 566.)*

4. If not taken within the past 5 years, take and pass the CSLB law and business examination.

5. Take and pass a course in Contractors License Law or a course related to construction law at an accredited community college. All courses must be approved in advance by the Registrar.

6. Community Service as determined by CSLB; 5-21 days.

7. Pay CSLB investigation and enforcement costs.

860. (CCR) Penalty for Failure to Comply with Rules

Minimum Penalty: 5 day suspension, stayed, 1 year probation

Maximum Penalty: Revocation

If warranted:

1. Actual suspension of 5 days or more.

2. Standard terms and conditions in cases of probation. *(See page 566.)*

3. If not taken within the past 5 years, take and pass the CSLB law and business examination.

4. Take and pass a course in Contractors License Law or a course related to construction law at an accredited community college. All courses must be approved in advance by the Registrar.

Section VI

5. Pay CSLB investigation and enforcement costs.

7018.5. Notice to Owner; Mechanics' Lien Law

Minimum Penalty: 5 day suspension, stayed, 1 year probation

Maximum Penalty: 60 day suspension, 1 year probation

If warranted:

1. Standard terms and conditions in cases of probation. *(See page 566.)*

2. Submit copies of construction contracts to the Registrar upon demand during the probation period.

3. If not taken within the past 5 years, take and pass the CSLB law and business examination.

4. Take and pass a course in Contractors License Law or a course related to construction law at an accredited community college. All courses must be approved in advance by the Registrar.

5. Pay CSLB investigation and enforcement costs.

7027.3. Fraudulent Use of a License Number

Minimum Penalty: Revocation

Maximum Penalty: Revocation

If warranted:

1. Pay CSLB investigation and enforcement costs.

7029.1. Contracting Jointly Without a Joint Venture License

Minimum Penalty: 5 day suspension, stayed, 1 year probation

Maximum Penalty: 60 day suspension, 1 year probation

If warranted:

1. Actual suspension of 5 days or more.

2. Standard terms and conditions in cases of probation. *(See page 566.)*

3. If not taken within the past 5 years, take and pass the CSLB law and business examination.

4. Take and pass a course in Contractors License Law or a course related to construction law at an accredited community college. All courses must be approved in advance by the Registrar.

5. Pay CSLB investigation and enforcement costs.

7029.5. Identification on Vehicle, Plumbing, Electrical Sign, and Well-drilling

Minimum Penalty: 5 day suspension, stayed, 1 year probation

Maximum Penalty: 60 suspension, 1 year probation

If warranted:

1. Standard terms and conditions in cases of probation. *(See page 566.)*

2. Pay CSLB investigation and enforcement costs.

7068.2. Failure to Notify; Disassociation of RMO/RME

Minimum Penalty: 60 day suspension, stayed, 1 year probation

Maximum Penalty: Revocation

If warranted:

1. Standard terms and conditions in cases of probation. *(See page 566.)*

2. If not taken within the past 5 years, take and pass the CSLB law and business examination.

3. Take and pass a course in Contractors License Law or a course related to construction law at an accredited community college. All courses must be approved in advance by the Registrar.

4. Pay CSLB investigation and enforcement costs.

7071.11. Judgment, Admitted Claim or Good Faith Payment on Bond

Minimum Penalty: 60 day suspension, stayed, 1 year probation

Maximum Penalty: Revocation

If warranted:

1. Actual suspension of 5 days or more.

2. Standard terms and conditions in cases of probation. *(See page 566.)*

3. Make restitution.

4. Pay CSLB investigation and enforcement costs.

7071.13. Reference in Advertising; Contractors Bond

Minimum Penalty: 5 day suspension, stayed, 1 year probation

Maximum Penalty: 60 day suspension, 1 year probation

Section VI

If warranted:

1. Standard terms and conditions in cases of probation. *(See page 566.)*

2. Submit copies of advertisements relating to contracting business to the Registrar prior to their being displayed or published during the probation period.

3. If not taken within the past 5 years, take and pass the CSLB law and business examination.

4. Take and pass a course in Contractors License Law or a course related to construction law at an accredited community college. All courses must be approved in advance by the Registrar.

5. Pay CSLB investigation and enforcement costs.

7071.15. Failure to Maintain a Sufficient Bond

Minimum Penalty: 60 day suspension, stayed, 1 year probation

Maximum Penalty: Revocation

If warranted:

1. Actual suspension of 5 days or more.

2. Standard terms and conditions in cases of probation. *(See page 566.)*

3. If not taken within the past 5 years, take and pass the CSLB law and business examination.

4. Take and pass a course in Contractors License Law or a course related to construction law at an accredited community college. All courses must be approved in advance by the Registrar.

5. Pay CSLB investigation and enforcement costs.

7076. Failure to Notify; Death or Disassociation of Licensee Personnel

Minimum Penalty: 60 day suspension, stayed, 1 year probation

Maximum Penalty: Revocation

If warranted:

1. Standard terms and conditions in cases of probation. *(See page 566.)*

2. If not taken within the past 5 years, take and pass the CSLB law and business examination.

3. Take and pass a course in Contractors License Law or a course related to construction law at an accredited community college. All courses must be approved in advance by the Registrar.

4. Pay CSLB investigation and enforcement costs.

7083. Failure to Notify, Changes of Personnel, Business Name, Address, Bond Exemption, and Multiple License Exemption

Minimum Penalty: 60 day suspension, stayed, 1 year probation

Maximum Penalty: Revocation

If warranted:

1. Standard terms and conditions in cases of probation. *(See page 566.)*

2. If not taken within the past 5 years, take and pass the CSLB law and business examination.

3. Take and pass a course in Contractors License Law or a course related to construction law at an accredited community college. All courses must be approved in advance by the Registrar.

4. Pay CSLB investigation and enforcement costs.

7090. Failure to Obtain Building Permits

Minimum Penalty: 60 day suspension, stayed, 1 year probation

Maximum Penalty: Revocation

If warranted:

1. Actual suspension of 5 days or more.

2. Standard terms and conditions in cases of probation. *(See page 566.)*

3. Make restitution.

4. Submit copies of building permits to the Registrar upon demand for projects undertaken during the probation period.

5. If not taken within the past 5 years, take and pass the CSLB trade examination.

6. Take and pass a course in Contractors License Law or a course related to construction law at an accredited community college. All courses must be approved in advance by the Registrar.

7. Pay CSLB investigation and enforcement costs.

Section VI

7090.5. Fraud and Repeated Acts, Despite Corrections of Conditions

Minimum Penalty: Revocation, stayed, 3 years probation

Maximum Penalty: revocation

If warranted:

1. Actual suspension of 5 days or more.

2. Standard terms and conditions in cases of probation. *(See page 566.)*

3. Take and pass a course in accounting, bookkeeping and/or business management at an accredited community college. All courses must be approved in advance by the Registrar.

4. Submit copies of building permits to the Registrar upon demand for projects undertaken during the probation period.

5. Submit copies of construction contracts to the Registrar upon demand during the probation period.

6. Prohibit receipt of down payments.

7. Submit to the Registrar a detailed plan setting forth the procedure to be used to provide for direct supervising and control by the qualifying individual.

8. If not taken within the past 5 years, take and pass the CSLB law and business examination.

9. Take and pass a course in Contractors License Law or a course related to business law at an accredited community college. All courses must be approved in advance by the Registrar.

10. If not taken within the past 5 years, take and pass the CSLB trade examination.

11. Take and pass a vocational course(s) related to the trade(s) employed on the project. All courses must be approved in advance by the Registrar.

12. Pay CSLB investigation and enforcement costs.

7099.6. Failure to Comply with a Citation

Minimum Penalty: Revocation, stayed, 1 year probation

Maximum Penalty: Revocation

If warranted:

1. Actual suspension of 5 days or more.

2. Standard terms and conditions in cases of probation. *(See page 566.)*

3. Make restitution.

4. Take and pass a course in Contractors License Law or a course related to construction law at an accredited community college. All courses must be approved in advance by the Registrar.

5. Pay CSLB investigation and enforcement costs.

7103. Disciplinary Action by Another State

Minimum Penalty: Revocation, stayed, 3 years probation.

Maximum Penalty: Revocation

If warranted:

1. Actual suspension of 5 days or more.

2. Standard terms and conditions in cases of probation. *(See page 566.)*

3. Pay CSLB investigation and enforcement costs.

7107. Abandonment

Minimum Penalty: Revocation, stayed, 3 years probation

Maximum Penalty: Revocation

If warranted:

1. Absent compelling mitigating circumstances, abandonment of a project is a serious offense that warrants an actual period of suspension of at least 30 days.

2. Standard terms and conditions in cases of probation. *(See page 566.)*

3. Make restitution.

4. Submit copies of building permits to the Registrar upon demand for projects undertaken during the probation period.

5. Submit copies of construction contracts to the Registrar upon demand during the probation period.

6. Submit to the Registrar a detailed plan setting forth the procedure to be used to provide for direct supervision and control by the qualifying individual.

7. If not taken within the past 5 years, take and pass the CSLB law and business examination.

8. Take and pass a course in Contractors License Law or a course related to construction law at an accredited community college. All courses must be approved in advance by the Registrar.

9. If not taken within the past 5 years, take and pass the CSLB trade examination.

10. Take and pass a vocational course(s) related to the trade(s) employed on the project. All courses must be approved in advance by the Registrar.

11. During the period of probation, provide lien releases to project owners as soon as payment is received.

12. Pay CSLB investigation and enforcement costs.

7108. Misuse of Funds

Minimum Penalty: Revocation, stayed, 3 years probation

Maximum Penalty: Revocation

If warranted:

1. Absent compelling mitigating circumstances, misuse of funds is a serious offense that warrants an actual period of suspension of at least 30 days.

2. If diversion or misuse of funds is for personal use not related to construction work, outright revocation is appropriate.

3. Standard terms and conditions in cases of probation. *(See page 566.)*

4. Make restitution.

5. Take and pass a course in accounting, bookkeeping and/or business management at an accredited community college. All courses must be approved in advance by the Registrar.

6. Submit copies of construction contracts to the Registrar upon demand during the probation period.

7. If not taken within the past 5 years, take and pass the CSLB law and business examination.

8. Take and pass a course in Contractors License Law or course related to construction law at an accredited community college. All courses must be approved in advance by the Registrar.

9. Community Service as determined by CSLB; 5-21 days.

10. Pay CSLB investigation and enforcement costs.

7108.5. Prime Contractors and Subcontractors; Payment Required

Minimum Penalty: 60 day suspension, stayed, 1 year probation

Maximum Penalty: Revocation

If warranted:

1. Actual suspension of 5 days or more.

2. Standard terms and conditions in cases of probation. *(See page 566.)*

3. Make restitution.

4. Take and pass a course in accounting, bookkeeping and/or business management at an accredited community college. All courses must be approved in advance by the Registrar.

5. If not taken within the past 5 years, take and pass the CSLB law and business examination.

6. Take and pass a course in Contractors License Law or a course related to construction law at an accredited community college. All courses must be approved in advance by the Registrar.

7. Pay CSLB investigation and enforcement costs.

7109(a). Departure from Accepted Trade Standards for Workmanship

Minimum Penalty: Revocation, stayed, 2 years probation

Maximum Penalty: Revocation

If warranted:

1. Actual suspension of 5 days or more. If the departure from trade standards is substantial, actual suspension of at least 30 days.

2. Standard terms and conditions in cases of probation. *(See page 566.)*

3. Make restitution.

4. Submit copies of building permits to the Registrar upon demand for projects undertaken during the probationary period.

5. Submit copies of construction contracts to the Registrar upon demand during the probation period.

6. Submit to the Registrar a detailed plan setting forth the procedure to be used to provide for direct supervising and control by the qualifying individual.

7. If not taken within the last 5 years, take and pass the CSLB law and business examination.

8. Take and pass a course in Contractors License Law or a course related to construction law at an accredited community college. All courses must be approved in advance by the Registrar.

9. If not taken within the past 5 years, take and pass the CSLB trade examination.

10. Take and pass a vocational course(s) related to the trade(s) employed on the project. All courses must be approved in advance by the Registrar.

11. Pay CSLB investigation and enforcement costs.

7109(b). Departure from Plans and/or Specifications

Minimum Penalty: Revocation, stayed, 2 years probation

Maximum Penalty: Revocation

If warranted:

1. Actual suspension of 5 days or more. If the departure from plans and/or specifications is substantial, actual suspension of at least 30 days.

2. Standard terms and conditions in cases of probation. *(See page 566.)*

3. Make restitution.

4. Submit copies of building permits to the Registrar upon demand for all projects undertaken during the probationary period.

5. Submit copies of construction contracts to the Registrar upon demand during the probation period.

6. Submit to the Registrar a detailed plan setting forth the procedure to be used to provide for direct supervising and control by the qualifying individual.

7. If not taken within the past 5 years, take and pass the CSLB law and business examination.

8. Take and pass a course in Contractors License Law or a course related to construction law at an accredited community college. All courses must be approved in advance by the Registrar.

9. If not taken within the past 5 years, take and pass the CSLB trade examination.

10. Take and pass a vocational course(s) related to the trade(s) employed on the project. All courses must be approved in advance by the Registrar.

11. Pay CSLB investigation and enforcement costs.

7109.5. Violation of Safety Orders

Minimum Penalty: Revocation, stayed, 2 years probation

Maximum Penalty: Revocation

If warranted:

1. Actual suspension of 5 days or more.

2. Standard terms and conditions in cases of probation. *(See page 566.)*

3. If not taken within the past 5 years, take and pass the CSLB law and business examination.

4. Take and pass a course in Contractors License Law or a course related to construction law at an accredited community college. All courses must be approved in advance by the Registrar.

5. Establish a safety program.

6. Pay CSLB investigation and enforcement costs.

7110. Violations of Other Laws; Disciplinary Action

Minimum Penalty: Revocation, stayed, 2 years probation

Maximum Penalty: Revocation

If warranted:

1. Actual suspension of 5 days or more.

2. Standard terms and conditions in cases of probation. *(See page 566.)*

3. Make restitution.

4. Comply with orders or assessments of relevant agency.

5. If not taken within the past 5 years, take and pass the CSLB law and business examination.

6. Take and pass a course in Contractors License Law or a course related to construction law at an accredited community college. All courses must be approved in advance by the Registrar.

7. Submit copies of building permits to the Registrar upon demand for projects undertaken during the probation period.

8.   Establish a safety program.

9.   Pay CSLB investigation and enforcement costs.

7110.1. Violation of Labor Code Section 206.5; Requiring Release of Claim for Wages

Minimum Penalty: 60 day suspension, stayed, 1 year probation

Maximum Penalty: Revocation

If warranted:

1.   Actual suspension of 5 days or more.

2.   Standard terms and conditions in cases of probation. *(See page 566.)*

3.   If not taken within the past 5 years, take and pass the CSLB law and business examination.

4.   Take and pass a course in Contractors License Law or a course related to construction law at an accredited community college. All courses must be approved in advance by the Registrar.

5.   Pay CSLB investigation and enforcement costs.

7110.5. Violation Pursuant to Section 98.9 of the Labor Code

Minimum Penalty: 60 day suspension, stayed, 1 year probation

Maximum Penalty: Revocation

If warranted:

1.   Actual suspension of 5 days or more.

2.   Standard terms and conditions in cases of probation. *(See page 566.)*

3.   If not taken within the past 5 years, take and pass the CSLB law and business examination.

4.   Take and pass a course in Contractors License Law or a course related to construction law at an accredited community college. All courses must be approved in advance by the Registrar.

5.   Pay CSLB investigation and enforcement costs.

7111. Preservation of Records

Minimum Penalty: 60 day suspension, stayed, 1 year probation

Maximum Penalty: Revocation

If warranted:

1. Actual suspension of 5 days or more.

2. Standard terms and conditions in cases of probation. *(See page 566.)*

3. Take and pass a course in accounting, bookkeeping and/or business management at an accredited community college. All courses must be approved in advance by the Registrar.

4. If not taken within the past 5 years, take and pass the CSLB law and business examination.

5. Take and pass a course in Contractors License Law or a course related to construction law at an accredited community college. All courses must be approved in advance by the Registrar.

6. Pay CSLB investigation and enforcement costs.

7111.1. Failure of Licensee To Cooperate in an Investigation of a Complaint

Minimum Penalty: 60 day suspension, stayed, 1 year probation

Maximum Penalty: revocation

If warranted:

1. Actual suspension of 5 days or more.

2. Standard terms and conditions in cases of probation. *(See page 566.)*

3. If not taken within the past 5 years, take and pass CSLB law and business examination.

4. Take and pass a course in Contractors License Law or a course related to construction law at an accredited community college. All courses must be approved in advance by the Registrar.

5. Pay CSLB investigation and enforcement costs.

7112. Misrepresentation on an Application

Minimum Penalty: Revocation, stayed, 3 years probation

Maximum Penalty: Revocation

If warranted:

1. Absent compelling mitigating circumstances, misrepresentation is a serious offense that warrants an outright revocation.

2. Actual suspension of at least 30 days.

3. Standard terms and conditions in cases of probation. *(See page 566.)*

4. Community Service as determined by CSLB; 5-21 days.

5. Pay CSLB investigation and enforcement costs.

7113. Failure to Complete Project for Contract Price

Minimum Penalty: Revocation, stayed, 2 years probation

Maximum Penalty: Revocation

If warranted:

1. Actual suspension of 5 days or more. If injury is substantial, actual suspension of at least 30 days.

2. Standard terms and conditions in cases of probation. *(See page 566.)*

3. Make restitution.

4. Complete an education course in estimating construction costs or a related course in the field of construction science. All courses must be approved in advance by the Registrar.

5. Prohibit receipt of down payments.

6. If not taken within the past 5 years, take and pass the CSLB law and business examination.

7. Take and pass a course in Contractors License Law or a course related to construction law at an accredited community college. All courses must be approved in advance by the Registrar.

8. Pay CSLB investigation and enforcement costs.

7113.5. Settlement of Lawful Obligations

Minimum Penalty: Revocation, stayed, 2 years probation

Maximum Penalty: Revocation

If warranted:

1. Actual suspension of 5 days or more.

2. Standard terms and conditions in cases of probation. *(See page 566.)*

3. Make restitution.

4. Take and pass a course in accounting, bookkeeping and/or business management at an accredited community college. All courses must be approved in advance by the Registrar.

5. Submit a list of all subcontractors used on construction projects to the Registrar upon demand during the probation period.

6. Submit a list of all material suppliers used on construction projects to the Registrar upon demand during the probation period.

7. Pay CSLB investigation and enforcement costs.

7114. Aiding and Abetting an Unlicensed Person

Minimum Penalty: Revocation, stayed, 2 years probation

Maximum Penalty: Revocation

If warranted:

1. Actual suspension of 5 days or more.

2. Standard terms and conditions in cases of probation. *(See page 566.)*

3. If not taken within the past 5 years, take and pass the CSLB law and business examination.

4. Take and pass a course in Contractors License Law or a course related to construction law at an accredited community college. All courses must be approved in advance by the Registrar.

5. Submit a list of all subcontractors used on construction projects to the Registrar upon demand during the probation period.

6. Pay CSLB investigation and enforcement costs.

7114.1. Certifying to False Experience

Minimum Penalty: Revocation, stayed, 3 years probation

Maximum Penalty: Revocation

If warranted:

1. Absent compelling mitigating circumstances, certifying false experience is a serious offense that warrants an outright revocation.

2. Standard terms and conditions in cases of probation. *(See page 566.)*

3. Community Service as determined by CSLB; 5-21 days.

4. Pay CSLB investigation and enforcement costs.

7115. Violation of the Contractors License Law

Minimum Penalty: 5 day suspension, stayed, 1 year probation

Maximum Penalty: Revocation

If warranted:

Section VI

1. Actual suspension of 5 days or more.

2. Standard terms and conditions in case of probation. *(See page 566.)*

3. Pay CSLB investigation and enforcement costs.

7116. Any Willful or Fraudulent Act

Minimum Penalty: Revocation, stayed, 3 years probation

Maximum Penalty: revocation

If warranted:

1. Absent compelling circumstances, fraud is a serious offense that warrants an actual suspension of at least 60 days.

2. If the injury is substantial, outright revocation is appropriate.

3. Standard terms and conditions in case of probation. *(See page 566.)*

4. Make restitution.

5. If not taken within the past 5 years, take and pass the CSLB law and business examination.

6. Take and pass a course in Contractors License Law or a course related to construction law at an accredited community college. All courses must be approved in advance by the Registrar.

7. Community Service as determined by CSLB; 5-21 days.

8. Pay CSLB investigation and enforcement costs.

7117. Variance from License as to Name or Personnel

Minimum Penalty: 5 day suspension, stayed, 1 year probation

Maximum Penalty: 364 day suspension, 2 years probation

If warranted:

1. Standard terms and conditions in case of probation. *(See page 566.)*

2. If not taken within the past 5 years, take and pass the CSLB law and business examination.

3. Take and pass a course in Contractors License Law or a course related to construction law at an accredited community college. All courses must be approved in advance by the Registrar.

4. Pay CSLB investigation and enforcement costs.

7117.5. Contracting with an Inactive, Suspended or Expired License

Minimum Penalty: Revocation, stayed, 2 years probation

Maximum Penalty: Revocation

If warranted:

1. Actual suspension of 5 days or more.

2. Standard terms and conditions in case of probation. *(See page 566.)*

3. If not taken within the past 5 years, take and pass the CSLB law and business examination.

4. Take and pass a course in Contractors License Law or a course related to construction law at an accredited community college. All courses must be approved in advance by the Registrar.

5. Pay CSLB investigation and enforcement costs.

7117.6. Contracting Out of Classification

Minimum Penalty: 60 day suspension, stayed, 1 year probation

Maximum Penalty: Revocation

If warranted:

1. Actual suspension of 5 days or more.

2. Standard terms and conditions in case of probation. *(See page 566.)*

3. Submit copies of construction contracts to the Registrar upon demand during the probation period.

4. Submit copies of all advertisements relating to contracting business to the Registrar prior to their being displayed or published during the probation period.

5. Pay CSLB investigation and enforcement costs.

7118. Contracting with an Unlicensed Person

Minimum Penalty: Revocation, stayed, 2 years probation
Maximum Penalty: Revocation
If warranted:
1. Actual suspension of 5 days or more.

2. Standard terms and conditions in cases of probation. *(See page 566.)*

3. If not taken within the past 5 years, take and pass the CSLB law and business examination.

4. Take and pass a course in Contractors License Law or a course related to construction law at an accredited community college. All courses must be approved in advance by the Registrar.

5. Submit a list of all subcontractors used on construction projects to the Registrar upon demand during the probation period.

6. Community Service as determined by CSLB; 5-21 days.

7. Pay CSLB investigation and enforcement costs.

7118.4. Asbestos Related Inspection with Knowledge of Report being Required for Loan; Disclosure Required

Minimum Penalty: 60 day suspension, stayed, 1 year probation

Maximum Penalty: Revocation

If warranted:

1. Absent compelling mitigating circumstances, conducting an asbestos related inspection while maintaining a financial relationship with an entity which performs corrective work without disclosing this fact is a serious offense that warrants an actual suspension of 60 days.

2. Standard terms and conditions in cases of probation. *(See page 566.)*

3. If not taken within the past 5 years, take and pass the CSLB law and business examination.

4. Take and pass a course in Contractors License Law or a course related to construction law at an accredited community college. All courses must be approved in advance by the Registrar.

5. Community Service as determined by CSLB; 5-21 days.

6. Pay CSLB investigation and enforcement costs.

7118.5. Asbestos-related Work; Contracting with Uncertified Contractor

Minimum Penalty: 60 day suspension, stayed, 1 year probation

Maximum Penalty: Revocation

If warranted:

1. Absent compelling mitigating circumstances, contracting with an uncertified asbestos contractor to perform asbestos related work

is a serious offense that warrants an actual suspension of 60 days.

2. Standard terms and conditions in cases of probation. *(See page 566.)*

3. Submit a list of all subcontractors used on construction projects to the Registrar upon demand during the probation period.

4. Community Service as determined by CSLB; 5-21 days.

5. Pay CSLB investigation and enforcement costs.

7118.6. Asbestos-contracting with an Uncertified Person for Removal or Remedial Action

Minimum Penalty: 60 day suspension, stayed, 1 year probation

Maximum Penalty: Revocation

If warranted:

1. Absent compelling mitigating circumstances, contracting with an uncertified person for removal or remedial asbestos work is a serious offense that warrants an actual suspension of 60 days.

2. Standard terms and conditions in cases of probation. *(See page 566.)*

3. Submit a list of all subcontractors used on construction projects to the Registrar upon demand during the probation period.

4. Community Service as determined by CSLB; 5-21 days.

5. Pay CSLB investigation and enforcement costs.

7119. Lack of Reasonable Diligence

Minimum Penalty: 60 day suspension, stayed, 1 year probation

Maximum Penalty: Revocation

If warranted:

1. Actual suspension of 5 days or more.

2. Standard terms and conditions in cases of probation. *(See page 566.)*

3. Make restitution.

4. Prohibit receipt of down payments.

5. Pay CSLB investigation and enforcement costs.

7120. Failure to Pay Money

Minimum Penalty: 60 day suspension, stayed, 1 year probation

Maximum Penalty: Revocation

If warranted:

1. Actual suspension of 5 days or more.

2. Standard terms and conditions in cases of probation. *(See page 566.)*

3. Take and pass a course in accounting, bookkeeping and/or business management at an accredited community college. All courses must be approved in advance by the Registrar.

4. If not taken within the past 5 years, take and pass the CSLB law and business examination.

5. Take and pass a course in Contractors License Law or a course related to construction law at an accredited community college. All courses must be approved in advance by the Registrar.

6. Submit a list of all subcontractors used on construction projects to the Registrar upon demand during the probation period.

7. Submit a list of all material suppliers used on construction projects to the Registrar upon demand during the probation period.

8. Prohibit the receipt of down payments.

9. Provide lien releases to project owners on all future construction projects upon receipt of payments.

10. Pay CSLB investigation and enforcement costs.

7121. Prohibition against Association

Minimum Penalty: Revocation, stayed, 2 years probation

Maximum Penalty: Revocation

If warranted:

1. Actual suspension of 5 days or more.

2. Standard terms and conditions in cases of probation. *(See page 566.)*

3. Make restitution.

4. If not taken within the past 5 years, take and pass the CSLB law and business examination.

5. Take and pass a course in Contractors License Law or a course related to construction law at an accredited community college. All courses must be approved in advance by the Registrar.

6. Pay CSLB investigation and enforcement costs.

7123. Conviction of a Crime

Minimum Penalty: Revocation, stayed, 3 years probation

Maximum Penalty; Revocation

If warranted:

1. Absent compelling mitigating circumstances, conviction of a crime related to the functions of a contractor is a serious offense and warrants an outright revocation.

2. Actual suspension of at least 30 days.

3. Standard terms and conditions in cases of probation. *(See page 566.)*

4. Make restitution.

5. If not taken within the past 5 years, take and pass the CSLB law and business examination.

6. Take and pass a course in Contractors License Law or a course related to construction law at an accredited community college. All courses must be approved in advance by the Registrar.

7. Prohibit the receipt of down payments.

8. Community Service as determined by CSLB; 5-21 days.

9. Pay CSLB investigation and enforcement costs.

7123.5. Violation of Prohibition against Overpricing Following an Emergency or Disaster (Penal Code Section 396)

Minimum Penalty: 6 month suspension, 3 years probation

Maximum Penalty: Revocation

If warranted:

1. Absent compelling mitigating circumstances, overpricing following an emergency or disaster is a serious offense and warrants an outright revocation.

2. Actual suspension of 6 months.

3. Standard terms and conditions in cases of probation. *(See page 566.)*

4. Make restitution.

5. If not taken within the past 5 years, take and pass the CSLB law and business examination.

6. Take and pass a course in Contractors License Law or a course related to construction law at an accredited community college. All courses must be approved in advance by the Registrar.

7. Prohibit the receipt of down payments.

8. Community Service as determined by CSLB; 5-21 days.

9. Pay CSLB investigation and enforcement costs.

7125(b). Filing False Workers' Compensation Exemption Reports

Minimum Penalty: Revocation, stayed, 2 years probation

Maximum Penalty: Revocation

If warranted:

1. Actual suspension of 5 days or more.

2. Standard terms and conditions in cases of probation. *(See page 566.)*

3. If not taken within the past 5 years, take and pass the CSLB law and business examination.

4. Take and pass a course in Contractors License Law or a course related to construction law at an accredited community college. All courses must be approved in advance by the Registrar.

5. Submit a list of persons employed on construction related projects to the Registrar upon demand during the probation period.

6. Make restitution.

7. Pay CSLB investigation and enforcement costs.

7154. Employment of a Nonregistered Home Improvement Salesperson

Minimum Penalty: 60 day suspension, stayed, 1 year probation

Maximum Penalty: Revocation

If warranted:

1. Actual suspension of 5 days or more.

2. Standard terms and conditions in cases of probation. *(See page 566.)*

3. If not taken within the past 5 years, take and pass the CSLB law and business examination.

4. Take and pass a course in Contractors License Law or a course related to construction law at an accredited community college. All courses must be approved in advance by the Registrar.

5. Pay CSLB investigation and enforcement costs.

7155. Violation of Contractors License Law by Home Improvement Salesperson

Minimum Penalty: 60 day suspension, stayed, 1 year probation

Maximum Penalty: Revocation

If warranted:

1. Actual suspension of 5 days or more.

2. Standard terms and conditions in cases of probation. *(See page 566.)*

3. Submit copies of construction contracts to the Registrar upon demand during the probation period.

4. If not taken within the past 5 years, take and pass the CSLB law and business examination.

5. Take and pass a course in Contractors License Law or a course related to construction law at an accredited community college. All courses must be approved in advance by the Registrar.

6. Pay CSLB investigation and enforcement costs.

7155.5. Liability of a Contractor for a Home Improvement Salesperson

Minimum Penalty: Suspension, stayed, 1 year probation

Maximum Penalty: Revocation

If warranted:

1. Actual suspension of 5 days or more.

2. Standard terms and conditions in cases of probation. *(See page 566.)*

3. If not taken within the past 5 years, take and pass the CSLB law and business examination.

4. Take and pass a course in Contractors License Law or a course related to construction law at an accredited community college. All courses must be approved in advance by the Registrar.

5. Submit copies of construction contracts to the Registrar upon demand during the probation period.

6. Prohibit the receipt of down payments.

7. Pay CSLB investigation and enforcement costs

7156. Registered Salespersons Violations

Minimum Penalty: 60 day suspension, stayed, 1 year probation

Maximum Penalty: Revocation

If warranted:

1. Actual suspension of 5 days or more.

2. Standard terms and conditions in cases of probation. *(See page 566.)*

3. Submit copies of construction contracts to the Registrar upon demand during the probation period.

4. Pay CSLB investigation and enforcement costs.

7157. Home Improvement Inducements

Minimum Penalty: 60 day suspension, stayed, 1 year probation

Maximum Penalty: Revocation

If warranted:

1. Actual suspension of at least 5 days.

2. Standard terms and conditions in cases of probation. *(See page 566.)*

3. If not taken within the past 5 years, take and pass the CSLB law and business examination.

4. Take and pass a course in Contractors License Law or a course related to construction law at an accredited community college. All courses must be approved in advance by the Registrar.

5. Submit copies of advertisements relating to contracting business to the Registrar prior to their being displayed or published during the probation period.

6. Prohibit the receipt of down payments.

7. Pay CSLB investigation and enforcement costs.

7158. False Completion Certificate

Minimum Penalty: Revocation, stayed, 3 years probation

Maximum Penalty: Revocation

If warranted:

1. Absent compelling circumstances, knowingly using a false certificate is a serious offense that warrants an actual suspension of at least 30 days.

2. Standard terms and conditions in cases of probation. *(See page 566.)*

3. If not taken within the past 5 years, take and pass the CSLB law and business examination.

4. Take and pass a course in Contractors License Law or a course related to construction law at an accredited community college. All courses must be approved in advance by the Registrar.

5. Make restitution.

6. Submit copies of construction contracts to the Registrar upon demand during the probation period.

7. Prohibit receipt of down payments.

8. Community Service as determined by CSLB; 5-21 days.

9. Pay CSLB investigation and enforcement costs.

7159. Home Improvement Contract Requirements

Minimum Penalty: 60 day suspension, stayed, 1 year probation

Maximum Penalty: Revocation

If warranted:

1. If any injuries are involved, actual suspension of at least 30 days.

2. Standard terms and conditions in cases of probation. *(See page 566.)*

3. If not taken within the past 5 years, take and pass the CSLB law and business examination.

4. Take and pass a course in Contractors License Law or a course related to construction law at an accredited community college. All courses must be approved in advance by the Registrar.

5. Submit copies of construction contracts to the Registrar upon demand during the probation period.

6. Prohibit receipt of down payments.

7. Community Service as determined by CSLB; 5-21 days.

8. Pay CSLB investigation and enforcement costs.

7161. Misrepresentation; False Advertisement

Minimum Penalty: Revocation, stayed, 3 years probation

Maximum Penalty: Revocation

If warranted:

1. Absent compelling mitigating circumstances, misrepresentation and false or deceptive advertising are serious offenses that warrant an actual period of suspension of at least 30 days.

2. If injury is substantial, outright revocation is appropriate.

3. Standard terms and conditions in cases of probation. *(See page 566.)*

4. If not taken within the past 5 years, take and pass the CSLB law and business examination.

5. Take and pass a course in Contractors License Law or a course related to construction law at an accredited community college. All courses must be approved in advance by the Registrar.

6. Submit copies of construction contracts to the Registrar upon demand during the probation period.

7. Submit copies of advertisements relating to contracting business to the Registrar prior to their being displayed or published during the probation period.

8. Prohibit the receipt of down payments.

9. Community Service as determined by CSLB; 5-21 days.

10. Pay CSLB investigation and enforcement costs.

7162. Representation with Respect to Trademark or Brand Name; Quantity or Size

Minimum Penalty: Revocation, stayed, 2 years probation

Maximum Penalty: Revocation

If warranted:

1. Actual suspension of 5 days or more.

2. Standard terms and conditions in cases of probation. *(See page 566.)*

3. If not taken within the past 5 years, take and pass the CSLB law and business examination.

4. Take and pass a course in Contractors License Law or a course related to construction law at an accredited community college. All courses must be approved in advance by the Registrar.

5. Make restitution.

6. Submit copies of construction contracts to the Registrar upon demand during the probation period.

7. Submit copies of advertisements relating to contracting business to the Registrar prior to their being displayed or published during the probation period.

8. Prohibit the receipt of down payments.

9. Pay CSLB investigation and enforcement costs.

7164. Contract Form for Single Family Dwelling

Minimum Penalty: 60 day suspension, stayed, 1 year probation

Maximum Penalty: Revocation

If warranted:

1. Actual suspension of 5 days or more.

2. Standard terms and conditions in cases of probation. *(See page 566.)*

3. If not taken within the past 5 years, take and pass the CSLB law and business examination.

4. Take and pass a course in Contractors License Law or a course related to construction law at an accredited community college. All courses must be approved in advance by the Registrar.

5. Submit copies of construction contracts to the Registrar upon demand during the probation period.

6. Pay CSLB investigation and enforcement costs.

7165. Swimming Pool Construction Contract

Minimum Penalty: 60 day suspension, stayed, 1 year probation

Maximum Penalty: Revocation

If warranted:

1. Actual suspension of 5 days or more.

2. Standard terms and conditions in cases of probation. *(See page 566.)*

3. If not taken within the past 5 years, take and pass the CSLB law and business examination.

4. Take and pass a course in Contractors License Law or a course related to construction law at an accredited community college. All courses must be approved in advance by the Registrar.

5. Submit copies of construction contracts to the Registrar upon demand during the probation period.

6. Pay CSLB investigation and enforcement costs.

7183.5. Asbestos; Certification Obtained under False Pretenses

Minimum Penalty: Revocation, stayed, 3 years probation

Maximum Penalty: Revocation

If warranted:

1. Absent compelling mitigating circumstances, obtaining an asbestos certification under false pretenses is a serious offense and warrants an outright revocation.

2. Actual suspension of at least 30 days.

3. Standard terms and conditions in cases of probation. *(See page 566.)*

4. Community Service as determined by CSLB; 5-21 days.

5. Pay CSLB investigation and enforcement costs.

7189. Asbestos Certification; Conflicts of Interest

Minimum Penalty: 60 day suspension, stayed, 1 year probation

Maximum Penalty: Revocation

If warranted:

1. Absent compelling circumstances, a person defined as an "asbestos consultant" or a "site surveillance technician," having financial or proprietary interest in an asbestos contractor's company is a serious offense that warrants an actual suspension period of at least 30 days.

2. Standard terms and conditions in cases of probation. *(See page 566.)*

3. Submit copies of construction contracts to the Registrar upon demand during the probation period.

4. Prohibit the receipt of down payments.

5. Community Service as determined by CSLB; 5-21 days.

6. Pay CSLB investigation and enforcement costs.

All Other Violations

Minimum Penalty: 5 day suspension, stayed, 1 year probation

Maximum Penalty: Revocation

If warranted:

1. Actual suspension of 5 days or more.

2. Standard terms and conditions in cases of probation. *(See page 566.)*

3. If not taken within the past 5 years, take and pass the CSLB law and business examination.

4. Take and pass a course in Contractors License Law or a course related to construction law at an accredited community college. All courses must be approved in advance by the Registrar.

5. If not taken within the past 5 years, take and pass the CSLB trade examination.

6. Take and pass a vocational course(s) related to the trade(s) employed on the project. All courses must be approved in advance by the Registrar.

7. Submit copies of construction contracts to the Registrar upon demand during the probation period.

8. Make restitution

9. Pay CSLB investigation and enforcement costs.

Standard Terms and Conditions to Be Included in all Cases of Probation

1. Obey All Laws:

   Respondent shall comply with all federal, state and local laws governing the activities of a licensed contractor in California.

2. Interviews With Regional Deputy:

   Respondent and any of respondent's personnel of record shall appear in person for interviews with the Regional Deputy or designee upon request and reasonable notice.

3. Completion Of Probation:

   Upon successful completion of probation, the contractor's license will be fully restored.

4. Violation Of Probation:

   If respondent violates probation in any respect, the Registrar, after giving notice and opportunity to be heard, may revoke probation and impose the disciplinary order that was stayed. If the decision contains an order to make restitution, the Registrar may impose the disciplinary order without giving the respondent an opportunity to be heard should the respondent fail to comply with the restitution order.

5. Respondent shall submit copies of documents directly related to the person's construction operations to the Registrar upon demand during the probation period.

872. Disclosure of General Liability Insurance

(a) As used in this regulation, "home improvement contract" is defined in Code Section 7151.2 The following statement, must accompany every estimate (bid) intended to result in a home improvement contract and every home improvement contract. The heading shall be printed in at least 14-point type, the questions in at least 12-point type, and the comments in italics of at least 11-point type. The text should be bold where indicated. This is 14-point type. This is 12-point type. *This is 11-point type in italics.*

Information About Commercial General Liability Insurance Home Improvement

Pursuant to California Business & Professions Code § 7159.3 (SB 2029), home improvement contractors must provide this notice and disclose whether or not they carry commercial general liability insurance.

Did your contractor tell you whether he or she carries Commercial General Liability Insurance?

Home improvement contractors are required by law to tell you whether or not they carry Commercial General Liability Insurance. This written statement must accompany the bid, if there is one, and the contract.

What does this insurance cover?

Commercial General Liability Insurance can protect against third-party bodily injury and accidental property damage. It is not intended to cover the work the contractor performs.

Is this insurance required?

No. But the Contractors State License Board strongly recommends that all contractors carry it. The Board cautions you to evaluate the risk to your family and property when you hire a contractor who is not insured. Ask yourself, if something went wrong, would this contractor be able to cover losses ordinarily covered by insurance?

How can you make sure the contractor is insured?

If he or she is insured, your contractor is required to provide you with the name and telephone number of the insurance company. Check with the insurance company to verify that the contractor's insurance coverage will cover your project.

What about a contractor who is self-insured?

A self-insured contractor has made a business decision to be personally responsible for losses that would ordinarily be covered by insurance. Before contracting with a self-insured contractor, ask yourself, if something went wrong, would this contractor be able to cover losses ordinarily covered by insurance?

■ _____ does not carry Commercial General Liability
   (CONTRACTOR'S NAME)

Insurance.

■ _____ carries Commercial General Liability
   (CONTRACTOR'S NAME)

Insurance.

The insurance company is _____
                    (COMPANY NAME)

You may call the insurance company at _____
                        (TELEPHONE NUMBER)

to verify coverage.

For more information about Commercial General Liability Insurance, contact the Contractors State License Board at www.cslb.ca.gov or call 800-321-CSLB (2752).

(This form meets the requirements of Rule 872 and Sections 7159.3 and 7164, Business and Professions Code.)

(b) The following statement must accompany every contract described in Code Section 7164. The heading shall be printed in at least 14-

Section VI

point type, the questions in at least 12-point type, and the comments in italics of at least 11-point type. The text should be bold where indicated. **This is 14-point type.** **This is 12-point type.** *This is 11-point type in italics.*

Information About Commercial General Liability Insurance Single Family Home

Pursuant to California Business & Professions Code §7164 (SB 2029), contractors building single-family residences for owners who intend to occupy the home for at least a year must provide this notice and disclose whether or not they carry commercial general liability insurance.

Did your contractor tell you whether he or she carries Commercial General Liability Insurance?

Contractors building single-family residences for owners who intend to occupy the home for at least a year are required by law to tell you whether or not they carry Commercial General Liability Insurance. This written statement must accompany the contract.

What does this insurance cover?

Commercial General Liability Insurance can protect against third-party bodily injury and accidental property damage. It is not intended to cover the work the contractor performs.

Is this insurance required?

No. But the Contractors State License Board strongly recommends that all contractors carry it. The Board cautions you to evaluate the risk to your family and property when you hire a contractor who is not insured. Ask yourself, if something went wrong, would this contractor be able to cover losses ordinarily covered by insurance?

How can you make sure the contractor is insured?

If he or she is insured, your contractor is required to provide you with the name and telephone number of the insurance company.

Check with the insurance company to verify that the contractor's insurance coverage will cover your project.

What about a contractor who is self-insured?

A self-insured contractor has made a business decision to be personally responsible for losses that would ordinarily be covered by insurance. Before contracting with a self-insured contractor, ask yourself, if something went wrong, would this contractor be able to cover losses ordinarily covered by insurance?

■ _____ does not carry Commercial General Liability
    (CONTRACTOR'S NAME)

Insurance.

■ _____ carries Commercial General Liability
    (CONTRACTOR'S NAME)

Insurance.

The insurance company is _____
                    (COMPANY NAME)

You may call the insurance company at _____
                          (TELEPHONE NUMBER)

to verify coverage.

For more information about Commercial General Liability Insurance, contact the Contractors State License Board at *www.cslb.ca.gov* or call 800-321-CSLB (2752).

(This form meets the requirements of Rule 872 and Sections 7159.3 and 7164, Business and Professions Code.)

ARTICLE 8. CITATION

880. Order of Correction—Practical Feasibility

Before including an order of correction in a citation, due consideration shall be given to the practical feasibility of correction in accordance with, but not limited to, the following criteria:

(a) An order of correction is appropriate where it would not result in excessive destruction of or substantial waste of existing acceptable construction.

(b) An order of correction is appropriate where the owner of the construction project is willing to allow the cited licensee to correct.

(c) An order of correction is appropriate where it appears to the Registrar that the cited licensee has competence or ability to correct.

(Authority cited: Sections 7008 and 7099.1, Business and Professions Code. Reference: Sections 7099 and 7099.1, Business and Professions Code.)

881. Order of Correction—Alternative Compliance

A cited licensee may comply with an order of correction by having and paying for another licensee to do the corrective work. The cited licensee remains responsible, however, for any failure to fully comply with the order of correction.

An order of correction may, but need not, contain the alternative that the cited person may pay a specified sum to the owner of the construction project in lieu of correcting.

(Authority cited: Sections 7008 and 7099.1, Business and Professions Code. Reference: Sections 7099 and 7099.1, Business and Professions Code.)

882. Order of Correction—Time Required to Correct

Where an order of correction is included in a citation, due consideration shall be given to the time required to correct in accordance with, but not limited to, the following criteria:

(a) Accepted industry practice in that area relating to performance of such work under certain climate or weather conditions.

(b) A reasonable time in which to obtain necessary materials.

(c) The number of working days the construction project will be made accessible by the owner for corrections.

(Authority cited: Sections 7008 and 7099.1, Business and Professions Code. Reference: Sections 7099 and 7099.1, Business and Professions Code.)

883. Order of Correction—Extension of Time to Correct

If the cited person, after exercising substantial efforts and reasonable diligence, is unable to complete the correction within the time allowed because of conditions beyond his control, he may request an extension of time in which to correct. Such request must be made in writing, and must be made prior to the expiration of the time allowed in the order of correction. An extension may be granted upon showing of good cause which determination is within the discretion of the Registrar. If a request for extension of time is not made prior to the expiration of time allowed in the order of correction, failure to correct within the time allowed shall constitute a violation of the order of correction whether or not good cause for an extension of time existed.

(Authority cited: Sections 7008 and 7099.1, Business and Professions Code. Reference: Sections 7099 and 7099.1, Business and Professions Code.)

884. Assessments of Civil Penalties

(a) Civil penalties against persons who have been cited for violation of the Contractors State License Law shall be assessed in accordance with the following ranges of penalties.

Section Violated	Minimum Civil Penalty	Maximum Civil Penalty
7027.1	$100	$1,000
7028	200	8,000
7028.1	1,000	8,000
7028.5	200	8,000
7028.7	200	15,000
7029.1	200	2,500
7029.5	100	500
7029.6	100	500
7030	500	1,500
7030.1	1,000	8,000
7030.5	100	1,000
7031.5	100	500
7034	100	1,000
7058.7	500	8,000
7068.1	100	8,000
7068.2	100	1,000
7071.1	100	1,000
7071.1	100	500
7075	100	500
7076	100	1,000
7083	100	1,000
7083.1	100	1,000
7099.1	100	1,500
7099.1	100	1,500
7107	200	8,000
7108	200	8,000
7108.5	200	2,000
7108.6	200	2,000
7109	200	8,000
7109.5	500	8,000
7110	200	30,000
7110.1	100	1,000
7111	100	1,000

Section Violated	Minimum Civil Penalty	Maximum Civil Penalty
7111.1	100	1,500
7113	200	8,000
7114	500	30,000
7114.1	200	2,000
7115	100	8,000
7116	100	8,000
7117	100	1,000
7117.5	200	8,000
7117.6	200	8,000
7118	500	30,000
7118.4	3,000	8,000
7118.5	1,000	8,000
7118.6	1,000	8,000
7119	200	2,000
7120	200	2,000
7123	500	8,000
7125	100	500
7125.4	200	30,000
7154	100	1,000
7157	100	1,000
7158	500	8,000
7159	100	1,000
7159.5(a)(1), (a)(3), and (a)(5),	100	8,000
7159.5(a)(2), (a)(4), (a)(6), (a)(7), and (a)(8)	100	1,000
7159.1	100	500
7159.1	100	8,000
7161	100	8,000
7162	100	1,500
7164	100	1,000

(b) When determining the amount of assessed civil penalty, the Registrar shall take into consideration whether one or more of the following or similar circumstances apply:

(1) the citation includes multiple violations;

(2) the cited person has a history of violations of the same or similar sections of the Contractors State License Law;

(3) in the judgment of the Registrar, a person has exhibited bad faith;

(4) in the judgment of the Registrar, the violation is serious or harmful;

(5) the citation involves a violation or violations perpetuated against a senior citizen or disabled person; and/or

(6) the citation involves a violation or violations involving a construction project in connection with repairs for damages caused by a natural disaster as described in Section 7158 of the Code.

(c) Where a citation lists more than one violation and each of the violations relates to the same construction project, the total penalty assessment in each citation shall not exceed $ 8,000, except as provided for violations of Section 7028.7, in which case the total penalty assessment in each citation shall not exceed $ 15,000, and for violations of Sections 7110, 7114, 7118, or 7125.4, in which case the total penalty assessment in each citation shall not exceed $ 30,000.

(d) Where a citation lists more than one violation, the amount of assessed civil penalty shall be stated separately for each section violated.

(Authority cited: Sections 7008 and 7099.2, Business and Professions Code. Reference: Sections 7099, 7099.1 and 7115, Business and Professions Code.)

885. Appeal of Citation

Any person served with a citation pursuant to Section 7099 of the Business and Professions Code may contest the citation by appealing to the Registrar within 15 working days from the receipt of such citation. The 15 day period may be extended upon showing of good cause which determination is within the discretion of the Registrar.

The cited person may contest any or all of the following aspects of the citation:

1. The occurrence of a violation of the Contractors License Law;

2. The reasonableness of the order of correction, if an order of correction is included in the citation;

3. The period of time allowed for correction, if an order of correction is included in the citation;

4. The amount of the civil penalty, if a civil penalty is assessed in the citation.

(Authority cited: Section 7008, Business and Professions Code. Reference: Sections 7099.3, 7099.4 and 7099.5, Business and Professions Code.)

886. Service of Citation

Service of a citation shall be made in accordance with the provisions of Section 11505(c) of the Government Code, and, further, that a copy of the citation be sent by regular mail.

(Authority cited: Section 7008, Business and Professions Code. Reference: Sections 7099.3, 7099.4 and 7099.5, Business and Professions Code.)

887. Criteria to Evaluate the Gravity of a Violation of Business and Professions Code Section 7028.7

Before assessing a civil penalty under Section 7028.7 of the Business and Professions Code, the Registrar shall give due consideration to the gravity of the violation, including, but not limited to, a consideration of whether the cited person did one or more of the following:

1. Falsely represented that he/she was licensed.

2. Failed to perform work for which money was received.

3. Executed or used any false or misleading documents in order to induce a person to enter into a contract or to pay money.

4. Made false or misleading statements in order to induce a person to enter into a contract or pay money.

5. Failed to apply funds which were received for the purpose of obtaining or paying for services, labor, materials, or equipment.

6. Performed work that was potentially hazardous to the health, safety, or general welfare of the public.

7. Performed work in violation of the building laws, safety laws, labor laws, compensation insurance laws, or unemployment insurance laws.

8. Performed work that did not meet acceptable trade standards for good and workmanlike construction.

9. Was convicted of a crime in connection with the violation.

10. Committed any act which would be cause for disciplinary action against a licensee.

11. Committed numerous or repeated violations.

(Authority cited: Sections 7008 and 7028.7, Business and Professions Code. Reference: Section 7028.7, Business and Professions Code.)

ARTICLE 9. ARBITRATION

890. Minimum Qualification Standards for Arbitrators

For the purposes of Section 7085.5 of the Code, regardless of the method of appointment or selection, arbitrators shall possess the following minimum qualifications:

(a) (1) Five (5) years of experience in the construction industry as a licensed contractor or a professional in a construction related field, such as an architect or engineer, or

(2) Five (5) years of experience as an attorney, judge, administrative law judge, arbitrator, or a combination thereof, handling a minimum of 8 construction related matters.

(b) Completion of an arbitrator's course on construction arbitration within the last 5 years including, but not limited to, training on the process, the ethics and the laws relating to arbitration. The training on the process of arbitration may include such topics as the role of the arbitrator, the use of effective questioning techniques, and the role of an expert in an arbitration proceeding.

(c) Completion of 8 hours of continuing education on construction arbitration every 5 years, including, but not limited to, the topics set forth in subsection (b).

(d) Completion of a training program related specifically to the Board's arbitration procedures, laws and policies.

(Authority cited: Sections 7008 and 7085.5(b)(3), Business and Professions Code. Reference: Section 7085 et seq., Business and Professions Code.)

HISTORY NOTES FOR
CURRENT BOARD RULES AND REGULATIONS

(History notes for repealed rules and regulations appear at the end of this section.)

810. DEFINITIONS

1. *Repealer of Article 1 (Sections 700 and 701) and new Article 1 (Section 700) filed 5-25-83; effective thirtieth day thereafter (Register 83, No. 22).*
2. *Section renumbered from 700 to 810, filed 2-27-84; effective upon filing pursuant to Government Code Section 11346.2(d) (Register 84, No. 9).*
3. *New subsection (a), subsection relettering and amendment of newly designated subsection (b) filed 6-5-2024; operative 10-1-2024 (Register 2024, No. 23).*

811. FEES

1. *New section filed 12-31-2002 as an emergency; operative 1-1-2003 (Register 2003, No. 1). A Certificate of Compliance must be transmitted to OAL by 5-1-2003 or emergency language will be repealed by operation of law on the following day.*

2. *Certificate of Compliance as to 12-31-2002 order, including new subsection (e), subsection relettering and amendment of Note, transmitted to OAL 4-25-2003 and filed 6-5-2003 (Register 2003, No. 23).*

3. *Amendment of section and Note filed 11-18-2010; operative 12-18-2010 (Register 2010, No. 47).*

4. *Change without regulatory effect repealing subsections (a)-(a)(12) and subsection (b) designator and amending former subsection (b) and subsections (7)-(8) filed 8-7-2013 pursuant to section 100, title 1, California Code of Regulations (Register 2013, No. 32).*

5. *Redesignation of first paragraph and subsections (1)-(13) as subsections (a)-(a)(13) and amendment of newly designated subsections (a)(7), (a)(8) and (a)(11) filed 12-19-2019 as an emergency; operative 12-19-2019 (Register 2019, No. 51). A Certificate of Compliance must be transmitted to OAL by 6-16-2020 or emergency language will be repealed by operation of law on the following day.*

6. *Reinstatement of section as it existed prior to 12-19-2019 emergency amendment by operation of Government Code section 11346.1(f) (Register 2020, No. 44).*

7. *Redesignation of first paragraph and subsections (1)-(13) as subsections (a)-(a)(13) and amendment of newly designated subsections (a)(7), (a)(8) and (a)(11) refiled 11-10-2020 as an emergency; operative 11-10-2020. Emergency expiration extended 60 days (Executive Order N-40-20) plus an additional 60 days (Executive Order N-66-20) (Register 2020, No. 46). A Certificate of Compliance must be transmitted to OAL by 6-18-2021 or emergency language will be repealed by operation of law on the following day.*

8. *Certificate of Compliance as to 11-10-2020 order transmitted to OAL 4-8-2021 and filed 5-20-2021 (Register 2021, No. 21).*

9. *Change without regulatory effect repealing and adopting new section and amending Note filed 6-12-2024 pursuant to section 100, title 1, California Code of Regulations (Register 2024, No. 24).*

813. ABANDONMENT OF APPLICATION

1. *New section filed 8-25-83; effective upon filing pursuant to Government Code Section 11346.2(d) (Register 83, No. 35).*

2. *Section renumbered from 705 to 813, filed 2-27-84; effective upon filing pursuant to Government Code Section 11346.2(d) (Register 84, No. 9).*

816. APPLICATION FORM FOR ORIGINAL LICENSE

1. *Amendment filed 9-8-77; effective thirtieth day thereafter (Register 77, No. 37).*

2. *Editorial correction of subsection (c) (Register 77, No. 52).*

3. *Amendment filed 8-25-83; effective upon filing pursuant to Government Code Section 11346.2(d) (Register 83, No. 35).*

4. *Section renumbered from 706 to 816, filed 2-27-84; effective upon filing pursuant to Government Code Section 11346.2(d) (Register 84, No. 9).*

5. *Amendment of subsections (a)(1) and (c) filed 6-6-86; effective thirtieth day thereafter (Register 86, No. 23).*

6. *Change without regulatory effect repealing subsection (a)(1), renumbering subsections and amending subsection (c) and Note filed 11-15-2016 pursuant to section 100, title 1, California Code of Regulations (Register 2016, No. 47).*

819. REQUIREMENT OF CORPORATIONS

1. *Amendment filed 7-19-74; effective thirtieth day thereafter (Register 74, No. 29).*

2. *Amendment filed 8-25-83; effective upon filing pursuant to Government Code Section 11346.2(d) (Register 83, No. 35).*

3. *Section renumbered from 714 to 819, filed 2-27-84; effective upon filing pursuant to Government Code Section 11346.2(d) (Register 84, No. 9).*

824. APPLICATION INVESTIGATION REQUIRED

1. *New section filed 1-24-80; effective thirtieth day thereafter (Register 80, No. 4).*

2. *Amendment filed 8-25-83; effective upon filing pursuant to Government Code Section 11346.2(d) (Register 83, No. 35).*

3. *Section renumbered from 723.1 to 824, filed 2-27-84; effective upon filing pursuant to Government Code Section 11346.2(d) (Register 84, No. 9).*

825. EXPERIENCE REQUIREMENT OF APPLICANT

1. *Amendment filed 9-8-77; effective thirtieth day thereafter (Register 77, No. 37). For prior history, see Register 74, No. 29.*

2. *Editorial correction (Register 77, No. 52).*

3. *Amendment filed 8-25-83; effective upon filing pursuant to Government Code Section 11346.2(d) (Register 83, No. 35).*

4. *Section renumbered from 724 to 825, filed 2-27-84; effective upon filing, pursuant to Government Code Section 11346.2(d) (Register 84, No. 9).*

5. *Amendment of subsection (a) filed 4-12-84; effective upon filing pursuant to Government Code Section 11346.2(d) Register 84, No. 15).*

825.5. GENERAL MANUFACTURED HOUSING CONTRACTOR INITIAL INSTALLER TRAINING REQUIREMENT

1. *New section filed 9-30-2021; operative 9-30-2021 pursuant to Government Code section 11343.4(b)(3) (Register 2021, No. 40). Filing deadline specified in Government Code section 11349.3(a) extended 60 calendar days pursuant to Executive Order N-40-20.*

826. REGISTRAR TO PASS ON EXPERIENCE

1. *Amendment filed 9-8-77; effective thirtieth day thereafter (Register 77, No. 37).*

2. *Amendment filed 8-25-83; effective upon filing pursuant to Government Code Section 11346.2(d) (Register 83, No. 35).*

3. *Section renumbered from 725 to 826, filed 2-27-84; effective upon filing pursuant to Government Code Section 11346.2(d) (Register 84, No. 9).*

827. REVIEW OF APPLICATION FOR ORIGINAL LICENSE, ADDITIONAL CLASSIFICATION, OR REPLACEMENT OF QUALIFYING PERSON

1. *New section filed 12-3-85; effective thirtieth day thereafter (Register 85, No. 49).*

828. REVIEW OF APPLICATION FOR HOME IMPROVEMENT SALESMAN REGISTRATION

1. *New section filed 10-26-84; effective thirtieth day thereafter (Register 84, No. 43).*

830. CLASSIFICATION POLICY

1. *Amendment filed 9-8-77; effective thirtieth day thereafter (Register 77, No. 37).*

2. *Amendment filed 8-19-83; effective thirtieth day thereafter (Register 83, No. 35).*

3. *Section renumbered from 730 to 830, filed 2-27-84; effective upon filing pursuant to Government Code Section 11346.2(d) (Register 84, No. 9).*

831. INCIDENTAL AND SUPPLEMENTAL DEFINED

1. *New section filed 8-19-83; effective thirtieth day thereafter (Register 83, No. 35).*

2. *Section renumbered from 730.1 to 831, filed 2-27-84; effective upon filing pursuant to Government Code Section 11346.2(d) (Register 84, No. 9).*

832. SPECIALTY CONTRACTORS CLASSIFIED

1. *Amendment filed 4-29-64; effective thirtieth day thereafter (Register 64, No. 9). For prior history see Register 55, No. 11 and Register 61, No. 19.*

2. *Amendment filed 7-18-68; designated effective 10-15-68 (Register 68, No. 27).*

3. *Amendment filed 5-8-73; effective thirtieth day thereafter (Register 73, No. 19).*

4. *Amendment filed 4-16-74 as procedural and organizational; designated effective 5-16-74 (Register 74, No. 16).*

5. *Amendment filed 8-19-83; effective thirtieth day thereafter (Register 83, No. 35).*

6. *Section renumbered from 732 to 832, filed 2-27-84; effective upon filing pursuant to Government Code Section 11346.2(d) (Register 84, No. 9).*

7. *Amendment filed 6-6-86; effective thirtieth day thereafter (Register 86, No. 23).*

8. *Amendment filed 10-22-86; effective thirtieth day thereafter (Register 86, No. 43).*

9. *Amendment filed 9-15-88; operative 10-15-88 Register 88, No. 39).*

10. *Amendment filed 11-9-95; effective thirtieth day thereafter (Register 95, No. 45).*

11. *Change without regulatory effect amending section filed 11-15-2016 pursuant to section 100, title 1, California Code of Regulations (Register 2016, No. 47).*

12. *Amendment filed 3-30-2022; operative 1-1-2024 (Register 2022, No. 13)*

832.02. CLASS C-2—INSULATION AND ACOUSTICAL CONTRACTOR

1. *New section filed 9-18-47 as an emergency; effective upon filing (Register 9).*

2. *Amendment filed 4-12-61; effective 30th day thereafter (Register 61, No. 8).*

3. *Amendment filed 8-19-83; effective thirtieth day thereafter (Register 83, No. 35).*

4. *Section renumbered from 754.8 to 832.02, filed 2-27-84; effective upon filing pursuant to Government Code Section 11346.2(d) (Register 84, No. 9).*

832.04. CLASS C-4—BOILER, HOT-WATER HEATING AND STEAM FITTING CONTRACTOR

1. *New section filed 9-18-47 as an emergency; effective upon filing (Register 9).*

2. *Amendment filed 5-4-72; effective thirtieth day thereafter (Register 72, No. 19).*

3. *Amendment filed 4-28-82; effective thirtieth day thereafter (Register 82, No. 18).*

4. *Amendment filed 8-25-83; effective upon filing pursuant to Government Code Section 11346.2(d) (Register 83, No. 35).*

5. *Section renumbered from 754.1 to 832.04, filed 2-27-84; effective upon filing pursuant to Government Code Section 11346.2(d) (Register 84, No. 9).*

832.05. CLASS C-5—FRAMING AND ROUGH CARPENTRY CONTRACTOR

1. *New section filed 10-26-93; operative 11-25-93 (Register 93, No. 44).*

2. *Amendment filed 12-18-97; effective 01-01-98 (Register 97, No. 172)*

3. *Amendment of section heading, section and Note filed 5-24-2002; operative 1-1-2003 Register 2002, No.21).*

4. *Change without regulatory effect repealing second paragraph filed 8-7-2013 pursuant to section 100, title 1, California Code of Regulations (Register 2013, No. 32).*

832.06. CLASS C-6—CABINET, MILLWORK AND FINISH CARPENTRY CONTRACTOR

1. *New section filed 5-24-2002; operative 1-1-2003 (Register 2002, No. 21). For prior history, see Register 97, No. 51.*

2. *Change without regulatory effect repealing second paragraph filed 8-7-2013 pursuant to section 100, title 1, California Code of Regulations (Register 2013, No. 32).*

832.07. CLASS C-7—LOW VOLTAGE SYSTEMS CONTRACTOR

1. *New section filed 9-15-88; operative 10-15-88 (Register 88, No. 39).*

2. *Amendment filed 5-17-95; operative 6-16-95 (Register 95, No. 20).*

832.08. CLASS C-8—CONCRETE CONTRACTOR

1. *Amendment filed 10-12-72; effective thirtieth day thereafter (Register 72, No. 42).*

2. *Amendment filed 8-25-83; effective upon filing pursuant to Government Code Section 11346.2(d) (Register 83, No. 35).*

3. *Section renumbered from 739 to 832.08, filed 2-27-84; effective upon filing pursuant to Government Code Section 11346.2(d) (Register 84, No. 9).*

832.09. CLASS C-9—DRYWALL CONTRACTOR

1. *New section filed 4-29-64; effective thirtieth day thereafter (Register 64, No. 9).*

2. *Amendment filed 10-14-65; effective thirtieth day thereafter (Register 65, No. 19).*

3. *Amendment filed 8-19-83; effective thirtieth day thereafter (Register 83, No. 34).*

4. *Section renumbered from 754.13 to 832.09, filed 2-27-84; effective upon filing pursuant to Government Code Section 11346.2(d) (Register 84, No. 9).*

5. *Amendment filed 5-8-2002; operative 6-7-2002 (Register 2002, No.19).*

832.10. CLASS C-10—ELECTRICAL CONTRACTOR

1. *Amendment filed 4-28-82; effective thirtieth day thereafter (Register 82, No. 18).*

2. *Amendment filed 8-19-83; effective thirtieth day thereafter (Register 83, No. 34).*

3. *Section renumbered from 733 to 832.10, filed 2-27-84, effective upon filing pursuant to Government Code Section 11346.2(d) (Register 84, No. 9)*

4. *Amendment filed 6-5-2024; operative 10-1-2024 (Register 2024, No. 23).*

832.11. CLASS C-11—ELEVATOR CONTRACTOR

1. *New section filed 9-18-47 as an emergency; effective upon filing (Register 9).*

2. *Amendment filed 8-25-83; effective upon filing pursuant to Government Code Section 11346.2(d) (Register 83, No. 35).*

3. *Section renumbered from 754.3 to 832.11, filed 2-27-84; effective upon filing pursuant to Government Code Section 11346.2(d) (Register 84, No. 9).*

832.12. CLASS C-12—EARTHWORK AND PAVING CONTRACTORS

1. *Originally published 12-5-46 (Title 16).*

2. *Amendment filed 9-18-47 as an emergency; effective upon filing (Register 9).*

3. *Amendment filed 8-3-72; effective thirtieth day thereafter (Register 72, No. 32).*

4. *Amendment filed 8-25-83; effective upon filing pursuant to Government Code Section 11346.2(d) (Register 83, No. 35).*

5. *Section renumbered from 745 to 832.12, filed 2-27-84; effective upon filing pursuant to Government Code Section 11346.2(d) (Register 84, No. 9).*

832.13. CLASS C-13—FENCING CONTRACTOR

1. *New section filed 4-16-74; effective thirtieth day thereafter (Register 74, No. 16).*

2. *Amendment filed 8-25-83; effective upon filing pursuant to Government Code Section 11346.2(d) (Register 83, No. 35).*

3. *Section renumbered from 754.15 to 832.13, filed 2-27-84; effective upon filing pursuant to Government Code Section 11346.2(d) (Register 84, No. 9).*

832.14. CLASS C-14—METAL ROOFING CONTRACTOR

1. *New section filed 10-22-86; effective thirtieth day thereafter (Register 86, No. 43).*

2. *Repealer and new section filed 6-22-98; operative 7-1-98 pursuant to Government Code section 11343.4(d) (Register 98, No. 26).*

832.15. CLASS C-15—FLOORING AND FLOOR COVERING CONTRACTORS

1. *Originally published 12-5-46 (Title 16).*

2. *Amendment filed 9-18-47 as an emergency; effective upon filing (Register 9).*

3. *Amendment filed 8-3-72; effective thirtieth day thereafter (Register 72, No. 32).*

4. *Amendment filed 8-25-83; effective upon filing pursuant to Government Code Section 11346.2(d) (Register 83, No. 35).*

5. *Section renumbered from 741 to 832.15, filed 2-27-84; effective upon filing pursuant to Government Code Section 11346.2(d) (Register 84, No. 9).*

832.16. CLASS C-16—FIRE PROTECTION CONTRACTOR

1. *New section filed 4-27-49 (Register 16, No. 2).*

2. *Amendment filed 8-12-83; effective thirtieth day thereafter (Register 83, No. 33).*

3. *Section renumbered from 754.9 to 832.16, filed 2-27-84; effective upon filing pursuant to Government Code Section 11346.2(d) (Register 84, No. 9).*

4. *Amendment filed 8-21-90; operative 9-20-90 (Register 90, No. 41).*

5. *Change without regulatory effect amending section filed 11-15-2016 pursuant to section 100, title 1, California Code of Regulations (Register 2016, No. 47).*

832.17. CLASS C-17—GLAZING CONTRACTOR

1. *Amendment filed 10-29-69; effective thirtieth day thereafter (Register 69, No. 44).*

2. *Amendment filed 8-25-83; effective upon filing pursuant to Government Code Section 11346.2(d) (Register 83, No. 35).*

3. *Section renumbered from 750 to 832.17, filed 2-27-84; effective upon filing pursuant to Government Code Section 11346.2(d) (Register 84, No. 9).*

832.20. CLASS C-20—WARM-AIR HEATING, VENTILATING AND AIR-CONDITIONING CONTRACTOR

1. *Originally published 12-5-46 (Title 16).*

2. *Amendment filed 9-18-47 as an emergency; effective upon filing (Register 9).*

3. *Amendment filed 5-4-72; effective thirtieth day thereafter (Register 72, No. 19).*

4. *Amendment filed 4-28-82; effective thirtieth day thereafter (Register 82, No. 18).*

5. *Amendment filed 11-1-83; effective upon filing pursuant to Government Code Section 11346.2(d) (Register 83, No. 45).*

6. *Section renumbered from 746 to 832.20, filed 2-27-84; effective upon filing pursuant to Government Code Section 11346.2(d) (Register 84, No. 9).*

7. *Editorial correction filed 7-19-84 (Register 84, No. 29).*

832.21. CLASS C-21--BUILDING MOVING/DEMOLITION CONTRACTOR

1. *Amendment filed 1-31-72; effective thirtieth day thereafter (Register 72, No. 6). For prior history see Register 55, No. 11.*

2. *Amendment filed 8-3-72; effective thirtieth day thereafter (Register 72, No. 32).*

3. *Amendment filed 8-25-83; effective upon filing pursuant to Government Code Section 11346.2(d) (Register 83, No. 35).*

4. *Section renumbered from 752 to 832.21, filed 2-27-84; effective upon filing pursuant to Government Code Section 11346.2(d) (Register 84, No. 9).*

832.22. CLASS C–22—ASBESTOS ABATEMENT CONTRACTOR

1. *New section filed 12-30-2014; operative 1-1-2015 pursuant to Government Code section 11343.4(b)(3) (Register 2015, No. 1).*

832.23. CLASS C-23—ORNAMENTAL METAL CONTRACTOR

1. *Amendment filed 8-25-83; effective upon filing pursuant to Government Code Section 11346.2(d) (Register 83, No. 35).*

2. *Section renumbered from 749 to 832.23, filed 2-27-84; effective upon filing pursuant to Government Code Section 11346.2(d) (Register 84, No. 9).*

832.27. CLASS C-27—LANDSCAPING CONTRACTOR

1. *Amendment filed 10-14-68; effective thirtieth day thereafter (Register 68, No. 39).*

2. *Amendment filed 8-19-83; effective thirtieth day thereafter (Register 83, No. 34).*

3. *Section renumbered from 747 to 832.27, filed 2-27-84; effective upon filing pursuant to Government Code Section 11346.2(d) (Register 84, No. 9).*

4. *Amendment filed 6-1-88; operative 7-1-88 (Register 88, No. 23).*

832.28. CLASS C-28—LOCK AND SECURITY EQUIPMENT CONTRACTOR

1. *New section filed 1-31-95; operative 3-1-95 (Register 95, No.6Z).*

832.29. CLASS C-29—MASONRY CONTRACTOR

1. *Amendment filed 8-25-83; effective upon filing pursuant to Government Code Section 11346.2(d) (Register 83, No. 35).*

2. *Section renumbered from 740 to 832.29, filed 2-27-84; effective upon filing pursuant to Government Code Section 11346.2(d) (Register 84, No. 9).*

832.31. CLASS C-31—CONSTRUCTION ZONE TRAFFIC CONTROL CONTRACTOR

1. *New section filed 9-18-2000; operative 9-18-2000 pursuant to Government Code Section 11343.4 (d) (Register 2000, No.38).*

832.32. CLASS C-32—PARKING AND HIGHWAY IMPROVEMENT CONTRACTOR

1. *New section filed 7-18-68; designated effective 10-15-68 (Register 68, No. 27).*

2. *Amendment filed 8-19-83; effective thirtieth day thereafter (Register 83, No. 34).*

3. *Section renumbered from 754.14 to 832.32, filed 2-27-84; effective upon filing pursuant to Government Code Section 11346.2(d) (Register 84, No. 9).*

832.33. CLASS C-33—PAINTING AND DECORATING CONTRACTORS

1. *Amendment filed 8-19-83; effective thirtieth day thereafter (Register 83, No. 34).*

2. *Section renumbered from 735 to 832.33, filed 2-27-84; effective upon filing pursuant to Government Code Section 11346.2(d) (Register 84, No. 9).*

832.34. CLASS C-34—PIPELINE CONTRACTOR

1. *New section filed 7-24-56; designated effective sixtieth day thereafter (Register 56, No. 14).*

2. *Amendment filed 8-19-83; effective thirtieth day thereafter (Register 83, No. 34).*

3. *Section renumbered from 754.11 to 832.34, filed 2-27-84; effective upon filing pursuant to Government Code Section 11346.2(d) (Register 84, No. 9).*

832.35. CLASS C-35—LATHING AND PLASTERING CONTRACTOR

1. *Amendment of section heading, new subsection (a) designator and new subsections (b) and (c) filed 12-18-97; operative 1-1-98 pursuant to Government Code section 11343.4(d) (Register 97, No. 51).*

2. *Change without regulatory effect repealing subsection (c) filed 8-7-2013 pursuant to section 100, title 1, California Code of Regulations (Register 2013, No. 32).*

832.36. CLASS C-36—PLUMBING CONTRACTOR

1. *Amendment filed 4-29-64; effective thirtieth day thereafter (Register 64, No. 9).*

2. *Amendment filed 4-28-82; effective thirtieth day thereafter (Register 82, No. 18).*

3. *Amendment filed 8-12-83; effective thirtieth day thereafter (Register 83, No. 33).*

4. *Section renumbered from 734 to 832.36, filed 2-27-84; effective upon filing pursuant to Government Code Section 11346.2(d) (Register 84, No. 9).*

5. *Amendment filed 5-25-89; operative 6-24-89 (Register 89, No. 22). 2. Editorial correction of printing error and restoration of History 1. (Register 92, No. 29).*

6. *Amendment filed 12-1-94; operative 12-31-94 (Register 94, No. 50Z).*

832.38. CLASS C-38—REFRIGERATION CONTRACTOR

1. *Amendment filed 5-4-72; effective thirtieth day thereafter (Register 72, No. 19).*

2. *Amendment filed 8-19-83; effective thirtieth day thereafter (Register 83, No. 34).*

3. *Section renumbered from 748 to 832.38, filed 2-27-84; effective upon filing pursuant to Government Code Section 11346.2(d) (Register 84, No. 9).*

832.39. CLASS C-39—ROOFING CONTRACTOR

1. *Amendment filed 8-25-83; effective upon filing pursuant to Government Code Section 11346.2(d) (Register 83, No. 35).*

2. *Section renumbered from 737 to 832.39, filed 2-27-84; effective upon filing pursuant to Government Code Section 11346.2(d) (Register 84, No. 9).*

3. *Amendment filed 6-22-98; operative 7-1-98 pursuant to Government Code section 11343.4 (d) (Register 98, No. 26).*

832.42. CLASS C-42—SANITATION SYSTEM CONTRACTOR

1. *New section filed 9-18-47 as an emergency; effective upon filing (Register 9).*

2. *Amendment filed 8-3-72; effective thirtieth day thereafter (Register 72, No. 32).*

3. *Amendment filed 8-19-83; effective thirtieth day thereafter (Register 83, No. 34).*

4. *Section renumbered from 754.4 to 832.42, filed 2-27-84; effective upon filing pursuant to Government Code Section 11346.2(d) (Register 84, No. 9).*

832.43. CLASS C-43—SHEET METAL CONTRACTOR

1. *Originally published 12-5-46 (Title 16).*

2. *Amendment filed 9-18-47 as an emergency; effective upon filing (Register 9).*

3. *Amendment filed 8-19-83; effective thirtieth day thereafter (Register 83, No. 34).*

4. *Section renumbered from 742 to 832.43, filed 2-27-84; effective upon filing pursuant to Government Code Section 11346.2(d) (Register 84, No. 9).*

5. *Amendment filed 6-22-98; operative 7-1-98 pursuant to Government Code section 11343.4 (d) (Register 98, No. 26).*

832.45. CLASS C-45—ELECTRICAL SIGN CONTRACTOR

1. *New section filed 9-18-47 as an emergency; effective upon filing (Register 9).*
2. *Amendment filed 8-25-83; effective upon filing pursuant to Government Code Section 11346.2(d) (Register 83, No. 35).*
3. *Section renumbered from 754.2 to 832.45, filed 2-27-84; effective upon filing pursuant to Government Code Section 11346.2(d) (Register 84, No. 9).*
4. *Amendment of section heading and section filed 11-30-2009; operative 12-30-2009 (Register 2009, No. 49).*

832.46. CLASS C-46—SOLAR CONTRACTOR

1. *New section filed 10-20-78; effective thirtieth day thereafter (Register 78, No. 42).*
2. *Amendment filed 4-28-82; effective thirtieth day thereafter (Register 82, No. 18).*
3. *Amendment filed 8-25-83; effective upon filing pursuant to Government Code Section 11346.2(d) (Register 83, No. 35).*
4. *Section renumbered from 754.16 to 832.46, filed 2-27-84; effective upon filing pursuant to Government Code Section 11346.2(d) (Register 84, No. 9).*
5. *Amendment filed 11-30-2009; operative 12-30-2009 (Register 2009, No. 49).*
6. *Amendment filed 6-5-2024; operative 10-1-2024 (Register 2024, No. 23).*

832.47. CLASS C-47—GENERAL MANUFACTURED HOUSING CONTRACTOR

1. *New section filed 3-15-83; effective thirtieth day thereafter (Register 83, No. 12).*
2. *Section renumbered from 754.18 to 832.47, filed 2-27-84; effective upon filing pursuant to Government Code Section 11346.2(d) (Register 84, No. 9).*
3. *Amendment of section and Note filed 10-7-2008; operative 11-6-2008 (Register 2008, No. 41).*

832.49. CLASS C-49—TREE AND PALM CONTRACTOR

1. *New section filed 3-30-2022; operative 1-1-2024 (Register 2022, No. 13).*

832.50. CLASS C-50—REINFORCING STEEL CONTRACTOR

1. *New section filed 9-18-47 as an emergency; effective upon filing (Register 9).*
2. *Amendment filed 8-19-83; effective thirtieth day thereafter (Register 83, No. 34).*
3. *Section renumbered from 754.5 to 832.50, filed 2-27-84; effective upon filing pursuant to Government Code Section 11346.2(d) (Register 84, No. 9).*
4. *Amendment filed 6-1-88; operative 7-1-88 (Register 88, No. 23).*

832.51. CLASS C-51—STRUCTURAL STEEL CONTRACTOR

1. *New section filed 9-18-47 as an emergency; effective upon filing (Register 9).*
2. *Amendment filed 8-19-83; effective thirtieth day thereafter (Register 83, No. 34).*
3. *Section renumbered from 754.6 to 832.51, filed 2-27-84; effective upon filing pursuant to Government Code Section 11346.2(d) (Register 84, No. 9).*
4. *Amendment filed 11-30-98; effective thirtieth day thereafter (Register 98, No. 49).*

832.53. CLASS C-53—SWIMMING POOL CONTRACTOR

1. *New section filed 5-3-55; effective thirtieth day thereafter (Register 55, No. 7).*
2. *Amendment filed 4-28-82; effective thirtieth day thereafter (Register 82, No. 18).*
3. *Amendment filed 8-19-83; effective thirtieth day thereafter (Register 83, No. 34).*
4. *Section renumbered from 754.10 to 832.53, filed 2-27-84; effective upon filing pursuant to Government Code Section 11346.2(d) (Register 84, No. 9).*

832.54. CLASS C-54—TILE CONTRACTORS (CERAMIC AND MOSAIC)

1. Originally published 12-5-46 (Title 16).
2. Amendment filed 9-18-47 as an emergency; effective upon filing (Register 9).
3. Amendment filed 8-25-83; effective upon filing pursuant to Government Code Section 11346.2(d) (Register 83, No. 35).
4. Section renumbered from 738 to 832.54, filed 2-27-84; effective upon filing pursuant to Government Code Section 11346.2(d) (Register 84, No. 9).
5. Amendment filed 5-16-2002; operative 5-16-2002 pursuant to Government Code section 11343.4 (Register 2002, No. 20).

832.55. CLASS C-55—WATER CONDITIONING CONTRACTOR

1. New section filed 5-24-61; designated effective 8-22-61 (Register 61, No. 10).
2. Amendment filed 8-19-83; effective thirtieth day thereafter (Register 83, No. 34).
3. Section renumbered from 754.12 to 832.55, filed 2-27-84; effective upon filing pursuant to Government Code Section 11346.2(d) (Register 84, No. 9).

832.57. CLASS C-57—WELL DRILLING CONTRACTOR

1. Originally published 12-5-46 (Title 16).
2. Amendment filed 10-19-48 as an emergency (Register 14, No. 3).
3. Amendment filed 8-25-83; effective upon filing pursuant to Government Code Section 11346.2(d) (Register 83, No. 35).
4. Section renumbered from 751 to 832.57, filed 2-27-84; effective upon filing pursuant to Government Code Section 11346.2(d) (Register 84, No. 9).

832.60. CLASS C-60—WELDING CONTRACTOR

1. New section filed 9-18-47 as an emergency; effective upon filing (Register 9).
2. Amendment filed 8-19-83; effective thirtieth day thereafter (Register 83, No. 34).
3. Section renumbered from 754.7 to 832.60, filed 2-27-84; effective upon filing pursuant to Government Code Section 11346.2(d) (Register 84, No. 9).

832.61. CLASSIFICATION C-61, LIMITED SPECIALTY

1. New section filed 9-5-61; effective thirtieth day thereafter (Register 61, No. 19).
2. Amendment filed 4-29-64; effective thirtieth day thereafter (Register 64, No. 9).
3. Amendment filed 9-8-77; effective thirtieth day thereafter (Register 77, No. 37).
4. Editorial correction (Register 77, No. 52).
5. Amendment filed 8-19-83; effective thirtieth day thereafter (Register 83, No. 34).
6. Section renumbered from 732.1 to 832.61, filed 2-27-84, effective upon filing pursuant to Government Code Section 11346.2(d) (Register 84, No. 9).

832.62. SOLAR SYSTEM WORK WITHIN SCOPE OF CLASS A, CLASS B, AND CLASS C-61 (SWIMMING POOL MAINTENANCE)

1. New section filed 4-28-82; effective thirtieth day thereafter (Register 82, No. 18).
2. Section renumbered from 754.17 to 832.62, filed 2-27-84, effective upon filing pursuant to Government Code Section 11346.2(d) (Register 84, No. 9).

833. ASBESTOS CLASSIFICATION AND CERTIFICATION LIMITATIONS AND EXAMINATION REQUIREMENT

1. New section filed 12-30-2014; operative 1-1-2015 pursuant to Government Code section 11343.4(b)(3) (Register 2015, No. 1). For prior history, see Register 86, No. 23.

834. LIMITATION OF CLASSIFICATION

1. *New section filed 7-17-47 as an emergency (Register 9).*
2. *Amendment filed 4-29-64; effective thirtieth day thereafter (Register 64, No. 9).*
3. *Amendment filed 9-8-77; effective thirtieth day thereafter (Register 77, No. 37).*
4. *Editorial correction (Register 77, No. 52).*
5. *Amendment filed 11-1-83; effective upon filing pursuant to Government Code Section 11346.2(d) (Register 83, No. 45).*
6. *Section renumbered from 760 to 834, filed 2-27-84; effective upon filing pursuant to Government Code Section 11346.2(d) (Register 84, No. 9).*
7. *Editorial correction filed 7-19-84 (Register 84, No. 29).*
8. *Amendment of subsection (b) filed 8-10-99; effective thirtieth day thereafter (Register 99, No. 33).*

840. WRITTEN EXAMINATIONS REQUIRED OF ALL APPLICANTS

1. *Amendment filed 9-8-77; effective thirtieth day thereafter (Register 77, No. 37).*
2. *Editorial correction (Register 77, No. 52).*
3. *Amendment filed 5-6-83; effective thirtieth day thereafter (Register 83, No. 19).*
4. *Section renumbered from 765 to 840, filed 2-27-84; effective upon filing pursuant to Government Code Section 11346.2(d) (Register 84, No. 9).*
5. *Amendment filed 6-6-86; effective thirtieth day thereafter (Register 89, No. 23).*

841. ELIMINATION AND REVISION OF EXAMINATION QUESTIONS

1. *Amendment filed 9-8-77; effective thirtieth day thereafter (Register 77, No. 37).*
2. *Editorial correction (Register 77, No. 52).*
3. *Amendment filed 5-6-83; effective thirtieth day thereafter (Register 83, No. 19).*
4. *Section renumbered from 768 to 841, filed 2-27-84; effective upon filing pursuant to Government Code Section 11346.2(d) (Register 84, No. 9).*

853. RENEWAL APPLICATION FORM

1. *Amendment of subsections (b) and (c) and Note filed 2-9-2021; operative 4-1-2021 (Register 2021, No. 7).*

856. SECURITY IN LIEU OF BOND

1. *Amendment filed 11-23-71; effective thirtieth day thereafter (Register 71, No. 48). For prior history see Register 67, No. 17.*
2. *Amendment filed 1-28-77; effective thirtieth day thereafter (Register 77, No. 5).*
3. *Amendment filed 5-25-83; effective thirtieth day thereafter (Register 83, No. 22).*
4. *Section renumbered from 791 to 856, filed 2-27-84; effective upon filing pursuant to Government Code Section 11346.2(d) (Register 84, No. 9).*
5. *Amendment filed 11-9-95; effective thirtieth day thereafter (Register 95, No. 45).*

858. BLANKET PERFORMANCE AND PAYMENT BOND DEFINED

1. *New section filed 11-22-2011; operative 12-22-2011 (Register 2011, No. 47).*

858.1. BLANKET PERFORMANCE AND PAYMENT BOND REQUIREMENTS

1. *New section filed 11-22-2011; operative 12-22-2011 (Register 2011, No. 47).*
2. *Change without regulatory effect amending subsections (a) and (f) filed 11-10-2021 pursuant to section 100, title 1, California Code of Regulations (Register 2021, No. 46).*

858.2. APPLICATION FOR APPROVAL OF BLANKET PERFORMANCE AND PAYMENT BOND

1. *New section filed 11-22-2011; operative 12-22-2011 (Register 2011, No. 47).*
2. *Change without regulatory effect amending subsections (a)(3), (a)(4) and (b) and amending Note filed 11-10-2021 pursuant to section 100, title 1, California Code of Regulations (Register 2021, No. 46).*
3. *Change without regulatory effect amending subsections (a) and (a)(4) filed 9-6-2022 pursuant to section 100, title 1, California Code of Regulations (Register 2022, No. 36).*

858.3. MINIMUM STANDARDS FOR BLANKET PERFORMANCE AND PAYMENT BOND APPROVAL—CAUSE FOR DENIAL

1. *New section filed 11-22-2011; operative 12-22-2011 (Register 2011, No. 47).*

858.4. BLANKET PERFORMANCE AND PAYMENT BOND BIENNIAL CERTIFICATION AND FINANCIAL REPORTING REQUIREMENTS

1. *New section filed 11-22-2011; operative 12-22-2011 (Register 2011, No. 47).*

858.5. BLANKET PERFORMANCE AND PAYMENT BOND AUDIT AUTHORIZATION AND PROCEDURES

1. *New section filed 11-22-2011; operative 12-22-2011 (Register 2011, No. 47).*

858.6. AUTHORIZATION AND PROCEDURES FOR ORDERING THE AMOUNT OF BLANKET PERFORMANCE AND PAYMENT BOND TO BE INCREASED

1. *New section filed 11-22-2011; operative 12-22-2011 (Register 2011, No. 47).*

858.7. MAINTENANCE OF THE BLANKET PERFORMANCE AND PAYMENT BOND

1. *New section filed 11-22-2011; operative 12-22-2011 (Register 2011, No. 47).*

858.8. RESCISSION OF BLANKET PERFORMANCE AND PAYMENT BOND APPROVAL

1. *New section filed 11-22-2011; operative 12-22-2011 (Register 2011, No. 47).*

858.9. POSTING OF BLANKET PERFORMANCE AND PAYMENT BOND INFORMATION TO LICENSE RECORDS

1. *New section filed 11-22-2011; operative 12-22-2011 (Register 2011, No. 47).*

860. PENALTY FOR FAILURE TO COMPLY WITH RULES

1. *Amendment filed 5-25-83; effective thirtieth day thereafter (Register 83, No. 22).*
2. *Section renumbered from 794 to 860, filed 2-27-84; effective upon filing pursuant to Government Code Section 11346.2(d) (Register 84, No. 9).*

861. LICENSE NUMBER REQUIRED IN ADVERTISING

1. *New section filed 10-20-78; effective thirtieth day thereafter (Register 78, No. 42).*
2. *Amendment filed 10-21-83; effective thirtieth day thereafter (Register 83, No. 43).*
3. *Section renumbered from 794.1 to 861, filed 2-27-84; effective upon filing pursuant to Government Code Section 11346.2(d) (Register 84, No. 9).*
4. *Editorial correction filed 7-19-84 (Register 84, No. 29).*

5. *Amendment of section heading and section filed 11-30-2009; operative 12-30-2009 (Register 2009, No. 49).*

861.5 DEFINITION OF "STRUCTURAL DEFECT"

1. *New section filed 08-28-96; effective thirtieth day thereafter (Register 96, No. 35).*

863. PUBLIC ACCESS TO INFORMATION

1. *Repealer filed 8-1-62; effective thirtieth day thereafter (Register 62, No. 16).*
2. *New section filed 5-15-80; designated effective July 1, 1980 (Register 80, No. 20).*
3. *Amendment filed 10-24-83; effective thirtieth day thereafter (Register 83, No. 43).*
4. *Section renumbered from 722 to 863, filed 2-27-84; effective upon filing pursuant to Government Code Section 11346.2(d) (Register 84, No. 9).*
5. *Editorial correction filed 7-19-84 (Register 84, No. 29).*
6. *Amendment filed 4-10-92; operative 5-11-92 (Register 92, No. 18).*

864. CONTINUANCE OF LICENSE UNDER SECTION 7068.2

1. *Originally published 12-5-46 (Title 16).*
2. *Amendment filed 5-5-48 as an emergency (Register 12, No. 6).*
3. *Amendment filed 10-14-65; effective thirtieth day thereafter (Register 65, No. 19).*
4. *Amendment filed 5-25-83; effective thirtieth day thereafter (Register 83, No. 22).*
5. *Section renumbered from 796 to 864, filed 2-27-84; effective upon filing pursuant to Government Code Section 11346.2(d) (Register 84, No. 9).*
6. *Change without regulatory effect amending section filed 11-15-2016 pursuant to section 100, title 1, California Code of Regulations (Register 2016, No. 47).*

865. CONTINUANCE OF LICENSE UNDER SECTION 7076

1. *Amendment filed 10-14-68; effective thirtieth day thereafter (Register 68, No. 39). For prior history, see Section 65, No. 19.*
2. *Amendment filed 5-25-83; effective thirtieth day thereafter (Register 83, No. 22).*
3. *Section renumbered from 796.5 to 865, filed 2-27-84; effective upon filing pursuant to Government Code Section 11346.2(d) (Register 84, No. 9).*
4. *Amendment of subsections (a) and (b) filed 6-6-86; effective thirtieth day thereafter (Register 86, No. 23).*
5. *Change without regulatory effect separating second sentence of subsection (a)(3) into new paragraph filed 11-15-2016 pursuant to section 100, title 1, California Code of Regulations (Register 2016, No. 47).*

867. PROCEDURE TO REINSTATE INACTIVE LICENSE

1. *New section filed 8-1-62; designated effective 10-1-62 (Register 62, No. 16).*
2. *Amendment filed 5-25-83; effective thirtieth day thereafter (Register 83, No. 22).*
3. *Section renumbered from 799 to 867, filed 2-27-84; effective upon filing pursuant to Government Code Section 11346.2(d) (Register 84, No. 9).*
4. *Amendment filed 6-6-86; effective thirtieth day thereafter (Register 86, No. 23).*
5. *Change without regulatory effect amending subsection (a) filed 11-15-2016 pursuant to section 100, title 1, California Code of Regulations (Register 2016, No. 47).*

868. CRITERIA TO AID IN DETERMINING IF CRIMES, PROFESSIONAL MISCONDUCT, OR ACTS ARE SUBSTANTIALLY RELATED TO QUALIFICATIONS, FUNCTIONS, OR DUTIES OF A LICENSEE OR REGISTRANT.

1. *Amendment of section heading, section and Note filed 5-31-2006; operative 6-30-2006 (Register 2006, No. 22).*

2. *Amendment of section heading, section and Note filed 5-3-2021; operative 5-3-2021 pursuant to Government Code section 11343.4(b)(3) (Register 2021, No. 19). Filing deadline specified in Government Code section 11349.3(a) extended 60 calendar days pursuant to Executive Order N-40-20 and an additional 60 calendar days pursuant to Executive Order N-71-20.868.1.*

868.1 CRITERIA TO AID IN DETERMINING IF FINANCIAL CRIMES ARE DIRECTLY AND ADVERSELY RELATED TO FIDUCIARY QUALIFICATIONS, FUNCTIONS, OR DUTIES OF A LICENSEE OR REGISTRANT FOR THE PURPOSE OF CONSIDERING DENIALS OF APPLICATIONS.

1. *New section filed 5-3-2021; operative 5-3-2021 pursuant to Government Code section 11343.4(b)(3) (Register 2021, No. 19). Filing deadline specified in Government Code section 11349.3(a) extended 60 calendar days pursuant to Executive Order N-40-20 and an additional 60 calendar days pursuant to Executive Order N-71-20.*

869. CRITERIA FOR REHABILITATION

1. *Amendment of section and Note filed 5-31-2006; operative 6-30-2006 (Register 2006, No. 22).*

2. *Amendment of section and Note filed 5-3-2021; operative 5-3-2021 pursuant to Government Code section 11343.4(b)(3) (Register 2021, No. 19). Filing deadline specified in Government Code section 11349.3(a) extended 60 calendar days pursuant to Executive Order N-40-20 and an additional 60 calendar days pursuant to Executive Order N-71-20.*

869.1. APPLICANT DEFINED

1. *New section filed 3-17-2005; operative 4-16-2005 (Register 2005, No. 11).*

2. *Change without regulatory effect amending subsection (c) filed 11-15-2016 pursuant to section 100, title 1, California Code of Regulations (Register 2016, No. 47).*

869.2. EXEMPTIONS

1. *New section filed 3-17-2005; operative 4-16-2005 (Register 2005, No. 11).*

869.3. METHODS FOR SUBMITTING FINGERPRINTS

1. *New section filed 3-17-2005; operative 4-16-2005 (Register 2005, No. 11).*

869.4. SUBSEQUENT ARREST HISTORY

1. *New section filed 3-17-2005; operative 4-16-2005 (Register 2005, No. 11).*

869.9. CRITERIA TO AID IN DETERMINING EARLIEST DATE A DENIED APPLICANT MAY REAPPLY FOR LICENSURE

1. *New section filed 5-31-2006; operative 6-30-2006 (Register 2006, No. 22).*

2. *Amendment of section heading, section and Note filed 5-3-2021; operative 5-3-2021 pursuant to Government Code section 11343.4(b)(3) (Register 2021, No. 19). Filing deadline specified in Government Code section 11349.3(a) extended 60 calendar days pursuant to Executive Order N-40-20 and an additional 60 calendar days pursuant to Executive Order N-71-20.*

870. FACTORS TO APPLY IN DETERMINING EARLIEST DATE A REVOKED LICENSEE MAY APPLY FOR LICENSURE

1. *New section filed 5-11-89; operative 6-10-89 (Register 89, No. 19).*

2. *Change without regulatory effect amending subsection (b) filed 11-15-2016 pursuant to section 100, title 1, California Code of Regulations (Register 2016, No. 47).*

871. DISCIPLINARY GUIDELINES

1. *New section filed 5-29-97; operative 5-29-97 pursuant to Government Code 11343.4(d) (Register 97, No. 22).*

872. DISCLOSURE OF GENERAL LIABILITY INSURANCE

1. *New section filed 11-28-2001; operative 2-26-2002 (Register 2001, No. 48).*

880. ORDER OF CORRECTION—PRACTICAL FEASIBILITY

1. *New Article 8 (Sections 803-806.1) filed 4-7-81; effective thirtieth day thereafter (Register 81, No. 15).*

2. *Section renumbered from 803 to 880, filed 2-27-84; effective upon filing pursuant to Government Code Section 11346.2(d) (Register 84, No. 9).*

881. ORDER OF CORRECTION—ALTERNATIVE COMPLIANCE

1. *New section filed 4-7-81; effective thirtieth day thereafter (Register 81, No. 15).*

2. *Section renumbered from 803.1 to 881, filed 2-27-84; effective upon filing pursuant to Government Code Section 11346.2(d) (Register 84, No. 9).*

882. ORDER OF CORRECTION—TIME REQUIRED TO CORRECT

1. *New section filed 4-7-81; effective thirtieth day thereafter (Register 81, No. 15).*

2. *Section renumbered from 804 to 882, filed 2-27-84; effective upon filing pursuant to Government Code Section 11346.2(d) (Register 84, No. 9).*

883. ORDER OF CORRECTION—EXTENSION OF TIME TO CORRECT

1. *New section filed 4-7-81; effective thirtieth day thereafter (Register 81, No. 15).*

2. *Section renumbered from 804.1 to 883, filed 2-27-84; effective upon filing pursuant to Government Code Section 11346.2(d) (Register 84, No. 9).*

3. *Editorial correction (Register 2017, No. 8).*

884. RECOMMENDED ASSESSMENTS OF CIVIL PENALTIES

1. *New section filed 4-7-81; effective thirtieth day thereafter (Register 81, No. 15).*

2. *Section renumbered from 805 to 884, filed 2-27-84; effective upon filing pursuant to Government Code Section 11346.2(d) (Register 84, No. 9).*

3. *Amendment filed 5-23-94; operative 6-22-94 (Register 94, No. 21).*

4. *Amendment of section and Note filed 1-31-2007; operative 3-2-2007 (Register 2007, No. 5).*

5. *Change without regulatory effect amending section and Note filed 11-10-2021 pursuant to section 100, title 1, California Code of Regulations; operative 1-1-2022 (Register 2021, No. 46).*

6. *Change without regulatory effect amending subsections (a) and (c) filed 8-17-2023 pursuant to section 100, title 1, California Code of Regulations (Register 2023, No. 33).*

885. APPEAL OF CITATION

1. *New Section filed 4-7-81; effective thirtieth day thereafter (Register 81, No. 15).*
2. *Section renumbered from 806 to 885, filed 2-27-84; effective upon filing pursuant to Government Code Section 11346.2(d) (Register 84, No. 9).*

886. SERVICE OF CITATION

1. *New Section filed 4-7-81; effective thirtieth day thereafter (Register 81, No. 15).*
2. *Section renumbered from 806.1 to 886, filed 2-27-84; effective upon filing pursuant to Government Code Section 11346.2(d) (Register 84, No. 9).*

887. CRITERIA TO EVALUATE THE GRAVITY OF A VIOLATION OF BUSINESS AND PROFESSIONS CODE SECTION 7028.7

1. *New section filed 5-13-82; effective thirtieth day thereafter (Register 82, No. 20).*
2. *Section renumbered from 807 to 887, filed 2-27-84; effective upon filing pursuant to Government Code Section 11346.2(d) (Register 84, No. 9).*

890. MINIMUM QUALIFICATION STANDARDS FOR ARBITRATORS

1. *New article 9 (section 890) and section filed 10-31-2001; operative 11-30-2001 (Register 2001, No. 44).*

HISTORY NOTES FOR
REPEALED BOARD RULES AND REGULATIONS

701. PURPOSE OF LAW—PROTECTION, HEALTH AND SAFETY OF PUBLIC

1. *Repealer filed 5-25-83; effective thirtieth day thereafter (Register 83, No. 22).*

702. FEES

1. *New Article 1.5 (Section 702) filed 12-21-81; designated effective 2-1-82 (Register 81, No. 52).*
2. *Repealer filed 3-15-83; effective thirtieth day thereafter (Register 83, No. 12).*

707. ALL MEMBERS OF APPLICANT TO FURNISH INFORMATION

1. *Repealer filed 8-25-83; effective upon filing pursuant to Government Code Section 11346.2(d) (Register 83, No. 35).*

708. SIGNING AND VERIFICATION OF APPLICATION

1. *Amendment filed 7-19-74; effective thirtieth day thereafter (Register 74, No. 29).*
2. *Repealer filed 8-25-83; effective upon filing pursuant to Government Code Section 11346.2(d) (Register 83, No. 35).*

709. FURNISHING REFERENCES

1. *Repealer filed 3-3-53; effective thirtieth day thereafter (Register 53, No. 4).*

710. POWER OF REGISTRAR TO DENY INSUFFICIENT APPLICATIONS

1. *Amendment filed 9-8-77; effective thirtieth day thereafter (Register 77, No. 37).*
2. *Repealer filed 8-25-83; effective upon filing pursuant to Government Code Section 11346.2(d) (Register 83, No. 35).*

711.1. ABANDONMENT OF APPLICATION

1. *New section filed 1-22-76; effective thirtieth day thereafter (Register 76, No. 4).*

2. Repealer filed 8-25-83; effective upon filing pursuant to Government Code Section 11346.2(d) (Register 83, No. 35).

712. POWER OF REGISTRAR TO WAIVE FORMAL REQUIREMENTS

1. Amendment filed 9-8-77; effective thirtieth day thereafter (Register 77, No. 37).

2. Repealer filed 8-25-83; effective upon filing pursuant to Government Code Section 11346.2(d) (Register 83, No. 35).

713. TENDER OF FEE

1. Originally published 12-5-46 (Title 16).

2. Amendment filed 9-18-47 as an emergency (Register 9).

3. Repealer filed 1-23-50 (Register 19, No. 2).

716. POWER IN REGISTRAR TO WAIVE POSTING

1. Originally published 12-5-46 (Title 16).

2. Amendment filed 9-18-47 as an emergency (Register 9).

3. Repealer filed 1-27-71; effective thirtieth day thereafter (Register 71, No. 5).

719. BOND REQUIREMENT OF APPLICANTS

1. Repealer filed 8-1-62; effective thirtieth day thereafter (Register 62, No. 16).

720. POSTING OF BOND AS CONDITION OF REINSTATEMENT

1. Repealer filed 8-1-62; effective thirtieth day thereafter (Register 62, No. 16).

721. REGISTRAR MAY WAIVE BOND

1. Repealer filed 8-1-62; effective thirtieth day thereafter (Register 62, No. 16).

723. POLICY OF THE BOARD REGARDING EXPERIENCE

1. Amendment filed 9-8-77; effective thirtieth day thereafter (Register 77, No. 37).

2. Editorial correction (Register 77, No. 52).

3. Repealer filed 12-22-82; effective thirtieth day thereafter (Register 82, No. 52).

726. CREDIT FOR ADDITIONAL EXPERIENCE

1. Originally published 12-5-48 (Title 16).

2. Amendment filed 3-12-47 (Register 8).

3. Repealer filed 2-28-80; effective thirtieth day thereafter (Register 80, No. 9).

731. ALL CONTRACTORS TO BE CLASSIFIED

1. Repealer filed 12-22-82; effective thirtieth day thereafter (Register 82, No. 52).

753. CLASS C-22—STRUCTURAL PEST CONTROL CONTRACTOR

1. Repealer filed 10-18-55; effective thirtieth day thereafter (Register 55, No. 16).

754. CLASS C-56—WATERPROOFING, WEATHERPROOFING AND DAMP-PROOFING CONTRACTORS

1. Originally published 12-5-46 (Title 16).

2. Repealer filed 9-18-47 as an emergency; effective upon filing (Register 9).

755. PRIMARY AND SUPPLEMENTAL CLASSIFICATIONS

1. Amendment filed 9-8-77; effective thirtieth day thereafter (Register 77, No. 37).

2. Editorial correction (Register 77, No. 52).

Section VI

3. *Repealer filed 12-22-82; effective thirtieth day thereafter (Register 82, No. 52).*

756. ASSIGNMENT OF PRIMARY CLASSIFICATION

1. *Amendment filed 2-7-75; effective thirtieth day thereafter (Register 75, No. 6).*
2. *Amendment filed 9-8-77; effective thirtieth day thereafter (Register 77, No. 37).*
3. *Repealer filed 12-22-82; effective thirtieth day thereafter (Register 82, No. 52).*

756.1. ASSIGNMENT OF SUPPLEMENTAL SOLAR CLASSIFICATION

1. *New section filed 10-20-78; effective thirtieth day thereafter (Register 78, No. 42).*
2. *Repealer filed 3-15-83; effective thirtieth day thereafter (Register 83, No. 12).*

756.2. QUALIFICATION FOR SUPPLEMENTAL SOLAR CLASSIFICATION

1. *New section filed 10-20-78; effective thirtieth day thereafter (Register 78, No. 42).*
2. *Repealer filed 4-28-82; effective thirtieth day thereafter (Register 82, No. 18).*

756.3. SOLAR PROJECT REPORTING REQUIREMENTS

1. *New section filed 10-20-78; effective thirtieth day thereafter (Register 78, No. 42).*
2. *Repealer filed 4-28-82; effective thirtieth day thereafter (Register 82, No. 18).*

756.4. EFFECTIVE DATE OF REGULATION

1. *New section filed 10-20-78; effective thirtieth day thereafter (Register 78, No. 42).*
2. *Repealer filed 4-28-82; effective thirtieth day thereafter (Register 82, No. 18).*

757. NO "SUPPLEMENTAL" CLASSIFICATION WHERE NO SPECIAL EXAMINATION

1. *Originally published 12-5-46 (Title 16).*
2. *Repealer filed 9-18-47 as an emergency; effective upon filing (Register 9).*

759. WAIVER OF RECLASSIFICATION EXAMINATIONS

1. *Amendment filed 9-8-77; effective thirtieth day thereafter (Register 77, No. 37).*
2. *Repealer filed 2-28-80; effective thirtieth day thereafter (Register 80, No. 9).*

764. POLICY OF THE BOARD REGARDING EXAMINATIONS

1. *Amendment filed 9-8-77; effective thirtieth day thereafter (Register 77, No. 37).*
2. *Editorial correction (Register 77, No. 52).*
3. *Repealer filed 12-22-82; effective thirtieth day thereafter (Register 82, No. 52).*

766. TYPES OF EXAMINATIONS

1. *Repealer filed 5-6-83; effective thirtieth day thereafter (Register 83, No. 19).*

767. "SPECIFIC" AND "BLANKET" EXAMINATIONS APPROVED

1. *Originally published 12-5-46 (Title 16).*
2. *Repealer filed 9-18-47 as an emergency; effective upon filing (Register 9).*

769. REGISTRAR TO REQUIRE EXAMINATION OF APPLICANTS

1. *Repealer filed 12-22-82; effective thirtieth day thereafter (Register 82, No. 52).*

770. REGISTRAR MAY CHANGE WRITTEN EXAMINATIONS

1. *Amendment filed 9-8-77; effective thirtieth day thereafter (Register 77, No. 37).*
2. *Repealer filed 5-6-83; effective thirtieth day thereafter (Register 83, No. 19).*

772. GRADING OF EXAMINATIONS

1. Originally published 12-5-46 (Title 16).

2. Amendment filed 3-17-47 (Register 8).

3. Amendment filed 2-28-80; effective thirtieth day thereafter (Register 80, No. 9).

4. Repealer filed 4-15-83; effective upon filing pursuant to Government Code Section 11346.2(d) (Register 83, No. 16).

773. REGISTRAR MAY MAKE RULES ON EXAMINATION PROCEDURE

1. Amendment filed 9-8-77; effective thirtieth day thereafter (Register 77, No. 37).

2. Editorial correction (Register 77, No. 52).

3. Repealer filed 5-6-83; effective thirtieth day thereafter (Register 83, No. 19).

774. NO EXAMINATION REQUIRED

1. Sections 774 and 775 originally published 12-5-46 (Title 16).

2. Amendments to same filed 10-19-48 as emergencies (Register 14, No. 3).

3. Amendment filed 8-6-64; effective thirtieth day thereafter (Register 64, No. 17).

4. Repealer filed 8-25-83; effective upon filing pursuant to Government Code Section 11346.2(d) (Register 83, No. 35).

812. DISHONORED CHECK SERVICE CHARGE

1. New section filed 9-30-82; effective thirtieth day thereafter (Register 82, No. 40).

2. Section renumbered from 703 to 812, filed 2-27-84; effective upon filing pursuant to Government Code Section 11346.2(d) (Register 84, No. 9).

3. Change without regulatory effect repealing section filed 6-12-2024 pursuant to section 100, title 1, California Code of Regulations (Register 2024, No. 24).

817. OPERATING CAPITAL DEFINED

1. New section filed 1-24-80; effective thirtieth day thereafter (Register 80, No. 4).

2. Amendment filed 8-25-83; effective upon filing pursuant to Government Code Section 11346.2(d) (Register 83, No. 35).

3. Section renumbered from 707.1 to 817, filed 2-27-84; effective upon filing pursuant to Government Code Section 11346.2(d) (Register 84, No. 9).

4. Change without regulatory effect repealing section filed 11-15-2016 pursuant to section 100, title 1, California Code of Regulations (Register 2016, No. 47).

818. INSUFFICIENT OR INCOMPLETE APPLICATIONS—REJECTION

1. Amendment filed 2-7-75; effective thirtieth day thereafter (Register 75, No. 6).

2. Amendment filed 8-25-83; effective upon filing pursuant to Government Code Section 11346.2(d) (Register 83, No. 35).

3. Section renumbered from 711 to 818, filed 2-27-84; effective upon filing pursuant to Government Code Section 11346.2(d) (Register 84, No. 9).

4. Repealer filed 11-9-95; effective thirtieth day thereafter (Register 95, No. 45).

820. POSTING OF NAMES OF APPLICANTS

1. Originally published 12-5-46 (Title 16).

2. Amendment filed 7-31-50 as a procedural rule; effective upon filing (Register 21, No. 4).

3. Amendment filed 1-27-71; effective thirtieth day thereafter (Register 71, No. 5).

4. Amendment filed 2-7-75; effective thirtieth day thereafter (Register 75, No. 6).

5. *Amendment filed 8-25-83; effective upon filing pursuant to Government Code Section 11346.2(d) (Register 83, No. 35).*

6. *Section renumbered from 715 to 820, filed 2-27-84; effective upon filing pursuant to Government Code Section 11346.2(d) (Register 84, No. 9).*

7. *Repealer filed 11-9-95; effective thirtieth day thereafter (Register 95, No.45).*

821. JOINT VENTURE LICENSE DEFINED

1. *Originally published 12-5-46 (Title 16).*

2. *Amendment filed 10-18-49 as an emergency (Register 18, No. 3).*

3. *Amendment filed 12-16-63; effective thirtieth day thereafter (Register 63, No. 25).*

4. *Amendment filed 8-25-83; effective upon filing pursuant to Government Code Section 11346.2(d) (Register 83, No. 35).*

5. *Section renumbered from 717 to 821, filed 2-27-84; effective upon filing pursuant to Government Code Section 11346.2(d) (Register 84, No. 9).*

6. *Repealer filed 11-9-95; effective thirtieth day thereafter (Register 95, No.45).*

822. LICENSING REQUIREMENTS FOR JOINT VENTURE LICENSE

1. *Amendment filed 9-8-77; effective thirtieth day thereafter (Register 77, No. 37). For prior history, see Register 71, No. 5.*

2. *Amendment filed 8-25-83; effective upon filing pursuant to Government Code Section 11346.2(d) (Register 83, No. 35).*

3. *Section renumbered from 718 to 822, filed 2-27-84; effective upon filing pursuant to Government Code Section 11346.2(d) (Register 84, No. 9).*

4. *Repealer filed 11-9-95; effective thirtieth day thereafter (Register 95, No.45).*

823. DEFINITIONS: BONA FIDE EMPLOYEE; DIRECT SUPERVISION AND CONTROL

1. *Editorial correction filed 7-19-84 (Register 84, No. 29).*

2. *Change without regulatory effect repealing section filed 6-2-2022 pursuant to section 100, title 1, California Code of Regulations (Register 2022, No. 22).*

829. CREDIT FOR EXPERIENCE

1. *New section filed 5-30-90; operative 6-29-90 (Register 90, No. 29).*

2. *Repealer filed 8-10-2006; operative 9-9-2006 (Register 2006, No. 32).*

832.06. CLASS C-6—CABINET AND MILLWORK CONTRACTORS

1. *Amendment filed 8-25-83; effective upon filing pursuant to Government Code Section 11346.2(d) (Register 83, No. 35).*

2. *Section renumbered from 744 to 832.06, filed 2-27-84; effective upon filing pursuant to Government Code Section 11346.2(d) (Register 84, No. 9).*

3. *Repealer filed 12-18-97; effective 01-01-98 (Register 97, No.172).*

832.14. CLASS C-14—METAL ROOFING CONTRACTOR

1. *New section filed 10-22-86; effective thirtieth day thereafter (Register 86, No. 43).*

2. *Repealer and new section filed 6-22-98; operative 7-1-98 pursuant to Government Code section 11343.4(d) (Register 98, No. 26).*

3. *Change without regulatory effect repealing section filed 8-7-2013 pursuant to section 100, title 1, California Code of Regulations (Register 2013, No. 32).*

832.26. CLASS C-26—LATHING CONTRACTORS

1. *Amendment filed 9-23-83; effective upon filing pursuant to Government Code Section 11346.2(d) (Register 83, No. 39).*

2. *Section renumbered from 743 to 832.26, filed 2-27-84; effective upon filing pursuant to Government Code Section 11346.2(d) (Register 84, No. 9).*

3. *Repealer filed 12-18-97; effective 01-01-98 (Register 97, No.172).*

833. ADDITIONAL CLASSIFICATIONS

1. *Sections 758 and 759 originally published 12-5-46 (Title 16).*

2. *Amendments to same filed 10-19-48 as emergencies (Register 14, No. 3).*

3. *Amendment filed 9-8-77; effective thirtieth day thereafter (Register 77, No. 37).*

4. *Amendment filed 8-19-83; effective thirtieth day thereafter (Register 83, No. 35).*

5. *Section renumbered from 758 to 833, filed 2-27-84; effective upon filing pursuant to Government Code Section 11346.2(d) (Register 84, No. 9).*

6. *Repealer filed 6-6-86; effective thirtieth day thereafter (Register 86, No. 23).*

842. APPLICANTS MAY BE RE-EXAMINED

1. *Amendment filed 7-19-66; effective thirtieth day thereafter (Register 66, No. 23).*

2. *Amendment filed 9-8-77; effective thirtieth day thereafter (Register 77, No. 37).*

3. *Amendment filed 5-6-83; effective thirtieth day thereafter (Register 83, No. 19).*

4. *Section renumbered from 771 to 842, filed 2-27-84; effective upon filing pursuant to Government Code Section 11346.2(d) (Register 84, No. 9).*

5. *Amendment filed 6-6-86; effective thirtieth day thereafter (Register 86, No. 23).*

6. *Repealer filed 11-30-2009; operative 12-30-2009 (Register 2009, No. 49).*

843. WAIVER OF EXAMINATION

1. *New section filed 7-2-81; effective thirtieth day thereafter (Register 81, No. 27). For history of former section, see Registers 80, No. 9; 77, No. 52; 77, No. 37; 62, No. 1 and 57, No. 6.*

2. *Section renumbered from 775 to 843, filed 2-27-84; effective upon filing pursuant to Government Code Section 11346.2(d) (Register 84, No. 9).*

3. *Repealer filed 6-6-86; effective thirtieth day thereafter (Register 86, No. 23).*

844. FAILURE TO APPEAR FOR EXAMINATION

1. *Originally filed 12-5-46 (Title 16).*

2. *Amendment filed 4-30-47 (Register 8).*

3. *Amendment filed 9-8-77; effective thirtieth day thereafter (Register 77, No. 37).*

4. *Amendment filed 8-25-83; effective upon filing pursuant to Government Code Section 11346.2(d) (Register 83, No. 35).*

5. *Section renumbered from 776 to 844, filed 2-27-84; effective upon filing pursuant to Government Code Section 11346.2(d) (Register 84, No. 9).*

6. *Repealer filed 6-6-86; effective thirtieth day thereafter (Register 86, No. 23).*

852. RENEWAL OF LICENSES

1. *New section filed 6-22-78; effective thirtieth day thereafter (Register 78, No. 25). For history of prior section 780, see Register 66, No. 23.*

2. *Amendment filed 5-25-83; effective thirtieth day thereafter (Register 83, No. 22).*

3. *Section renumbered from 780 to 852, filed 2-27-84; effective upon filing pursuant to Government Code Section 11346.2(d) (Register 84, No. 9).*

4. *Change without regulatory effect repealing section filed 11-9-95 pursuant to section 100, title 1, California Code of Regulations (Register 95, No. 45).*

854. RENEWAL FEE AND REACTIVATION CREDIT

1. *New section filed 6-3-97; operative 6-3-97 pursuant to Government Code section 11343.4(d) (Register 97, No. 23).*

2. *Change without regulatory effect repealing section filed 8-7-2013 pursuant to section 100, title 1, California Code of Regulations (Register 2013, No. 32).*

862. NOTICE TO OWNER

1. *New section filed 6-5-80; effective thirtieth day thereafter (Register 80, No. 23).*

2. *Amendment filed 3-26-82; effective thirtieth day thereafter (Register 82, No. 13).*

3. *Section renumbered from 794.2 to 862, filed 2-27-84; effective upon filing pursuant to Government Code Section 11346.2(d) (Register 84, No. 9).*

4. *Amendment filed 3-6-84; effective upon filing pursuant to Government Code Section 11346.2(d) (Register 84, No. 9).*

5. *Change without regulatory effect repealing section filed 11-9-95 pursuant to section 100, title 1, California Code of Regulations (Register 95, No. 45).*

866. PROCEDURE TO INACTIVATE LICENSE

1. *New section filed 8-1-62; designated effective 10-1-62 (Register 62, No. 16).*

2. *Amendment filed 5-25-83; effective thirtieth day thereafter (Register 83, No. 22).*

3. *Section renumbered from 798 to 866, filed 2-27-84; effective upon filing pursuant to Government Code Section 11346.2(d) (Register 84, No. 9).*

4. *Repealer filed 6-6-86; effective thirtieth day thereafter (Register 86, No. 23).*

869.5. INQUIRY INTO CRIMINAL CONVICTIONS

1. *New section filed 3-17-2005; operative 4-16-2005 (Register 2005, No. 11).*

2. *Change without regulatory effect amending section filed 11-15-2016 pursuant to section 100, title 1, California Code of Regulations (Register 2016, No. 47).*

3. *Repealer filed 5-3-2021; operative 5-3-2021 pursuant to Government Code section 11343.4(b)(3) (Register 2021, No. 19). Filing deadline specified in Government Code section 11349.3(a) extended 60 calendar days pursuant to Executive Order N-40-20 and an additional 60 calendar days pursuant to Executive Order N-71-20.*

872.1. CHECKLIST FOR HOMEOWNERS

1. *New section filed 11-28-2001; operative 2-26-2002 (Register 2001, No. 48).*

2. *Change without regulatory effect amending subsections (b) and (c) and Note filed 11-22-2021 pursuant to section 100, title 1, California Code of Regulations (Register 2021, No. 48)*

Abbreviations Key for Cited Index Codes	
B&P	Business and Professions Code
CC	Civil Code
CCP	Code of Civil Procedure
CCR	California Code of Regulations
FC	Family Code
GC	Government Code
H&S	Health and Safety Code
IC	Insurance Code
LC	Labor Code
PC	Penal Code
PCC	Public Contract Code
PRC	Public Resources Code
PUC	Public Utilities Code
RTC	Revenue and Taxation Code
S&H	Streets and Highways Code
UIC	Unemployment Insurance Code
VC	Vehicle Code
WC	Water Code

Index

A

ABANDONMENT OF CONTRACT,
Ch 8 B&P 7107

ABATEMENT, ORDER OF, Ch 8 B&P
7028.6, Ch 8 B&P 7028.7
Violations, criteria to evaluate gravity
of, Ch 9 T 16 CCR 887

ACCOUNTING CONTROL.
Financial responsibility and control.
(*See* **Business Management**)

ACTIONS AND PROCEEDINGS.
Reporting of civil actions against
licensees to registrar.
Confidential settlements or other
agreements.
Report not considered violation of
confidentiality, Ch 8 B&P
7071.22
Insurers of licensees, reporting, Ch
8 B&P 7071.21
Requirement to report, Ch 8 B&P
7071.20

Index

Index

Y

**YELLOW CORRUGATED
STAINLESS STEEL.**